SCIENCEPOWER™ 9

McGraw-Hill Ryerson SCIENCEPOWER™ Program

SCIENCEPOWER™ 7
SCIENCEPOWER™ 8
SCIENCEPOWER™ 9
SCIENCEPOWER™ 10

Chenelière/McGraw-Hill OMNISCIENCES Program

OMNISCIENCES 7
OMNISCIENCES 8
OMNISCIENCES 9
OMNISCIENCES 10

This program is available directly from Chenelière/McGraw-Hill.

Teacher Support for Each Grade Level
Teacher Resource Binder
Blackline Masters
Computerized Assessment Bank
Web site: *http//www.mcgrawhill.ca*
Videotape series

Our cover According to today's knowledge, as two galaxies collide in the depths of space, gas falls into an immensely powerful black hole at nearly the speed of light. A beam of energy is generated that we detect on Earth, billions of light years away, as a quasar.

SCIENCEPOWER™ 9

SCIENCE • TECHNOLOGY • SOCIETY • ENVIRONMENT

Author Team

Elgin Wolfe
Ontario Institute for Studies in Education of the University of Toronto
Toronto, Ontario

Christina Clancy
Loyola Catholic Secondary School
Mississauga, Ontario

Gordon Jasper
Dr. E.P. Scarlett Senior High School
Calgary, Alberta

Dawn Lindenberg
Ross Sheppard High School
Edmonton, Alberta

David Lynn
Belle River District High School
Belle River, Ontario

Frank Mustoe
University of Toronto Schools
Toronto, Ontario

Rob Smythe
Iroquois Ridge High School
Oakville, Ontario

Senior Program Consultants

Malisa Mezenberg
Loyola Catholic Secondary School
Mississauga, Ontario

Douglas A. Roberts
University of Calgary
Calgary, Alberta

McGraw-Hill Ryerson

Toronto   Montreal   New York   Burr Ridge   Bangkok   Bogotá   Caracas
Lisbon   London   Madrid   Mexico City   Milan   New Delhi
Seoul   Singapore   Sydney   Taipei

McGraw-Hill Ryerson Limited
A Subsidiary of The McGraw·Hill Companies

SCIENCEPOWER™ 9
Science • Technology • Society • Environment

Copyright © 1999, McGraw-Hill Ryerson Limited, a Subsidiary of The McGraw-Hill Companies. All rights reserved. No part of this publication may be reproduced or transmitted in any form or by any means, or stored in a data base or retrieval system, without the prior written permission of McGraw-Hill Ryerson Limited, or, in the case of photocopying or other reprographic copying, a licence from CANCOPY (Canadian Copyright Licensing Agency) One Yonge Street, Suite 1900, Toronto, Ontario M5E 1E5.

Any request for photocopying, recording, or taping of this publication shall be directed in writing to CANCOPY.

0-07-560361-6

http//www.mcgrawhill.ca

1 2 3 4 5 6 7 8 9 0 GTC 99

Printed and bound in Canada

Care has been taken to trace ownership of copyright material contained in this text. The publishers will gladly take any information that will enable them to rectify any reference or credit in subsequent printings.

Canadian Cataloguing in Publication Data

Main entry under title:

Sciencepower 9: science, technology, society, environment

Includes index.

ISBN 0-07-560361-6

1. Science – Juvenile literature. I Wolfe, Elgin. II Title: Sciencepower nine.

Q161. Z. S386 1999 500 C99-931204-9

The SCIENCEPOWER™ Development Team
SCIENCE PUBLISHER: Trudy Rising
DEVELOPMENTAL EDITORS: Janis Barr, Jean Bullard, Gerry De Iuliis, Lois Edwards, Tom Gamblin, Dan Kozlovic, Jane McNulty, Georgina Montgomery, Louise Oborne
SENIOR SUPERVISING EDITOR: Nancy Christoffer
PROJECT CO-ORDINATORS: Kelli Legros, Crystal Shortt
ASSISTANT PROJECT CO-ORDINATOR: Janie Reeson
EDITORIAL ASSISTANT: Joanne Murray
SPECIAL FEATURES: Jill Bryant, Trudee Romanek, Elma Schemenauer, Lauri Seidlitz
COPY EDITORS: Sarah Swartz, Paula Pettitt-Townsend, Grace D'Alfonso
PERMISSIONS EDITORS: Jane Affleck, Jacqueline Donovan
SENIOR PRODUCTION CO-ORDINATOR: Yolanda Pigden
COVER DESIGN: Pronk & Associates
INTERIOR DESIGN: Pronk & Associates/ArtPlus Limited
ELECTRONIC PAGE MAKE-UP: Pronk & Associates/ArtPlus Limited — Valerie Bateman
SET-UP PHOTOGRAPHY: Trent Photography/Michael Cullen
SET-UP PHOTOGRAPHY CO-ORDINATOR: Grant Ball
TECHNICAL ILLUSTRATIONS: Imagineering Scientific and Technical Artworks Inc.
ILLUSTRATIONS: Paulette Dennis, Deborah Crowle, William Kimber, Dorothy Siemens, Tina Holdcroft, Malcolm Cullen, Alan Gaunt, Margo Pronk
ArtPlus Limited — Sue Ledoux, Paul Payer, Cory McCargar
COVER IMAGE: Painting © 1999 by Don Dixon

Acknowledgements

Pedagogical Reviewers

Nancy Dalgarno Aldred
Trinity College School
Port Hope, Ontario

Ray Bowers
Toronto District School Board
Toronto, Ontario

Stewart Buchanan
Harrison Trimble High School
Moncton, New Brunswick

John Caranci
Toronto District School Board
Toronto, Ontario

Phonse Chiasson
Sherwood Park Education Centre
Sydney, Nova Scotia

Peter Chin
Queen's University
Kingston, Ontario

Audrey Cook
George Street Middle School
Fredericton, New Brunswick

Gail de Souza
St. Joseph Secondary School
Mississauga, Ontario

Barry Edgar
Strathcona Composite High School
Edmonton, Alberta

Dan Forbes
Ste. Anne Elementary School
Ste. Anne, Manitoba

Keith Gibbons
Catholic Central High School
London, Ontario

Derrick Grant
Stanley High School
Stanley, New Brunswick

Greg Kingston
Saint John High School
Saint John, New Brunswick

Steve Karrel
Bible Hill Junior High School
Truro, Nova Scotia

Ping Lai
University of Toronto Schools
Toronto, Ontario

James Lewko
Toronto District School Board
Toronto, Ontario

Penny McLeod
Thornhill Secondary School
Thornhill, Ontario

Henry Pasma
Cawthra Park Secondary School
Mississauga, Ontario

Terry Price
Huron Heights Secondary School
Thornhill, Ontario

Garry Rasmussen
Sydenham High School
Sydenham, Ontario

Taunya Sheffield
Central Kings Rural High School
Cambridge Station, Nova Scotia

Susan Tanner
Queen Elizabeth High School
Halifax, Nova Scotia

Paul Weese
Lambdon-Kent Composite School
Dresden, Ontario

Sandy M. Wohl
Hugh Boyd Secondary School
Richmond, British Columbia

Academic Reviewers

Gerry De Iuliis, Ph.D., Biology
Lois Edwards, Ph.D., Biophysics
Tom Gamblin, Ph.D., Mathematics
Eric Grace, Ph.D., Biology
Dan Kozlovic, Ph.D., Biology
Penny McLeod, Ph.D., Chemistry
Lawrence Pitt, Ph.D., Astronomy

Safety Reviewer

Margaret Redway
Fraser Scientific & Business Services
Delta, British Columbia

Contents

Unit 1 The Power of Reproduction

Unit 2 Atoms and Elements 152

Unit 3 Characteristics of Electricity   292

Unit 4 Exploration of the Universe   426

To the Teacher

We are very pleased to have been part of the team of experienced science educators and editors working together to bring you and your students this new program — the *SCIENCEPOWER*™ *7-10* series of textbooks, and its French equivalent, *OMNISCIENCES 7-10*. The *SCIENCEPOWER*™ and *OMNISCIENCES* student and teacher resources were specifically developed to provide 100 percent congruence with the new Ontario curriculum. As the titles *SCIENCEPOWER*™ and *OMNISCIENCES* suggest, these resources are designed to foster an appreciation of the power of scientific explanation as a way of understanding our world and to empower students to critically examine issues and questions from a societal and environmental perspective.

SCIENCEPOWER™*9/OMNISCIENCES 9* provide:

- A science inquiry emphasis, in which students address questions about the nature of science involving broad explorations as well as focussed investigations. Skill areas emphasized include: careful observing; questioning; proposing ideas; predicting; hypothesizing; making inferences; designing experiments; gathering, processing, and interpreting data; and explaining and communicating.

- A technological problem-solving emphasis, in which students seek answers to practical problems. Problem solving may either precede knowledge acquisition or provide students with opportunities to apply their newly acquired science knowledge in novel ways. Skill areas emphasized include: understanding the problem; setting and/or understanding criteria; developing a design plan, carrying out the plan; evaluating; and communicating.

- A societal decision-making emphasis, in which students draw upon those science and technology concepts and skills that will inform the question or issue under consideration. Students are encouraged to give particular attention to sustainability. Skill areas emphasized include: identifying the issue; identifying alternatives; researching, reflecting, and deciding; taking action; evaluating; and communicating.

The particular emphases within a unit are, in part, suggested by the topic itself. The primary and secondary emphases for *SCIENCEPOWER*™ *9* and *OMNISCIENCES 9* are as follows:

SCIENCEPOWER™ 9/ OMNISCIENCES Unit	Primary Emphasis	Secondary Emphasis or Emphases
Unit 1 The Power of Reproduction	Societal Decision Making	Science Inquiry
Unit 2 Atoms and Elements	Science Inquiry	Technological Problem Solving
Unit 3 Characteristics of Electricity	Technological Problem Solving	Science Inquiry
Unit 4 Exploration of the Universe	Science Inquiry	Technological Problem Solving, Societal Decision Making

Scientific literacy has become the goal in science education throughout the world, and this goal has been given expression in Canada in the *Common Framework of Science Learning Outcomes, K-12: Pan-Canadian Protocol for Collaboration on School Curriculum* (Council of Ministers of Education, Canada, 1997).

> "Scientific literacy is an evolving combination of the science-related attitudes, skills, and knowledge students need to develop inquiry, problem-solving, and decision-making abilities, to become lifelong learners, and to maintain a sense of wonder about the world around them. To develop scientific literacy, students require diverse learning experiences which provide opportunity to explore, analyze, evaluate, synthesize, appreciate, and understand the inter-relationships among science, technology, society, and the environment that will affect their personal lives, their careers, and their future."

Through varied text features, *SCIENCEPOWER™ 9* enables students to under-stand basic concepts in Biology (Unit 1: The Power of Reproduction), Chemistry (Unit 2: Atoms and Elements), Physics (Unit 3: Characteristics of Electricity), and Earth and Space Science (Unit 4: Exploration of the Universe). The program also develops skills in the processes of scientific inquiry, and in relating science to tech-nology, society, and the environment.

In *SCIENCEPOWER™ 9*, students learn scientific theories and conduct investi-gations related to cell division and reproduction; atomic and molecular structures and the properties of elements and compounds; the principles of electricity; and the universe and space exploration.

Like the other textbooks in our series, *SCIENCEPOWER™ 9* builds on the three basic goals of the curriculum, and reflects the essential triad of knowledge, skills, and the ability to relate science to technology, society, and the environment (STSE). Science is approached both as an intellectual pursuit, and also as an activ-ity-based enterprise operating within a social context.

Our extensive *Teacher's Resource Binder* provides essential planning and implemen-tation strategies that you will find helpful and practical. Our *Blackline Masters* provide you with materials that you can use for vocabulary building, skill building, concept clarification, alternative activities for multiple learning styles, forms for performance task assessment of student achievement that are specific to the unit of study, and others that focus on larger encompassing skills of science, technology, and societal decision making. Our *Computerized Assessment Bank* will assist you in your full implementation of the *SCIENCEPOWER™ 9* program.

We feel confident that we have provided you with the best possible program to help ensure your students achieve excellence and a high degree of scientific literacy in their course of study.

The Authors and Senior Program Consultants

A TOUR OF YOUR TEXTBOOK

Welcome to *SCIENCEPOWER™ 9*. This textbook introduces you to the cellular processes that make reproduction possible, the atoms and molecules upon which our existence relies, the electricity that "lights up our lives," and the wonders of space that loom before us in the distance. To understand the book's structure, begin by taking a brief tour on the following pages.

UNIT OPENER

- *SCIENCEPOWER™ 9* has four major units.
- Each unit opener provides a clear overview of the unit's contents.
- The unit opener stimulates interest in the topic by suggesting a problem to think about, presenting science concepts to consider, or outlining a societal issue to explore.
- The unit opener identifies each chapter in the unit.

CHAPTER OPENER

- Each chapter opener gives you a clear idea of what this chapter is about.
- **Opening Ideas** give you a chance to think about what you already know (or do not know) about the topic.
- **Science Log** suggests various ways to answer the *Opening Ideas* questions, and provides an opportunity to keep a record of what you learn in the same way that scientists log their observations and the results of their findings. (Your teacher may call this record a *Science Journal* instead of a *Science Log*.)

- The **Starting Point Activity** launches each chapter in a variety of ways. Like the *Opening Ideas,* the *Starting Point Activity* helps you think about what you already know (or do not know) about the chapter's main topics.

- **Key Concepts, Key Skills,** and **Key Terms** focus your attention on the major concepts, skills, and terms that you will be expected to know by the time you have completed the chapter.

- The **introductory paragraphs** of each chapter invite you to learn more about the topic and clearly tell you what you will be studying in the chapter.

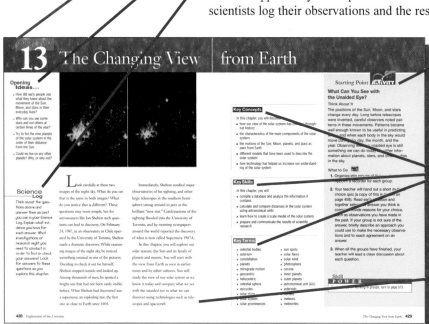

DESIGN & DO INVESTIGATIONS set challenges to design and construct, your own models, systems, or products.

- The co-operative group work icon shows that you will be doing these investigations in a team.
- The Design Criteria provide a framework for evaluating your results.
- You and your team members are then on your own to design and construct!

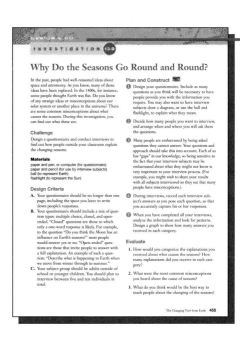

OUTSIDE LINK ACTIVITY

- This is a short, informal inquiry activity to do outside of class.
- Activities involve simple materials and equipment.

WordCONNECT

- Word origins and a variety of language activities provide links to language arts.

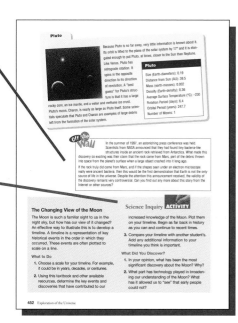

CONDUCT AN INVESTIGATION

- One- to four-page "formal" labs provide an opportunity to develop science inquiry skills using various equipment and materials.
- These investigations provide a chance to ask questions about science, to make observations, and to obtain results.
- You then analyze your results to determine what they tell you about the topic you are investigating.
- Safety icons and Safety Precautions alert you to any special precautions you should take.

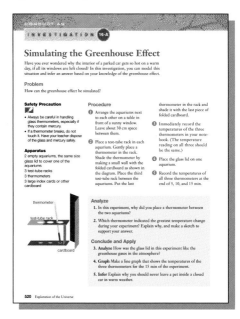

Off the Wall

- This item features intriguing situations, discrepant events, or weird facts.
- Ideas for connecting science with other curriculum areas are often included.

SCIENCE INQUIRY ACTIVITY

- This short, informal inquiry activity provides practice in science inquiry skills: predicting, estimating, hypothesizing, and so on.

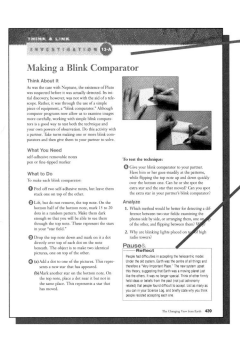

THINK & LINK INVESTIGATION

- These one- to two-page "thought" or "paper-based" investigations enable you to explore concepts or ideas that might be impractical and/or dangerous in the science classroom.
- These investigations emphasize a variety of skills, including data analysis, interpretation of a diagram or flowchart, issue analysis, and formulation of ideas, opinions, or recommendations based on a case study.

Pause & Reflect

- These items supply opportunities to reflect on what you know (or do not know) and to make connections among ideas throughout the text.
- This recurring feature encourages you to construct your own learning on an ongoing basis and to keep track of how your knowledge is building.

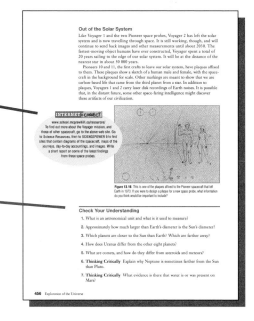

InternetCONNECT

- This feature encourages productive use of the Internet by offering content-appropriate sites.
- Web site suggestions will save you time as you do research.

CHECK YOUR UNDERSTANDING

- A set of review questions appears at the end of each numbered section in a chapter.
- These questions provide opportunities for ongoing self-assessment.
- "Apply" and "Thinking Critically" questions present additional challenges.

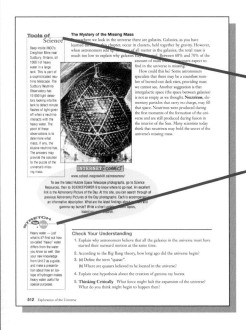

Tools of Science

- This feature provides information about some of the instruments and equipment invented to help us explore the unknown.
- The information is often related to a variety of occupations and situations.

Stretch Your Mind

- These brain teasers are often mathematics-related.
- They draw upon your problem-solving skills and your imagination.

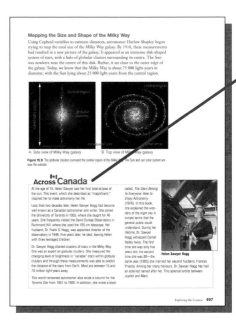

Mapping the Size and Shape of the Milky Way

Using Cepheid variables to estimate distances, astronomer Harlow Shapley began trying to map the total size of the Milky Way galaxy. By 1918, these measurements had resulted in a new picture of the galaxy. It appeared as an immense disk-shaped system of stars, with a halo of globular clusters surrounding its centre. The Sun was nowhere near the centre of this disk. Rather, it sat close to the outer edge of the galaxy. Today, we know that the Milky Way is about 75 000 light-years in diameter, with the Sun lying about 25 000 light-years from the central region.

A. Side view of Milky Way galaxy   B. Top view of Milky Way galaxy

Figure 15.9 The globular clusters surround the central region of the Milky Way. The Sun and our solar system are near the outside.

▌▲▐ Across Canada

At the age of 15, Helen Sawyer saw her first total eclipse of the sun. This event, which she described as "magnificent," inspired her to make astronomy her life.

Less than two decades later, Helen Sawyer Hogg had become well known as a Canadian astronomer and writer. She joined the University of Toronto in 1935, where she taught for 40 years. She frequently visited the David Dunlap Observatory in Richmond Hill, where she used the 185 cm telescope. Her husband, Dr. Frank S. Hogg, was appointed director of the observatory in 1946. Five years later, he died, leaving Helen with three teenaged children.

Dr. Sawyer Hogg charted clusters of stars in the Milky Way. She was an expert on globular clusters. She measured the changing level of brightness in 'variable' stars within globular clusters and through these measurements was able to predict the distance of the stars from Earth. Most are between 15 and 70 million light-years away.

This world-renowned astronomer also wrote a column for the *Toronto Star* from 1951 to 1980. In addition, she wrote a book

called, *The Stars Belong to Everyone: How to Enjoy Astronomy* (1976). In this book, she explained the wonders of the night sky in simple terms that the general public could understand. During her lifetime, Dr. Sawyer Hogg witnessed Comet Halley twice. The first time she was only five years old; the second time she was 80—the same year (1985) she married her second husband, Frances Priestly. Among her many honours, Dr. Sawyer Hogg has had an asteroid named after her. This asteroid orbits between Jupiter and Mars.

Helen Sawyer Hogg

Exploring the Cosmos **497**

Across Canada

- This "mini-essay" features information on Canadian scientists involved in important research and discoveries.
- *Across Canada* increases awareness and appreciation of the work of Canadian scientists, as well as providing role models for those of you interested in careers or further study in science.

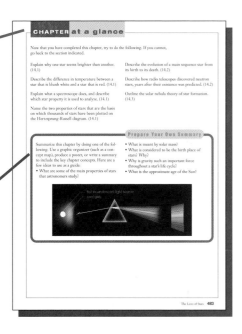

CHAPTER at a glance

Now that you have completed this chapter, try to do the following. If you cannot, go back to the section indicated.

Explain why one star seems brighter than another. (14.1)

Describe the difference in temperature between a star that is bluish white and a star that is red. (14.1)

Explain what a spectroscope does, and describe which star property it is used to analyze. (14.1)

Name the two properties of stars that are the basis on which thousands of stars have been plotted on the Hertzsprung-Russell diagram. (14.1)

Describe the evolution of a main sequence star from its birth to its death. (14.2)

Describe how radio telescopes discovered neutron stars, years after their existence was predicted. (14.2)

Outline the solar nebula theory of star formation. (14.3)

Prepare Your Own Summary

Summarize this chapter by doing one of the following. Use a graphic organizer (such as a concept map), produce a poster, or write a summary to include the key chapter concepts. Here are a few ideas to use as a guide:
- What are some of the main properties of stars that astronomers study?

- What is meant by solar mass?
- What is considered to be the birth place of stars? Why?
- Why is gravity such an important force throughout a star's life cycle?
- What is the approximate age of the Sun?

The Lives of Stars **483**

CHAPTER AT A GLANCE

- Located at the end of each chapter, this page provides self-assessment opportunities as you look back at the chapter as a whole.
- It gives parents or guardians an overview of what you have accomplished.
- **Prepare Your Own Summary** encourages you to summarize your understanding in a variety of ways — using diagrams, flowcharts, concept maps, artwork, and writing.

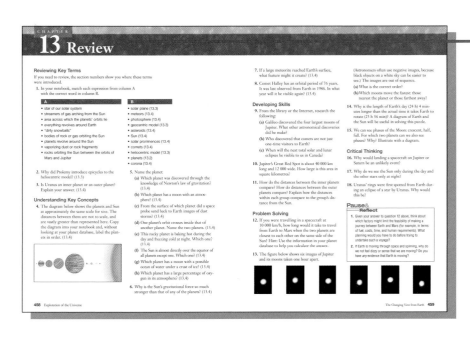

CHAPTER

13 Review

Reviewing Key Terms

If you need to review, the section numbers show you where these terms were introduced.

1. In your notebook, match each expression from column A with the correct word in column B.

A	B
• star of our solar system	• solar plane (13.3)
• streamers of gas arching from the Sun	• meteors (13.4)
• ansa across which the planets' orbits lie	• photospheres (13.4)
• everything revolves around Earth	• geocentric model (13.3)
• "dirty snowballs"	• asteroids (13.4)
• bodies of rock or gas orbiting the Sun	• Sun (13.4)
• planets revolve around the Sun	• solar prominences (13.4)
• vaporizing dust or rock fragments	• comets (13.4)
• rocks orbiting the Sun between the orbits of Mars and Jupiter	• heliocentric model (13.3)
	• planets (13.2)
	• corona (13.4)

2. Why did Ptolemy introduce epicycles to the heliocentric model? (13.3)

3. Is Uranus an inner planet or an outer planet? Explain your answer. (13.4)

Understanding Key Concepts

4. The diagram below shows the planets and Sun at approximately the same scale for size. The distances between them are not to scale, and are vastly greater than represented here. Copy the diagram into your notebook and, without looking at your planet database, label the planets in order. (13.4)

5. Name the planet:
(a) Which planet was discovered through the knowledge of Newton's law of gravitation? (13.4)
(b) Which planet has a moon with an atmosphere? (13.4)
(c) From the surface of which planet did a space probe send back to Earth images of dust storms? (13.4)
(d) One planet's orbit crosses inside that of another planet. Name the two planets. (13.4)
(e) This rocky planet is baking hot during the day and freezing cold at night. Which one? (13.4)
(f) The Sun is almost directly over the equator of all planets except one. Which one? (13.4)
(g) Which planet has a moon with a possible ocean of water under a crust of ice? (13.4)
(h) Which planet has a large percentage of oxygen in its atmosphere? (13.4)

6. Why is the Sun's gravitational force so much stronger than that of any of the planets? (13.4)

7. If a large meteorite reached Earth's surface, what feature might it create? (13.4)

8. Comet Halley has an orbital period of 76 years. It was last observed from Earth in 1986. In what year will it be visible again? (13.4)

Developing Skills

9. From the library or the Internet, research the following:
(a) Galileo discovered the four largest moons of Jupiter. What other astronomical discoveries did he make?
(b) Who discovered that comets are not just one-time visitors to Earth?
(c) When will the next total solar and lunar eclipses be visible to us in Canada?

10. Jupiter's Great Red Spot is about 40 000 km long and 12 000 km wide. How large is this area in square kilometres?

11. How do the distances between the inner planets compare? How do distances between the outer planets compare? Explain how the distances within each group compare to the group's distance from the Sun.

Problem Solving

12. If you were travelling in a spacecraft at 10 000 km/h, how long would it take to travel from Earth to Mars when the two planets are closest to each other on the same side of the Sun? Hint: Use the information in your planet database to help you calculate the answer.

13. The figure below shows six images of Jupiter and its moons taken one hour apart.

(Astronomers often use negative images, because black objects on a white sky can be easier to see.) The images are out of sequence.
(a) What is the correct order?
(b) Which moons move the fastest: those nearest the planet or those farthest away?

14. Why is the length of Earth's day (24 h) 4 minutes longer than the actual time it takes Earth to rotate (23 h 56 min)? A diagram of Earth and the Sun will be useful in solving this puzzle.

15. We can see phases of the Moon: crescent, half, full. For which two planets can we also see phases? Why? Illustrate with a diagram.

Critical Thinking

16. Why would landing a spacecraft on Jupiter or Saturn be an unlikely event?

17. Why do we see the Sun only during the day and the other stars only at night?

18. Uranus' rings were first spotted from Earth during an eclipse of a star by Uranus. Why would this be?

Pause & Reflect

1. Given your answer to question 12 above, think about which factors might limit the feasibility of making a journey between Earth and Mars (for example, in terms of fuel, costs, time, and human requirements). What planning would you have to do before trying to undertake such a voyage?

2. If Earth is moving through space and spinning, why do we not feel dizzy or sense that we are moving? Do you have any evidence that Earth is moving?

458 Exploration of the Universe

The Changing View from Earth **459**

CHAPTER REVIEW

- This final wrap-up of each chapter reviews basic concepts, skills of inquiry and communication, and skills relating science to technology, society, and the environment.
- These questions help you recall, think about, and apply what you have learned.

A Tour of Your Textbook **XV**

END OF UNIT FEATURES

ASK AN EXPERT

- Experts in every area of science and technology are working to understand better how the world "works" and to try to find solutions to difficult problems. The *Ask an Expert* feature at the end of each unit is an interview with one of these many people.
- After the interview, you will have a chance to do an activity that is related to the kind of work the expert does.

UNIT ISSUE ANALYSIS

- You, your community, and society in general face complex issues in today's world. Understanding science and technology cannot provide a "correct" answer to the problems these issues present, but understanding will lead to more informed decisions. A *Unit Issue Analysis* gives you a chance to start thinking now about how you can help make the best decisions for yourself and your community, today and in the future.
- The *Unit Issue Analysis* takes the form of a case study, a simulation, or a debate.

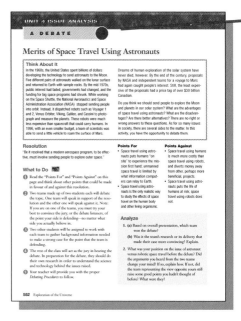

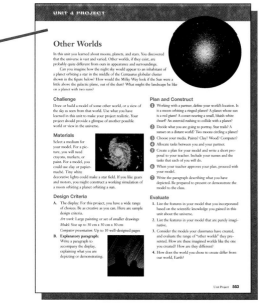

UNIT PROJECT

- A *Unit Project* gives you a chance to use key concepts and skills from the unit to build a device, system, or model of your own.
- Your teacher might ask you to begin to consider early in the unit how you might design, plan, and build your wrap-up project.
- You will complete the project as part of a team.

UNIT REVIEW

- Appearing at the end of each unit, a four-page *Unit Review* gives you one more opportunity to assess your understanding of the entire unit.

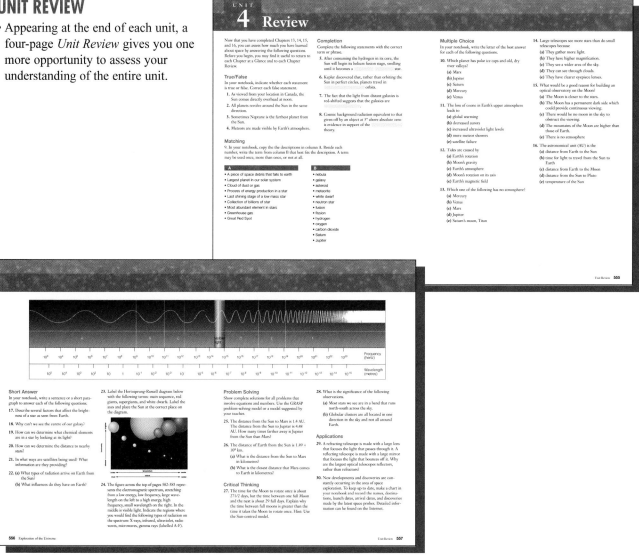

OTHER IMPORTANT FEATURES

DidYou**Know**?

- Presents interesting facts related to science, technology, nature, and the universe.

Skill POWER

- Skill development tips refer you to the *Science Skills Guide* at the back of the student text.
- These tips provide specific skill development strategies and activities as they are needed, for example, in use of the microscope and in scientific drawing.

Math CONNECT

- Reviews math skills as they are required to do activities.
- Makes connections between your science studies and your math studies.

Computer CONNECT

- Highlights opportunities where using spreadsheet or data base applications would be helpful.

Career CONNECT

- Portrays people with various levels of education making practical use of science and technology in their jobs.

WRAPPING UP THE TOUR

At the back of **SCIENCEPOWER™ 9,** you will find some additional features to help you review and develop skills and knowledge that you will need to be successful in this course. Are you having trouble with graphing? Would you like help setting up a data table? Have you forgotten how to make a concept map? Do you need a reminder about scientific notation? The *Science Skills Guide* will help you review and/or develop your skills. A *Glossary* provides all the key vocabulary for the whole course, and an *Index* will help you find your way to a topic.

Special Icons

The co-operative group work icon alerts you to opportunities to work within a group. The safety icons are extremely important because they alert you to any safety precautions you must take, for example, the need for safety goggles or a lab apron. Other safety icons used in this book are shown on page 597. Make certain you become familiar with what they mean, and make sure that you follow their precautions.

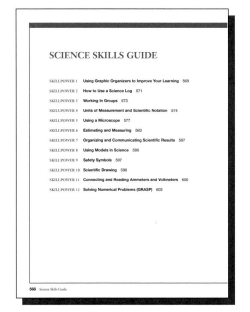

SCIENCE SKILLS GUIDE

568   Science Skills Guide

Safety in Your Science Classroom

Become familiar with the following safety rules and procedures. It is up to you to use them and your teacher's instructions to make your activities and investigations in *SCIENCEPOWER™ 9* safe and enjoyable. Your teacher will give you specific information about any other special safety rules to be used in your school.

1. **General Rules**
   - Listen carefully to any instructions your teacher gives you.
   - Inform your teacher if you have any allergies, medical conditions, or other physical problems that could affect your work in the science classroom. Tell your teacher if you wear contact lenses or a hearing aid.
   - Obtain your teacher's approval before beginning any activity or investigation you have designed yourself.
   - Know the location and proper use of the nearest fire extinguisher, fire blanket, first aid kit, and fire alarm.

2. **Before Each Activity or Investigation**
   - Before starting any activity or investigation, read all of it carefully. If you do not understand how to do a step, ask your teacher for help.
   - Be sure you have read and understand the *Safety Precautions*.
   - Begin an activity only after your teacher tells you to start.

3. **Special Dress Precautions**
   - When you are directed to do so, wear protective clothing, such as a lab apron, safety goggles, and/or safety gloves. Always wear protective clothing when you are using materials that could pose a safety problem, such as when you are using unidentified materials, or when you are heating anything.
   - Tie back long hair, and avoid wearing scarves, ties, long necklaces, and earrings.

4. **Doing Activities and Investigations**
   - Work carefully with a partner and make sure your work area is clear.
   - Handle equipment and materials carefully.
   - Make sure stools and chairs are resting securely on the floor.
   - If other students are doing something that you consider dangerous, report it to your teacher.
   - Do not chew gum, eat, or drink in your science classroom.
   - Do not taste any substances or draw any material into a tube with your mouth.
   - Make sure you understand all safety labels on school materials or those you bring from home. Familiarize yourself, as well, with the WHMIS symbols and the special safety symbols used in this book found on page 597.
   - Be careful when carrying equipment for an activity or investigation. Carry only one object or container at a time.
   - Be aware of others during activities and investigations. Make room for students who may be carrying equipment to their work station.

5. Sharp Object Precautions

- Always cut away from yourself and others when using a knife or razor blade.
- Always keep the pointed end of scissors or any pointed object facing away from yourself and others if you have to walk with such objects.
- If you notice sharp or jagged edges on any equipment, take special care with it and report it to your teacher.
- Dispose of broken glass as your teacher directs.

6. Electrical Equipment Precautions

- Make sure your hands are dry when touching electrical cords, plugs, or sockets.
- Pull the plug, not the cord when unplugging electrical equipment. Report damaged equipment or frayed cords to your teacher.
- Place electrical cords in places where people will not trip over them.

7. Heat Source Precautions

- Wear safety goggles, heat-resistant safety gloves, and any other safety equipment that the text or your teacher suggests, when heating any item.
- Always use heat-proof containers.
- Do not use broken or cracked containers.
- Point the open end of a container that is being heated away from yourself and others.
- Do not allow a container to boil dry.
- Handle hot objects carefully. Be especially careful with a hot plate that might look as though it has cooled down.
- If you use a Bunsen burner, make sure you understand how to light and use it safely.
- If you do receive a burn, inform your teacher. Apply cold water to the burned area immediately.

Use this method to smell a substance in the laboratory.

8. Chemical Precautions

- If any part of your body comes in contact with a potentially dangerous substance, wash the area immediately and thoroughly with water. If you get anything in your eyes, do not touch them. Wash them immediately and continuously for 15 min, and inform your teacher.
- Always handle substances carefully. If you are asked to smell a substance, never smell it directly. Hold the container slightly in front of and beneath your nose, and waft the fumes toward your nostrils, as shown here.
- Hold containers away from your face when pouring liquids, as shown on the next page.

9. Working with Living Things

On a field trip:

- Try not to disturb the area any more than is absolutely necessary.
- If you move something, do it carefully, and always replace it carefully.
- If you are asked to remove plant material, remove it gently, and take as little as possible.

In the classroom:

- Treat living creatures with respect.
- Make sure that living creatures receive humane treatment while they are in your care.
- If possible, return living creatures to their natural environment when your work is complete.

10. Cleaning Up in the Science Classroom

- Clean up any spills, according to your teacher's instructions.
- Clean equipment before you put it away.
- Wash your hands thoroughly after doing an activity or an investigation.
- Dispose of materials as directed by your teacher. Never discard materials in the sink unless your teacher requests it.

11. Technology Projects

- Use tools safely to cut, join, and shape objects.
- Handle modelling clay correctly. Wash your hands after using modelling clay.
- Follow proper procedures when comparing mechanical systems and their operations.
- Use special care when observing and working with objects in motion (e.g., objects that spin, swing, bounce, or vibrate; gears and pulleys; and elevated objects).
- Do not use power equipment such as drills, sanders, saws, and lathes unless you have specialized training in handling such tools. Make sure you obtain information and support for designing and building devices from a specialist teacher in this area for all *Design & Do Investigations* and *Unit Projects* that ask you to design and build models and/or devices or structures.

Instant Practice

1. Select four or five of the main safety points listed and use them to create a poster that communicates the message of the importance of safety.

2. Use the *SkillPower* on page 597 to ensure you are familiar with all of the safety icons used in this textbook and in workplaces.

What is science? What is technology? How are they related and what do they mean to each of us and to society at large, especially in terms of the environment in which we live? In your grade 9 course, you will be actively involved in science investigations, gaining new skills and knowledge. You will be asked to consider relationships among science, technology, society, and the environment (abbreviated STSE). Today, science and technology affect everyone. Whether you decide to become a scientist or a technologist yourself, or whether you are more interested in other areas — from art to architecture, from music to mechanics — you will need to know the basic concepts and skills you will develop in this program. Start with the *Instant Practice* below to consider what you already know about the nature of science and technology.

Instant Practice

Close your textbook and, as a class, have a brainstorming session. List the first 5 to 10 ideas that come to mind when you consider each of these words:
- science
- technology
- society
- environment

Science, Technology, and Society

You and your classmates probably thought of a number of important ideas about what each of the terms "science" and "technology" mean. Because everyone comes from a slightly different background, there were probably a number of different opinions expressed about the meanings of these terms.

Some people think of science as a body of knowledge or facts. It *is* that, but it is more than that. Science is also a way of thinking, a "mind-set" which you will explore throughout this course. Likewise, many people think of technology as applied science, and it certainly can be that. Again, however, technology is also a process. Think about this. People used technology long before they understood the science behind the processes they were using. Egyptian wall paintings, for example, show many scenes of people wearing jewellery, such as this one of the Egyptian queen, Nefertari. This means that people were extracting metals from ores about 2000 years before the chemical process involved was understood.

Nefertari, Egyptian queen

Basically, science asks questions that aim to increase our understanding of the physical universe and our ability to explain nature. Technology aims to design and develop devices and processes for practical purposes. For example, science asks questions about how gravity and friction act. On the other hand, technology gave us the wheel long before people understood gravity and friction through years and years of scientific inquiry.

How can you easily grasp what science, technology, and society are, especially in terms of issues surrounding our environment? The diagram below presents one way to think about the meanings of these words and the interrelationships among these concepts.

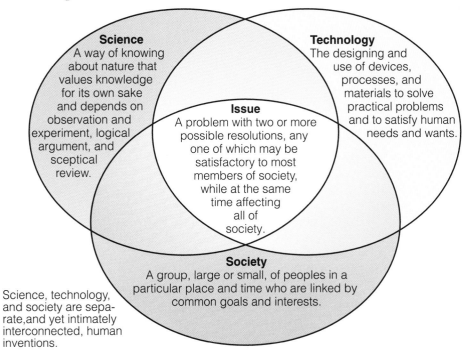

Science
A way of knowing about nature that values knowledge for its own sake and depends on observation and experiment, logical argument, and sceptical review.

Technology
The designing and use of devices, processes, and materials to solve practical problems and to satisfy human needs and wants.

Issue
A problem with two or more possible resolutions, any one of which may be satisfactory to most members of society, while at the same time affecting all of society.

Society
A group, large or small, of peoples in a particular place and time who are linked by common goals and interests.

Science, technology, and society are separate, and yet intimately interconnected, human inventions.

Science and Science Inquiry

You have just read that science involves understanding and explaining nature. However, when you think about nature, science is probably not the first thing that comes to mind. You might think about a grassy hillside on a warm summer evening. You see the grass and the trees and hear a frog croaking in a pond. You look up at the evening sky and, although it is still light, you can see the Moon and a star. In a few hours, the darkened sky will be filled with many sparkling stars. An artist or a poet may try to capture the beauty of this scene in a painting or verse. A scientist will ask questions about the same scene and then seek answers using the methods of science inquiry.

Why do frogs croak? How far away is that star? Why does day become night? How did that huge rock end up in the middle of a field when there are no other rocks like it anywhere nearby? Why did lightning hit that tall tree and how could it do so much damage? What makes red streaks in those rocks? The questions could go on and on, seemingly forever. No one can possibly learn all the answers to questions that scientists have wondered about over the centuries. How, therefore, can you find answers to specific questions?

Knowledge in science is organized by dividing it into logical categories. Each category is subdivided several times. The concept map below shows one way to categorize scientific knowledge. There are many more subdivisions for each category presented.

By following the concept map, you can figure out where to look for the answer to the question, "Why do frogs croak?" First, you would go to print or electronic resources in the life sciences category because frogs are living creatures. Then you would look up zoology, the study of animals. Further subdivisions would lead you to a group of cold-blooded animals, called amphibians. Amphibians can live on land or in water but they always begin their lives and go through their early development stages in water. By exploring further in this way, you would eventually discover why frogs croak.

Categories of Science

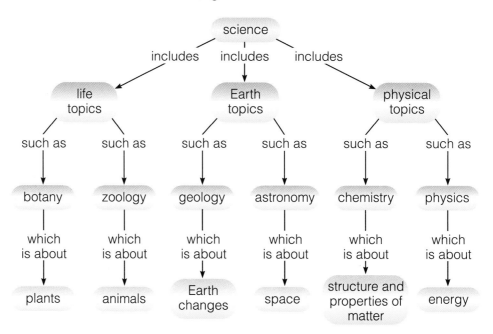

Although no one can master all scientific knowledge, everyone can learn enough in each major category to permit a focus of interest, and a good general overview. In this course, you will gain knowledge in four different categories. First, you will learn how and why plants and animals reproduce. Where would you add this subtopic to the concept map? Next, you will find out about atoms and their properties and how scientists were able to discover objects that are much too small to see. Where do atoms fit in the concept map? Then you will learn about the characteristics of electricity, how scientists learned about these characteristics, and how we can use electricity in beneficial ways. In which category in the concept map does the subtopic "electricity" belong? Finally, you will learn about Earth's place in the universe. How did the solar system form? What is a galaxy? How far away are the stars?

You will probably discover that one category interests you more than another. In fact, you might discover a career that you could enjoy for many years to come. Even if you do not choose to pursue science as a career, you will gather information in four areas of knowledge that will help make you a scientifically literate person. You will then be able to contribute to the decision-making processes that are so important in society today.

Science Inquiry

How has this body of knowledge, called science, been accumulated? Why has this tremendous amount of knowledge been accumulated? It all starts with curiosity, with someone asking "how?" or "why?" Scientists' curiosity motivates them to find answers to questions. The most valid answers are found by using a logical, step-by-step process. As more and more curious individuals have sought answers and communicated their methods and results with each other, they developed an orderly process of asking and investigating scientific questions. One model of science inquiry is shown in the diagram.

As you have seen, science includes an accumulated body of knowledge. Science is also, however, a unique method of thinking or inquiry that allows us to find answers to questions about the world around us. As well, and equally as important, science allows us to learn about ourselves.

What is science inquiry and why is it so useful in answering questions? An example will help clarify the science inquiry process. In your mind, go back to that grassy hillside and imagine that you are observing some objects fall. Why does one leaf seem to glide from side to side when it falls? Why does that seed twirl on its path to the ground? Why does a walnut fall straight down? For that matter, why does any object fall to the ground in the first place?

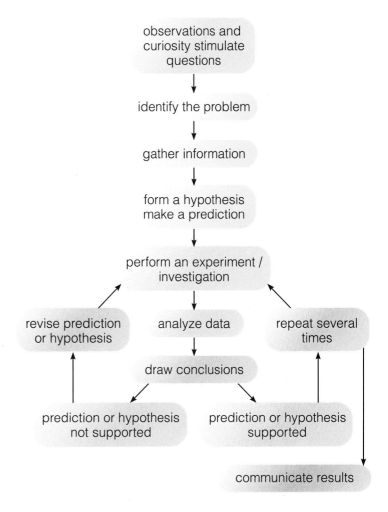

The answer to the last question is found in the **Law** of Universal Gravitation. All massive objects attract each other. Since Earth is enormous, it exerts a large attractive force — the force of gravity — on all objects. Thus, objects fall to the ground when they drop from a height.

> **law:** an action or condition that has been observed so consistently that scientists are convinced it will always happen. A law has no theoretical basis. In previous studies, you probably learned about the two laws of reflection, for example.

Now that you know why something falls, you can formulate your own question about why an object falls in a particular way. How do the characteristics of the object itself influence its motion during its fall? To answer this question, you will need to state the problem clearly and narrow the investigation down to one, specific object that you can control. Even when you study one object, many characteristics of the object might influence its motion. These characteristics are called the **variables** of the investigation.

You must control all of the variables except one when you make observations. The one factor or variable that you change is called the **independent** (or **manipulated**) **variable.** The factor or variable that changes as a result of the independent variable is called the **dependent** (or **responding**) **variable**. If you change two different variables at the same time, you will not know which one was responsible for the effect that you observed. If your investigation is to be valid and unbiased (a **fair test**), you must carry out the procedure in precisely the same way more than once, changing only the variable you are measuring. Many experiments have a **control** — a treatment or experiment that you can compare with the result of your test groups.

> **variable:** any factor that will influence the outcome of an experiment

In an investigation of the motion of a particular falling object, the height of the falling object above the ground is a variable.

Next, review all of the information that you already have about the object. You have acquired this information through your **observations** .

> **Qualitative observations:** describe something using only words; for example, a yellow short-haired dog. **Quantitative observations:** use numbers as well as words to describe something; for example, a dog with a mass of 14 kg, a height of 46 cm, an ear length of 10 cm, and an age of 150 days.

Use the information obtained through your observations to formulate a **hypothesis**. Design an **experiment** to test your hypothesis. Carry out the investigation, then record your data and analyze the results. Did your results support or contradict the hypothesis? If the data you recorded during the investigation did not support your hypothesis, review the results and formulate a new hypothesis, then start the testing process again. Even if the data did support your hypothesis, you must repeat the experiment at least once more. Scientific evidence must be reproducible.

hypothesis: a possible explanation for a question or observation, stated in a way that makes it testable. Example: If a plant is deprived of water, then it will begin to wilt.

experiment: an activity or procedure designed to falsify a hypothesis. It may seem strange to attempt to prove something wrong. However, it is not possible to prove something to be absolutely true because there might always be one more experiment that would reveal a flaw. It only takes one experiment to falsify a hypothesis. If you do not falsify a hypothesis, then the results support it.

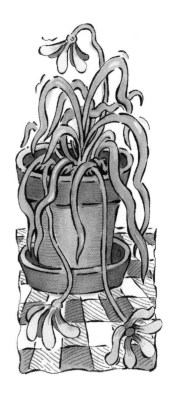

Experimental results and **conclusions** can contribute to the growing body of scientific knowledge only if they are communicated. Scientists communicate their findings by submitting articles to scientific journals, by presenting papers at conferences, and by discussing their work with colleagues. Before an article is published in a print resource, other scientists review it to ensure that the research and conclusions are based on proper methods of science inquiry.

conclusion: an interpretation of the results of an experiment as it applies to the hypothesis being tested. Example: Based on quantitative data for gasoline consumption, we found that regular gasoline is more efficient than premium gasoline.

As a final step in the science inquiry process, you write a report on your experiment, presenting the procedural results clearly so that someone else who reads your report could repeat the experiment. End your report with a discussion of your interpretation of the results and the conclusion.

The example you just read is a **model** of science inquiry designed to show you how scientific knowledge accumulates. However, this model is the first phase in a broader process. When many different scientists make observations based on the same hypothesis, and come to the same conclusions, the hypothesis gains more and more support. Eventually, scientists agree that the hypothesis has been tested so thoroughly that it should be universally accepted. At this point, the hypothesis has earned the status of a **theory**.

model: a mental image, diagram, structure, or mathematical expression that attempts to explain a concept or hypothesis. A working model of a volcano can be made from clay, a small amount of baking soda, vinegar, and a bottle cap. Other models can be devised on a computer.

theory: an explanation of an observation or event that has been supported by consistent, repeated experimental results, and has therefore been accepted by a majority of scientists. In earlier studies, you learned about the particle theory of matter. Another example is Einstein's theory of relativity.

Now that you have reviewed the key processes of science inquiry, you are ready to use the processes yourself. Do the *Conduct an Investigation* on the following pages to get the experience you need before carrying out activities and investigations throughout this book.

Observing Falling Motion

In this investigation, you will put your knowledge of science inquiry to work. You will look for variables that affect the falling motion of a structure called a rotocopter. The directions for making a rotocopter are given in the diagrams on the right.

Some features of the rotocopter that might affect its falling motion are the length of the blades, the length of the stem, the width of the blades, the weight (number of paper clips attached), and the stiffness of the paper. These are **independent variables** (sometimes called manipulated variables) because they do not depend on the design you have chosen. The features of the rotocopter will influence the rate at which the rotocopter falls or the rate at which it rotates while falling. These motions are **dependent variables** (sometimes called responding variables) because they depend on the design you have chosen.

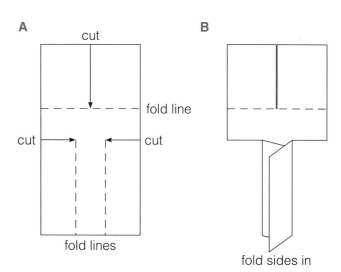

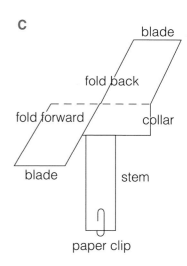

Problem

Find at least two relationships between a feature of the rotocopter (an independent variable) and motion while falling (a dependent variable).

Safety Precautions

Be careful when using sharp objects such as scissors.

Apparatus
ruler
pencil
scissors
paper clips

Materials
paper (several different types with varying thickness and stiffness)

Procedure

1. Each member of the group will choose the type of paper and the dimensions of his or her own rotocopter and then build it.

2. Make observations about the falling motion of rotocopters. The group as a whole will observe the motion of each rotocopter in order to collect general information about the falling motion. When dropping the rotocopters, hold them by the tips of their blades, about 2 m above the floor, and let them fall freely.

3. As a group, choose at least two different, independent variables to test. For each of the variables that the group chooses, formulate a hypothesis that predicts how the variable will affect the falling motion.

4 Choose a basic design and decide exactly how you will vary each feature of the rotocopter you have decided to test. For example, if you choose to test the effect of the stiffness of the paper, all of the rotocopters must be identical in size and shape. If you choose to test the width of the blade, then the type of paper and the length of the blade and the stem must remain the same for each rotocopter. Only one feature can be varied at a time.

5 For each of the variables that you have chosen to test, build at least three rotocopters with variations in that feature only.

6 Test your rotocopters, as shown in the photograph. Test only one variable at a time. To make good comparisons, have different members of the group hold the rotocopters at the same height and drop them at the same time. As they fall, observe the rate of rotation and observe the order in which they reach the floor. Carry out at least five trials on each of the variations you are testing.

Analyze

1. Was there a relationship between either one of your independent variables and the rate of rotation? If so, state the relationship.

2. Was there a relationship between either one of your independent variables and the rate of fall? If so, state the relationship.

Conclude and Apply

3. Did your results support or falsify your hypotheses? Explain.

4. Write a statement describing any relationship between an independent variable and a dependent variable that you observed.

Technology and Technological Problem Solving

Engineers, architects, technologists, and designers use technological problem-solving skills to develop technologies that solve specific problems or challenges. As stated earlier, technology is any tool, device, or technique that humans use to help do work or to make daily life easier.

Technological devices can be simple or complex. For example, a shovel is a simple technology that makes it easier to dig a hole. Precision lasers are complex devices that specially trained physicians can use to perform delicate brain or eye surgery, for example. Today, technology can be developed or improved more easily if we know and understand the science that makes it work. As you have read, however, it has not always been necessary to know the science first. Some technology has been developed simply as a response to a challenge, without complete scientific understanding, and that will probably continue.

Children use their own experiences all the time with little knowledge of science to solve technological problems they encounter in their daily lives. For example, if they need to cross a shallow stream or puddle without getting their feet wet, they put a wooden plank across it. As a child, perhaps you clipped a card to your bicycle to create a buzzing noise as the card hit the spokes of the wheel when you pedalled. You were probably not thinking about the science involved. However, you *were* using technological problem-solving skills. You were also using your own prior experience and knowledge about sound, materials, and fasteners. The flowchart below shows the basic steps in the process of technological problem-solving:

Solving a Technological Problem

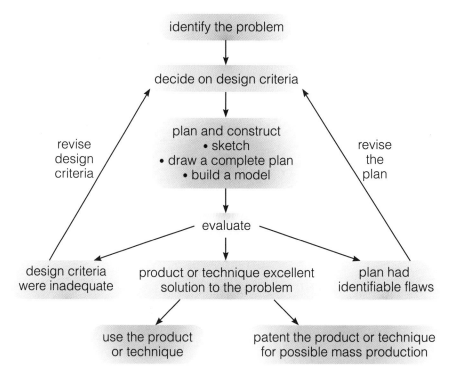

Instant Practice

Using the flowchart for Solving a Technological Problem, consider the challenge mentioned earlier — to make a buzzing sound as a bicycle moves.

1. What was the child's challenge or problem?

2. What were some design criteria the child might want to consider?

3. What planning would the child need to do before constructing the "buzz-making" device?

4. How would the child most likely evaluate the buzz-maker?

Technological Problem Solving in This Course

You will use technological problem-solving skills in this course in a type of investigation called *Design & Do*. This kind of investigation asks you to develop strategies for meeting a challenge. You will be asked to develop and carry out a plan based on specific design criteria. You will also be asked to evaluate the plan, and to reflect on and communicate the results. It is unlikely that you will try to patent any of your products or techniques, but who knows!

Look at the design for a flying machine conceptualized and sketched by Leonardo da Vinci, the great Italian inventor and artist of the fifteenth century. Consider what object in nature might have given him some of his ideas for the flying machine shown here (he thought of and designed many others, as well). Use the same rotocoptor design you used in the Science and Science Inquiry section to solve a technological problem. You've seen how this design can be used to ask a science-related question. How can this same simple design be used to address a technological problem?

How to Make a 'Copter Fall As Slowly As Possible

You work for an airplane manufacturer early in the 1900s. Airplanes have been invented recently and are flying successfully. You and some of your colleagues have an idea. Is it possible to build a flying machine that has a rotor at the top of it so it will lift straight up and also land upright? Think of some of the places you could travel to in such a vehicle. You start your thinking and planning with paper, cardboard, and paper clips in your company's office. By the way, this is not so different from how ideas for many inventions were first conceived!

Challenge

Design and construct a rotocopter that will take the longest time to fall to the ground from a height of 2 m and that will remain intact for three trials.

Materials

construction paper or poster board, pencil, ruler, paper clips, scissors, stopwatch or watch with a second hand

Safety Precaution

Be careful when using sharp objects such as scissors.

Design Criteria

A. Your rotocopter must be designed and built by a team of students in no more than 20 min.

B. Your rotocopter must withstand three drops.

C. It must be no more than 30 cm long and no more than 10 cm wide.

D. The stabilizer of your rotocopter must be no more than 30 cm long.

E. You must use at least one paper clip.

F. You must draw a clearly labelled sketch before you begin to construct your rotocopter.

Plan and Construct

1. Brainstorm as many ideas as you can about how rotocopters behave when they are dropped. Consider what you learned in the previous investigation about the characteristics of rotocopters. How could you modify the design to meet the design criteria of this challenge, based on what you learned in the first investigation?

2. (a) Consider a few possible designs and make rough sketches of them.

   (b) Select the design that you think will work best. Check once more to ensure it meets all the design criteria.

3. Make a detailed sketch of your selected design. Label the rotor, the stabilizer, and their dimensions (measurements), as well as the position and number of paper clips you will use. Show your design to your teacher.

④ Use the materials provided to build your roto-copter design.

⑤ (a) Each model is allowed three trials.

(b) Drop the rotocopter from a height of 2 m, and time how long it takes to reach the ground. Record the results in a table like this one.

⑥ Calculate the average time for each group's roto-copter to fall to the ground. Which design had the slowest falling time?

Group	Dimensions used	Materials used	Time in trial # 1	Time in trial # 2	Time in trial # 3	Average time

Evaluate

1. Evaluate your design. Consider the dimensions and materials of the slowest falling rotocopter. If your design was not the slowest (or did not withstand three drops), how would you revise it? What was the same and what was different between your model and the slowest one?

2. If you have enough time and the appropriate materials, make a revised model. Test your new rotocopter against the one that fell most slowly. How does your rotocopter's falling time compare now?

Societal Decision Making

In your science course this year, you will often be asked to think about interactions among science, technology, society, and the environment (abbreviated STSE). Why? No one lives in isolation from one another, the environment, and the effects of science and technology on our lives. For example, the photograph above was taken by astronauts who were orbiting the Moon. At the time (1968), the use of technology for space travel seemed new and exciting. This image of Earth made people throughout the world aware of our environment's fragility in a way that nothing else ever had.

Today, hundreds of unpiloted satellites are orbiting Earth. Each year, astronauts ride space shuttles into orbit to release more satellites, repair existing ones, and carry out science experiments that cannot be performed on Earth's surface. Some orbiting space stations have been continuously occupied for years.

STSE interactions often lead to issues that range from public to personal. For example:

- *Space junk* is largely an environmental issue. Older nonworking satellites may break apart and spiral to Earth, causing damage and requiring costly cleanup efforts. Should these satellites be removed from orbit before this can happen? If so, who is responsible for retrieving them?

- *Funding space programs* is an economic issue. Space travel costs an enormous amount of money, much of which is raised through taxes. Some people ask, "Why not use this money to solve problems, such as poverty, here on Earth?"

Issues like these can be addressed more effectively by societies made up of scientifically literate citizens: those able to sort information from misinformation and to evaluate whether claims made in the name of science are valid or invalid.

This textbook is designed to help you progress toward scientific literacy. The knowledge and thinking skills you develop as a result will help you become scientifically literate. The same thinking skills can be used throughout your life to help you make important decisions about personal and community issues.

Science can provide basic information to help you evaluate risks, but science alone is not enough to make final decisions about either public or personal issues. Art, literature, philosophy, music, history, and cultural beliefs — each may play a part in influencing how each person interprets our world. All viewpoints should be examined with respect. This textbook's content will help you to appreciate and understand the science underlying many societal issues that will arise in the future, and it also provides you with critical skills and concepts you need to succeed in future science courses.

Use the Developing Decision-Making Skills flowchart shown here as a guide to analyzing issues.

Your **SCIENCEPOWER™ 9** textbook, in general, promotes an understanding of issue analysis, but two special features will be especially useful in helping you to develop your decision-making skills.

Many of the *Think & Link* investigations in this textbook examine issues. All of the *Unit Issue Analysis* activities provide an issue to debate, a simulation to role-play, or a case study giving you experience in developing your critical-thinking and decision-making skills.

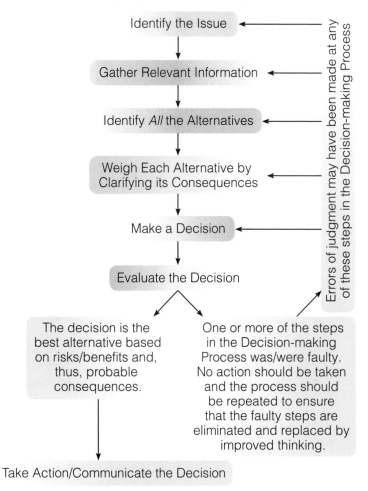

Developing Decision-making Skills

Identify the Issue

Gather Relevant Information

Identify *All* the Alternatives

Weigh Each Alternative by Clarifying its Consequences

Make a Decision

Evaluate the Decision

The decision is the best alternative based on risks/benefits and, thus, probable consequences.

One or more of the steps in the Decision-making Process was/were faulty. No action should be taken and the process should be repeated to ensure that the faulty steps are eliminated and replaced by improved thinking.

Take Action/Communicate the Decision

Errors of judgment may have been made at any of these steps in the Decision-making Process

Instant Practice

1. Describe how each of the following technological developments affected society positively (a "benefit"):
   (a) television
   (b) electricity
   (c) telephone
   (d) jet aircraft
   (e) mass production of the automobile

2. Now describe one or two ways in which the above technology has affected society negatively (a "risk").

3. For each of the technologies in question 1, identify what kinds of science understandings were necessary for its development.

4. Analyze the two following quotations, discussing them with others, and explain what they mean:

> (a) "Science and technology are essential social enterprises, but alone they can only indicate what can happen, not what should happen. [What should happen] involves human decisions about the use of knowledge."
>
> NATIONAL SCIENCE EDUCATION STANDARDS
>
> (b) "Attention to the language of the discourse is important. Much clarification can be gained by focusing on the language as an expression of values and priorities. Whenever someone talks to you about benefits and costs of a particular project, don't ask 'What benefit?', ask 'Whose benefits and whose costs?'".
>
> DR. URSULA FRANKLIN, PROFESSOR EMERITUS OF CHEMICAL AND MECHANICAL ENGINEERING, UNIVERSITY OF TORONTO, AND HUMAN RIGHTS ACTIVIST

5. Identify whether each of the following is a question of science, a question of technology, or an STSE issue. Explain each of your answers.
    (a) How much anti-freeze do I need to add to my car's radiator in winter?
    (b) Why don't frogs freeze to death in Canadian winters?
    (c) Why can't a landfill site be built on this property?
    (d) What are the causes of cancer?

6. Did you identify any of the items in question 5 as an issue? If so, use it or another issue of your choice to begin getting some practice using the *Developing Decision-Making Skills* flowchart.
    (a) Identify the issue.
    (b) Where would you go to begin gathering relevant information? Provide three or four sources.
    (c) What alternatives do there appear to be?

The Power of Reproduction

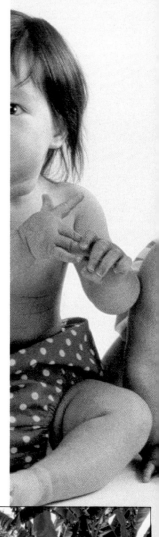

Perhaps the greatest difference between living and non-living things is that living things are able to reproduce, or make more of themselves. Recognizing the power of reproduction helped people of ancient times develop agriculture and domesticate animals. Understanding the power of reproduction has helped modern scientists develop medicines, such as antibiotics, as well as new varieties of food plants, such as Canola.

This banana plantation is the product of asexual reproduction, in which many identical plants develop from a single parent. Similarly, all McIntosh apple trees are descended from a single original plant. Techniques to produce plants with desirable features were first developed centuries ago, and are still being improved.

In contrast, these babies are far from identical. They are the product of sexual reproduction, which brings two parents together to produce offspring that differ from each other and from either parent.

Asexual and sexual reproduction depend on the basic unit of life — the cell. In fact, your own growth and development involve cellular processes in which your body cells "reproduce," or divide to make identical copies of themselves. Understanding the cellular processes of reproduction is an ongoing journey of scientific discovery that has taken many years and will continue for many more. Every technology has benefits and risks associated with it. As new reproductive technologies are developed to increase food production, reduce disease, and improve genetic therapies, society must continually weigh the benefits and risks.

Unit Contents

1

The Cell Cycle

Opening Ideas...

- How do organisms grow?
- How do broken bones mend?
- How do people age?
- What is cancer?
- How do organisms make more of themselves?

110 x

Science Log

In your Science Log, answer the above questions as best you can, recalling your previous studies and what you have read or heard from other sources. Look for answers to these questions as you explore this chapter.

These students are part of a research project investigating wetland habitats. They are studying the plants and microscopic organisms that live in a pond environment. If you could examine this scene at the cellular level, you would find that these students have something in common with the organisms they are researching. The cells that make up the students, the water plants, and the one-celled organisms scooped up in the sample container all grow and divide.

The cell and its extraordinary abilities have been a focus of human study for the last two centuries. In this chapter, you will retrace the scientific journey that led to an understanding of the cell as the basic unit of life. You will also observe the cycle responsible for cell growth and reproduction, and explore the asexual reproduction of organisms.

Skill POWER

For tips on how to use a Science Log, turn to page 571.

and Asexual Reproduction

Key Concepts

In this chapter, you will discover
- how the cell theory was developed
- the important role that mitosis and cell division play in the cell cycle
- the various types of asexual reproduction in living organisms
- some advantages and disadvantages to asexual reproduction
- how knowledge of asexual reproduction is used in plant production

Key Skills

In this chapter, you will
- update your skills in using a microscope to observe the process of cell division
- predict the number of cell divisions required to produce a certain number of organisms
- investigate the phases of mitosis and cell division
- research a number of issues, integrating information from a variety of sources and presenting your findings

Key Terms

- cell theory
- organelles
- nucleus
- DNA
- chromatin
- nucleolus
- ribosomes
- cell membrane
- cytoplasm
- endoplasmic reticulum
- mitochondria
- Golgi bodies
- vacuoles

- lysosomes
- cell wall
- chloroplasts
- mitosis
- replication
- chromosomes
- centromere
- prophase
- metaphase
- anaphase
- telophase
- spindle fibres
- centrioles

- cell plate
- interphase
- cell cycle
- regeneration
- asexual reproduction
- binary fission
- fragmentation
- budding
- spore
- meristem
- cloning

Skill POWER

To review the safety symbols used in this book, turn to page 597.

What's in the Pond?

Imagine that you are part of a student research team studying a pond. What kinds of organisms might you expect to find in a drop of pond water? Unicellular (one-celled)? Multicellular (many-celled)? Take a look under a microscope to find out.

What to Do

1. Before you do this activity, make sure you have thorough knowledge and skills for proper microscope handling techniques and effective use of a microscope. Turn to page 577 and practise the techniques described there.

2. Obtain a drop of pond water.

3. Prepare a wet mount by placing the drop of water on a slide, using a medicine dropper. Carefully place the cover slip at an angle of about 45° at one edge of the drop, slowly releasing it over the entire drop. If you have too much water in the drop, place a tissue at the edge of the cover slip to draw the excess water up.

4. Now you are ready to observe your wet mount under the low-power lens of your microscope. What can you see? Change carefully to medium power, focus, and then go to high power. What can you see now?

5. Draw the organisms and try to identify them.

6. Wash your hands after this activity.

What Did You Discover?

1. Your teacher will give you some illustrations of common pond organisms. Use these to help identify the organisms you see.

2. Note whether you think each organism is unicellular or multicellular.

1.1 The Cell: Understanding the Basic Unit of Life

Today we know that all the living organisms in these photographs are made up of one or more cells. However, we have not always had this knowledge. The human journey into the cell stretches over many centuries and involves many people and cultures. In this section, you will retrace the development of **cell theory** — that the cell is the basic unit of life — and explore its fundamental role in biology, the study of life. You will also look into the cell itself to see cell structures and processes at work. Understanding the cell as the basic unit of life will draw on your previous knowledge about cells and on your ability to use a microscope.

Pause& Reflect

Do a knowledge check on what you already know about cells and microscopes. Try to answer the following questions in your Science Log. Then update your knowledge as you work through this section.

- How do we know that the cell is the basic unit of life?

- How are plant and animal cells alike and how are they different?

- What must you know about the microscope and its parts to use it effectively?

Figure 1.1 All organisms begin life as a single cell. Redwood trees that grow to a height of more than 90 m, blue whales that have a mass of more than 100 t, microscopic organisms, and every person in your class began as a single cell.

A Theory is Born

Think About It

The history of science includes periods when remarkable progress in knowledge was made in a fairly short time. For instance, there were periods during which scientific ideas about life pointed gradually and increasingly toward what became known as the *cell theory*. Like many important ideas in science, the cell theory combines, or *synthesizes*, the contributions of a great many people. In its final form, the cell theory was synthesized by one person, German physiologist Rudolph Virchow (1821-1902). In this investigation, you will trace the scientific, technological, and social developments that led to this synthesis.

What to Do

1 On pages 6 to 9, you will see the four-page Cell Theory Timeline, which summarizes several centuries of biological history. The information is set up to show you how various ideas led to other ideas. You might find it useful to work in a group of three, with three copies of SCIENCEPOWER™ 9 available. That way, you can open one book to this page, the second book to page 6, and the third book to page 8.

2 Before you begin to explore the Cell Theory Timeline, study the colour key below. It defines four categories of historical information:

COLOUR 1 scientific developments (discoveries, theories, ideas)

COLOUR 2 reactions and attitudes (of scientists or of the general public)

COLOUR 3 technological developments (tools or techniques that led to scientific discoveries)

COLOUR 4 scientific communications (books, letters, lectures)

Skill
POWER

For tips on working in groups, turn to page 573.

3 Scan the timeline to find one example of each category above. Notice the kind of information each example contains. Trace each example back to the date line. What year did each event happen?

4 Read across the timeline to view the progression of discoveries that built up biological knowledge of cells, bit by bit. To form a picture of the science, attitudes, and beliefs of people during a particular time period, you may find it helpful to continue tracing each event back to the date line. Use the following points as guidelines to help you summarize the most important information in your notebook:

- When were cells first seen? Next seen? Seen as the basic unit of life?

- What technological developments made each of these events possible?

- What was the public reaction to each event? The scientific reaction?

- Did public and scientific attitudes help or hinder progress?

5 The cell theory, as we now know it, was first stated in the 1850s by Rudolph Virchow in a series of 20 lectures. Scientists make a demanding audience, so Virchow had to build up the background picture for them before presenting his synthesis. Read the timeline and try to see the big picture as Virchow saw it. Then select the most essential issues. What main points do you think Virchow made? Record these in your notebook. What evidence might he have presented to change the minds of those who challenged/opposed his ideas?

6 After completing the above steps, turn to page 10 and answer the questions. If possible, leave two books open so that the entire timeline is still visible.

CONTINUED

Cell Theory Timeline

ANCIENT TIMES

People everywhere focus on how living organisms can be used. They pass along their accumulated knowledge to the next generation orally.

1268: First recorded reference is made to eyeglasses from the writings of English friar and philosopher Roger Bacon (1214?-1294).

1600s
Scientists debate the nature of reproduction. Where does life come from? Some say the appearance of mushrooms on logs and maggots in unsalted meat supports Aristotle's theory of spontaneous generation — that living organisms can arise from non-living matter.

Scholars, such as English physician William Harvey (1578-1657), begin to look directly at nature. This defies strongly held views about the origin of life. Harvey says maggots hatch from eggs too small to be seen.

500 B.C.E.: Some civilizations, such as Ancient Greece, support full-time scholars, who ask questions about life, but seek answers through thought rather than observation or experiment.

---

ancient times   **1500**   **1600**

c334 B.C.E.: One scholar, Greek philosopher Aristotle (384-322 B.C.E.), does observe nature directly. He (1) classifies all known organisms into two kingdoms: plant and animal; (2) visualizes a "ladder of life" with plants on the bottom rungs; (3) writes that living organisms can arise spontaneously from non-living matter.

1500s
Most European scholars regard knowledge as unchangeable. For information about nature, they rely on ancient books based on Aristotle's original writings.

1662: English monarch King Charles II (1636-1685) grants a charter to the Royal Society of London for the Promotion of Natural Knowledge.

1590: Dutch eyeglass makers, such as Zacharias Janssen (exact dates unknown), invent the first compound microscopes, by lining up two lenses to produce extra-large images.

1665: A new book by English scientist Robert Hooke (1635-1703) entitled *Micrographia*, shows illustrations of once-living matter (tree bark lining) as observed with a compound (two-lens) microscope. Magnification reveals empty room-like compartments or "cells."

c1667: A published letter by English naturalist John Ray (1627-1705) defines "species" as a set of individual organisms that can reproduce their own kind (*like from like*).

1674: In an illustrated letter, Dutch amateur scientist Anton van Leeuwenhoek (1632-1723) reports living "beasties" as small as 0.002 mm observed with a simple single-lens microscope.

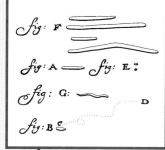

1700s
Horrified by the sight of a magnified flea, a prominent individual publicly denounces the microscope as an instrument of evil. Scientists begin to doubt the theory of spontaneous generation. The general public still accepts it.

1753: With the work of Swedish biologist Carolus Linnaeus (1707-1778), biology begins to focus on discovering, naming, and classifying new species from all over the world. Exploration makes scientists aware of the great diversity of organisms.

1665

1700

1665: The Royal Society sets up a communication network. Editor Henry Oldenburg (1617-1677) collects letters from all over Europe, translates them into English, and publishes them in a journal called *Philosophical Transactions.*

1668: One of the first controlled biological experiments conducted by Italian scientist Francesco Redi (1626-1697) demonstrates that maggots do not appear in meat if flies cannot land on it.

1770s
Mechanical improvements make microscopes sturdier and easier to use, but low-quality glass produces blurry, distorted images with coloured halos.

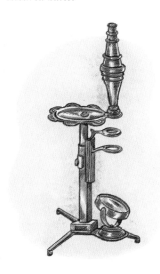

CONTINUED

1800s
Support for and interest in science is very high. Public lectures are popular. Wealthy merchants and monarchs fund expeditions for the sole purpose of collecting biological specimens. The English vessel HMS Investigator *embarks on a five-year voyage of discovery.*

1831: Scottish botanist Robert Brown (1773-1858) is the first to consider the nucleus as a regular part of the living cell. He has difficulty observing the faintly-coloured specimens without electric light.

1820s
Better glass leads to improved lens quality. Many English manufacturers compete to produce the best microscope.

1838: "All plants are made of cells."
German botanist Matthias Jacob Schleiden (1804-1881)

1810s
Biology lags behind chemistry and physics in theories and discoveries. However, there is much synthesizing of earlier ideas. For example, a lecture series by Swiss botanist Professor de Candolle (exact dates unknown) focusses on properties of plants rather than classification.

1825: *"Omnis cellula e cellula."* Latin for "every cell is derived from a preexisting cell".
French chemist and free thinker François Vincent Raspail (1794-1878)

1839: "All animals are made of cells."
Schleiden's colleague German physiologist Theodor Schwann (1810-1882)

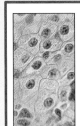

1800   1810   1820   1830

1809: With the work of English science writer Jane Haldimand (1769-1858), textbooks designed to help young people learn science start to appear. Terms such as "cell," "cellular system," and "cellular tissue" are used in these books.

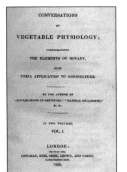

1830s
Biology is evolving from a collection of miscellaneous facts into a true body of knowledge. Better optical theory leads to improved microscopes, which biologists use to study cells intensively.

1839: "All living things are composed of cells and cell products."
Theodor Schwann

Late 1830s
The conclusions of Brown, Schleiden, and Schwann are based on repeated observations, but many scientists reject them. Aristotle's influence is still strong: if plants are inferior to animals, how could they have such similar structures?

c1845: "The cell is the basic unit of life."

German botanist Alexander Carl Heinrich Braun (1805-1877)

1856: At 18 years of age, English chemistry student William Henry Perkin (1838-1907) develops an intense new purple dye. Microscopists quickly develop techniques for staining slide specimens with it.

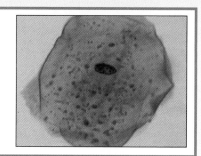

1846: "Protoplasm is the living substance of the cell."

German biologist Jugo von Mohl (1805-1872)

1858: "Cells are the last link in a great chain [that forms] tissues, organs, systems, and individuals…Where a cell exists, there must have been a preexisting cell…Throughout the whole series of living forms…there rules an eternal law of continuous development."
German physiologist Rudolph Virchow (1821-1902)

c1847: "Cells are made of protoplasm enveloped by a flexible membrane."

Alexander Braun

1840

1850

1860

1840s
Improved microscopy allows scientists to observe "live beasts" appear in matter such as decomposing food. This revives the scientific debate about spontaneous generation.

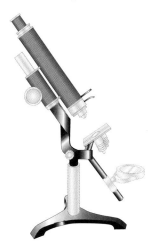

1858: A 17-page paper written by English biologists Charles Darwin (1809-1882) and Alfred Wallace (1823-1913) on "the tendency of species to form variations" is read aloud at a meeting of the Linnaean Society. (You can find this paper on the Internet.)

1850s
Biological knowledge advances rapidly in several areas: medicine, as well as botany and zoology.

1860: The Paris Academy of Sciences offers a prize to anyone who can settle the debate on spontaneous generation. French biologist Louis Pasteur (1822-1895) decides to take up the challenge. Through a series of experiments using microorganisms, he disproves spontaneous generation and concludes that living organisms do not arise from non-living matter.

CONTINUED

Analyze

1. Examine the postulates, or claims, of the cell theory on page 11. Are any of these postulates based on something not shown in the chart?

2. Like all sciences, biology has its own set of tools, techniques, and investigative methods.
   (a) What tools helped scientists develop the cell theory?
   (b) What methods helped scientists develop the cell theory?

3. Jan Batista van Helmont (1577-1544) was the first scientist to use an approach called the scientific method, yet he wrote that mice could be generated by placing rags and bran together in a tub. This "recipe for life" may seem absurd, but it works. Why do mice appear? Explain why their appearance is not evidence of spontaneous generation.

4. In science, a theory is accepted only if it can explain known facts, and lasts only as long as it continues to explain new observations.
   (a) Explain why the cell theory was accepted after Virchow's series of lectures.
   (b) Explain why the cell theory is still accepted today.

5. Every science has two major aspects: process and knowledge. From the timeline, give an example of:
   (a) process in biology, such as a tool or technique used to investigate living things.
   (b) knowledge in biology, such as an observation, fact, generalization, or theory.

6. Around 1900, a new book *The Cell: Its Role in Development and Heredity* argued that the cell theory is not a theory at all, but only a comprehensive general statement of fact. In the glossary, look up the scientific definitions of the terms "fact" and "theory." Now that you know the scientific meaning of these terms, do you agree with the book?

7. Many reference books state that Schleiden and Shwann developed the cell theory. Do you agree or disagree with this statement? Support your position.

8. Raspail was jailed for his political views in 1827. What effect did this probably have on the development of the cell theory?

9. The Internet was originally designed to allow scientists all over the world to communicate quickly and easily with each other. What invention had a similar effect on scientific communication in earlier centuries?

Extend Your Knowledge

Research the importance to biology of a single discovery, scientist, or technology. Identify your own topic with help from your teacher or choose one from the following: binocular (stereoscopic) microscope, chromosomes, DNA, Charles Darwin, Barbara McClintock, Johann Gregor Mendel, mitochondria, Thomas Morgan, Louis Pasteur, phase-contrast microscope, scanning electron microscope, transmission electron microscope. Share your findings with your classmates to extend the timeline on the previous four pages.

The Cell Theory

You have learned that technological developments, such as improved microscopes and new slide preparation techniques, have made the detailed study of living things possible. Scientists such as Schwann, Schleiden, and Virchow made thousands of observations of living tissues. Their ability to organize and interpret this information led to the formal cell theory that we use to explain our observations of living things today. The postulates of the cell theory are:

- All living organisms are composed of one or more cells.

- Cells are the basic units of structure and function in all organisms.

- All cells come from previously existing cells.

- The activity of an entire organism depends on the total activity of its independent cells.

Figure 1.2 All the life functions performed by this bald eagle are carried out by its cells.

Pause& Reflect

All living organisms carry out a variety of life functions to ensure their growth and survival. These include: (1) taking in nutrients and using energy; (2) eliminating wastes; (3) detecting and responding to changes in surroundings; (4) building and repairing body parts; (5) storing information needed to control these functions; (6) reproducing. Which of your organs or body systems are responsible for carrying out each of these functions? Recall what you already know about the parts of a cell. Which cell parts might be responsible for carrying out the same functions? Make a table in your Science Log to present your answers.

Inside the Basic Unit of Life

A typical cell has numerous membrane-bound **organelles**, specialized structures that perform specific functions in the cell. To refresh your knowledge of organelles, look closely at Figures 1.3 and 1.4, which show a typical animal cell and a typical plant cell. Now cover up the figures and make a labelled sketch of each type of cell from memory. Recall what you know about each organelle and write down your ideas. Don't worry if you do not know them all. Read the next section to correct or update your knowledge.

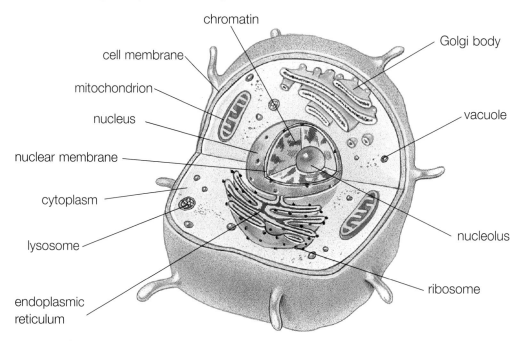

Figure 1.3 The parts of a typical animal cell. How many organelles do you know?

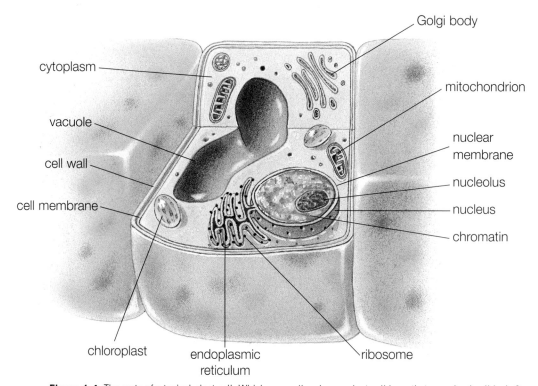

Figure 1.4 The parts of a typical plant cell. Which organelles does a plant cell have that an animal cell lacks?

The Composition of Living Cells

As you read through these paragraphs, locate each organelle on your sketch. Add any that you may not have included. The **nucleus** is an organelle bounded by a double-layered porous membrane. This **nuclear membrane** encloses the cell's genetic material or **DNA** (**D**eoxyribo**n**ucleic **A**cid). You will learn more about the important function of the nucleus in the next investigation. The DNA forms long strands called **chromatin** that are scattered throughout the nucleus. DNA holds the instructions to assemble the necessary substances for building the cell and making it work. You will learn more about DNA in Chapter 4.

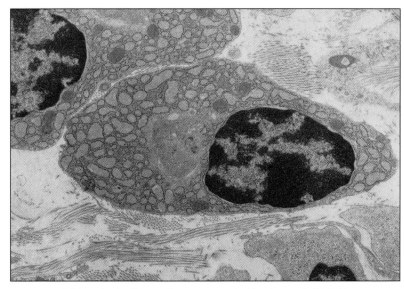

Figure 1.5 Which animal cell organelles can you see in this micrograph (6000x)?

The **nucleolus** is a darker area within the nucleus that manufactures ribosome parts. **Ribosomes** contribute to the manufacture of substances important for cell function. The parts are assembled outside the nucleus. Enclosing the cell contents is the **cell membrane**, which separates the contents of the cell from its surroundings. This membrane controls the movement of materials in and out of the cell. The jelly-like material enclosed by the cell membrane is called **cytoplasm**. It supports the nucleus and other organelles.

Within the cytoplasm, a folded membrane called the **endoplasmic reticulum** forms a series of canals. Materials are transported through these canals to different parts of the cell. Some of the ribosomes are attached to the endoplasmic reticulum, and others float freely in the cytoplasm. Other organelles in the cytoplasm include mitochondria, Golgi bodies, vacuoles and lysosomes. **Mitochondria** transform energy for the cell. **Golgi bodies** package useful materials and secrete them to the outside of the cell for use elsewhere in the organism. **Vacuoles** are fluid-filled storehouses that contain water, food, wastes, and other materials. **Lysosomes** break down food and digest wastes and worn-out cell parts.

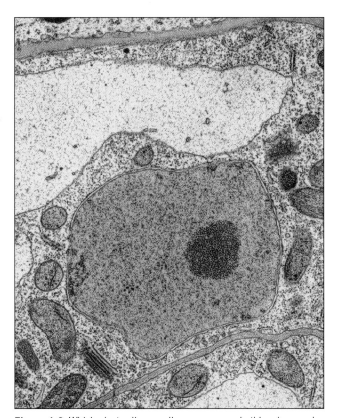

Figure 1.6 Which plant cell organelles can you see in this micrograph (6000x)?

Differences Between Animal and Plant Cells

Unlike animal cells, plant cells have a rigid **cell wall** that lies outside the cell membrane. This fibrous wall provides structure and support for the cell. Fungi and most bacteria also have a cell wall. Multicellular plants rely on the strength of their cell walls to provide support for the entire organism. As well, unlike animal cells, plant cells contain **chloroplasts**, organelles that enable them to make their own food through the process of photosynthesis.

Who's the Instructor?

Think About It

Observing cells through electron microscopes gave scientists tremendous new knowledge, but much more research had to occur to determine how each organelle "worked." In the 1940s and 1950s, researchers used precise micro-surgical techniques to remove various organelles from cells. Their experiments showed that individual organelles need instructions for carrying out their particular functions. In this investigation, you will be imagining yourself as a scientist who is part of a research team trying to determine which organelle — "the instructor" — gives these instructions.

What to Do

Experiment 1: Developing a Hypothesis

To test your ideas about how organelles function, you and your colleagues have decided to conduct an experiment using an alga known as *Acetabularia*. This alga is a large single cell, about 1 to 2 cm in height. (Although it is a single cell, you and other scientists, for convenience, refer to its parts as the foot, stalk, and cap.) Your procedures and results are summarized in illustration A.

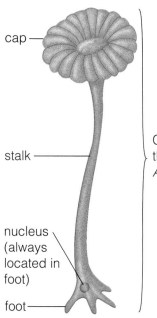

cap

stalk

nucleus (always located in foot)

foot

Cytoplasm extends through all parts of *Acetabularia*.

A. Experiment 1: Developing a Hypothesis

Procedure:

1. One *Acetabularia* cell is cut into three sections: foot, stalk, and cap.
2. All three sections receive the same light and nutrients.

Results

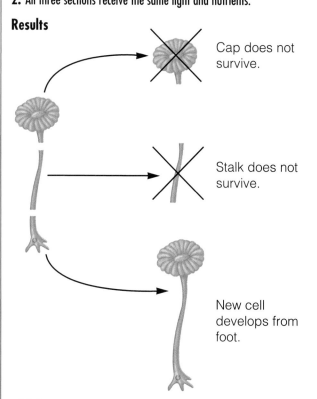

Cap does not survive.

Stalk does not survive.

New cell develops from foot.

Interpret the Results

1. How do you think the cytoplasm in the cut-off foot got the information it needed to rebuild an entire *Acetabularia* cell?

2. What can you infer about the function of the nucleus in the cell's foot?

Experiment 2: Testing the Hypothesis

The inference you drew from Experiment 1 is not a final conclusion. Rather, it is a "working hypothesis," an intelligent guess about how the *Acetabularia* cell gets the information it needs to perform its functions. To test your hypothesis, design a second experiment, this time using two *Acetabularia* cells. Your procedures and results are summarized in illustration B.

B. Experiment 2: Testing the Hypothesis

Procedure

1. The first cell is cut into three sections. The stalk is kept and the rest is discarded.
2. The nucleus is removed from the second cell and everything else is discarded.
3. The nucleus from the second cell is injected into the stalk of the first cell.

Results

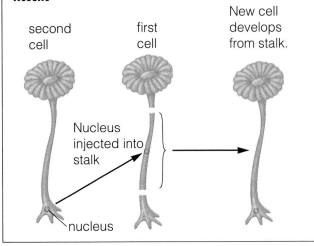

second cell   first cell   New cell develops from stalk.

Nucleus injected into stalk

nucleus

Interpret the Results

1. Do the results of Experiment 2 support your working hypothesis?

2. How do you think the cytoplasm in the stalk got the information it needed to rebuild an entire cell?

3. What can you infer about the function of the nucleus, even when it is moved to a new location?

4. How does the cell get the information it needs to perform all its life functions?

Experiment 3: Testing the Hypothesis Another Way

The *Acetabularia* cells you have been using in the previous two experiments have an umbrella-like cap. However, there is another kind of *Acetabularia* with a cap shaped like flower petals. This other type of alga gives you another way of testing your hypothesis. Using both types of alga, design a third experiment. Your procedure and results are summarized in illustration C.

C. Experiment 3: Testing the Hypothesis Another Way

Procedure:

1. The nucleus is removed from the umbrella-cap cell and all other parts discarded.
2. The stalk is cut from the petal-cap cell and all other parts discarded.
3. The umbrella-cap nucleus is injected into the petal-cap stalk.

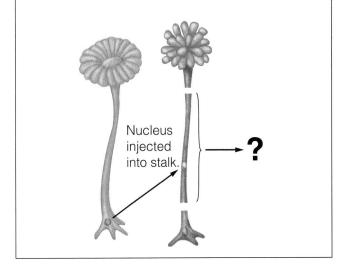

Nucleus injected into stalk.   **?**

Predict the Results

If your hypothesis is correct, what do you predict you will observe? Draw a sketch of the expected result.

Analyze

1. Every time a researcher tests a hypothesis, there are two possibilities. Either the expected results are observed, or they are not. Suppose the result is exactly what you expected.
   (a) Does this result support your original hypothesis?
   (b) What conclusion can you draw?
   (c) Can you draw a final conclusion yet? Explain.

2. Suppose you did not observe the expected results. Which of the following would you do next? Choose one of the following and give reasons for your choice.
   (a) Discard your hypothesis.
   (b) Try Experiment 3 again.
   (c) Try Experiments 1 and 2 again.
   (d) Design new experiments to test the same hypothesis.
   (e) Form a new hypothesis.

The Nucleus in Control

Over time, scientists performed numerous experiments that involved removing and replacing cell organelles. These experiments established that the nucleus was the control centre of the cell. Only when the nucleus was present could a cell perform all of its functions. The nucleus co-ordinates, controls, and manages cell functions. It is the storage centre for all information and instructions for the organelles.

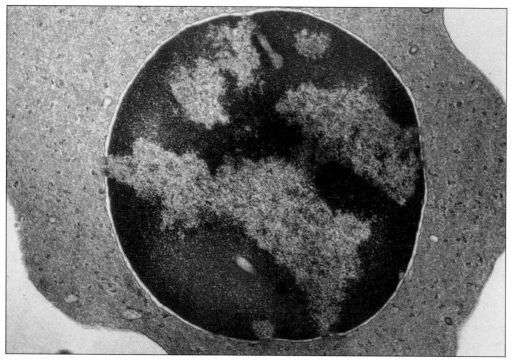

Figure 1.7 Without its nucleus, this cell would be unable to perform the functions it needs to survive (10 000x).

Check Your Understanding

1. **(a)** What are the four basic statements of the cell theory?
   (b) Sketch a timeline showing the major scientific and technological discoveries that contributed to the development of the cell theory.
   (c) Name three people whose ideas, research, or discoveries contributed to the cell theory. Briefly describe their contributions.

2. Define "organelles." State which organelles a plant cell has that an animal cell does not. How else does a plant cell differ from an animal cell?

3. **(a)** How did scientists discover the importance of the nucleus?
   (b) What information does the nucleus contain? Why is this information important and how does it affect cell function?

4. **Thinking Critically** In an experiment, you remove the nucleus from an amoeba. Predict what will happen to the amoeba and explain why.

5. **Thinking Critically** Why was communication through books, letters, and lectures such an important factor in the development of the cell theory? What do you think would happen if scientists today were unable to communicate with each other?

1.2 Understanding the Cell Cycle

You began life as a single cell. When you become an adult, your body will be made up of several hundred trillion cells. Where do all these cells come from? Each one can be traced back to that first cell, which divided into two. Then those two cells became four, and so on. Without cell division, living organisms cannot grow and develop. By itself, however, the process of cell division is not enough (see Figure 1.8).

If cell division is all that happens, then each new cell in Figure 1.8 would contain only a fraction of the original nucleus. You know that each new cell must have a complete nucleus. The process that ensures each new cell has a nucleus with a complete set of instructions (DNA) is called **mitosis**.

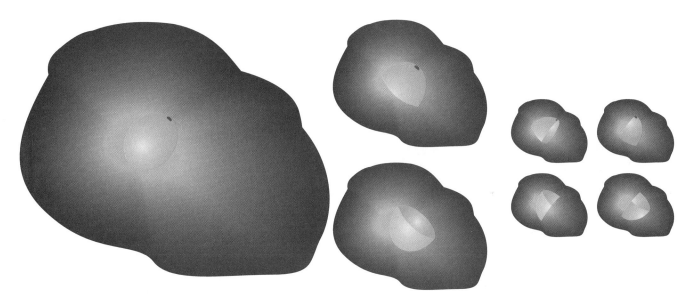

Figure 1.8 Imagine this ball of jelly is a cell and the grape inside is the nucleus. As the cell continues to divide, what happens to the nucleus?

How the Cell Gets Ready for Mitosis

Before mitosis can begin, the nucleus must make a copy, or a replica, of its chromatin, so that there are two complete sets of DNA. This step is known as **replication**. At this stage, the replicated strands of chromatin cannot be seen with a light microscope. The replicated chromatin coils up to form double-stranded **chromosomes**, which are joined in the middle by a **centromere** (see Figure 1.9). After replication, two complete sets of DNA are bundled up together as double-stranded chromosomes. Now the nucleus is ready for mitosis to begin.

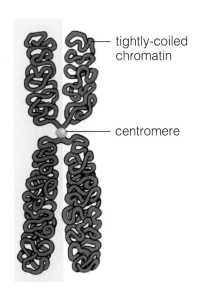

tightly-coiled chromatin

centromere

Figure 1.9 The centromere cinches around the double-stranded chromosomes, joining them together.

The Phases of Mitosis in an Animal Cell

The end result of mitosis is the separation of replicated DNA into two complete identical sets of DNA, one for each new cell's nucleus. This involves four major phases that always take place in the same order: **prophase**, **metaphase**, **anaphase**, and **telophase**. These phases are shown in Figure 1.10. Cover the explanation of each phase with a piece of paper. In your notebook, make quick sketches of the cells in each phase. Describe what is happening during each phase. Now read the explanations, carefully following the process on the diagrams as you read. Update your information and label your sketches as completely as possible.

Phase 1: Prophase

When prophase begins, the double-stranded chromosomes are large and dense enough to be seen with a light microscope. The nucleolus and the nuclear membrane disappear. In animal cells, **spindle fibres** begin to form and stretch across the cell from **centrioles** that have moved to opposite ends of the cell. (You can observe a similar process in the cells of plants, fungi, and some protists. They also form spindle fibres, but not centrioles.) Spindle fibres attach to one side of each centromere.

Figure 1.10 The phases of mitosis in a typical animal cell magnified about 450x.

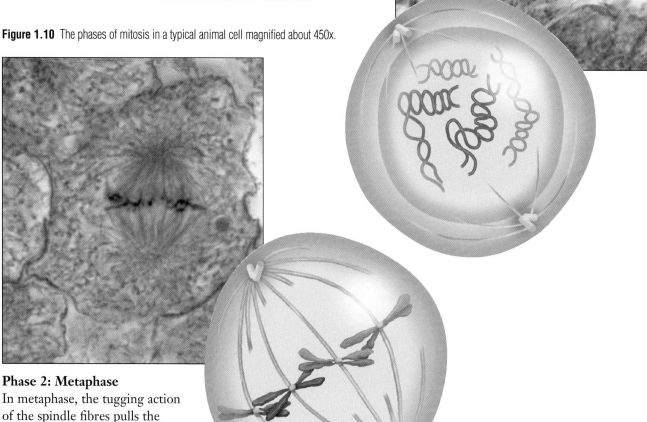

Phase 2: Metaphase

In metaphase, the tugging action of the spindle fibres pulls the double-stranded chromosomes into a line across the middle of the cell.

Phase 3: Anaphase

In anaphase, the spindle fibres begin to contract and shorten. This action pulls the centromere apart, allowing one of each of the replicated strands to move to opposite ends (poles) of the cell.

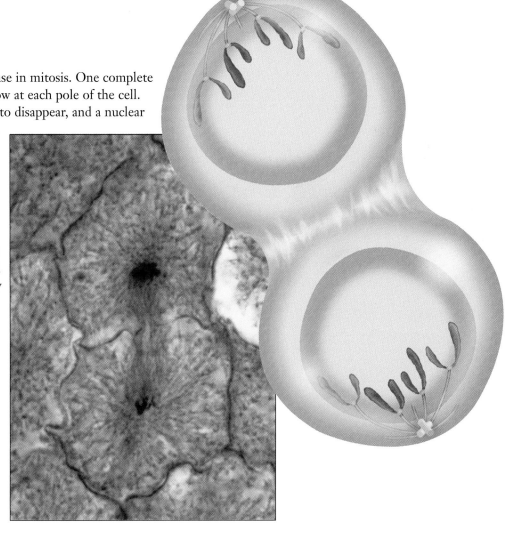

Phase 4: Telophase

Telophase is the final phase in mitosis. One complete set of chromosomes is now at each pole of the cell. The spindle fibres begin to disappear, and a nuclear membrane forms around each set of chromosomes. A nucleolus appears within each new nucleus. Single-stranded chromosomes start to uncoil into thin strands of chromatin. Now there are two nuclei in one cell and the cell itself is ready to divide.

Observing Mitosis in Plant and Animal Cells

Mitosis takes place in both plant and animal cells. In this investigation, you will observe mitosis in onion root cells and in whitefish cells, while looking for differences.

Problem

Are there any differences between the way plant and animal cells divide?

Safety Precautions

- Be sure your hands are dry when you plug in or disconnect the cord of the microscope.
- Handle the microscope slides carefully, so that they do not break or cause cuts or scratches.

Apparatus

microscope
prepared slide of an onion root tip
prepared slide of a whitefish embryo

Procedure

① Place the onion root tip slide on the microscope stage and observe it under low power. Focus on the area just behind the tip of the root.

② Carefully change to medium power, focus, and go to high power to observe the cells. As you look at each cell, determine which phase of mitosis it is in. Try to find cells in each phase of mitosis and draw a cell in each phase. Refer to the diagrams to help you identify what you are observing.

B.

A.

whitefish embryo cells, 320 x

onion root tip cells, 330 x

Skill
POWER

To review how to make proper diagrams in science, turn to page 598.

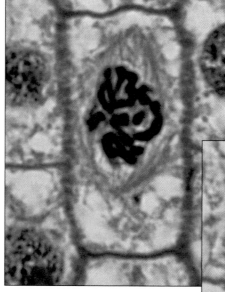

prophase

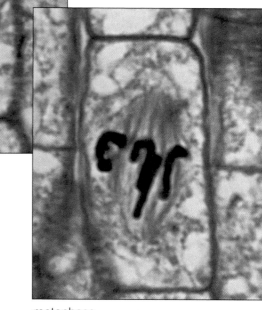

metaphase

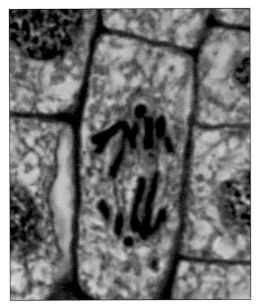

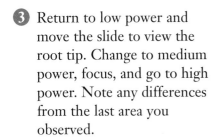

anaphase

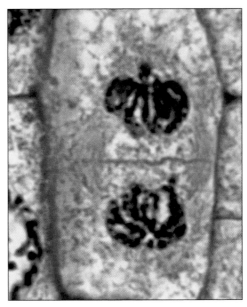

telophase

③ Return to low power and move the slide to view the root tip. Change to medium power, focus, and go to high power. Note any differences from the last area you observed.

④ Change back to low power and remove the onion root tip slide. Place the whitefish embryo slide on the stage and observe it under low power.

⑤ Find an area of dividing cells. Change to medium power, focus, and go to high power. As you look at each cell, determine which of the stages of mitosis it is in. Refer to the photographs in Figure 1.10 to recall how animal cells undergoing mitosis look. Draw one cell from each of the stages. Note any differences between mitosis in animal cells and mitosis in plant cells.

⑥ Change back to low power and remove the slide.

Analyze

1. Describe any differences you noticed in the cells behind the root tip, compared to those in the tip.

2. What differences did you notice between the onion root tip cells and the whitefish embryo cells that were dividing in:
   (a) size of the cells
   (b) the shape of the cells
   (c) the chromosomes in the cells

Conclude and Apply

3. What other parts of an onion plant might be used to study mitosis?

Extend Your Skills

4. Simulate the process of mitosis in a cell with four chromosomes. Start with four strips of construction paper or four twist-ties to represent chromosomes. Use paper clips to represent centrioles and extra paper strips (or twist-ties) for the phase during which the chromosomes replicate. You can use string or yarn to represent the cell's nuclear and cell membranes, if you like. Be prepared to explain mitosis using your model.

Skill
P O W E R

To review proper microscope handling techniques and effective use of a microscope, turn to page 577.

Cell Division

At the end of mitosis, there is still only one cell, but it now has two identical nuclei. The next event in a cell's life is cell division. In animal cells, the cell

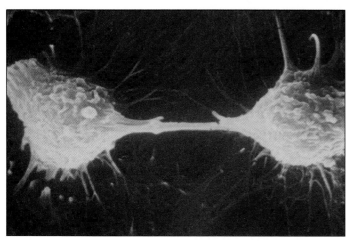

membrane pinches in near the middle of the cell, dividing the cytoplasm into two new cells (see Figure 1.11). In plant cells, a **cell plate** develops across the centre of the cell, forming a new cell wall between the two new cells (see Figure 1.12). In both plant and animal cells, each new cell after division is an exact copy of the original. Early cell biologists called these daughter cells. As a result of mitosis, the number of chromosomes in the nucleus of each cell is identical to each other and to the number in the original cell.

Figure 1.11 After telophase in an animal cell, the cell membrane pinches together and the cytoplasm of the cell divides (400x).

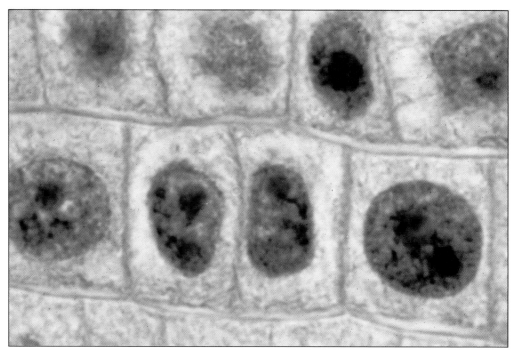

Figure 1.12 Plant cells also divide after mitosis (500 x). Can you identify the cell plate?

Interphase: How the Cell Spends Most of Its Time

Mitosis and cell division occupy only a tiny fraction of a cell's life. By far, the greater portion of its time is spent in **interphase**. The prefix *inter* means "between." Early researchers used interphase to describe what appeared to be an inactive phase in the cell between periods of activity. However, later research showed that interphase is anything but inactive. It makes up most of a cell's life when it is not dividing by mitosis. During interphase, the cell grows, replicates its DNA, and becomes prepared for the first phase of mitosis.

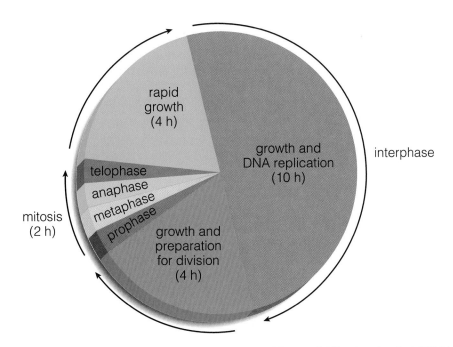

Word CONNECT

The word "mitosis" comes from the Greek word *mitos,* meaning thread. Why do you think the word mitosis is used to describe a process in the cell cycle?

Figure 1.13 A typical cell cycle. How long is the cell cycle in this example? How long is mitosis? Which stages of the cell cycle make up interphase?

The continuous processes of mitosis, cell division, and interphase are called the **cell cycle** as shown in Figure 1.13. In the next section, you will find out more about this cycle as it occurs in the human body.

Check Your Understanding

1. What must happen in a nucleus before it can undergo mitosis?

2. Explain the function of mitosis.

3. Briefly describe the phases of mitosis. In which phase are there two nuclei?

4. Compare what occurs in animal cells during cell division to what occurs in plant cells during the same process.

5. Explain what occurs in a cell during interphase.

6. **Thinking Critically** Why must the nuclear membrane break down in mitosis?

7. **Thinking Critically** What cell part controls the process of mitosis?

1.3 The Cell Cycle in Your Body

The cell cycle is responsible for the growth and development of all your body cells. In fact, cell division and growth were occurring in your body even before you were born. Cells that divided over and over are the basis for each of the tissues that form the organs and organ systems in your body (see Figure 1.14). You started out as a single cell, but through the process of mitosis, you became a living system composed of hundreds of trillions of cells working together. To understand how mitosis and growth are linked, try the activity on the next page.

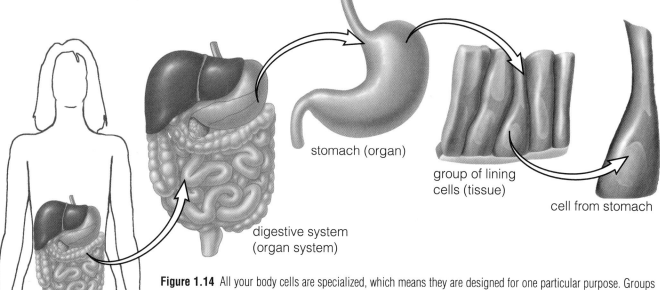

stomach (organ)

group of lining cells (tissue)

cell from stomach

digestive system (organ system)

Figure 1.14 All your body cells are specialized, which means they are designed for one particular purpose. Groups of specialized cells form tissues. Groups of specialized tissues work together to form organs, and groups of organs form organ systems.

The cell cycle ensures that the number of chromosomes in the nuclei of your body cells will remain constant, no matter how many body cells you have when you are fully grown. All humans have the same number of chromosomes in each nucleus of their body cells. Chromosome number varies from species to species. Dogs, for example, have 78 chromosomes; tomato plants have 24; humans have 46 chromosomes.

Figure 1.15 Though you have the same number of chromosomes (46) as this popular aquarium fish, the black molly, you are very different from this fish. Obviously, the number of chromosomes alone does not distinguish one species from another. It is the information carried on the chromosomes that does.

Graphing Human Body Growth

Much of human growth cannot be easily measured. For example, you cannot tell by looking in the mirror how large your heart, liver, or brain has become. Neither is the length of a muscle or nerve obvious. However, one part of the body in which growth can easily be seen is the skeletal system, your bones. What evidence have you observed in your own body that bones grow? In this activity, you will analyze height as an indication of skeletal growth.

What to Do

Joy's father kept a record of her height from the time she was born until she was eight years old. Study the record shown in the following chart. Make a line graph from these data.

Skill
P O W E R

To review how to prepare a line graph, turn to page 587.

Year	Height	Year	Height
birth	42 cm	5	112 cm
1	50 cm	6	118 cm
2	86 cm	7	124 cm
3	92 cm	8	128 cm
4	104 cm		

What Did You Discover?

1. On your graph, find the two years between which Joy's skeleton grew the most.

2. Between which two years did her skeleton grow the least?

3. From your graph, can you infer a general pattern of skeletal growth?

4. When do you think mitosis and cell division occurred most rapidly in Joy's skeleton?

Normal Cell Replacement

While you are growing, mitosis and cell division add to the total number of cells in your body. These processes continue even after you are fully grown. Why? Cells don't live forever. Some cells have definite life spans programmed into their genetic material. They die when they receive "instructions" to do so or when they are no longer needed or cannot function normally. Figure 1.16 shows the different life spans of different human body cells.

Mitosis and cell division are necessary for cells to be replaced after they die. In your body, some three billion cells die every minute. Cells also die as a result of damage or when they do not receive enough food or oxygen. They must also be replaced to maintain a healthy body.

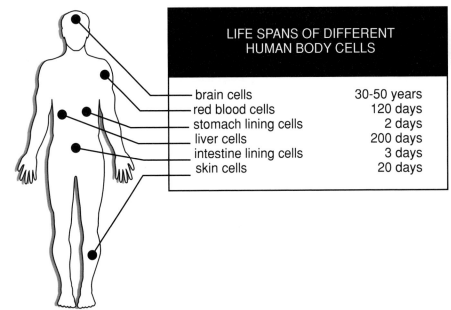

LIFE SPANS OF DIFFERENT HUMAN BODY CELLS

brain cells	30-50 years
red blood cells	120 days
stomach lining cells	2 days
liver cells	200 days
intestine lining cells	3 days
skin cells	20 days

Figure 1.16 Which cells live the longest? Which cells are replaced most often? How would their cell cycles be different?

Pause&
Reflect

Spinal cord injuries cause permanent damage because nerve and brain cells do not regenerate. Once damaged, these cells no longer send information from the brain to the muscles. Find out how scientists are trying to develop techniques to stimulate nerve cells to repair themselves. In your Science Log, list the resources that are available in your community to help those with spinal cord injuries.

Regeneration

If you cut your skin, it will usually heal in a short time. A bone break may take longer. Because both skin and bone cells undergo mitosis, they are capable of repairing injured tissue. Repair of injured cells or the making of lost body parts is called **regeneration**.

Figure 1.17 Unlike this northern plateau lizard, which can regenerate its tail, humans cannot regenerate lost body parts, once they are adults. However, the accidentally severed fingertips of children up to the age of 12 may regenerate completely.

Aging — The Slowing of the Cell Cycle

In this chapter, you have seen that as scientists were able to look deeper and deeper into the cell, their understanding of cell processes increased. Aging and its connection to cell division has been the subject of intense scientific investigation for many decades.

Figure 1.18 Look carefully at these pictures. What evidence do you see of aging? What do you think is happening to this person's body cells?

Research suggests that we age because, as cells die, they either are not replaced or are replaced more slowly. This process results in changes to the structure and function of major body systems. Our skin wrinkles, our bones lose their density, and our ability to fight off disease is weakened. Whether these events are the result of cells entering a state in which they no longer divide, or whether mitosis slows and stops in response to the aging process, is not entirely understood. Scientists theorize that certain changes take place in aging cells that affect their ability to repair themselves or to pass along the instructions new cells need to carry out their functions.

Cancer — The Cell Cycle Out of Control

Under normal conditions, instructions in a cell's DNA control its rate of cell division. A cell may also destroy itself, if the genetic material in its nucleus is damaged or if something inside the cell goes wrong. What happens if cells begin to divide uncontrollably? The result is cancer.

Cancerous cells interfere with surrounding cells and disrupt their normal functioning. They continue dividing and pile up on top of one another. These excess cells may produce a tumour or lump that stays contained in one area. In other cases, the cancerous cells may move to other parts of the organism, and continue to grow and divide uncontrollably. These cells gobble up oxygen and nutrients for themselves, crowding out other cells and robbing them of food. Scientists know that exposure to certain substances can increase the risk of cancer. Tobacco, asbestos, certain chemicals, some viruses, radioactivity, and ultraviolet radiation have all been linked to cancer in humans.

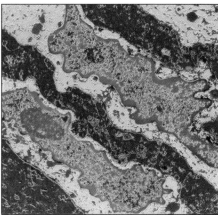

Figure 1.19 For reasons that are not quite clear to scientists, the DNA in this cell has been altered and the cell continues to divide indefinitely. How would you describe the nucleus of this cell (6000 x)?

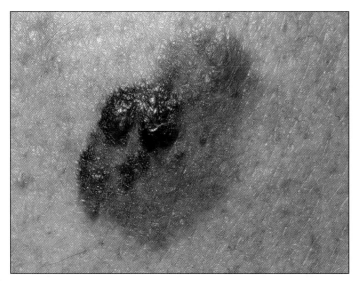

Figure 1.20 The dark spot shown in this photograph is skin cancer. About 20 000 Canadians develop skin cancer every year, and 500 to 600 die from it. Which environmental factor contributes to the development of skin cancer?

Math CONNECT

Statistically, each cigarette robs a regular smoker of 5.5 min of life. If the average smoker consumes 3000 cigarettes per year, how many days of life are lost in just one year of smoking?

Outside Link **ACTIVITY**

Reducing Cancer Risks

Our risk of getting some cancers, such as melanoma, or skin cancer, can be greatly reduced by staying out of the sun during peak periods of ultraviolet radiation. Making other simple lifestyle choices, such as not smoking, can also greatly reduce our risk of developing lung or throat cancer.

What to Do

1. In your group, brainstorm a list of questions related to cancer and lifestyle. For example: What are the most common types of cancer in Canada? What are the rates of these cancers in women and men? How do these compare with cancer rates in your community? What lifestyle changes could you make to reduce your risk of getting these cancers?

2. Next, brainstorm a list of possible resources and institutions in your community where you could get information about cancer. Make a list of web sites and collect pamphlets, if they are available.

3. Use your information to design a web site or create a poster. Present your findings to the class.

DidYou**Know**?

When most people think of cancer, they immediately think of a disease that affects humans. Cancer also affects other animal species and plants. For example, have your ever noticed a bulge on the stem of a plant? If so, you have probably witnessed a cancerous growth. As well, fish exposed to certain toxins develop cancerous tumours.

Check Your Understanding

1. Explain a process in the human body in which there is evidence of the cell cycle at work.

2. Give two reasons why cells die.

3. How do scientists currently explain the aging process?

4. Describe what happens when cells divide uncontrollably.

5. **Apply** The use of sunscreen can help reduce the risk of skin cancer. From your knowledge of cancer and cell division, propose a model to explain how sunscreen works. How could you determine whether your model is accurate?

6. **Thinking Critically** Some cells live for years, while others live for only a few days. Why do you think some cells might be replaced faster than others?

7. **Thinking Critically** The muscle cells of the heart were once thought to stop dividing when a person reached the age of nine. Thus, heart attacks, which kill heart cells, were believed to cause permanent damage to the heart muscle. New research has discovered that mitosis does occur in the heart later in life. Infer what this discovery could mean to people who have heart attacks.

1.4 Asexual Reproduction in Bacteria, Protists, Fungi, and Animals

In the last section, you learned how important the cell cycle is to human growth and tissue repair. Mitosis and cell division are important for another reason. They are the basis for the asexual reproduction of many organisms. **Asexual reproduction** is the formation of a new individual that has identical genetic information to its parent. In this section, you will explore the ways in which bacteria, protists, fungi, and some animals reproduce asexually. Before you begin reading this section, refresh your knowledge of the five-kingdom classification system by studying Appendix A.

Asexual Reproduction in Bacteria

Members of the kingdom Monera, such as bacteria shown if Figure 1.21, are unicellular organisms that do not contain a true nucleus. Bacteria reproduce asexually through a process called **binary fission**. In this process, a parent cell divides so that each new cell contains a single chromosome carrying a complete set of DNA identical to that of the parent (see Figure 1.22 on page 30.)

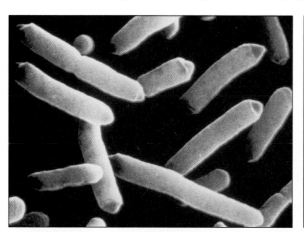
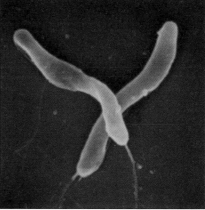
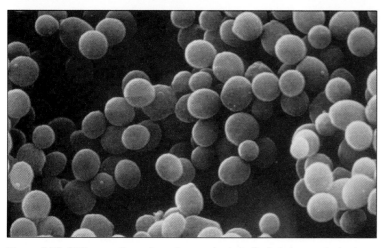

Figure 1.21 All the organisms shown here are bacteria. Bacteria have a single chromosome that is not surrounded by a nuclear membrane. How is this different from the cells you have already investigated in this chapter?

Did You Know?

Cells that lack a true nucleus, such as bacteria, are known as *prokaryotes*. All other cells — those of animals, plants, fungi, and protists — have a nucleus and other membrane-bound organelles and are known as *eukaryotes*.

Pause & Reflect

Bacteria, such as *Clostridium botulinum,* can cause a serious form of food poisoning. Other bacteria, such as *Lactobacillus acidophilus,* help digest food and destroy other harmful bacteria in your intestinal tract. In your Science Log, write a one-page essay explaining why bacteria can be both harmful and beneficial to humans. Search the Internet for information about "useful" bacteria, such as those that are used to break down toxins in the environment.

A. The cell prepares for replication. Do you see where the cell wall has ruptured?

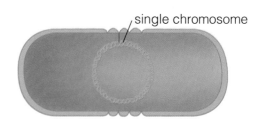
single chromosome

B. The cell makes a copy of its single chromosome. Do you see the new membrane that has formed? Why do you think it is needed?

C. The original chromosome and its copy soon separate as the cell grows larger, each moving to opposite ends of the cell.

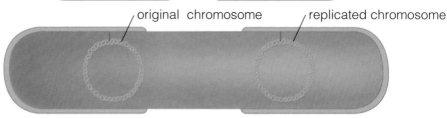
original chromosome   replicated chromosome

D. The cell membrane begins to pinch inward near the middle of the cell, creating two smaller parts, each with a single chromosome carrying identical genetic information.

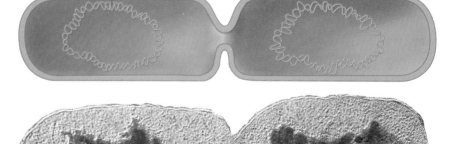

E. A new cell wall forms around each of the two new cells.

17 000x

Figure 1.22 Binary fission is one method of asexual reproduction used by bacteria. Under ideal conditions, the entire process takes about 20 minutes. Why might such a short cell cycle be an advantage?

Suppose you get on a bus to go to school. At 8:20 A.M., you yawn, and a single *Streptococcus* bacterium drifts into your open mouth and settles in your throat. Under ideal conditions, a single bacterium can reproduce in 20 min. So, by the time the bus drops you off at school at 8:40 A.M., there are two bacteria in your throat. When your homeroom period starts at 9:00 A.M., there are four.

1. Assume that the bacteria continue to reproduce asexually every 20 min. How many bacteria will be in your throat by: (a) lunchtime (12:00 noon); (b) by the time you get the bus in the afternoon (3:20 P.M.); (c) suppertime (6:00 P.M.); (d) bedtime (10:00 P.M.)?

2. Make a graph showing the growth of the *Streptococcus* population in your throat.

3. Do you think the bacteria can keep multiplying in this way indefinitely? Explain.

4. At what time do you think your throat may feel sore? How many bacteria will be present in your throat?

Be a Biologist: Assess Asexual Reproduction

Think About It

Biologists are explorers of the living world. Some dive deep into the oceans to study the bacteria that live on shipwrecks, such as the *Titanic*. Some trek to the tops of mountains to find fossil evidence of ancient mosses. Others journey to the innermost regions of the cell. In this investigation, you will focus on one aspect of biological inquiry: How do organisms reproduce asexually? You will collect background information, do research, and assess the advantages and disadvantages of asexual reproduction.

What to Do

Part 1

Collecting Background Information

1 Make a table such as the one shown below.

	Background Information				
Name and Description of Organism	Kingdom	Habitat	Type and Description of Asexual Reproduction	Advantages of Asexual Reproduction	Disadvantages of Asexual Reproduction

2 Begin by reading through the rest of this chapter, which describes asexual reproduction in a variety of organisms. As you read, organize the information in your table. Go to other sources, such as senior level textbooks, a library, or the Internet to get all the information to complete your background research.

3 Once you have compiled your information, answer the following questions.
   (a) Which organisms have a true nucleus? Which ones do not?
   (b) Which organisms reproduce asexually?
   (c) Make a general statement about the advantages and disadvantages of asexual reproduction.

Part 2

Specializing in the Asexual Reproduction of an Organism

1 Organize into groups. Your teacher will assign each group an organism. Your group will become specialists on that organism. Your job is to develop a profile of the organism that describes its overall characteristics, its habitat, when it uses asexual reproduction, and what threats to its habitat could affect its ability to reproduce asexually.

2 Working with your group, brainstorm resources you might need to research the topic. Consider, for example, the library, the Internet, and subject experts at a local university or college. **Note**: For tips on researching topics and using the Internet effectively, refer to Appendix B.

3 As a group, organize the information you have gathered and prepare a class presentation. Use a variety of media and formats in your presentation, such as audio-visual aids, computer simulations, performance, flip charts, pictures, and diagrams. As well, prepare a one-page summary of your organism profile to distribute to the rest of the class at the end of your presentation. Remember to list your sources of information.

Analyze

1. Did your organism have any competitors for space and food? How might asexual reproduction have given it an advantage compared with its competitors?

2. Which environmental conditions did your organism require to carry out asexual reproduction?

3. Does your organism reproduce in any other way?

Asexual Reproduction in Protists

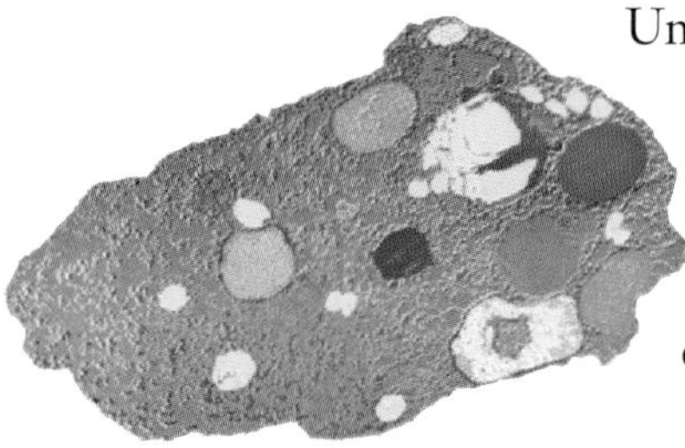

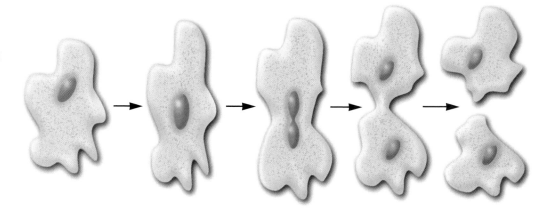

Unicellular organisms in the kingdom Protista, such as the amoeba, also rely mainly on asexual reproduction to increase their numbers. Unlike bacteria, the DNA of protists is contained within a true nucleus. Mitotic cell division in these unicellular organisms results in the formation of two identical off-spring. Protists are important because they form the basis of many food chains and because they are responsible for many diseases that affect humans.

Figure 1.23 *Entamoeba histolytica* is a famous amoeba that has its own disease named after it—amoebic dysentery. This disease causes diarrhea, fever, and abdominal cramps. Find out how *E. histolytica* is transmitted.

Figure 1.24 This simple sketch shows mitosis and cell division in an amoeba. How does this process differ from binary fission in bacteria?

Figure 1.25 This fungus grows by obtaining nutrients from a peach.

Asexual Reproduction in Fungi

Moulds, yeast, and mushrooms are members of the Fungi kingdom. The bodies of these organisms are composed of many thin filaments called hyphae. The hyphae grow over the surface of and into the bodies of other organisms to obtain food (see Figure 1.25). Three methods that fungi use to reproduce asexually are fragmentation, budding, and spores.

Fungi can reproduce asexually by **fragmentation**. A small piece, or fragment, breaks away from the main mass of hyphae and grows into a new individual. What must the fragment contain to enable it to develop into a new organism identical to its parent?

Word CONNECT

The word "hyphae" is descended from the Greek word "hyphos," meaning web. (The singular form of hyphae is hypha.) Why is hyphae a good word to describe the filaments that make up the body of a fungus?

Figure 1.26 Most fungi feed on dead and decaying organisms. How is this of benefit to the environment?

Yeast are unicellular fungi often used to make bread or alcohol products. When conditions are favourable for growth, yeast reproduce asexually by **budding**. First, a copy of the nucleus is made. Can you explain why is this necessary? Next, a tiny bud begins to form on the cell wall. This bud, containing the new nucleus, continues to grow larger. It eventually breaks away to become a single, independent cell. Look carefully at the micrograph in Figure 1.27. What are the small circles at the lower left of the parent cell?

Figure 1.27 A yeast cell forming a bud (4000 x).

To reproduce asexually, moulds, such as *Rhizopus*, produce spores. A **spore** is a reproductive cell that can grow into a new individual through mitotic cell division. Spores are stored in a case called a *sporangium*. When spores are mature, they take on a characteristic colour, such as black, yellow, blue, or red. Think of some places where you have seen mould recently. Was the place moist or dry? Hot or cold? You can test which conditions favour mould growth in the next activity.

Figure 1.28 This bread is covered by the common mould *Rhizopus*.

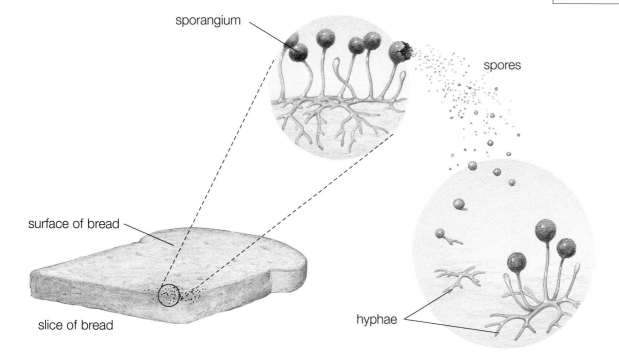

sporangium

spores

surface of bread

slice of bread

hyphae

Figure 1.29 Sporangia form on the tips of hyphae that have grown up from the surface of the bread. In each sporangium, hundreds of spores develop by mitotic cell division. Why do you think each spore is capable of starting a new colony of mould?

Making a Mould

Like all living organisms, bread mould requires suitable conditions in which to reproduce. You know that mould will grow on bread, but does any kind of bread provide the right food source? Is there a difference between home-made bread and store-bought bread? What other conditions must be present for bread mould to grow?

What To Do

1. Propose a hypothesis about the growth of bread mould that you would like to explore.

2. Design an experiment to test your hypothesis. In your design proposal, be sure to include your hypothesis, the materials you will need, and the steps you will follow to conduct your research. You should include the use of a low-power microscope or dissection scope to examine the bread for results. Be sure to

include steps to dispose of materials properly at the end of the experiment. **Note**: For tips on how experiments are designed, turn to page IS-2.

3. When you have received approval from your teacher, conduct your experiment.

What Did You Discover?

1. Describe your results. Use charts, diagrams, or photographs. Write brief descriptions to accompany your illustrations.

2. Did your results support your hypothesis? Why or why not?

3. What additional research or experiments could you carry out, based on your results?

4. Suggest how the spread of harmful moulds could be controlled.

Asexual Reproduction in Animals

In the kingdom Animalia, animals can be divided into two main groups — vertebrates (those with backbones) and invertebrates (those without backbones). Invertebrates, such as sponges, jellyfish, worms, shellfish, and insects, make up about 97% of all animal species. Many invertebrates can reproduce asexually to form one or more identical offspring from a single parent.

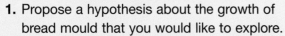

Planaria are a type of flatworm that can reproduce asexually by dividing in two and regenerating the parts they are missing. The part of the planarian that retains the head will grow a new tail. The part with the tail will grow a new head. What happens in the process of dividing that enables the two new planaria to grow the body parts they need? Planaria can also regenerate injured body parts, as shown in Figure 1.30.

Figure 1.30 An injury to the head of this planarian divided its head into two sections. Two complete heads are forming as a result of regeneration.

Figure 1.31 Sea stars reproduce asexually and can grow new body parts through the process of regeneration.

Some animals, such as sponges and hydras, reproduce asexually by budding. A cell, usually near the base of these organisms, undergoes mitosis and cell division repeatedly to produce a group of new cells, or a bud. Eventually, when the bud completes its development, it detaches and becomes independent.

Figure 1.32 Sponge buds may remain attached to the parent, which result in a colony. What advantage does the bud have by being attached to its parent?

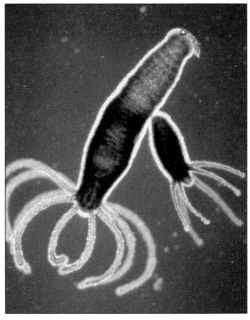

Figure 1.33 Hydras are microscopic organisms that live in water. Based on what you have learned about budding, describe what is happening in this picture.

Check Your Understanding

1. What is binary fission? How does binary fission differ from mitotic cell division?

2. Describe three ways fungi can reproduce asexually.

3. (a) Describe how an animal reproduces by budding.

    (b) What is one advantage of this type of reproduction?

4. **Apply** Explain why covering and refrigerating food helps to reduce spoilage from moulds.

5. **Thinking Critically** One arm of a sea star with part of the central disk attached can grow into a complete sea star. Sea stars are considered a nuisance by people who raise oysters. A sea star can attach itself to an oyster's shell, open it, and eat the contents. In the past, oyster farmers tried to destroy the sea stars by cutting them into pieces and throwing them back into the ocean. What do you think was the outcome of this action?

6. **Thinking Critically** Some invertebrates, such as crabs, have the ability to regrow body parts that have been lost through injury. What cell part do you think scientists study to learn more about the process of regeneration in these animals?

1.5 Asexual Reproduction in Plants

The trees, bushes, and lawns you pass on your way to school are such a familiar part of your landscape that you probably pay little attention to them. The only time you might notice them is when a tree limb is broken off or a bush has been pruned, or a lawn mowed. After a few weeks, you can see the branches and twigs growing back, and the grass needs cutting again. The ability of plants to reproduce asexually and to repair themselves is, as in all other kingdoms, the result of mitotic cell division. Asexual reproduction in plants ensures that each new plant will have the same DNA as its parent.

Meristem: The Basis of Asexual Reproduction in Plants

Unlike many animals, plants continue to grow throughout their lives. The tips of their roots and stems contain growing areas called **meristem**. Meristem is made up of unspecialized cells that undergo mitosis and cell division repeatedly, producing new cells. At a certain point in a plant's growth, meristematic cells specialize into the cells that make up the roots, stems, and leaves of the plant. Once these plant structures mature, their cells do not divide under normal conditions. If any of these structures becomes damaged, meristematic cells activate and repairs are made. Asexual reproduction can occur in plants by activating the meristematic cells in different plant structures.

Figure 1.34 It seems hard to believe that this uprooted tree could survive, but this willow is able to send up new growth. Where do you think mitosis and cell division are occurring here?

For centuries, plant growers have been using their knowledge of the ability of plants to reproduce asexually. One of the simplest methods of propagating, or increasing the number of, a plant is through the use of cuttings. Cuttings are lengths of a "parent" stem that are used to establish offspring that are exact copies of the parent. This is called **cloning**, the process by which identical offspring are produced from a single cell or tissue. In the next investigation, you will clone a plant using a cutting.

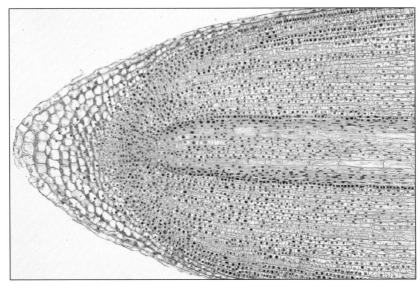

Figure 1.35 A micrograph of the tip of a growing plant root. Where are the meristematic cells?

INVESTIGATION 1-E

Clone a Plant

Plant-growers who produce plants commercially rely on cloning because it guarantees that the plants they want to reproduce will always be the same. In this investigation, you will clone a plant using a cutting and record its development over several weeks.

Coleus plant

Problem

How can you clone several plants from the same parent plant?

Your cutting should include 2 to 3 leaves.

Safety Precautions

- Be careful when using scissors or other sharp objects.

Apparatus

250 mL beaker (or glass jar)
scissors (or utility-knife)
metric ruler
small flower pot (or plastic cup)

Materials

label (or wax marker)
aluminum foil
several large *Coleus* plants (or equivalent)
water
sterilized potting soil

Procedure

1 Prepare a table with the following headings and give the table a title.

Date	Appearance of Bottom Tip of Cutting

2 Label the beaker with your name, and fill it with water. Cover the top of the beaker with foil, and use a pencil or pen to punch a small hole in the centre of the foil.

3 Use scissors to cut off a small cutting from the plants. Be sure the cutting has two to three leaves on it. Note: Several students should take cuttings from the same plant.

4 Insert the cut end of the cutting through the hole in the foil, ensuring the bottom 3 cm of the cutting dips into the water.

5 In your table, write the date, and draw what the cut end of the cutting looks like.

6 Check the cutting each day for the next week, observing any changes. (Add water as needed to keep the bottom 3 cm of your cutting in water.)

7 Record the date in your table when you first see roots, and draw what you see. Repeat this in two or three more days, using your ruler to measure root growth.

8 When the roots are about 3 cm in length, put soil in the small pot, and carefully plant the cutting. Clean the beaker.

9 Wash your hands thoroughly after this activity.

Analyze

1. Compare cuttings taken from the same plant. In what ways are they similar? In what ways are they different.

Conclude and Apply

2. Why was it necessary to leave two or three leaves on your cutting?

3. What advantage is there to planting the young plant in soil rather than leaving it in water?

Extend Your Knowledge and Skills

4. Is bright light or partial sunlight better for the growth of your plants? Design an experiment to determine optimal light conditions for the plant you used.

Pause&
Reflect

Think back to Investigation 1-C on page 20. Study the observations of cell division in an onion root cell that you made. In your Science Log, write a paragraph connecting what you saw occurring in the tips of the root with what you now know about meristematic cells.

Surveying Asexual Reproduction in Plants

Not all plants reproduce asexually in the same way. Asexual reproduction in the plant world has several different forms. As our knowledge has improved, so has our ability to use these natural processes in growing plants for commercial and non-commercial purposes. As you read through this section, make sketches in your notebook of the different ways in which new plants can be produced from the same parent.

New Plants from Roots

Have you ever pulled dandelions out of a lawn? What happens if you don't remove the entire root from the ground? Why does this occur? In some plants, meristem cells in the roots divide mitotically to produce stems, leaves, and other roots. This is what happens in dandelions and makes them so difficult to get rid of.

Because of the reliability of some plants to reproduce asexually from their roots (asparagus, for example), growers can sell just the roots, instead of a whole plant. Can you think of any advantages to developing and selling plants in this way? Are there any disadvantages?

Figure 1.36 Asparagus plants die back to the ground in the winter. In the spring, new plants regrow from their roots.

Off the Wall

What do you see when you look at this photograph? A forest, right? What you actually see is a forest of one — a single male aspen in the Wasatch Mountains of Utah. Researchers estimate that this plant has been growing for tens of thousands of years. The continuous asexual reproduction of this aspen has produced a root system that connects 47 000 stems and occupies 43 ha. This plant could live forever as long as environmental conditions continue to favour asexual reproduction. What environmental threats might this magnificent giant face in the future?

New Plants from Stems

In some plants, meristematic cells in the stem can divide to produce cells that will become a new plant. Strawberries have special stems called runners. New strawberry plants grow from the tips of these runners, and the new strawberry plants can be removed and planted.

Growers have developed a technique called *layering*, which uses the ability of some plants to reproduce more easily from stems than from other plant parts (see Figure 1.37). Blackberry, raspberry, and rose bushes can be grown from a parent plant using this technique. A branch of the parent plant is bent down to the ground and part of it is covered with soil. Roots will grow from the buried stem and the exposed tip will grow into a new shoot. This new plant can be cut away and replanted.

Pause&
Reflect

Based on what you have learned in this section, write a brief description in your Science Log of how a plant might be reproduced asexually from its leaves. Research the African violet and make a sketch of a technique that could be used to grow several African violets asexually from a leaf.

mound of soil

Figure 1.37 A new plant is produced by layering. What advantage does the offspring plant have by remaining attached to its parent while it develops?

Grafting is another technique plant growers have developed to use the ability of stems to reproduce asexually. Stems from plants with desirable qualities can be attached, or grafted, to the rooted stock of related or similar plants. This technique is commonly used with apples, grapes, and roses. For example, McIntosh apples are produced through grafting. Figure 1.38 shows two methods of grafting.

DidYou**Know**?

The potatoes we eat are actually part of an underground stem called a tuber. The eyes of the potato are the buds of a new plant. The bulbs of daffodils and tulips are other kinds of underground stems. These plants reproduce asexually by growing new shoots from underground stems.

A

B

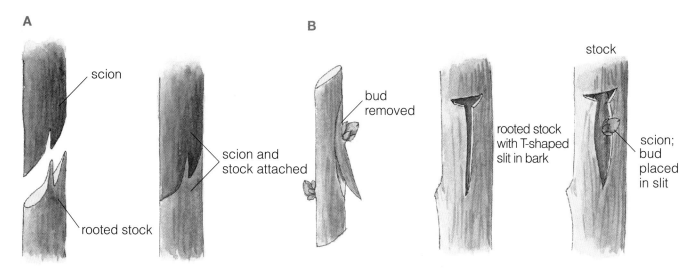

scion

scion and stock attached

rooted stock

bud removed

rooted stock with T-shaped slit in bark

stock

scion; bud placed in slit

Figure 1.38 What is the stem being grafted onto the rooted stock in A called? Where is this part in B?

Word CONNECT

Although plants have been cloned for thousands of years using the techniques you have learned in this section, cloning is more often used to refer to modern reproductive technologies such as tissue culturing. What is the origin of the word "clone"? Write a science fiction story that features a clone.

Tissue Culture

Tissue culture is a technique scientists have developed, which allows identical plants to be grown quickly and economically. Chrysanthemums, orchids, and fast-growing pine trees can be grown by taking a few specialized cells from one plant, and growing them in a special solution in the laboratory (see Figure 1.39). These cells grow quickly into mature plants that are identical to each other. Find out more about the types of plants that are being raised commercially in this way.

Figure 1.39 Tissue culture requires less space than producing plants through cuttings. Why would this be advantageous to a grower?

Check Your Understanding

1. (a) What is meristem?

   (b) What is the role of these cells in the asexual reproduction of plants?

2. (a) Explain and give an example of how plants can reproduce from roots, stems, and leaves.

   (b) Why are the plants produced by these methods considered to be identical to the parent plant?

3. **Apply** Describe how grafting can be used to produce an apple tree that yields four different kinds of apples.

4. **Apply** The number of plants in a flower bed, such as daffodils, can increase without additional bulbs being planted. Explain how this can happen.

5. **Thinking Critically** How can you find out which type of soil is best for growth of young plants? Describe how you would design an experiment to find out.

Now that you have completed this chapter, try to do the following. If you cannot, go back to the sections indicated.

Summarize the major events and discoveries that led to the development of the cell theory. (1.1)

State the four major claims of the cell theory. (1.1)

Name and describe the organelles found in a typical animal cell, and give the function of each. (1.1)

Name and describe the organelles that are found only in a typical plant cell, and give the function of each. (1.1)

Explain how you could design a series of experiments to determine the function of the nucleus. (1.1)

Sketch the four main phases of mitosis, and label each sketch with the name of the phase. Include a brief description of what happens in the cell at each phase. (1.2)

Describe the sequence of events in a typical cell cycle. (1.2)

Explain how mitosis and the cell cycle are responsible for the growth and development of body cells. (1.3)

Describe how cancer is related to the process of mitosis. (1.3)

Compare the advantages and disadvantages of asexual reproduction in bacteria and protists. (1.4)

What are the three types of asexual reproduction in fungi and how do they differ? (1.4)

Explain how meristem enables a plant to grow continuously. (1.5)

Describe how plants can reproduce asexually from roots, stems, and leaves. (1.5)

Prepare Your Own Summary

Summarize this chapter by doing one of the following. Use a graphic organizer (such as a concept map), produce a poster, or write the summary to include the key chapter concepts. Here are a few ideas to use as a guide:
- What is the cell theory?
- Sketch diagrams of typical animal and plant cells. Label and give the functions of the organelles in each.
- What is mitosis?
- List the steps in a typical cell cycle, and explain what takes place at each step.
- Describe the processes of growth, cell replacement, regeneration, aging, and uncontrolled cell division in multicellular organisms.

- Describe and give examples of asexual reproduction in bacteria, protists, fungi, and animals.
- Explain how plants are propagated, or grown commercially, using roots, stems, or leaves.
- Name the organelle shown in the micrograph, and describe its function.

Skill
POWER

For tips on using graphic organizers, turn to to page 569.

Reviewing Key Terms

If you need to review, the section numbers show you where these terms were introduced.

1. Copy this table and complete it for each of the cell organelles listed. Under the heading "Role," describe what part each organelle might play if it were part of a city. For example, the nucleus, as the control centre of the cell, could play the role of city hall. (1.1)

Organelle	Description	Function	Role
nucleus	has a double-layered membrane that surrounds the cell's DNA	control centre	city hall
mitochondria			
ribosomes			
cell membrane			
chromatin			
cytoplasm			

2. In your notebook, match the description in column A with the correct term in column B.

A

- membrane-bound parts of cell
- how a cell spends most of its life
- double-stranded carriers of genetic material
- forms across a plant cell during cell division
- unspecialized cells in the tips of roots and stems
- the making of lost body parts
- a reproductive cell found in fungi
- joins double-stranded chromosomes

B

- cell plate (1.2)
- centromere (1.2)
- regeneration (1.3)
- organelles (1.1)
- spore (1.4)
- interphase (1.2)
- chromosomes (1.2)
- meristem (1.5)
- prophase (1.2)

3. How does binary fission differ from mitosis? (1.2, 1.4)

Understanding Key Concepts

Section numbers are provided if you need to review.

4. Make a timeline showing the main events in the development of the cell theory. (1.1)

5. How does cell division in plant cells differ from cell division in animal cells? Make a sketch to illustrate your explanation. (1.2)

6. The phases of mitosis in the figure below are not in order. In your notebook, sketch the phases in the correct order and name them. (1.2)

7. (a) Explain why mitosis is such an important part of the cell cycle.

   (b) Explain what would happen to human body growth and cell repair if mitosis did not take place. (1.3)

8. (a) List the various types of asexual reproduction in bacteria, protists, fungi, and animals.

   (b) Describe the advantages and disadvantages of asexual reproduction to these organisms. (1.4)

9. What is the importance of meristem in the reproduction of plants? (1.5)

10. Describe and illustrate one example of plant propagation that relies on the ability of plants to reproduce asexually. (1.5)

Developing Skills

11. Make a model to represent each stage of mitosis in a typical animal cell.

12. From the library, a senior level biology textbook, or the Internet research the following:

    (a) How long is the cell cycle of a human brain cell? Make a labelled sketch in your notebook or use a computer program to make a diagram representing this cell cycle.

    (b) How long is the cell cycle of a human liver cell? Make a labelled sketch or diagram representing this cell cycle.

    (c) How long is the cell cycle of a yeast cell? Make a labelled sketch or diagram representing this cell cycle.

Problem Solving

13. Why might exposure to certain substances increase the risk of cancer? Propose a model to explain this.

14. In most Canadian cities, salt is used on roads and walkways in the winter. What happens to plants that come into direct contact with the salt or its runoff? The use of salt by road crews has presented a problem to city foresters who look after the trees and plant life that line roadways. Foresters have learned that one type of honey locust tree has roots that are resistant to high salt levels. However, this tree does not usually grow straight, and it produces lots of messy seed pods. There is another type of locust that grows a straight trunk and produces fewer seed pods. Explain which plant propagation technique foresters could use to produce a locust tree that has salt-resistant roots and a straight trunk.

Critical Thinking

15. Explain what might happen if the chromosomes did not separate properly during anaphase in mitosis.

16. How would you explain the difference between cells that can repair damaged tissue, such as skin cells, and other types of cells, such as nerve cells, that cannot repair damaged tissue?

17. The meristem in most plants is found at the tips of the roots and stems. Explain why homeowners must continually cut their grass in the summer, since each mowing cuts off the tips of grass blades.

Pause & Reflect

1. Write a one-page essay supporting this statement: "The cell is the basic unit of life."

2. Explain how knowledge of asexual reproduction in plants might lead to improvement in the food supplies for developing nations?

3. Look back at your answers to the Opening Ideas questions on page 2. How has your thinking changed? Write your revised answers in your Science Log.

2 Sexual Reproduction

Opening Ideas...

- Why do people differ in appearance from each other and from other members of their family?

- What is the difference between the eggs you eat and the eggs that become chicks?

- Why do frogs develop outside their parents' bodies?

- How do plants produce seeds?

Science Log

You may already have some answers to the questions above. Jot them down in your Science Log. Develop more detailed explanations as you read through this chapter.

Marine biologists who study humpback whales in the North Atlantic use photo identification techniques to track how these animals reproduce, migrate, and interact with each other and their environment. Because each humpback has unique black and white markings on the underside of its fluke (tail), skilled marine photographers are able to capture these whale "fingerprints" on film when the whale dives and raises its fluke.

The flukes of humpbacks are varied for the same reason you do not exactly resemble any member of your family. Similarly, each acorn from an oak tree is unique. In Chapter 1, you learned that asexual reproduction involves only one parent and produces identical offspring. In this chapter, you will examine how sexual reproduction ensures that offspring will not be identical and how this can be advantageous. You will also investigate how sexual reproduction occurs in a variety of organisms, such as animals and plants.

and Variation

Key Concepts

In this chapter, you will discover
- that meiosis produces special cells for sexual reproduction, which leads to offspring with different characteristics
- how sexual and asexual reproduction differ
- the various types of sexual reproduction that occur in animals and plants
- the advantages and disadvantages of sexual and asexual reproduction

Key Skills

In this chapter, you will
- distinguish the phases of meiosis from those of mitosis
- research and integrate your findings from a variety of sources to make a presentation on sexual reproduction
- make drawings of a biological part or process
- practise preparing microscope slides

Key Terms

- variation
- sexual reproduction
- gametes
- fertilization
- zygote
- homologous pairs
- diploid
- haploid
- meiosis
- gonads
- testes
- ovaries
- sperm
- eggs
- embryo
- external fertilization
- internal fertilization

- incomplete metamorphosis
- complete metamorphosis
- hermaphrodites
- seed
- angiosperm
- gymnosperm
- pistil
- stamen
- pollination
- pollen tube
- cotyledon
- fruit
- germination
- sporophyte
- gametophyte
- conjugation

Starting Point ACTIVITY

Observing Human Characteristics

Every person is a collection of characteristics, or traits. Some traits occur in distinct forms. For example, your hairline can be either smooth or pointed. In this activity, you will observe some traits displayed by your fellow students.

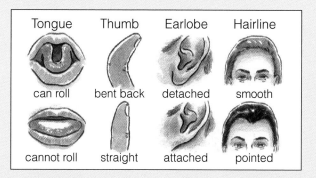

Tongue	Thumb	Earlobe	Hairline
can roll	bent back	detached	smooth
cannot roll	straight	attached	pointed

What to Do

1. Study the forms of each trait shown in the illustrations. Complete a table such as the one below, using the total number of students in your class.

Characteristic	Tongue		Thumb		Earlobe		Hairline	
Traits	Can Roll	Cannot Roll	Bent Back	Straight	Attached	Detached	Smooth	Pointed
Student 1								

In your table, check off which of the two forms of each trait each class member displays. Plot your results on a bar graph.

What Did You Discover?

1. Are some forms of a trait more common than others?

2. What can you conclude about the way traits vary among your class members? Why do you think some students show one form of a trait while others show a different form?

Skill
P O W E R

To review how to prepare a bar graph, turn to page 587.

2.1 Understanding the Basis of Sexual Reproduction

You have observed how several characteristics are displayed by the students in your class. The **variation**, or differences in characteristics, you noticed is not surprising as each of your class members comes from a different family. However, a variety of characteristics can also be seen within a family.

You have learned that when a body cell, such as a skin cell, undergoes mitosis and cell division, two new identical skin cells are produced. You have also learned that in asexual reproduction one parent divides mitotically to produce two identical offspring. The differences among family members in Figure 2.1, however, suggest that another process is responsible for producing such unique or non-identical individuals. This process is called **sexual reproduction**. Your body has specialized organs that make specialized cells, or **gametes**, for sexual reproduction. In sexual reproduction, the gametes from two parents combine during a process called **fertilization** to form a new cell, or **zygote**. This zygote is the first body cell of a new organism. Where do gametes come from and how are they different from body cells? Why are gametes necessary for sexual reproduction?

Figure 2.1 What evidence do you see that both parents in this family must have contributed to the genetic information their children received?

Word CONNECT

The word "homologous" comes from the Greek word "*homologos*," meaning agreeing. How do the chromosomes in a homologous pair "agree" with each other?

A Closer Look at Chromosomes

The differences among your classmates can be explained, because they come from different families. However, the differences among family members must have another explanation.

If you observe the chromosomes in a body cell through a microscope, you will discover that your 46 chromosomes could be arranged into 23 pairs of chromosomes that resemble each other in size and shape. These "matching" pairs of chromosomes are known as **homologous pairs**. You receive one member of each pair from your mother, the other from your father.

The total number of chromosomes in a human body cell is 46. Human body cells are referred to as **diploid** ("di" means double). The human diploid number is 46 (2 × 23). Human gametes have 23 chromosomes and are called **haploid**. You can remember haploid by thinking of "half" the diploid number.

The Reason for Meiosis

The body cells of every typical organism in a species have the same number of chromosomes in each cell, the diploid number. This number stays the same from one generation to the next. The gametes of the same species have the haploid number.

In order for the human chromosome number to remain at 46, gametes must have one-half the number of chromosomes. Only haploid gametes can combine during fertilization to form a diploid zygote. Only a diploid zygote can function as the offspring's first body cell. You know that mitosis ensures that chromosome number does not change. The process that ensures each gamete contains only one-half set of chromosomes is called **meiosis**.

Meiosis also ensures that each gamete has a *different* combination of the chromosomes that were present before meiosis. Because of these non-identical nuclei, the gametes have the potential to produce offspring different from their parents. Why are some of the chromosomes in the new nuclei not identical to the originals? During the early part of meiosis, double-stranded chromosomes come together. During this time, an event called *crossing over* can occur (see Figure 2.4). In the next investigation, you will examine the events that occur inside the nucleus during meiosis.

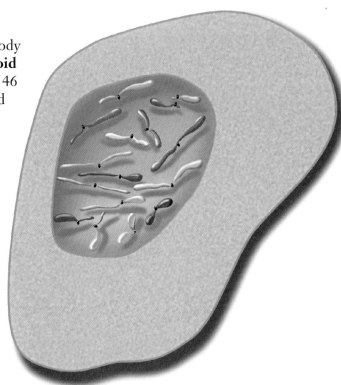

Figure 2.2 This illustration shows a body cell of an imaginary organism. It has a chromosome number of 16. How many homologous pairs are there? What is the organism's diploid number? What is its haploid number?

single strands from each double-stranded chromosome cross over and exchange segments of DNA

homologous pair

Figure 2.4 How does crossing over alter the original chromosomes? With a partner, brainstorm a way to construct a simple model to show this event.

Figure 2.3 Why is the zygote now able to undergo mitosis to produce body cells?

Meiosis: The Power of Reduction

Think About It

The word "meiosis" comes from the Greek word "*meioo*," meaning to lessen, or reduce. How does this reducing process occur to produce gametes with one-half the number of chromosomes of body cells? In this investigation, you will use your knowledge of mitosis to help you interpret the cellular events that occur in the nucleus during meiosis.

What to Do

Part 1

Investigating Meiosis I

1 Work with a partner. Open your textbook to page 18, so you can refer to Figure 1.10, which shows mitosis. Review the diagram and the notes you made about mitosis.

2 Look at the figure of meiosis I. How many double-stranded chromosomes are there in prophase I? Sketch their appearance. Does this

differ from what you observed in prophase of mitosis? (Hint: Are the chromosomes scattered around the cell as in prophase or are they paired up?) Write a brief description to go with your sketch.

3 Make a sketch of what is happening across the centre of the cell in metaphase I. Does this differ from what occurs in metaphase in mitosis? If so, how?

4 Explain what happens in anaphase I, using the words "homologous pairs" and "double-stranded chromosomes." Does this differ from what occurs in anaphase of mitosis? If so, how?

5 Compare telophase I to telophase of mitosis. Note that in both processes two nuclei have been produced. In which case do the two new nuclei contain double-stranded chromosomes Can you explain why?

Meiosos I

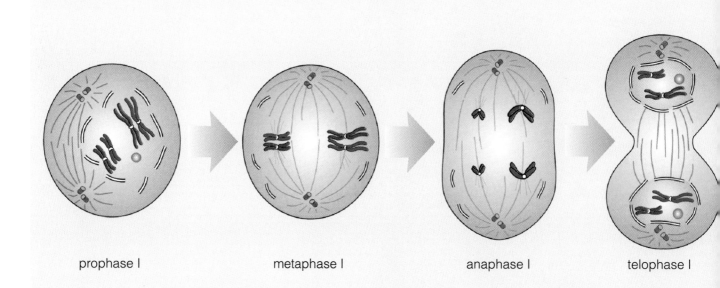

prophase I   metaphase I   anaphase I   telophase I

Part 2

Investigating Meiosis II

1 Look at the figure of meiosis II. Compare prophase II to prophase I. Explain any differences or similarities.

2 Explain what is happening in metaphase II. Does this differ from what happens in metaphase I? If so, explain how.

3 Compare anaphase II to anaphase I. Explain which one is similar to anaphase of mitosis.

4 Explain how telophase II compares to telophase I. What is different about the chromosomes?

5 Now compare the chromosomes in telophase II to the chromosomes in telophase of mitosis. Describe what you notice in a short paragraph.

6 Draw the new cells that will be produced after the cytoplasm divides following telophase II. How many new cells are there?

Analyze

1. By the end of telophase II, how many new nuclei have been produced?

2. How many chromosomes does each new nucleus have compared to the number of chromosomes contained by the original cell in prophase I?

3. What does your answer to question 2 tell you about the type of cells that have been produced? Explain why the new cells are gametes and not body cells.

4. Compared to mitosis, how many times does a cell divide in meiosis?

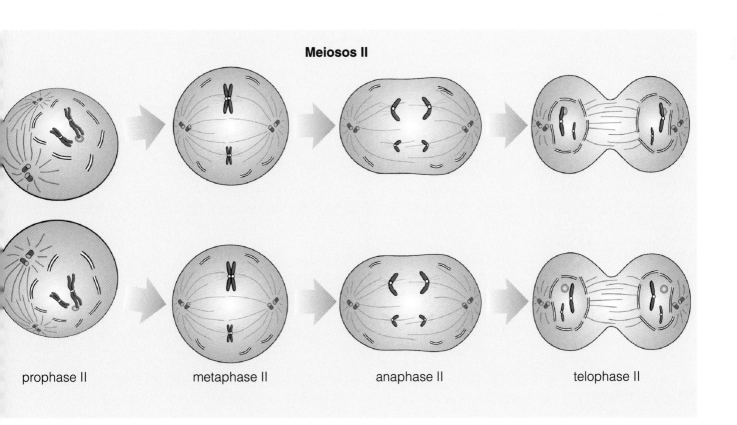

Meiosos II

prophase II   metaphase II   anaphase II   telophase II

Formation of Sperm

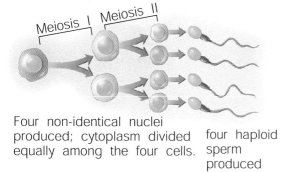

Four non-identical nuclei produced; cytoplasm divided equally among the four cells.

four haploid sperm produced

Formation of Egg

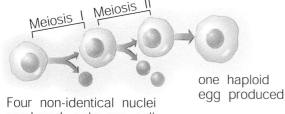

Four non-identical nuclei produced; only one cell receives sufficient cytoplasm to mature.

one haploid egg produced

Figure 2.5 Meiosis occurs continuously in the testes of human males once their gonads are sexually mature. In females, meiosis begins in the ovaries before birth, then stops until the age of about 12 to 15.

The Formation of Sperm and Eggs

Sexually reproducing animals produce gametes in reproductive organs called **gonads**. Male gonads are called **testes** and female gonads are called **ovaries**.

The diagram of meiosis you studied in Investigation 2-A shows the formation of gametes, or **sperm**, in the testes of a male animal. The gametes, or **eggs**, of female animals are produced by meiosis in the ovaries. However, the way in which male and female gametes are finally formed differs. Study Figure 2.5 carefully. What is the final outcome of meiosis for male gametes? For female gametes?

In this section, you have seen how gametes are produced. During the process of fertilization, they come together to produce a zygote, which then starts to divide through mitosis to develop all the cells of a new organism. In the remainder of this chapter, you will learn about sexual reproduction and development in a variety of organisms.

Check Your Understanding

1. For each pair of the following terms, explain how they are related or how they are different.
   (a) asexual reproduction and sexual reproduction
   (b) body cells and gametes
   (c) haploid and diploid

2. How are zygotes produced?

3. What are homologous pairs and why are they important?

4. What is the main difference between mitosis and meiosis?

5. **Apply** Are cells in your muscles haploid or diploid? Explain why.

6. **Apply** An organism has five pairs of chromosomes. Answer the following questions.
   (a) One of the organism's body cells undergoes mitosis. How many cells are formed? How many chromosomes does each new cell have?
   (b) How many chromosomes are in each sperm cell?

7. **Thinking Critically** Explain why all organisms that reproduce sexually have even diploid numbers.

8. **Thinking Critically** Based on what you now know about meiosis, explain the differences among the family members in Figure 2.1.

2.2 Sexual Reproduction in Animals

Look at the animals in Figure 2.6. Some are vertebrates and some are invertebrates. Some live on land and others live in water. The animal kingdom includes a wide variety of organisms with different body forms and ways of living.

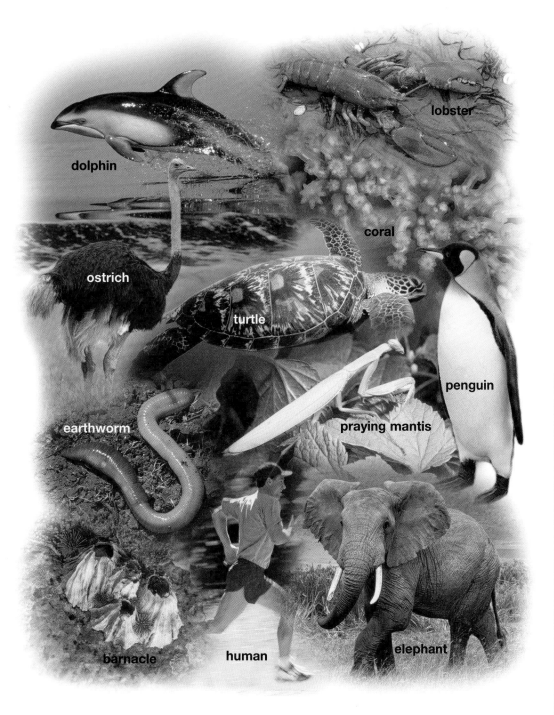

Figure 2.6 All of these organisms are classified as animals. Why are some organisms considered to be animals, while others are classified as plants or fungi? If you need a reminder, go to Appendix A on page 558 to find out.

Pause& Reflect

Television, movies, zoos, and the Internet have made many animals familiar to us that most people living in Canada 100 years ago would never have seen. Based on what you already know about the animals on this page, answer the following questions in your Science Log. Which animals live mostly in water? Which live mostly on land? Which animals are able to move around? Which stay in the same place? Which animals lay eggs? Which give birth to live young?

Despite the differences among these animals, the fundamental sequence that allows them to reproduce sexually is the same.
- Meiosis produces gametes.
- A male gamete (sperm) combines with a female gamete (egg).
- A zygote is produced and develops into an **embryo**.
- The embryo develops through mitosis and cell division into a mature offspring.

Once the offspring matures and is able to produce its own gametes, the sequence can begin again. Figure 2.7 illustrates this "cycle of life."

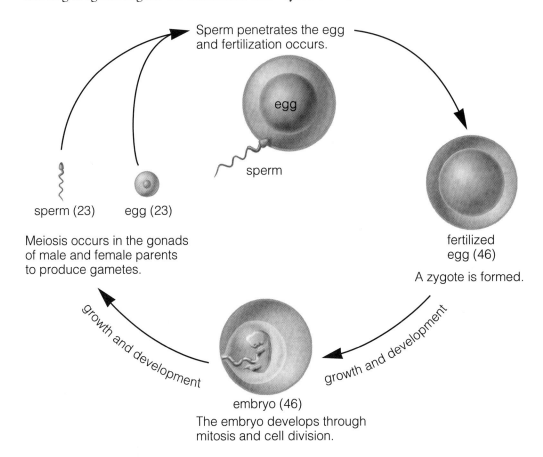

Figure 2.7 Recall what you learned about haploid and diploid numbers in the previous section. Which cells in this cycle are haploid? Which are diploid? How does this cycle ensure variation in offspring?

The first event in the cycle shown in Figure 2.7 depends on meiosis taking place in the gonads of the parents. The final event in the cycle depends on repeated cell division, which enables the zygote's single cell to divide by mitosis into two cells, then four, then eight, and so on.

For sexual reproduction to be successful, the following two requirements must be met.

1. Both male and female gametes must arrive in the same place at the same time for fertilization.
2. The zygote must receive adequate food, moisture, warmth, and protection to develop.

Different animal species meet these requirements through a wide variety of reproductive patterns.

Design a Reproductive Biology Website

In this investigation, you will be part of a design team working for a company that designs web pages. Your client is a university that wants to develop a website about animal reproduction that high-school students can use. Your client is looking for an interactive website that contains a variety of text and pictures linked together in an imaginative way. You and your team will make a presentation to your client on what you intend to include in the website and how it will work.

Challenge

Design a website featuring the reproductive biology of an animal group.

Materials

poster board
overhead projector acetates
coloured markers

Design Criteria

A. Your website will feature the reproductive biology of a particular animal group, for example how the male and female mate, how fertilization occurs, how the zygote develops.

B. Your website must be interactive and not simply display text and pictures.

C. Your website design may be presented as a flow chart or story board. You may also use web page software, if available, to create a design on a computer. You may illustrate your design with pictures.

D. Your team will have one class period to plan how you will design your website. Additional time will be provided to complete your project.

E. You may use any of the information presented in this chapter. However, not all of the information you will need is in the text. Your team will have to investigate other resources.

Plan and Construct

1 Decide the role of each member of your team. Some individuals will research the reproductive biology of the animal group, while others will work on how the material will be presented.

2 Determine what kind of information to include about the reproductive biology of the animal group.

3 What types of links, pictures, and type fonts will you include?

4 Be prepared to show an outline of your plan.

Evaluate

1. Was your website design similar to that of another team? If not, in what ways was it unique?

2. Was your design easy to follow? What changes would you like to make?

3. Did your design include the necessary information about the reproductive biology of your animal group? What other information would you like to include?

4. Was a team approach useful in working on your design? Did you encounter any problems? What were they? How could you improve your teamwork?

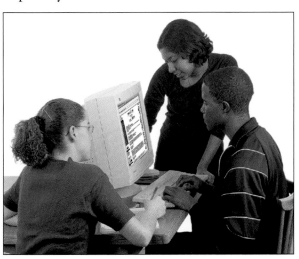

Figure 2.8 Male elk battle for the right to mate with a nearby female.

Figure 2.9 Desert toads mate only after a rainfall. How does this ensure their successful reproduction?

Mating Patterns in the Animal Kingdom

Mating is the process by which two members of a population come together to combine their gametes for fertilization. (A population is a group of individuals of the same species that live and reproduce in the same area.) For some animals, there is only one mating season each year. It is usually timed so that the offspring will hatch or be born when environmental conditions are favourable for their growth and development.

Mating once a year is not the only pattern. For example, a fish called the grunion mates when tides are highest, usually at the full or new moon. In contrast, the honeybee mates only once in a life-time. On her single mating flight, the queen bee will mate with several male bees (drones). The sperm she receives during this flight will fertilize all the eggs she produces for the rest of her life.

Fertilization Patterns in the Animal Kingdom

Fertilization occurs only if a sperm meets an egg from the same species. Both sperm and egg cells are very delicate and will die if they dry out, so a moist environment is an important requirement. Moisture also keeps the egg's cell membrane supple, so that a sperm can pierce it. As well, sperm can swim only in a wet environment.

In animals, there are two main patterns of fertilization: external and internal. In **external fertilization**, the sperm and egg meet outside the bodies of both parents. This pattern is common in water-dwelling animals such as fish. In most land animals, however, the sperm travels from the male's body into the female's body to meet the egg. This pattern is called **internal fertilization**.

Fertilization is only the beginning of animal reproduction. The resulting zygote must develop into a independent individual.

Figure 2.10 Arctic hares depend on internal fertilization for reproduction. What favourable conditions do their offspring need to survive?

External Fertilization

Most water-dwelling animals reproduce through external fertilization. Perhaps the simplest method of external fertilization occurs in animals such as the sea anemone.

Adult anemones cannot move around to mate with each other. However, they can reproduce sexually by releasing their eggs and sperm directly into the water. This method relies on water currents to bring gametes together. The resulting zygotes develop into free-swimming, self-feeding larvae (an immature form of the organism), which may travel some distance before settling down and developing into non-swimming adults (see Figure 2.12).

Many free-swimming animals reproduce by a less random form of external fertilization. For example, the female fish usually lays a cluster of eggs. The male then releases sperm directly onto the egg cluster. This form of external fertilization is known as spawning.

Figure 2.11 To increase the chance that their gametes will meet, all neighbouring anemones release their eggs and sperm at the same time, usually in response to an environmental cue, such as a full moon.

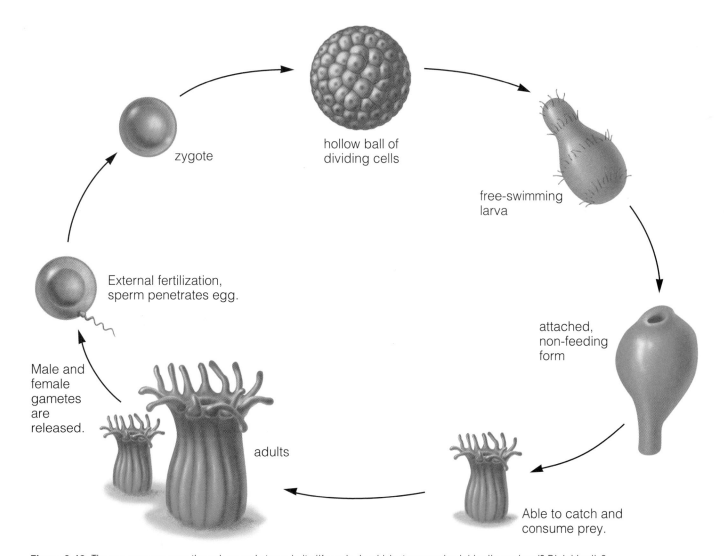

zygote

hollow ball of dividing cells

free-swimming larva

External fertilization, sperm penetrates egg.

attached, non-feeding form

Male and female gametes are released.

adults

Able to catch and consume prey.

Figure 2.12 The sea anemone goes through several stages in its life cycle. In which stages are haploid cells produced? Diploid cells?

Figure 2.13A The female sockeye salmon scrapes out a shallow nest in the stream bed before laying her eggs.

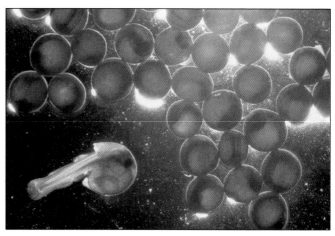

Figure 2.13B How do you think nest building increases the hatchling's chances of survival?

Frogs carry out a similar form of external fertilization. However, during mating, the male frog embraces the female. As the female lays her eggs, the male releases sperm over them.

The young that hatch from the eggs of anemones, fish, or frogs bear little resemblance to their parents. All must develop through several stages before they become adult individuals capable of reproduction. Adult anemones and fish normally spend their entire lives in the water, but most frogs spend at least some time on land (see Figure 2.14).

When sponges reproduce sexually, they use internal fertilization. Because sponges cannot travel for mating, sperm must be released externally into the water. Once the sperm find their way to another sponge, they are captured by special cells, taken into the sponge's body, and transferred to the eggs internally.

Young tadpoles have a tail for swimming.

Older tadpoles start to develop legs.

Young frogs have well-developed legs, but no tail.

adult frog

fertilized eggs

Figure 2.14 The developmental cycle of a frog. Compare this diagram to Figure 2.7. Present this information in your own diagram similar to Figure 2.7.

Internal Fertilization

Most animals that live on land reproduce through internal fertilization. To accomplish this, a specialized structure is often used by the male to transfer sperm directly into the female.

For instance, all reptiles, such as snakes and turtles, reproduce by internal fertilization. Males transfer sperm into the female's *cloaca*, a chamber where the reproductive, urinary, and digestive ducts leave the body. The sperm travel up the reproductive duct to meet the eggs from the female's ovary.

Most all reptiles lay eggs that have tough, leathery shells. Inside each shell, a fluid-filled sac surrounds and protects the zygote as it becomes an embryo. The egg also contains a large supply of food for the developing embryo. When development is complete, the young reptile makes its way out of the shell (see Figure 2.15).

Figure 2.15 Young reptiles, such as these snakes, are miniature versions of their adult parents. As soon as they leave their shells, they begin to feed and protect themselves.

Like reptiles, birds reproduce by internal fertilization. However, few bird species have a specialized structure for transferring sperm. Both males and females have a cloaca and internal fertilization is accomplished through close body contact. The sperm swim from the male's cloaca into the female's cloaca to fertilize her gametes. Birds also lay eggs, but the shells are hard rather than leathery.

Unlike most fish, amphibians, and reptiles, birds care for their young. They sit on the eggs to keep them warm and guard them from predators. In most species, both parents invest a great deal of energy in feeding the young. The young of species such as the killdeer look like miniature adults when they hatch. Although they cannot fly and feed themselves immediately, they can run. In a species such as the American robin, however, hatchlings are helpless. They are unfeathered, blind, and need to be fed by their parents before leaving the nest.

Elsewhere in the animal kingdom, organisms may pass through different forms during development. For example, insects such as grasshoppers and crickets pass through the different stages of development shown in Figure 2.16. This process is called **incomplete metamorphosis**.

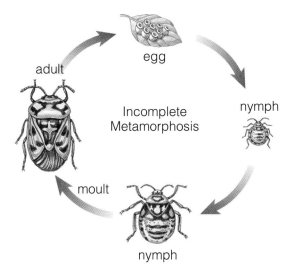

adult
egg
Incomplete Metamorphosis
nymph
moult
nymph

1. Eggs hatch into nymphs, which appear as small adults but have no wings.

2. To develop into a winged adult, a nymph must shed its external sketeton by moulting several times.

Figure 2.16 Incomplete metamorphosis includes three stages: egg, nymph, and adult.

1. The female moth lays fertilized eggs near a food supply, such as a plant, so the worm-like larva (caterpillar) can start feeding as soon as it hatches.

2. After a period of growth, the larva forms a cocoon around itself and enters the pupa stage.

3. The body tissues of the pupa gradually transform into an adult form.

4. The adult moth emerges from the cocoon and can mate to begin the cycle again.

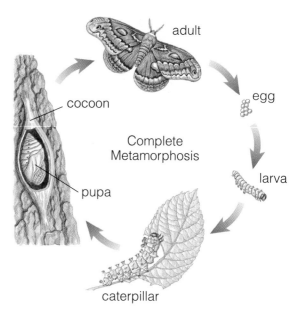

Figure 2.17 Complete metamorphosis of the moth includes four stages: egg, larva, pupa, and adult. At which stage is an insect most likely to survive a cold winter? How might this affect its reproductive success?

Other insects such as houseflies and butterflies go through **complete metamorphosis** (see Figure 2.17) in which the adult form has little resemblance to earlier stages.

You and the deer shown in Figure 2.18 have something in common. You are both mammals. All mammals fertilize their eggs internally. However, most mammals do not lay eggs. Instead, the mother retains and nourishes the embryo within her body. This ensures additional development and protection of the young before birth. Also, mammals produce milk for nourishment of their young. You will learn more about human reproductive cycles and development in Chapter 3.

Marsupials, such as the kangaroo and the opossum, give birth to offspring in a very early stage of development. The young animal uses a hook-like claw to crawl to its mother's pouch (the marsupium). There it latches onto a nipple to obtain milk for completion of its development.

Figure 2.18 The reproductive cycle of mammals and birds requires a great deal of one or both parents' energy. For this reason, mammals and birds produce fewer young per cycle than most other animals.

Figure 2.19 The female opossum gives birth to offspring that are smaller than a honeybee. To complete their development, they must remain in the mother's pouch for another three months.

Hermaphrodites

Hermaphrodites are animals that have both female and male reproductive organs in each individual. For example, flatworms such as the planarian are hermaphrodites. (Recall what you learned about the planarian in Chapter 1.) During mating, each planarian injects sperm into a reproductive pore on the other flatworm's body. Each planarian then lays fertilized eggs.

The common earthworm, often seen on lawns and roads after a rainstorm, is also a hermaphrodite (see Figure 2.20). Internal fertilization ensures that sperm have a moist environment in which to travel and increases the chances that all the eggs will be fertilized.

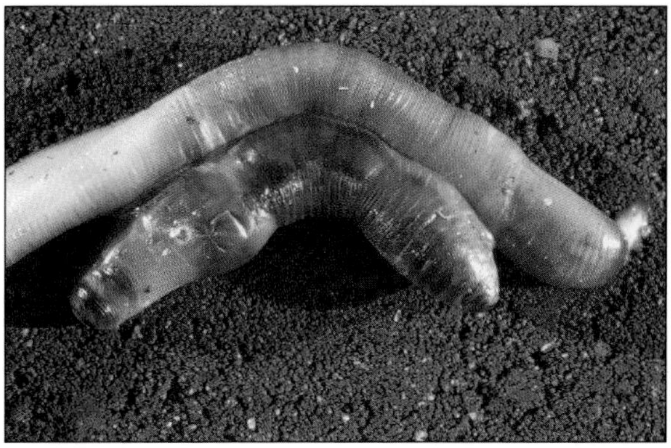

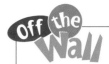

Figure 2.20 These earthworms are mating. Although earthworms produce both types of gametes, they still exchange sperm in order to reproduce.

Off the Wall

Many gastropods such as snails and slugs are hermaphrodites. Each individual has both female and male gonads. This is called simultaneous hermaphroditism. Others, however, are sequential hermaphrodites. They are male when younger and female when older and become large enough to produce and carry eggs.

Check Your Understanding

1. (a) Describe the fundamental cycle that allows all animals to reproduce sexually.
   (b) Explain how this cycle ensures variation in offspring.
2. (a) What is the function of mating? Explain why mating alone does not ensure successful reproduction.
   (b) What is the function of fertilization? Explain why fertilization alone does not ensure successful reproduction.
   (c) What else must occur before reproduction can be considered successful?
3. (a) Which animal probably releases more gametes at a time: the frog or the sea anemone? Explain why.
   (b) Which animal probably gives birth to more young at a time: the salmon or the whale? Explain why.
4. List the requirements for successful fertilization.
5. How does the reproductive pattern of the sea anemone help to ensure successful fertilization? How does it ensure variation among its offspring?
6. **Apply** Turtles are reptiles. Why might newly hatched turtles be less likely to survive than newly hatched birds. Explain.
7. **Thinking Critically** During mating, a female frog may try to dislodge the male who embraces her. Only males that can remain attached long enough will fertilize the eggs. How might this behaviour affect the characteristics of the offspring?

Computer CONNECT

Organize information about reproduction in various types of animals on a spreadsheet. Include any new information you learned about stages of development. In groups, discuss some general factors that affect the type of fertilization or number of stages of development.

2.3 Sexual Reproduction in Plants

If you were asked to name ten plants, what would they be? All of the pictures on this page show members of the plant kingdom. Like the animal kingdom, the plant kingdom includes a wide variety of organisms that live and reproduce in many different environments.

Figure 2.21 All of these organisms are classified as plants. How many do you recognize?

Pause & Reflect

In the previous section, you learned that many animals mate and care for their young. Plants do not follow this reproductive pattern. Most plants are rooted to one place and do not move around. In your Science Log, explain how you think plant gametes are able to meet. Propose a hypothesis about how a parent plant provides for a zygote's needs.

In Chapter 1, you learned that many plants are able to reproduce successfully through asexual reproduction. Plants can also reproduce sexually. The fundamental sequence that allows plants to reproduce sexually is the same to that in animals. What are the main stages and requirements of sexual reproduction? If you need to review, go back to page 52.

How Plants Meet the Challenge of Sexual Reproduction

Seeds are the products of sexual reproduction in most plants. A **seed** is a complete reproductive package that contains an embryo, a food supply, and a seed coat, which protects it from drying out. The Scottish botanist Robert Brown (recall Investigation 1-A) was first to classify seed-bearing plants into two major groups based on seed structure. These groups are called angiosperms and gymnosperms.

Angiosperms are flowering plants. They are probably the first plants you thought of at the beginning of this section. The seeds of angiosperms form inside flowers. When mature, the seeds are enclosed in a case, such as a pod, or shell. Which of the plants on page 60 would you classify as angiosperms?

Unlike angiosperms, **gymnosperms** do not produce flowers. Instead, most gymnosperms produce seeds inside cones. Gymnosperm seeds have a coat that protects them from dehydration, but they are not enclosed in a case. Which of the plants on page 60 would you classify as gymnosperms?

Not all plants fit into these two categories, however. For example, ferns and mosses are neither angiosperms nor gymnosperms. Such plants reproduce sexually, but do so without bearing seeds. Which plants on page 60 do not produce seeds?

Figure 2.22 Some angiosperms, such as these sunflowers, have large blossoms.

Figure 2.23 Gymnosperm seeds are well protected while they are still in the cone. Once they fall out, however, they have only a seed coat for protection.

Figure 2.24 Ferns are common forest plants that reproduce without forming seeds.

Word CONNECT

The word "*angio*" is a Greek word meaning inside a vessel. The word "*gymno*" is a Greek word that means naked. What is the "vessel" in an angiosperm? Why are gymnosperms "naked"? Why do you think the term "sperm" is added to the end of these words?

Sexual Reproduction in Angiosperms

Over half of all known plant species are angiosperms. Some, such as chrysanthemums, produce large, showy flowers. Others, such as grasses, produce flowers that are tiny and easily overlooked. Regardless of their size, all flowers have the same function. They contain the plant's reproductive organs. The female reproductive organ is called the **pistil** and the male reproductive organ is called the **stamen** (see Figure 2.25 on page 62).

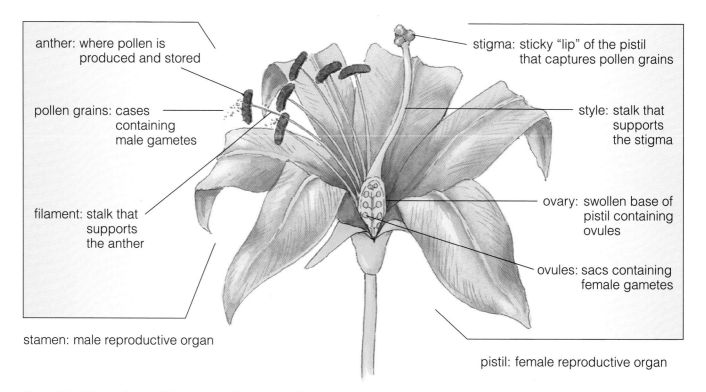

anther: where pollen is produced and stored

stigma: sticky "lip" of the pistil that captures pollen grains

pollen grains: cases containing male gametes

style: stalk that supports the stigma

filament: stalk that supports the anther

ovary: swollen base of pistil containing ovules

ovules: sacs containing female gametes

stamen: male reproductive organ

pistil: female reproductive organ

Figure 2.25 This is a diagram of the parts that make up the reproductive system of an angiosperm. Where are the female gametes formed? The male gametes?

What Is the Role of the Flower?

Science Inquiry

Most flowers contain parts for making both male and female gametes. In this activity, you will identify the parts with the most direct role in reproduction: *stamen, anther, filament, pollen grains, pistil, stigma, style, ovary,* and *ovules.*

What You Need

a real flower
magnifying lens
dark-coloured paper

What to Do

1. Make a sketch of your flower showing the different parts.

2. Make a table with the following headings.

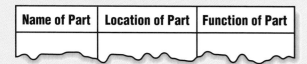

Name of Part	Location of Part	Function of Part

3. Refer to Figure 2.25 as you examine your flower and fill in your table.

4. Examine the stamens. Remove one anther and brush it against a piece of dark-coloured paper. Use the magnifying lens to observe the pollen grains.

5. Locate the pistil. Look for its three parts. Break open the ovary and look for the ovules.

6. Without referring to your table or textbook, label as many reproductive parts as you can on your diagram. Include a short definition of each part.

What Did You Discover?

1. How similar was your flower to Figure 2.25? How did it differ?

3. **(a)** What feature of the stigma makes it suited for capturing pollen grains?

   (b) What feature of the pollen grain makes it suited for being brushed off on insects? Blown away by air currents?

4. Where do you think the seeds are formed?

Pollination and Fertilization in Angiosperms

Before seeds can develop inside a flower, pollen grains from the anthers must reach the stigma of the pistil. This process is called **pollination**. In *self-pollination*, both male and female gametes come from the same plant. In most angiosperms, however, *cross-pollination* brings together gametes from two different parent plants. This means that the pollen from one flower is transferred to a flower on a different plant. Which type of pollination do you think produces more variation in seeds? The two most common agents of cross-pollination are wind and insects (see Figure 2.26B).

Pollination alone is not enough to ensure fertilization. The pollen grain must grow an extension called a **pollen tube** to reach the ovule as shown in Figure 2.27.

INTERNET·CONNECT

www.school.mcgrawhill.ca/resources/

Many of our most important food plants, such as wheat and barley, are self-pollinators. To find out how seed growers maintain vigorous, hardy grain crops, go to the above web site. Go to **Science Resources**, then to **SCIENCEPOWER 9** to find out where to go next. Find out how growers pollinate wheat flowers artificially.

Figure 2.26A Scanning electron micrograph of pollen grains (300x).

Figure 2.26B Pollen rubs off on insects and other small animals, as they travel from flower to flower. Do you think bees also promote self-pollination?

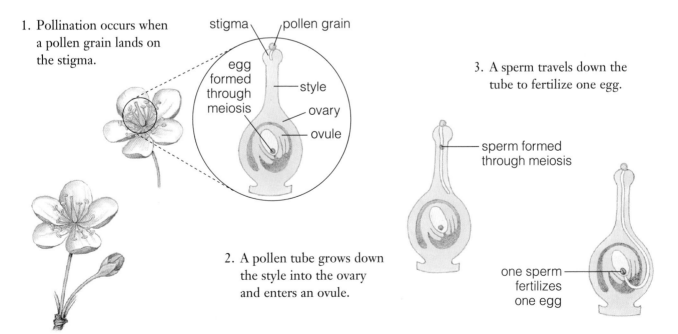

1. Pollination occurs when a pollen grain lands on the stigma.

stigma   pollen grain

egg formed through meiosis   style   ovary   ovule

2. A pollen tube grows down the style into the ovary and enters an ovule.

3. A sperm travels down the tube to fertilize one egg.

sperm formed through meiosis

one sperm fertilizes one egg

Figure 2.27 Development of a pollen tube. A what point does fertilization occur in an angiosperm?

In vitro Pollen Tube Formation

Observing pollen tube formation inside a living pistil is very difficult. In this investigation, you will observe the same process *in vitro*, which is a Latin term meaning in glass. This technique will allow you to study a biological process outside of an organism.

Problem

What conditions are necessary for a pollen grain to form a pollen tube?

Safety Precautions

- Be careful when using sharp objects.
- Be careful not to break the coverslip or slide. Use proper microscope techniques, such a looking from the side while adjusting the coarse adjustment knob.

Apparatus
microscope
cavity slide or depression slide (2)
coverslip (2)
medicine dropper or pipette (2)
tweezers

Materials
toothpick (2)
petroleum jelly
sucrose solution (10%)
pollen grains of lily, tulip, or daffodil
water

Procedure

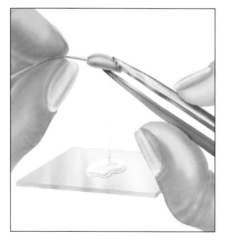

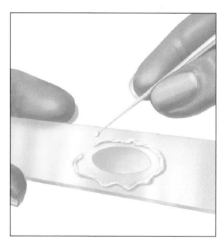

➊ Use the medicine dropper to place a single drop of sucrose solution on the coverslip.

➋ Use the tweezers to carefully transfer a few pollen grains from the anthers of the flower to the drop of sucrose.

➌ Use the toothpick to apply a thin ring of petroleum jelly around the edge of the cavity (depression) in the slide.

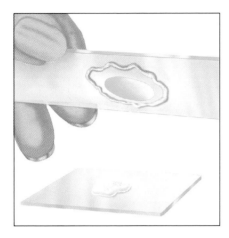

4 Slowly invert the slide over the drop of sucrose on the coverslip. Press very gently so that the petroleum jelly makes a seal around the drop. Quickly invert the slide and coverslip.

5 Examine the slide under low power. Then make a drawing of what you see.

(a) Make three more drawings after 20, 30, and 40 min. Record the elapsed time on each drawing.

(b) Increase the magnification. If you see any new features, include them in your drawings.

6 Repeat steps 1 to 5, using water instead of sucrose solution.

(a) When finished, clean and dry all equipment.

(b) Wipe up any spills and wash your hands thoroughly.

Skill
P O W E R
To review how to make a biological drawing, turn to page 598.

Analyze

1. Describe the results you obtained using the two liquids.

2. Does a pollen tube grow at a steady rate, or does its growth speed up or slow down as time passes?

3. In Figure 2.27, what structure appears inside the pollen tube? When you increased the magnification, were you able to see a similar structure inside your pollen tube?

Conclude and Apply

4. (a) What substances does a pollen grain need to grow a pollen tube? Explain how you know.

(b) What role do you think the water plays? What is the role of the sugar? Hint: Unlike a seed, a pollen grain contains no food supply of its own.

5. A gardener's lilies are in full bloom. A heavy rain falls overnight and washes much of their pollen to the ground. Will pollen tubes form on the ground where the rain soaked in? Explain why or why not.

6. If you were asked to perform a chemical analysis of the sticky material on a stigma, what substances would you expect to find? Explain your answer.

Extend Your Knowledge

7. In spring winds blow literally millions of pollen grains through the air at once. How do seed-bearing plants prevent the egg from being fertilized by sperm from a different species? Obtain pollen from several plant species. Add a grain or two of pollen from each flower to the same water drop on a new slide and place a coverslip over it. Observe the pollen grains under medium to high power and sketch the different shapes and features you see. How do pollen grains differ? Make a hypothesis about why pollen grains differ.

Seed Development in Angiosperms

Pause&
Reflect

Earlier in this section, you learned that a seed is a "complete reproductive package." Based on what you now know about seed development, write two or three sentences to explain the meaning of this statement in your Science Log.

While the pollen tube is growing, cells inside the ovule have been preparing for its arrival. Once a sperm reaches an egg, a zygote is formed, but this is just one step in seed development. Other cells in the ovule have been developing into a **cotyledon**, a structure which contains stored food. The zygote itself must now go through mitotic divisions to form a many-celled embryo with a miniature leaf, root, and stem. The cotyledon surrounds the embryo, and the sac around the ovule develops into a seed coat, as shown in Figure 2.28.

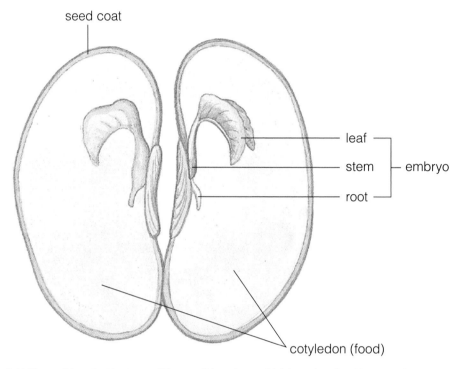

seed coat

leaf
stem — embryo
root

cotyledon (food)

Figure 2.28 The seed is a plant in storage. What conditions do you think it needs to be able to grow?

In angiosperms, the developing seed is further surrounded by the walls of the ovary. As the ovary matures, it forms a **fruit**, such as a pod or case, around the seed (see Figure 2.29).

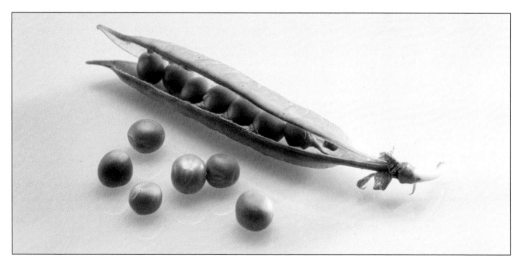

Figure 2.29 A pea pod is actually a fruit, the matured remains of the flower's ovary. Tomatoes, cucumbers, and strawberries are also fruits.

Seed Dispersal in Angiosperms

An angiosperm's fruit often aids in its *dispersal*. Dispersal is the transport of seeds away from the parent plant. Some fruits are able to launch their own seeds a considerable distance when disturbed. Others need help from outside agents. Look carefully at Figures 2.30A, B, C, and D. Notice the methods of seed dispersal they show.

Figure 2.30A Birds eat berries for their soft, tasty fruit, but they cannot digest the hard seed. It passes through them unharmed and falls in droppings far from the parent plant.

Figure 2.30B Seeds such as burdock may "hitch a ride" on the furry coats of mammals, where they stick until they are rubbed off or removed.

Figure 2.30C Milkweed pods open to release seeds with fluffy "sails" that are easily swept away by the slightest breeze to distant locations. Can you name other seeds dispersed by the wind?

Figure 2.30D Running water can also help to disperse seeds. For example, seeds that have fallen to the ground near a parent plant may be carried away to a new location by run-off after a rain.

Math CONNECT

Have you ever watched a maple seed as it falls to the ground? It spins around like a tiny helicopter. You can calculate the distance a maple seed can disperse using the formula $d = v \times t$, where d is the distance from the tree in metres, v is the wind speed in metres/second, and t is the time it takes for the maple seed to fall to the ground in seconds. If a maple seed takes 5 s to fall to the ground in a 5 m/s breeze, how far will the seed travel from the tree?

Regardless of the method, dispersal means that a seed gets away from the parent plant. Why is this important? A seed that stays near its parent will be competing with a mature plant for available moisture, soil, and sunlight. Dispersal can increase the likelihood that offspring will survive long enough to reproduce.

Germination and Growth in Angiosperms

Germination is the process in which a seed begins to grow. The seeds of some angiosperms can stay dormant, or inactive, for years, germinating only when they encounter the right amount of warmth, moisture, and oxygen in the soil. Study Figure 2.31 to see how a bean seed germinates and grows into a young bean plant. The young bean plant in Figure 2.31 will gradually grow larger and eventually develop its own flowers. When this happens the plant is mature and ready for sexual reproduction to produce the next plant generation.

Germination in a Bean Seed

1. Water in the soil softens the seed coat. The growing embryo absorbs food from the cotyledons.

2. The miniature root, stem, and leaf grow and emerge from the seed. The root develops a web of hairs to collect water and minerals from the soil.

3. The growing stem lifts the cotyledons and the true leaves into the sunlight.

4. The cotyledons turn green like leaves and continue to feed the young plant.

5. As the true leaves grow, they begin manufacturing food by photosynthesis. The cotyledons wither and eventually fall off.

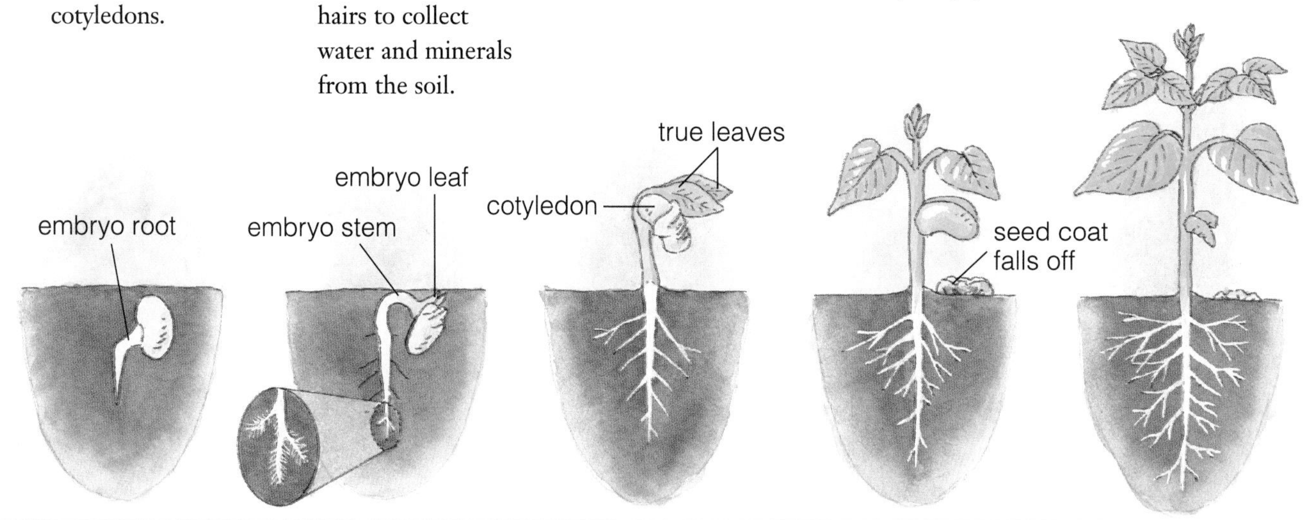

true leaves

embryo leaf

cotyledon

embryo root

embryo stem

seed coat falls off

Figure 2.31 Germination and early growth in a bean plant.

Sexual Reproduction in Gymnosperms

What you have learned about angiosperms will help you understand sexual reproduction in gymnosperms. The life cycle of a gymnosperm, such as the spruce, is similar to that of an angiosperm in many ways. However, gymnosperms do not bear flowers. At the beginning of this section, you learned that most gymnosperms produce their seeds inside cones. For this reason, such plants are often called *conifers*.

In some gymnosperm species, male and female cones are produced on separate trees. However, in most familiar species the same tree produces both types of cone. Examine Figure 2.33. It illustrates fertilization in a typical gymnosperm.

Like an angiosperm, the seed of a gymnosperm contains an embryo, a food supply, and a coat that protects it from drying out. However, the seed is not contained in a fruit.

Pause&
Reflect

Based on what you have learned about seed germination, how would you demonstrate the events shown in Figure 2.31, using a bean seed, a jar, and a moist paper towel? Sketch the set-up you would use in your Science Log.

Figure 2.32 This spruce is a typical gymnosperm. This photograph shows the leaves and cones of a white spruce.

Life Cycle of a Typical Gymnosperm

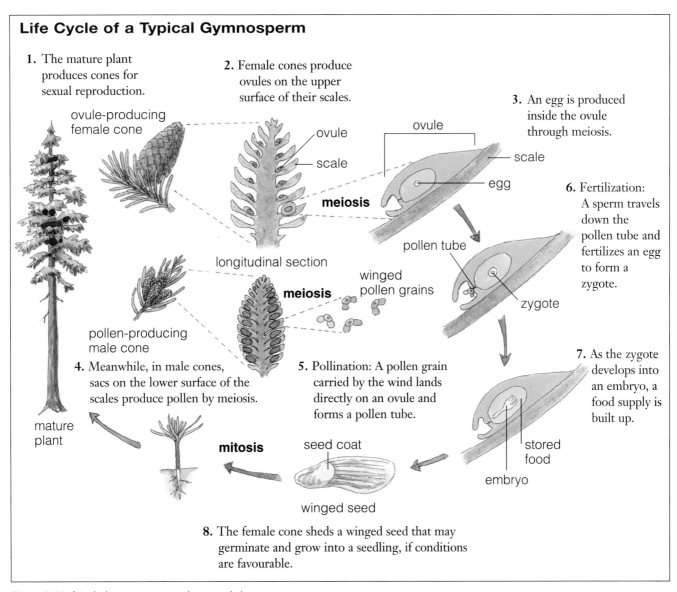

1. The mature plant produces cones for sexual reproduction.

ovule-producing female cone

2. Female cones produce ovules on the upper surface of their scales.

ovule

scale

ovule

scale

3. An egg is produced inside the ovule through meiosis.

egg

meiosis

longitudinal section

pollen tube

winged pollen grains

meiosis

zygote

6. Fertilization: A sperm travels down the pollen tube and fertilizes an egg to form a zygote.

pollen-producing male cone

4. Meanwhile, in male cones, sacs on the lower surface of the scales produce pollen by meiosis.

5. Pollination: A pollen grain carried by the wind lands directly on an ovule and forms a pollen tube.

7. As the zygote develops into an embryo, a food supply is built up.

mature plant

mitosis

seed coat

winged seed

stored food

embryo

8. The female cone sheds a winged seed that may germinate and grow into a seedling, if conditions are favourable.

Figure 2.33 A typical gymnosperm produces seeds in cones.

Sexual Reproduction in Plants Without Seeds

Many of the most familiar plants on the forest floor, such as mosses and liverworts, reproduce without seeds (see Figures 2.34A, B on page 70). These plants reproduce through spores. Like gametes, spores are haploid, but there is an important difference. A spore can develop into a new plant body without being fertilized.

To see how a spore-bearing plant reproduces sexually, examine Figure 2.35 on page 70, which shows the life cycle of a moss. The mature form with fine stalks is called a **sporophyte**, because it produces spores. Given suitable conditions, such as moisture, warmth, and a food supply, the spore develops into a **gametophyte**. What do you think the gametophyte produces?

DidYou**Know**?

Like angiosperms such as maples, ginkgo trees shed their distinctively-shaped leaves in autumn. However, ginkgoes are actually gymnosperms, the last of an ancient group whose other members are now extinct.

Figure 2.34B Liverworts are small, low-growing seedless plants that survive in very wet conditions. What can you infer is a main requirement of mosses and liverworts for reproduction?

Figure 2.34A Thick, green, and soft, mosses thrive in environments that are damp.

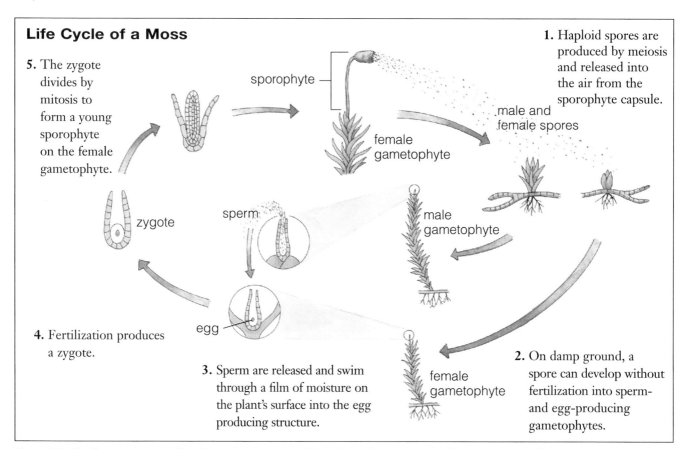

Life Cycle of a Moss

5. The zygote divides by mitosis to form a young sporophyte on the female gametophyte.

sporophyte

female gametophyte

zygote

sperm

egg

4. Fertilization produces a zygote.

3. Sperm are released and swim through a film of moisture on the plant's surface into the egg producing structure.

1. Haploid spores are produced by meiosis and released into the air from the sporophyte capsule.

male and female spores

male gametophyte

female gametophyte

2. On damp ground, a spore can develop without fertilization into sperm- and egg-producing gametophytes.

Figure 2.35 The life cycle of a moss. Study the numbered events carefully, following the process on the diagram as you read. Where are the reproductive structures located? How does this differ from seed-bearing plants?

Spores have two main advantages that suit them for dispersal. They are very light and can be carried great distances to locations that may have favourable growing conditions. Secondly, spores can survive unfavourable temperatures and periods of drought. Thus, spores can stay dormant for a very long time and still produce healthy plants when good growing conditions return.

Figure 2.36 Other spore-bearing plants, such as this fern, release spores from tiny cases found on the underside of the leaf.

Pause&
Reflect

There are about 35 000 species of spore-bearing plants, 700 species of gymnosperms, and 200 000 species of angiosperms living on Earth today. Based on these numbers, which type of sexual reproduction in plants appears to be the most successful in today's climate? Why? At one time, large spore-bearing plants were the most numerous of all plant species. In your Science Log, write a hypothesis to explain the type of climate Earth must have had to support such populations of spore-bearing plants. Infer how climate change can affect plant survival.

Check Your Understanding

1. Describe the fundamental cycle that allows all plants to reproduce sexually.

2. For each pair of terms below, explain what they have in common and how they differ.
   (a) pistil and stamen
   (b) flower and cone
   (c) angiosperm and gymnosperm
   (d) seed and spore

3. What is the function of pollination? Explain why pollination alone does not ensure successful reproduction.

4. (a) Explain why seeds can be referred to as "plants in storage."
   (b) Can spores also be thought of as plants in storage? Explain your answer.

5. (a) Can a gamete develop into a complete plant by itself, without fertilization? Explain.
   (b) Can a spore develop into a complete plant by itself without fertilization? Explain.

6. **Apply** Explain how the cycle in question 1 ensures variation in plants.

7. **Apply** A beech tree has small, green-coloured flowers. Explain why it is unlikely that beech flowers are pollinated by insects. Suggest the most likely method of pollination.

8. **Thinking Critically** Fireweed flowers are shaped so that they cannot pollinate themselves. Near the end of the growing season, however, a change occurs in any flower that has not been pollinated. The stamens curve around so that the anthers touch the stigmas within the same flower.
   (a) Explain the reproductive advantage of preventing self-pollination.
   (b) Explain the reproductive advantage of permitting self-pollination.

2.4 The Value of Variation

Pause& Reflect

In your Science Log, record your answers to the following. Which form of reproduction produces "more of the same"? Which form produces "more, but not the same"? Briefly describe the cellular process that is behind each type of reproduction. In which type do all offspring receive identical sets of chromosomes? In which type does each offspring receive a different set of chromosomes? What makes variation possible? Use sketches to support your answers.

No individual plant or animal lives forever. Plants and animals exist today because their ancestors reproduced, either sexually or asexually. Remember that asexual reproduction requires only a single cell to divide by mitosis. This process enables an organism to produce many offspring, usually in a short period of time. Because only one individual is involved in reproduction, all the offspring are genetically the same as the parent. In contrast, sexual reproduction requires the gametes of two individuals to combine to form a zygote. Sexual reproduction requires more energy than asexual reproduction. As a result, fewer offspring tend to be produced. However, the genetic information of two parents is represented in the offspring. Both methods produce more individuals of the same species, but which is better for offspring survival? The answer depends on the environment in which an organism lives.

We tend to think of our world as static, but it is in fact very changeable. A change, such as bad weather, disease, or inadequate food, can stress organisms in a population. For example, if all *Paramecia* in the same pond were identical, all might perish from a small environmental change. If they vary, even an environmental catastrophe may leave some survivors. See how variation in a population can be advantageous in the following activity.

Science Inquiry ACTIVITY

Survival: The Ultimate Advantage

The fictional animal species, *Shellshapus shiftia*, varies only in shape. It reproduces asexually or sexually. Individuals mate without regard to shape. In this activity, you will model reproduction, variation, and survival in a fictional population.

What to Do

1. Suppose a population of *Shellshapus shiftia* is composed of four types of shapes: squares, triangles, circles, and ovals. Draw the four shapes on a piece of paper to represent the types of individuals in the population.

2. Record the outcome of each environmental change described below.
   - **(a)** Autumn provides enough food for one cycle of asexual reproduction. Nobody dies.
   - **(b)** Winter cold kills all the squares.
   - **(c)** A large food supply in spring allows another cycle of asexual reproduction. Nobody dies.
   - **(d)** A virus in the summer kills all the ovals.

3. Begin again with the original shapes. Repeat step 2, replacing asexual with sexual reproduction. Model the potential outcome of sexual reproduction by showing what new variations might be produced by each possible pairing. List all possible pairings, for example, oval/oval; oval/circle; oval/square. List the new varieties you modelled. Use your imagination.

What Did You Discover?

1. Consider the impact of asexual reproduction on the population. Describe the makeup of the population after each environmental change. Does the population become more varied or less varied?

2. Consider the impact of sexual reproduction on the population. Does the population become more varied or less varied?

3. What can you conclude about the advantage of sexual reproduction over asexual reproduction in the survival of individuals?

Survival Through Variation

Variation is easy to observe in kittens, but not so obvious in penguins or sunflowers. The value of some variation is not always obvious. For example, earlobe shape does not seem to affect human survival. However, some variations that affect our survival are far less visible. Resistance to infectious disease is a good example.

A century ago, bacterial infections were a major cause of death in humans. With the discovery of bacteria-killing antibiotics in the late 1920s and their widespread use in the 1950s, we began to think such diseases had been conquered. We were wrong.

Suppose you catch strep throat, an infection caused by *Streptococcus* bacteria. Your body is their environment, and their population multiplies inside you. Before 1940, you would be sick for weeks while your immune system struggled to kill them off. By 1950, you would likely take an antibiotic to change their environment and quickly destroy the population. Today, your doctor may have difficulty finding an antibiotic that can do the job.

Figure 2.37 Bristlecone pines (*Pinus longaeva*, meaning long-living pine) are the oldest trees on Earth.

Figure 2.38 Can you see the variation among the individuals in each of the photographs above?

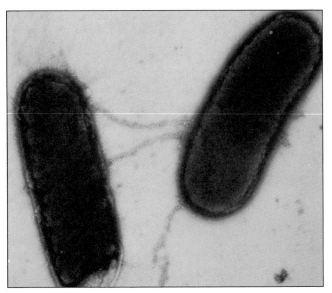

Figure 2.39 Sexual reproduction in bacteria does not involve meiosis. Instead, a conjugation tube allows a one-way transfer of a copy of DNA from one individual to another.

How did this happen? Before 1940, most *Streptococcus* bacteria had no ability to disable antibiotics, but a few did. These few surviving bacteria were able to pass on this ability, because bacteria are able to reproduce sexually by a process called conjugation. **Conjugation** is the transfer of DNA by cell-to-cell contact (see Figure 2.39). Conjugation allowed antibiotic resistant individuals to pass their DNA along to other *Streptococcus* bacteria. As a result of sexual reproduction, many resistant populations developed, especially in hospitals, where antibiotics are widely used.

Sexual reproduction combines DNA from two individuals to produce offspring that are varied. The nearly universal occurrence of sexual reproduction in all five kingdoms is strong evidence that variation must be an advantage. Because of variation, some individuals will survive to produce a new generation, even if their environment changes.

Check Your Understanding

1. What is the main value of variation?

2. What form of reproduction favours variation? Explain why by referring to DNA.

3. Describe conjugation in bacteria. How does this process favour variation?

4. How does the story of antibiotic resistance illustrate the value of variation?

5. **Apply** Do variations in colour affect the survival of the world's domestic cat population? Support your answer. Which cat population's survival might be affected by colour?

6. **Thinking Critically** Is variation always an advantage? Explain.

Now that you have completed this chapter, try to do the following. If you cannot, go back to the sections indicated.

State the main difference between meiosis and mitosis. (2.1)

Make a sketch to show how sperm and eggs in animals are formed. (2.1)

Define sexual reproduction and describe the cycle that enables animals to reproduce sexually. (2.2)

State the function of mating in animals and describe how it differs from fertilization. (2.2)

Compare and contrast external fertilization with internal fertilization and give examples of animals that use each of these methods to reproduce. (2.2)

Compare and contrast incomplete metamorphosis with complete metamorphosis. (2.2)

Explain, using an example, how mating and fertilization in hermaphrodites differ from that in other animals. (2.2)

Describe the cycle that enables plants to reproduce sexually. (2.3)

Compare and contrast gymnosperms, angiosperms, and spore-bearing plants. (2.3)

Explain the role of pollination in plant reproduction. (2.3)

In your notebook, make a copy of the diagram above and label the reproductive parts. (2.3)

Sketch a sequence of diagrams showing how a pollen tube develops in a flower. Indicate the point at which fertilization occurs. (2.3)

Compare and contrast seed development in angiosperms and gymnosperms. (2.3)

Explain the importance of dispersal within the plant kingdom and state examples of different dispersal methods. (2.3)

Explain the conditions needed for seed germination. (2.3)

Explain the role of sexual reproduction in ensuring variation. State the importance of variation to a population of organisms. (2.4)

Prepare Your Own Summary

Summarize this chapter by doing one of the following: Use a graphic organizer (such as a concept map), produce a poster, or write the summary to include key chapter concepts. Here are a few ideas to use as a guide:
- What is the importance of meiosis?
- How does fertilization occur?
- In animals using external fertilization, what features increase the chances for the eggs and sperm to meet?
- Why are sperm-transferring structures common in many organisms that have internal fertilization?

- How do animals such as the sea anemone benefit from a free-swimming stage during the reproductive cycle?
- Why do frogs return to the water to mate?
- How do hermaphrodites reproduce?
- Why can turtles leave their young as soon as they hatch, but birds cannot?
- Why do most mammals take much longer to be born than marsupial mammals?
- What reproductive structures must the simplest flower contain, and why?

Reviewing Key Terms

If you need to review, the section numbers show you where these terms were introduced.

1. Decide whether the following statements are true or false. If a statement is false, restate it to make it true.

   (a) Homologous pairs get separated in meiosis II. (2.1)

   (b) The ovaries and testes are an animal's gonads. (2.1)

   (c) If the haploid number of an organism is 28, its diploid number must be 56. (2.1)

   (d) Mating is required for internal fertilization, but not external fertilization. (2.2)

   (e) Cross-pollination guarantees that each plant offspring will be identical. (2.3)

   (f) Conjugation is a form of asexual reproduction. (2.4)

2. From the list of Key Terms on page 45, name the structure in plants that match the following:

   (a) A plant's "reproductive package" (2.3)

   (b) The female reproductive part of a flower (2.3)

   (c) This protective structure is also very tasty. (2.3)

   (d) Grows into a straw-like structure that delivers sperm (2.3)

   (e) Used for food storage in a seed (2.3)

   (f) Containers for spores grow on this. (2.3)

   (g) This part of a plant produces gametes. (2.3)

Understanding Key Concepts

Section numbers are provided if you need to review.

3. Why are fish eggs laid in the water? (2.2)

4. What are two features that suit reptile eggs for life on land? (2.2)

5. How is incomplete metamorphosis different from complete metamorphosis? (2.2)

6. How do new-born birds differ from new-born reptiles?(2.2)

7. Other than for protection, what is the role of fruit in seed plants?(2.3)

8. How are spores and pollen suited for dispersal? (2.3)

9. How are seeds adapted for dispersal by wind? By water? By animals? (2.3)

10. What happens to all the parts of a seed in the first few days of germination? (2.3)

Developing Skills

11. Complete the following life cycle by filling in the appropriate terms and processes.

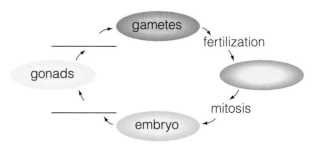

12. Using students to play the chromosomes, act out the steps of meiosis. Add students during each replication.

13. "Sexual reproduction is more effective than asexual reproduction, and it is only a matter of time before all living organisms reproduce that way exclusively." In teams, prepare arguments either for or against this statement. Support each argument with a quote or an example. Each team presents its arguments in a class debate.

Problem Solving

14. Adult anemones live in one location and do not move from it. Outline the ways in which sexual reproduction would help them overcome a toxic waste spill.

15. Which animal would you expect to lay more eggs at one time: a salamander (an external fertilizer) or a lizard (an internal fertilizer) of the same size? Give reasons to support your answer.

16. What is the haploid number for an organism with 18 homologous pairs?

17. Fern leaves grow from tightly coiled, tender spirals called *fiddleheads*. Although fiddleheads have been collected as a vegetable delicacy for ages, they are mildly toxic. How would this feature help a fern survive?

18. Why will organisms such as flatworms struggle to reproduce sexually, when their normally moist environment becomes dry?

Critical Thinking

19. (a) Which method of pollination demands more energy from a plant: animal or wind pollination?

(b) In what ways is animal pollination an advantage over wind pollination?

20. What are the advantages and disadvantages of asexual and sexual reproduction?

21. Some people call ferns and mosses the "amphibians" of the plant kingdom. Do you agree? In a table, compare reproduction in ferns and mosses with reproduction in amphibians.

22. When might people with pollen allergies experience the worst symptoms: on a windy spring day, on a rainy summer day, or on a sunny autumn day?

23. Check a Canadian atlas to see how much of Canada's land area is covered by coniferous forests. Suggest a reason why gymnosperms are especially suited for northern climates.

24. Some populations are more variable than others. Why do you think this is so?

25. Think about the reproductive role of a sporophyte fern plant compared with that of a gametophyte fern plant. What might you suppose "phyte" means?

Pause & Reflect

1. Using several examples, comment on how humans might help to disperse the seeds of angiosperms. Do humans play a similar role in dispersing the seeds of gymnosperms?

2. In seedless plants, the gametophytes produce sperm and egg cells. What are the gametophytes in seed-bearing plants?

3. In all mammals: (a) The female retains the fertilized egg in her body, providing protection and nourishment as it develops. (b) The female has mammary glands that produce milk to continue nourishing young mammals once they are born. (c) One or both parents care for the offspring until they can feed and defend themselves. In your Science Log, explain any advantages and disadvantages of these features of mammal reproduction.

Opening Ideas...

- How were all your limbs, bones, and tissues formed from only one cell?

- What changes take place inside a woman's body while she is pregnant?

- What factors can influence the development of a human fetus?

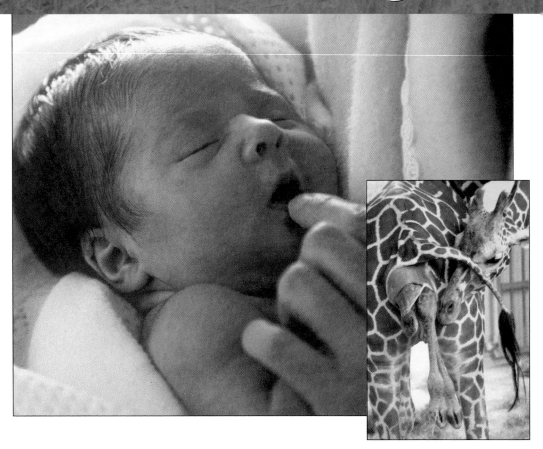

Science Log

In your Science Log, draw a zygote as you think it might look two days after fertilization. How would its appearance change after three months? Sketch your ideas. Then try to answer the three questions above.

All mammals, from giraffes to people, start life as tiny fertilized eggs about the size of the period at the end of this sentence. Over weeks or months, the new life grows and develops, eventually becoming a collection of cells, tissues, and organs that make up a baby giraffe or a baby human. Although these two babies look very different, the processes that produced them are quite similar.

In this chapter, you will learn about the changes that occur in the human body to prepare for reproduction. You will learn how a pregnant woman's body changes to protect and help a new life grow and how a single cell eventually becomes an independent living organism. You will also investigate how science and technology have helped us to identify certain factors that can sometimes affect the health of a developing fetus.

Human Development

Key Concepts

In this chapter, you will discover
- which organs are involved in human reproduction
- how hormones co-ordinate the reproductive process
- the stages of development, from zygote to birth
- some lifestyle/environmental factors that may affect fetal development

Key Skills

In this chapter, you will
- analyze statistics and predict trends
- formulate questions to investigate issues related to human reproduction and reproductive technologies
- investigate the effects of factors such as toxins, radiation, and disease on the reproductive process
- make and interpret graphs, tables, and diagrams

Key Terms

- gestation
- hormones
- puberty
- pituitary gland
- follicle stimulating hormone (FSH)
- testosterone
- estrogen
- scrotum
- seminiferous tubules
- epididymis
- vas deferens
- prostate gland
- seminal vesicles
- semen

- urethra
- ovum
- ovulation
- follicles
- oviducts
- uterus
- cervix
- vagina
- menstrual cycle
- luteinising hormone (LH)
- progesterone
- corpus luteum
- menstruation
- cleavages
- blastocyst
- placenta

- implantation
- gastrula
- germ layers
- endoderm
- mesoderm
- ectoderm
- yolk sac
- amnion
- allantois
- chorion
- umbilical cord
- differentiation
- trimester
- fetus
- oxytocin
- labour

Comparing Gestation Periods

Is there a difference in the time it takes for a mouse to develop before birth, compared to the time required for a human baby? The time needed for a mammal to develop to the point when it is ready to be born is called its **gestation** period.

Gestation Periods in Days for Some Common Mammals

Animal	Days	Animal	Days
ape	210	elephant	624
bear	208	giraffe	457
buffalo	275	hamster	16
cat	63	horse	336
chimpanzee	243	human	267
chipmunk	31	mouse	20
cow	281	rabbit	31
deer	215	sheep	151
dog	63	whale	450

What to Do

Make a bar graph using the data in the above table. List the animals in terms of shortest gestation period to longest gestation period.

What Did You Discover?

1. What general pattern does your graph show concerning the relationship between mammal size and gestation period?

2. Do humans fit this pattern? What might account for deviations from the general pattern you see in your graph?

3. What do you think is the benefit of a short gestation period?

4. Hypothesize some benefits of a longer gestation period.

3.1 Reproductive Systems

You learned in Chapter 2 that male and female gonads produce gametes. The human reproductive system is designed to produce these gametes and bring them together through internal fertilization. What makes the gonads start producing gametes?

It all begins with **hormones**. Hormones are substances that act like messengers in the body. They travel through the bloodstream and cause certain cells to respond in specific ways. Several hormones regulate the reproductive system.

Humans and Puberty

Most humans first experience the effects of reproductive hormones in their early to mid-teens. This period, called **puberty**, is when hormonal signals change the body so that it is able to reproduce. When puberty begins, the **pituitary gland** at the base of the brain (see Figure 3.1) starts to produce **follicle stimulating hormone (FSH)**. FSH travels through the bloodstream to the gonads—the ovaries in females and the testes in males. FSH signals the testes to produce sperm and the ovaries to produce mature eggs. Other hormones help in the development and maintenance of additional characteristics associated with being distinctly male or female — the *secondary sexual characteristics.*

Puberty in Males

When FSH reaches the testes, it promotes the development of sperm-producing tubes in the testes and the development of sperm cells. Once sperm production begins, males generally produce them daily for the rest of their lives. Other cells in the testes start to produce the hormone **testosterone**, which directs the development of secondary sexual characteristics. These characteristics include a deepening of the voice, the production of facial, underarm, and pubic hair, and a broadening of the shoulders.

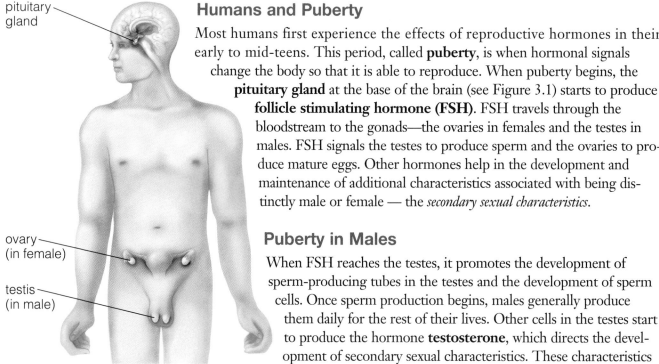

pituitary gland

ovary (in female)

testis (in male)

Figure 3.1 The pituitary gland at the base of the brain is about the size of a pea, yet it controls many important body functions, including reproduction.

Pause&Reflect

Do other mammals go through puberty? Think about what puberty is, and then answer this question in your Science Log. Indicate why you might be able to infer they, too, undergo such a reproductive change.

Figure 3.2 Male puberty usually begins between the ages of 13 and 16, and female puberty usually between the ages of 12 and 15.

Puberty in Females

When FSH reaches the ovaries, they are stimulated to begin maturing and releasing eggs. Generally one egg is released each month. FSH also stimulates the ovaries to produce **estrogen**, which is a reproductive hormone. Estrogen is also responsible for the appearance of female secondary sexual characteristics, including deposits of fat in the breasts and hips and the growth of pubic and underarm hair.

Outside Link ACTIVITY

Predicting Reproductive Trends

Only about 67% of women born in Canada in 1700 lived to the age of 15. By 1951, a woman's chances of reaching 15 were about 96%. Demographers analyze statistics such as these to understand and predict population trends. In this activity, you will predict and investigate patterns in women's reproductive lives.

Women's Reproductive Lives in Canada, 1700-1951

Variable	Year of Birth					
	1700	1831	1861	1891	1921	1951
Number of women per 1000 who lived at least to the age of 15	667	681	691	744	874	956
Number of women per 1000 who lived at least to the age of 50	365	490	527	627	820	928
Average life expectancy (years)	30-35	42	45	54	70	80
Average number of children born per woman	4.3	3.9	3.0	2.5	2.7	1.8

What to Do

Make two line graphs. Use the dates and the last two variables only to do the following: (a) Show the relationship of average life expectancy and year of birth. (b) Show the relationship of average number of children born per woman and year of birth.

What Did You Discover?

1. What general trend do you see in women's life expectancy from 1700 to 1951?

2. What general trend do you see in the average number of children born to each woman over the same period?

3. Based on the trends you have just assessed, predict the pattern in life expectancy and the average number of children born per woman for the period from 1951 to the present. Use the library or search the Internet to confirm or refute your predictions.

4. Predict what might happen during the first three decades of the twenty-first century. Justify your predictions in a short paragraph, indicating why you predict major changes or a continuation of a trend.

5. Why would knowing the number of women who reached the ages of 15 and 50 be important to someone studying patterns of reproduction? What generalizations can you make by examining these life expectancy statistics?

Extension

6. As a class, discuss how these statistics might be useful. For example, why might the Department of Health be interested in your results? How might a school division use the information to form its long-range plans? Do you think they would be more interested in the general trends or in quantitative data? Why?

Skill
POWER

For tips on organizing and communicating scientic results, turn to page 587.

Male Reproductive Anatomy

The male reproductive system is designed to produce as many healthy sperm as possible. As you read the next section, refer to Figure 3.3 to trace the path of sperm through the male body. Make a summary table in your notebook with structures of the male reproductive system listed in the first column and reproductive function in a second column.

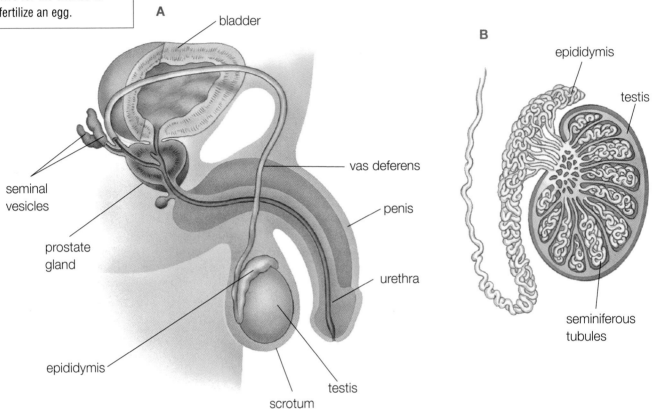

Figure 3.3 Structures of the male reproductive system (A), with a close-up of a testis (B). Where are the male gonads?

Sperm cells are produced in the testes, which are located outside the main body cavity in a sac of tissue called the **scrotum**. The external location of the scrotum keeps the testes slightly cooler than the rest of the body. A cooler temperature is required for the development of healthy sperm.

Sperm cells are produced in tiny tubes in the testes called **seminiferous tubules** (see Figure 3.4). About 350 to 500 million sperm are produced each day. When they move out of the tubules, the sperm cells are stored beside the testes in long, coiled tubes called the **epididymis**, until it is time for them to leave the body.

From the epididymis, sperm travels through tubes called the **vas deferens**, which circle the bladder. Recall from Chapter 2 that sperm move by swimming. To help sperm move, fluid is supplied by two glands, the **prostate gland** and **seminal vesicles** that are located at the base of the bladder. These glands produce and release thick, milky fluid into the vas deferens. The sperm cells mix with the milky fluid in the vas deferens. This mixture is called **semen**. Fluid produced by the prostate gland and seminal vesicles is rich in sugars. These nutrients provide energy for the sperm to swim.

If you examine Figure 3.3, you will see that the vas deferens joins the same tube that carries urine from the bladder through the penis to the outside of the body. This dual-function tube is the **urethra**. A small valve-like muscle at the bottom of the bladder prevents both urine and semen from being in the urethra at the same time.

Pause&
Reflect

Sperm cells need a lot of energy to travel from the male and unite with an egg in the female. Based on what you know about cells, which organelle might be found in large amounts in sperm? Record your answer in your Science Log and provide a brief explanation.

1. Sperm are produced from cells in the walls of the seminiferous tubules.

2. Diploid cells are forced away from the tubule walls by repeated mitotic cell divisions.

3. In a later stage of development, these cells undergo meiosis to produce mature sperm.

4. The entire process of sperm production takes nine to ten weeks.

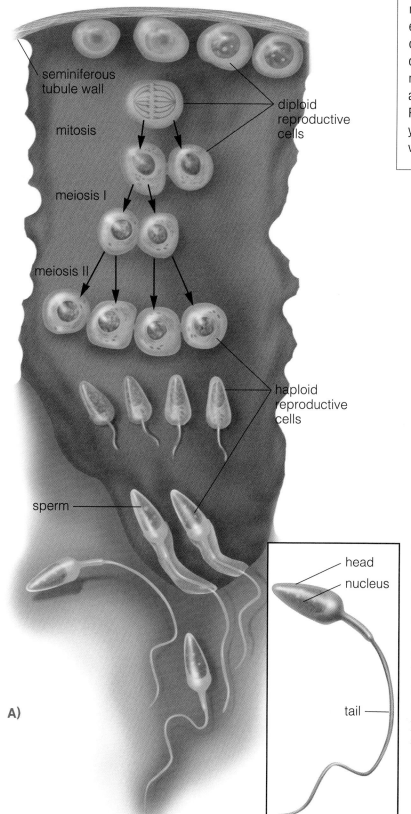

Sperm cells are unicellular and consist of a head and a tail. The head carries the nucleus, which contains the genetic material of the male. The tail-like structure, the *flagellum*, acts as a kind of propeller to move the sperm toward the egg.

Figure 3.4 Sperm development in a seminiferous tubule (A) with a close-up of a sperm (b).

Female Reproductive Anatomy

Ovaries are located inside a woman's main body cavity (see Figure 3.5). They are about 3 cm in length and almond-shaped. One egg, or **ovum** (plural ova), is released by the ovaries approximately every 28 days. This process is called **ovulation**. The two ovaries generally alternate, or take turns, releasing an egg.

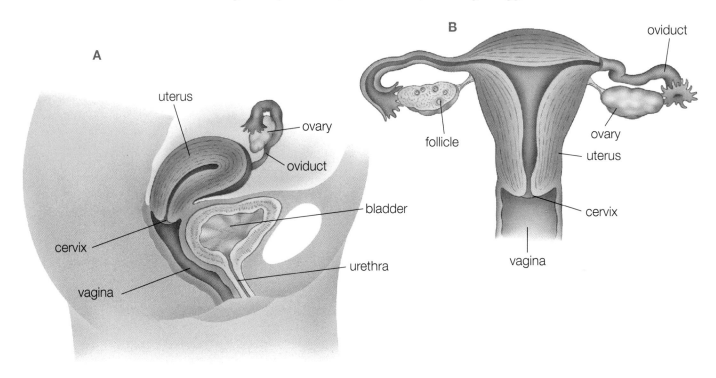

Figure 3.5 Structures of the female reproductive system shown from the side (A) and the front (B). Where are the female gonads in each drawing?

Near the time of ovulation, a woman's body temperature may drop slightly, then rise between 0.5° and 1°C (see Figure 3.6). Why might body temperature drop slightly before ovulation?

The surface of the ovaries contains many fluid-filled cavities called **follicles**. Each follicle contains an egg (see Figure 3.7). During ovulation, a mature egg breaks out of its follicle. The feathery ends of the **oviducts**, or Fallopian tubes, help to guide the tiny egg into the tube. Hair-like structures lining the oviducts

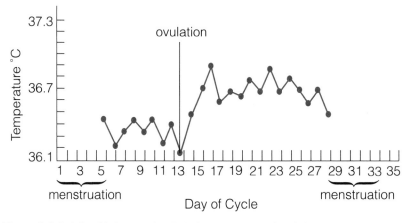

Figure 3.6 Relationship between female body temperature and ovulation

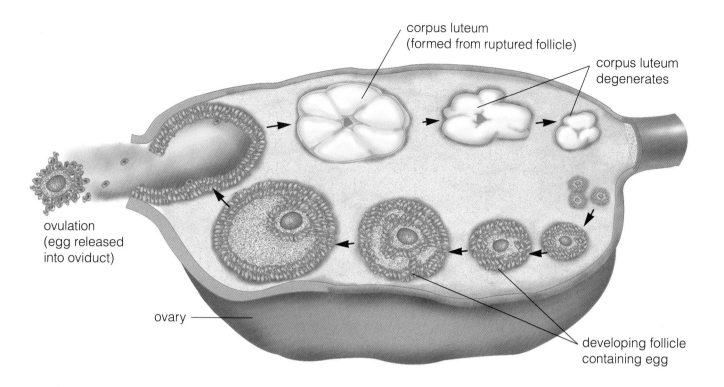

corpus luteum
(formed from ruptured follicle)

corpus luteum
degenerates

ovulation
(egg released
into oviduct)

ovary

developing follicle
containing egg

Figure 3.7 Egg development in the ovary

keep the egg moving toward the **uterus**. The egg can survive for only 24 h to 48 h after ovulation, unless a sperm fertilizes it. If the egg is not fertilized, it will die and disintegrate.

The uterus is a hollow, pear-shaped organ. It is here that a fertilized egg develops into a fetus. The lower entrance to the uterus, the **cervix**, is connected to a muscular passageway, the **vagina**. This passage is sometimes called the birth canal, because a baby passes through it on its way to the outside world. Unlike the male, the female has a separate urethra through which urine leaves the body.

Hormones and the Menstrual Cycle

Before and after ovulation, the female reproductive system undergoes changes in a cycle that lasts approximately one month. This cycle is known as the **menstrual cycle**. Hormones produced by the pituitary gland and the ovaries co-ordinate the entire sequence of events. The pituitary hormones "tell" the ovaries what to do and the ovarian hormones "tell" the uterus what to do. This type of communication between different parts of the body is called feedback. *Positive feedback* means that actions are stimulated, or begun. *Negative feedback* occurs when actions are inhibited, or prevented. You have already learned about some reproductive hormones, such as estrogen and FSH. Other important hormones in the menstrual cycle are **luteinising hormone (LH)** and **progesterone**. LH is released by the pituitary gland. Progesterone is released by a structure in the ovary called the **corpus luteum**, formed from the follicle after it releases its egg.

Word **CONNECT**

A gynecologist is a doctor who specializes in the human female reproductive system. Infer what the word "gyne" means in Greek and then use a dictionary to check the meaning. What other words can you find that use this root? Write three of these words in your Science Log.

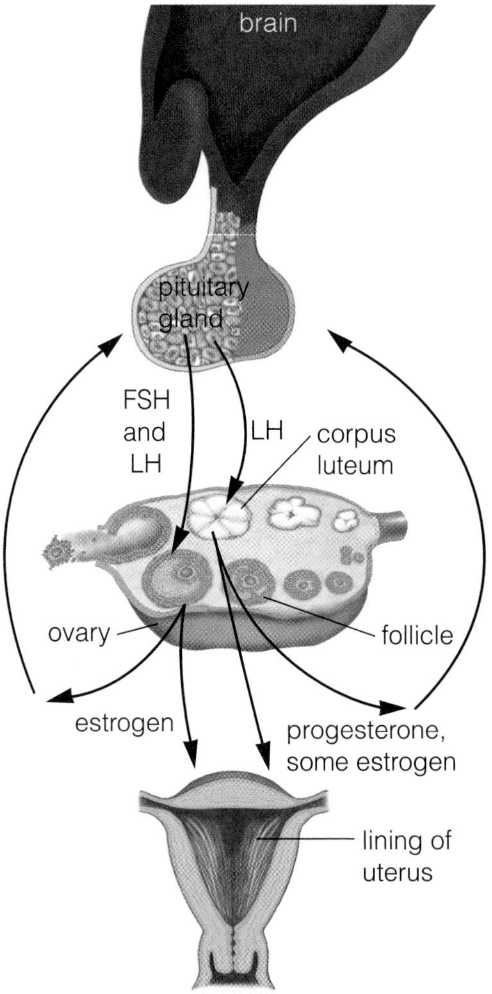

1. The pituitary gland releases FSH into the bloodstream.

2. FSH stimulates follicles to develop.

3. A developing follicle secretes estrogen into the bloodstream.

4. **(a)** Rising estrogen levels stimulate the lining of the uterus to thicken.
(b) Estrogen travels to the pituitary in the bloodstream, stimulating the pituitary gland to release LH.

5. LH causes the developing follicle to release a mature egg (ovulation).

6. LH also stimulates the empty follicle to develop into the corpus luteum.

7. The corpus luteum produces the hormone progesterone and some estrogen.

8. **(a)** Progesterone further increases the thickening of the uterine lining.
(b) Rising levels of progesterone in the bloodstream cause the pituitary to decrease its production of FSH and LH. Decreasing FSH and LH prevent more egg cells from being released until progesterone levels decrease once again (see steps 1-5).

Figure 3.8 Effects of hormones during stages of the menstrual cycle

Pause& Reflect

Draw a cause and effect chart in your Science Log. Record each step of the menstrual cycle as a cause in the first column, and list effects of each step in the second column. In a cycle, effects usually become causes of the next event. Begin and end with the pituitary gland sending FSH to the ovary. Assume no fertilized egg reaches the uterus.

Study the stages of the menstrual cycle in Figure 3.8 and identify the location of positive and negative feedback signals.

After an egg is released, the female's body waits for a signal. Has the egg been fertilized? If a fertilized egg does not reach the uterus, the corpus luteum breaks down, reducing progesterone in the bloodstream. In turn, declining progesterone levels cause the uterine lining to break down. The lining is shed from the body in the process known as **menstruation**. The menstrual flow, consisting mainly of dead cells and blood, continues for approximately four to seven days. When the level of progesterone reaches a certain level, the pituitary gland increases its production of FSH and the menstrual cycle starts over again.

How Do We Know What Ovarian Hormones Do?

Think About It

Hormones carry out many tasks in the human body, but their work is hidden from view. How do you think scientists found out about the roles of ovarian hormones? Use the following descriptions of three experiments on young female rats to think about how experiments were designed to determine how a reproductive system functions.

Experiment 1

Procedure: Rat 1 was anesthetized, its body wall opened, its ovaries removed, and its body wall closed again.

Result: The rat recovered completely, but it never had a reproductive cycle.

Experiment 2

Procedure: Rat 2 was anesthetized, its body wall was opened and closed, but its ovaries were not removed.

Result: The rat's reproductive cycle began at the usual age expected.

Experiment 3

Procedure: Experiment 1 was repeated with Rat 3, but the rat was injected with a substance from the ovaries of mature rats after it recovered from surgery.

Result: The rat's reproductive cycle began at the usual age expected.

What to Do

1. Read the descriptions of each of the three experiments. None of the rats used in the experiment had started their reproductive cycles.

2. State a hypothesis to explain the results of experiment 1.

3. Explain why the scientists performed experiment 2.

4. Infer what the injected substance might have been in experiment 3. (Hint: In writing your hypothesis, use the wording "If ..., then ..., because ...")

Analyze

1. What might a scientist conclude from the three experiments?

2. What hypothesis could a scientist make about the role of hormones in human reproduction, based on the results of the rat experiments?

Extend Your Knowledge

These kinds of experiments have led to our understanding of how reproductive systems function. Many people today object to using animals in experiments. What would be your argument for or against such experimentation?

Interpreting Hormonal Cycles

Think About It

Understanding how reproductive hormones work can help doctors diagnose some fertility problems. One important area of knowledge for human reproduction is how changes in the levels of female hormones relate to changes in the uterus and ovaries. How can quantitative data about hormone levels help you understand what is occurring in a woman's body? Refer to pages 85 to 86 and study the diagram below.

What to Do

1 Study the changing levels of pituitary hormones, ovarian hormones, and the changes in the uterine lining. Describe how the highest level of each hormone seems to affect the uterus.

2 Explain what happens to the follicle as the level of FSH in the blood changes.

Female hormone levels

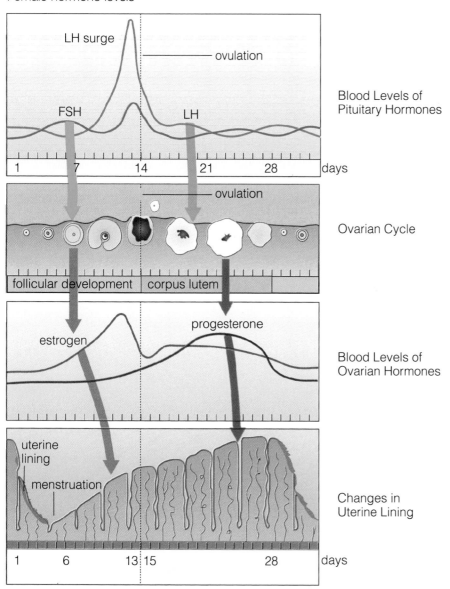

Analyze

1. How does an increased level of estrogen in the blood affect the pituitary gland? How can you tell from the graph?

2. Which hormones are at the highest levels in the blood when the uterine lining is thickest?

3. What appears to be the effect of the increased level of estrogen and progesterone on the secretion of FSH?

4. What effect does the increased level of LH appear to have on the follicle?

5. What is the effect of the drop in levels of estrogen and progesterone on the lining of the uterus on day 28?

6. Why is this process called a cycle?

7. Copy the diagram below into your notebook. It represents what is happening in the ovary and lining of the uterus during days 1 to 6 of the menstrual cycle. Use this drawing and the information from the graphs to draw four more diagrams to show what happens to the ovary and lining of the uterus during the menstrual cycle for days 7 to 12, 13 to 14, 15 to 20, and 21 to 28.

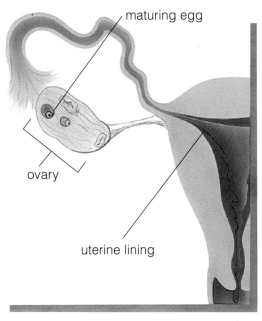

days 1 to 6

Extend Your Skills

1. Two main events of the menstrual cycle are (1) release of an egg from an ovary, and (2) buildup of the uterine lining. Use the table to predict which of the hormones A, B, or C would be associated with each of these two events. Assume that the cycle length is 28 days.

Relative Hormone Concentrations During the Menstrual Cycle

Day of menstrual cycle	Relative hormone concentration		
	A	B	C
1	12	5	10
5	14	5	14
9	14	5	13
13	70	10	20
17	12	60	9
21	12	150	8
25	8	100	8
1	12	5	10

2. **Apply** You are a gynecologist treating a patient who is having difficulty becoming pregnant. For the last month, her hormone levels have been measured on each of the eight days listed in the table. Hormone A remained steady at 12 for each test. Hormone B remained steady at 5. Hormone C had the levels shown in the table. How could these hormonal levels explain your patient's fertility problems? You might want to use a diagram or flow chart in your answer.

Menstruation and the Female Athlete

Very strenuous physical activity may delay the onset of the menstrual cycle in puberty. In adult women, strenuous exercise may cause the menstrual cycle to stop. What causes this effect? Research has shown that body fat deposits are needed to help produce estrogen. Body fat deposits may be very small in physically fit and healthy young women. A lack of estrogen results in a failure to build up the uterine lining, so menstruation stops. Why do you think the body responds this way?

A second problem of low body fat is that bone density declines if estrogen production stops. A reduction in bone density can lead to osteoporosis, which weakens bones and makes them more likely to break and fracture. Decreasing bone mass is especially dangerous for young athletes. Bones generally increase in density until age 30, when density begins to decrease. If a young woman does not develop enough bone mass, her bones may become weak later in life.

DidYouKnow?

Men can also get osteoporosis if they do not have enough testosterone in their bodies. Unlike women, however, low body fat in men does not decrease their ability to produce testosterone. Thus, male athletes do not require the same increase in calcium intake as do women.

Figure 3.9 Sufficient calcium is necessary for proper bone development. Female athletes are encouraged to increase their daily recommended intake of calcium by about 25% from 1200 mg to 1500 mg, in order to help prevent a decrease in bone density.

Check Your Understanding

1. List changes that males and females undergo during puberty.

2. Which hormones cause the appearance and maintenance of secondary sexual characteristics in males and females? Which hormone is produced at puberty in both sexes?

3. Draw a diagram showing the path taken by sperm from production to leaving the body.

4. What functions does the fluid portion of semen serve?

5. List the hormones involved in the menstrual cycle and their roles.

6. **Apply** Why do you think production of progesterone signals the pituitary gland to reduce secretion of FSH and LH?

3.2 Pregnancy

You have learned what happens in the female body if a mature egg is not fertilized. What happens, then, if an egg is fertilized (that is, the nucleus of a sperm cell fuses with the nucleus of the egg cell, creating a zygote)? Once sperm are deposited in the vagina, they move through the uterus and into the oviducts. Fertilization occurs in the oviduct. Only one sperm will fertilize the egg (see Figure 3.10).

After fertilization, the zygote continues down the oviduct toward the uterus as shown in Figure 3.11. On its way, approximately 24 to 36 hours after fertilization, it begins the process of mitosis. The zygote then undergoes a series of rapid **cleavages**, or cell divisions. By the time it reaches the uterus, it has become a mass of cells arranged to form an almost hollow ball of cells called a **blastocyst**. The blastocyst contains a group of cells called the inner cell mass. The outer cells of the blastocyst will eventually help form the **placenta**, a blood-vessel rich organ that is present only during pregnancy. (You will learn more about the placenta later in this chapter.) The inner cell mass forms the embryo.

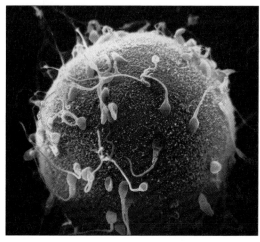

Figure 3.10 Here you can see the relative sizes of sperm and egg. The mature egg is the largest cell of the human body. Why would the egg be so much larger than sperm?

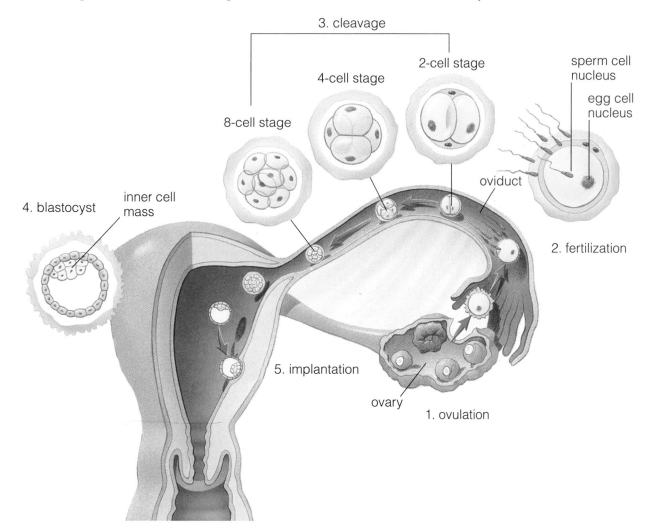

Figure 3.11 Human development from ovulation through implantation

In Vitro Fertilization (IVF)

Approximately 13% of Canadian couples experience infertility and are not able to conceive a child. In vitro fertilization (IVF) is a medical procedure that allows fertilization to be done outside the body. It has been used since 1978 to help couples have children. In this procedure, the woman is first treated with hormones to stimulate the development of ova in her ovaries. The ova are then collected with a suction apparatus inserted into the woman's abdomen. Ova are fertilized in a Petri dish with a sample of the man's semen. The fertilized ova are allowed to develop for several days. Then one or more embryos are transferred into the uterus. If successful, one of the embryos will implant in the uterine wall and develop. In this activity, you will explore some issues surrounding IVF. Discuss the issues in class.

What to Do

Conduct research at your local library and/or search the Internet to investigate the following questions.

- What are some causes and treatments of infertility?

- What is the success rate of IVF?
- What are some of the risks associated with IVF?
- Who should be eligible for this procedure?
- What are the costs involved and who should pay for them?
- What happens to unused embryos?
- What is a surrogate mother?
- What are the arguments in favour of and against surrogate mothers?

What Did You Discover?

1. When IVF first came to the attention of the public, it caused a great deal of controversy. Why do you think that happened? Is the procedure considered more acceptable today? Why do you think this is so?

2. Is it possible to preserve unused embryos for later use? If so, who should be held responsible for their use?

DidYou**Know**?

In some rare instances, a developing embryo may become implanted in the wall of the oviduct, rather than in the uterus. Because the oviduct is far too small to support a growing embryo, the oviduct may rupture in the second or third month of pregnancy. The embryo may die, or surgery may be required. Such an event is called an *ectopic* pregnancy.

Implantation

The embryo attaches itself to the thickened lining of the uterus in a process called **implantation**. This occurs six to ten days after fertilization of the egg. At this point, pregnancy begins. The attached embryo produces a hormonal signal that prevents the corpus luteum from disintegrating. The corpus luteum continues to produce progesterone. This keeps the uterine lining in place, which means there is no menstrual flow. The corpus luteum produces progesterone for approximately the first three months of pregnancy.

Off the Wall

Through a process called embryo splitting, scientists have been able to create genetically identical animal embryos. Scientists take embryos that are between the 4 and 8-cell stages and divide them in half. Each half is then allowed to develop again to the 4 or 8-cell stages, whereupon the scientists split the embryos again. They have successfully produced up to eight embryos using this technique. Based on what you learned about the benefits of sexual reproduction in Chapter 2, what are some potential drawbacks of this technique?

Embryo Development

When the embryo is in the blastocyst stage, its cells are mostly similar to each other. During its second week, however, cells begin to specialize to form a **gastrula,** in a process called gastrulation. In gastrulation, the cells of the growing embryo become arranged into distinct layers called **germ layers**. This arrangement occurs by continued mitotic division and cell movement, or migration. The cells move to specific positions to form three layers called the **endoderm**, the **mesoderm**, and the **ectoderm**. You can think of the germ layers as forming three tubes, one inside the other. Cells in each layer develop into different parts of the body, as shown in Figure 3.12.

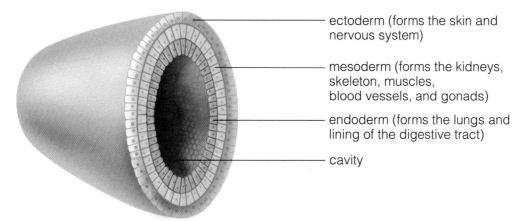

ectoderm (forms the skin and nervous system)

mesoderm (forms the kidneys, skeleton, muscles, blood vessels, and gonads)

endoderm (forms the lungs and lining of the digestive tract)

cavity

Figure 3.12 Idealized diagram showing development of germ layers during gastrulation and the tissues formed by each layer.

Supporting Tissues

Between the tenth and fourteenth days of development, the outer portions of the embryo develop four important tissues, as shown in Figure 3.13. The **yolk sac** supplies nutrients to the embryo for about the first two months of development. The **amnion** forms a fluid-filled sac around the embryo. The fluid serves as a kind of shock absorber, which helps protect the embryo. The **allantois** helps remove waste from the embryo.

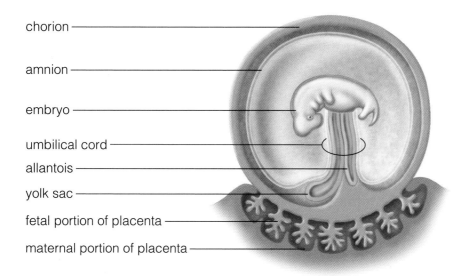

chorion

amnion

embryo

umbilical cord

allantois

yolk sac

fetal portion of placenta

maternal portion of placenta

Figure 3.13 Tissues supporting development of the embryo. In the placenta, nutrients and oxygen diffuse into the embryo's blood vessels from the mother's blood. Wastes move in the opposite direction.

Observing the Embryo

In this activity, you will use a microscope to observe a zygote and embryos at different stages of development.

What You Need

microscope
prepared slides showing stages of development
  of an animal from zygote to embryo

What to Do

1. Sketch the main features that you observe in each slide.

2. Add the following labels to your diagrams: egg, sperm, zygote, blastocyst, gastrula, endoderm, mesoderm, ectoderm.

What Did You Discover?

1. How do you know that cleavage had occurred?

2. What changes in the embryo indicate that a blastocyst had formed?

3. What changes indicate that a gastrula had formed?

4. Describe any recognizable tissues or limbs in the last phase of development you observed.

The **chorion** surrounds the embryo, yolk sac, amnion, and allantois. It develops many finger-like projections that extend into the uterine wall to serve as a kind of anchor. Inside the "fingers" are blood vessels. Together, the blood vessels and chorion make up the placenta. Once the placenta has formed, it takes over the yolk sac's role of supplying nutrients to the embryo. It also replaces the corpus luteum and maintains the high levels of progesterone necessary to sustain the pregnancy.

The placenta is the embryo's supply line for survival inside its enclosed world. It ensures the delivery of nutrients and oxygen to the developing organism and makes sure wastes are removed. The embryo is attached to the placenta by the **umbilical cord**. After birth, the doctor or midwife cuts the cord. The cord eventually shrivels, and its point of attachment to the fetus becomes the baby's navel.

Check Your Understanding

1. Describe the stages of human development from fertilization to gastrulation. Use a diagram to show the order of the stages.

2. What is cleavage? When does it occur?

3. What is the stage at which a pregnancy has truly begun?

4. Twins may be identical or non-identical. Infer how the two different kinds of twins may be produced.

5. **Thinking Critically** The human body's immune system normally tries to get rid of any foreign matter it encounters. This is how your body fights bacterial infections. This is also why organ transplants are sometimes rejected. Suggest what might prevent a mother's immune system from rejecting the "foreign material" of the developing fetus.

3.3 Differentiation and Birth

You saw in Figure 3.12 that the three layers in the gastrula develop into different parts of the body. This process is called **differentiation**. This means that different cells become specialized to perform the different tasks of various tissues and organs in the body. For example, a tube-like heart starts beating at about three weeks, even before there is any blood to pump. By the end of the fourth week, the embryo is 500 times its original size. The human gestation period (about 38 weeks) can be divided into three blocks of time based on the formation of different tissues and organs. Each block of time, or **trimester**, is approximately three months long. Major developmental changes occur within each trimester.

Did You Know?

About 25% of all pregnancies end during the first trimester, because of a natural *miscarriage*. The tiny embryo is expelled with the uterine lining. A miscarriage often results, if the embryo has serious genetic defects or if it has failed to implant properly in the uterus.

First Trimester (weeks 1-12)

At four weeks, the limbs, eyes and spine begin to form (see Figure 3.14). At eight to nine weeks, the embryo begins to form its first bone cells. Once this happens the embryo is called a **fetus** (see Figure 3.15). By the end of 12 weeks, all the major organs have begun their development. The fetus has the beginnings of its liver, stomach, brain, and heart and a noticeable head and limbs. The fetus has a length of 100 mm. At this time, the sex of the fetus can be identified using *ultrasound* technology.

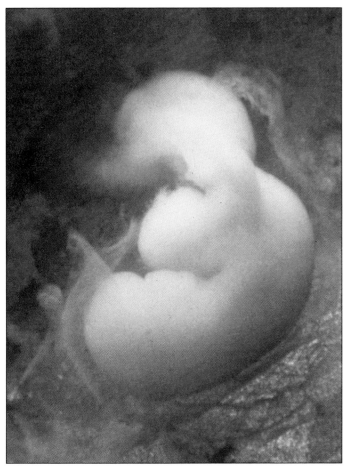

Figure 3.14 This photograph shows a 28-day-old human embryo. The brain and heart are among the first organs to develop.

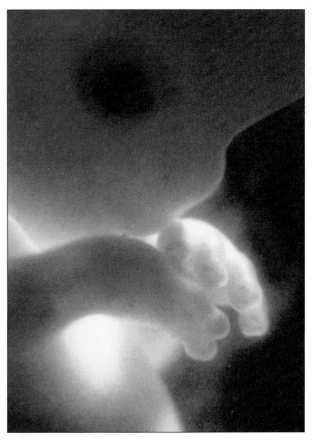

Figure 3.15 The fetus measures 3 cm by the end of eight weeks. Which limbs and organs can you identify in this photograph?

Comparing Vertebrate Embryos

Embryos of many vertebrates show similar stages of development. In this activity, you will compare the growth of embryos of six animals during three stages of development. Consider each stage of development to be a trimester.

What to Do

1. Study the diagram showing stages of development among several animals.

2. List at least three similarities and three differences among the embryos shown during each stage of development.

3. Look at the diagram you drew in your Science Log of the zygote after three months of development. Would you make any changes based on what you have learned so far in this chapter?

What Did You Discover?

1. At what stage of development do the differences among the animals become most obvious?

2. Which animal shown is most similar to humans in terms of development? Explain.

Extension

3. Why do the organisms shown below appear to be so similar in early development but not in later development? How are various tissues and organs formed? Research the development of one of the vertebrates shown and compare your findings to what you have learned about human development.

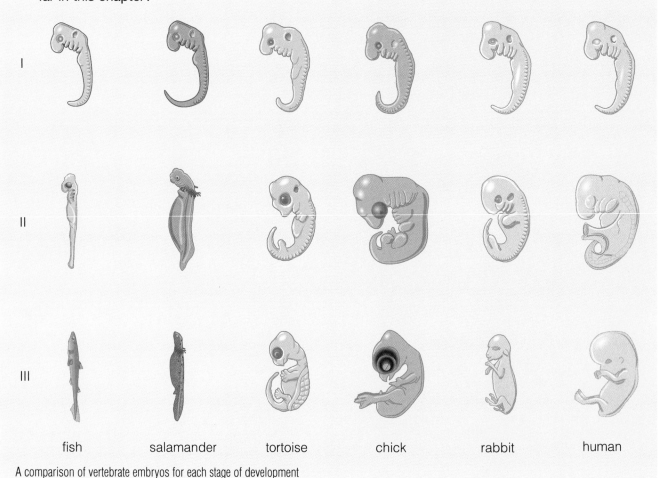

| | | | | | |
| fish | salamander | tortoise | chick | rabbit | human |

A comparison of vertebrate embryos for each stage of development

Second Trimester (weeks 12-24)

Figure 3.16 shows the fetus during the second trimester. At 16 weeks, the placenta is too small to surround the fetus, so it moves to one side. The skeleton begins to form, the brain grows rapidly, and the nervous system begins to function. The mother begins to feel the movements of the fetus as it flexes and moves its new muscles. By 24 weeks, the fetus is about 300 mm long. Its movements become more vigorous. Most organs are formed but are not yet fully developed. Thus, the fetus has little chance of survival if born prematurely.

What about the mother's health? Premature birth of the fetus can be accompanied by bleeding. Before current technology, some women died as a result of loss of blood or infection.

Tools of Science

It is possible to observe a developing fetus using *ultrasound* technology. High-frequency sound waves are transmitted through the mother's abdominal wall. These sound waves bounce off tissues of different densities at different rates. The waves can be recorded and used to create an image of the fetus on a computer monitor.

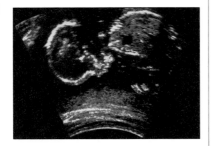

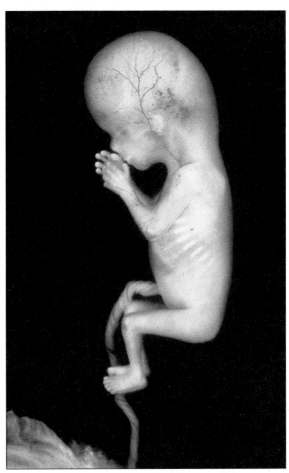

Figure 3.16 Can you identify the umbilical cord in this 22-week-old fetus? What other structures can you identify?

Career CONNECT

An Inside Look

Ultrasound images allow doctors to give a fetus a pre-birth check-up. Ultrasound sonographers like Cathy Babiak are specially trained to carry out the procedure on the patient. They carefully record information they "read" in the image, including measurements of the fetus. An ultrasound image isn't just a picture; it's a real-time movie. Thus, sonographers can also accurately measure the fetus's heart rate.

A radiologist then interprets the sonographer's information to assess the growth and health of the fetus. The radiologist's report is sent to the patient's family doctor or obstetrician.

Ultrasound imaging is part of a larger field called medical imaging. This field includes other methods of "seeing" inside the human body, such as echocardiographs, x-rays, CT (computer tomography) scans, and NMR (nuclear magnetic resonance) imaging. These procedures require a fair bit of training and experience to master. Technicians must be able to translate the

various bumps, bulges and lines in an image, as well as sounds the equipment produces, into useful medical information.

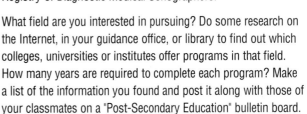

Cathy completed the Post Diploma Ultrasound Program at the Michener Institute for Applied Health Sciences and then took an exam to become registered with the American Registry of Diagnostic Medical Sonographers.

What field are you interested in pursuing? Do some research on the Internet, in your guidance office, or library to find out which colleges, universities or institutes offer programs in that field. How many years are required to complete each program? Make a list of the information you found and post it along with those of your classmates on a "Post-Secondary Education" bulletin board.

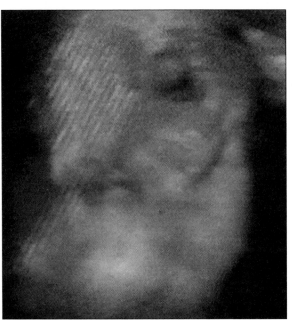

Figure 3.17 This image of a yawning fetus was made using 3-D ultrasound technology. In the ninth month, the fetus normally moves in the uterus, so that its head faces down. Why would this change in position be important?

Third Trimester (weeks 24-38)

During the last three months of pregnancy, the fetus rapidly increases in overall size and begins to move around in its amniotic sac, stretching and kicking. The immune system develops. Proper nutrition is more important than ever before, mainly for the building of vital brain tissue. By the eighth month, the fetus opens its eyes. By the end of the third trimester, the fetus has grown to an average length of 500 mm and an average weight of between 2700 and 4100 grams.

What about nutrition of the mother? If the mother does not properly nourish both herself and the fetus, nutrients from the mother's body tissues will be used to supply the developing fetus. An improper diet late in the third trimester may cause permanent health problems in some women.

INTERNET CONNECT

www.school.mcgrawhill.ca/resources/

To learn more about imaging techniques used to examine a developing fetus, visit the above web site. Go to **Science Resources**, then to **SCIENCEPOWER 9** to find out where to go next. Find out about the latest techniques and developments in imaging technology. What new information do these techniques provide? What are the main uses of ultrasound during pregnancy? What measurements are usually taken to determine the health and development of a fetus? Prepare a brief report on your findings.

AcrossCanada

Christopher Kovacs

How do the bones of a fetus develop? How do the developing fetus and placenta interact to regulate skeletal development? What roles do hormones play? These are among questions that intrigue Dr. Christopher Kovacs. An expert in fetal calcium physiology, he does research, practises medicine, and teaches at Memorial University in St. John's, Newfoundland.

"In grade 8," Christopher recalls, "I was selected to go to the Canada-Wide Science Fair held in Sudbury, Ontario that year. I learned right away that science people weren't necessarily geeks, that doing science had rewards....When you're doing research on a frontier level, you're the only one who knows this area that well, and you alone know certain facts until you've had a chance to publish them — that is what makes research fun and exciting."

Born in Toronto, Christopher studied and worked in several Canadian and American cities, including doing a postdoctoral fellowship at Harvard Medical School in Boston.

His research work takes him to places in Canada and abroad. Christopher is trained as a professional artist as well as a medical doctor and scientist. He notes that "science and art don't have to be mutually exclusive, as students may think. Many of my research presentations and medical school lectures are jazzed up with illustrations that I couldn't have done without my background in art."

Fetal Development

A human fetus usually requires 38 weeks to complete its development. During this period, different organs and systems develop at different times. The length of a developing fetus can be used to determine its age.

Problem

How can you assess the development of a fetus?

Materials

ruler

Procedure

1 Measure the length of each fetus in the diagram from its crown to its rump.

2 Multiply each measurement by 5.5 to determine the actual length.

3 Make a table with the headings shown below. Record the actual length and the events occurring to each fetus.

Fetus	ActualLength (mm)	Events
A		
B		
etc.		

Events are shown in the following table.

Fetal Development Data

Event	Length (mm)	Event	Length (mm)
24 weeks old	230	eyes open	300
sex can be determined	140	32 weeks old	300
eyes closed	50	mother feels movement	140
all organs well developed	230	body "chubby" looking	300
9 weeks old	50	body hair is gone	360
16 weeks old	140	can grasp with hand	360
body covered with hair	230	sex cannot be determined	50
38 weeks old	360		

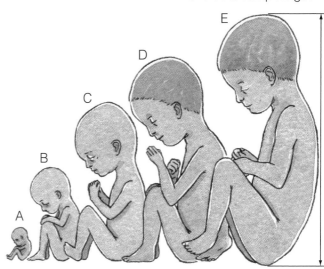

Crown to rump length

E

D

C

B

A

Growth of a fetus from 9 to 38 weeks. About one fifth scale.

Analyze

1. What changes occur in a fetus between 9 and 38 weeks in terms of
   (a) the eyes
   (b) body hair
   (c) sex determination

2. Images of a fetus can be made using ultrasound technology. How might the ultrasound images of a 9 and 24-week-old fetus differ?

Conclude and Apply

3. Why might a pregnant woman feel more tired or hungry than when she is not pregnant?

Extend Your Skills

4. Enter the data for fetal age and length into a spreadsheet. Make a line graph and label the *x*-axis and the *y*-axis. According to your graph, during which weeks does length increase the most? What events are occurring at this time?

Risk Factors During Fetal Development

The developing fetus receives all of its nutrients and oxygen from its mother's bloodstream, but it may also receive harmful substances. Whatever the mother eats, drinks, or inhales from her environment ends up in her blood. As her blood circulates through her body, substances in it can pass through the blood vessels in the placenta to the fetus. The first trimester is a period critical to the proper development of an embryo. Figure 3.18 shows critical periods of development for the embryo and fetus.

Some substances, such as cigarette smoke and alcohol, may affect the normal development of the fetus and can cause permanent damage. Cigarette smoke may constrict the fetus's blood vessels, which can prevent it from getting enough oxygen. Alcohol may affect the function of the fetus's brain, central nervous system, and physical development. These are symptoms of Fetal Alcohol Syndrome (FAS). Alcohol might remain in the bloodstream of the fetus for a longer time than in the mother. This can happen because the fetus's liver might not be fully formed and therefore might be unable to process the alcohol.

Other factors can affect the genetic material in some or all of the cells of the developing fetus. Some examples of such factors are radiation and certain pollutants, such as PCBs and mercury (see Figure 3.19). These factors may eventually lead to cancer

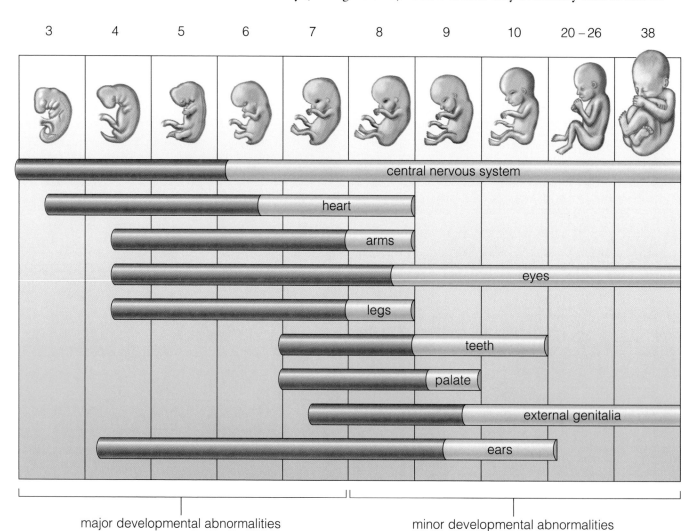

Figure 3.18 Critical periods of embryonic and fetal development. The periods marked in red indicate when organs are most sensitive to environmental factors. Numbers indicate age in weeks.

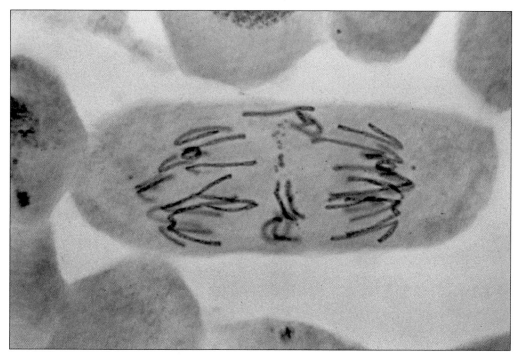

Figure 3.19 Here you can see the effects of radiation on mitosis; some chromosomes fail to move to opposite poles of the cell during anaphase. Children whose mothers have been exposed to high levels of radiation, especially early in their pregnancy, have been born with a higher than normal frequency of birth defects.

or some other form of genetic defect. Certain drugs may cause deformities in newborns. Thalidomide is a drug first prescribed in the 1950s to women to reduce nausea during the first few weeks of pregnancy. At the time, no adverse side-effects were known. Unfortunately, as a result of its use, many babies were born with missing or severely deformed limbs. This drug is no longer prescribed to pregnant women.

The risk of genetic disorders increases with the age of the mother. Women in their teens and twenties have only a one in several thousand chance of having a baby with chromosomal abnormalities, while the risks rise to one in 20 for women who are over 45. Figure 3.20 shows the relationship between the incidence of Down syndrome and the age of the mother. Down syndrome is a genetic disorder that affects neurological and physical development. You will learn more about genetic disorders in the next chapter.

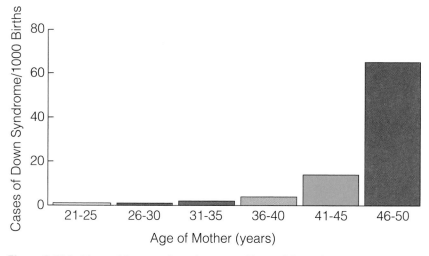

Figure 3.20 Incidence of Down syndrome increases with age of the mother.

Public Education Campaign

The development of an embryo and fetus is a very complex process. Even brief exposure to harmful situations or substances, if it occurs at a critical period, can result in serious defects in the developing fetus.

Challenge

Create a public awareness campaign about one factor that can endanger the development or life of an embryo or fetus.

Materials

poster board
coloured markers

Design Criteria

A. Be as creative as you like, but remember that you have two goals: (1) to catch attention and (2) to educate.

B. Your project must include a poster, one or more radio segments, and a list of community resources that prospective parents can use to get more information.

C. Each radio segment should be no longer than one or two minutes.

Plan and Construct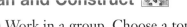

① Work in a group. Choose a topic from the following list of risk factors:
- toxic pollutants (including those in air, water, or food)
- alcohol
- cigarettes
- radiation
- prescription drugs
- non-prescription drugs (over-the-counter and illegal substances)
- German measles and other infectious diseases

② Research your topic using the library, the Internet and/or resources in your community.

③ Brainstorm ideas for your project. Decide how the poster and radio segments will be presented.

④ List the jobs to be done in order to complete the project.

⑤ Divide the tasks for your presentation among members of your group and prepare your project.

⑥ Display the posters and present your radio segments to the class. Post your list of community resources next to your poster, or decide on another way to present the resources.

Evaluate

1. Which posters are the most effective at catching your attention? Which are best at conveying important information? Which posters do a good job of both?

2. Which radio segment was most effective? Why?

3. For which risk factors does there appear to be many resources and help available? For which risk factors would prospective parents have trouble finding assistance and information?

Extend Your Knowledge

4. As a class, discuss some of the issues concerning who should be held responsible for the health of a developing fetus. For example, should it be against the law for a mother to drink alcohol during pregnancy? Should companies that produce materials dangerous for a developing fetus be held responsible for birth defects? Raise any other issues you may have thought about during your research. Conclude your discussion with ideas for how society might decide the answers to some of these problems.

Birth

Sudden, dramatic changes in hormone levels are responsible for starting the birth process. During pregnancy, high progesterone levels have maintained the pregnancy. A sharp drop in the levels of progesterone and estrogen causes the muscles of the uterus to begin to contract. At the same time, the mother's pituitary gland secretes another hormone, **oxytocin**, which stimulates the uterus to contract and open the birth canal. This process is known as **labour**, and ends in the birth of a new baby (see Figure 3.21).

Occasionally, problems occur during childbirth. Sometimes the mother's pelvis is too small for the baby to pass through the birth canal. In other cases, the baby is not in the correct position for birth. In many of these cases, the baby is delivered through a process called *Cesarean section*. In a Cesarean, doctors remove the baby through an incision in the mother's abdomen and uterus.

A *Dilation stage*. Uterine contractions and oxytocin cause the cervix to open, or dilate. During this stage the amnion breaks and the amniotic fluid is released through the vagina. The dilation stage lasts an average of 2 to 20 h.

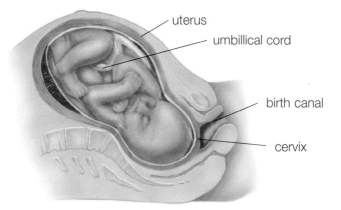

uterus

umbillical cord

birth canal

cervix

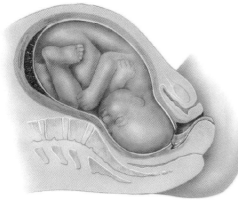

B *Expulsion stage*. Contractions in the uterus become so forceful that the baby is pushed through the cervix to the birth canal. This takes from 0.5 to 2 h. As the baby moves through the canal, its head rotates, making it easier for its body to pass through the birth canal.

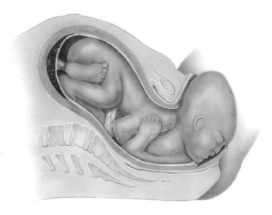

placenta detaching

umbillical cord

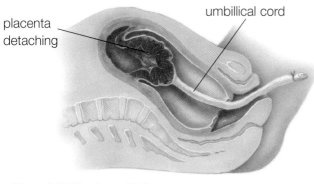

C *Placental stage*. The placenta and umbilical cord are expelled from the uterus. This usually happens within 10 or 15 min after the baby is born. The expelled placenta is called the *afterbirth*.

Figure 3.21 The stages of birth

After birth, the baby's umbilical cord is usually clamped, cut, and tied. For the first time, the baby must breathe air, ingest food, and eliminate wastes on its own. It must also become accustomed to light, louder sounds, and cooler temperatures. Growth continues after birth. Figure 3.22 shows how body proportions of a person change from infancy to young adulthood. For instance, notice how the proportion of the legs compared to the rest of the body changes with age. Why do you think body proportions change as we get older?

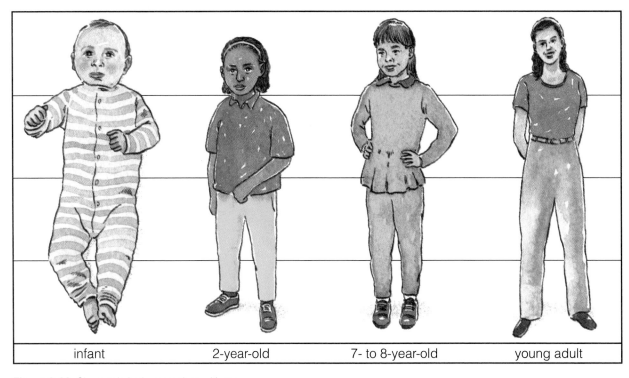

| infant | 2-year-old | 7- to 8-year-old | young adult |

Figure 3.22 Changes in body proportions with age

Math CONNECT

The head of a baby is about one quarter of the total length of its body. Measure the total body length and head length of ten class members. Calculate the proportion of each person's head length to body length.

Check Your Understanding

1. Explain what happens during differentiation. What controls differentiation?

2. Which development marks the change from an embryo to a fetus?

3. Outline some of the changes that occur during each trimester of fetal development.

4. Make a list of factors that can harm a developing embryo or fetus. Which factors are particularly dangerous at specific periods?

5. Describe the birth process. Which hormonal change signals the beginning of labour?

6. **Thinking Critically** Why do you think legs are slow to develop in a human fetus?

7. **Thinking Critically** A woman may not realize that she is pregnant during the first month of her pregnancy. How might this put the embryo at risk?

Now that you have completed this chapter, try to do the following. If you cannot, go back to the sections indicated.

Describe the effects of pituitary hormones on the development of male and female reproductive structures. (3.1)

Describe the chemical events leading up to the development of male and female secondary sexual characteristics. (3.1)

Explain why sperm cells require a nutrient-rich fluid in which to travel from the male's body. (3.1)

Suggest reasons why fewer eggs than sperm are produced. (3.1)

Describe the chemical relationship between the ovary, the pituitary gland, and the uterus. (3.1)

Explain how quantitative differences in hormone levels can lead to different responses by organs (3.1)

Explain why it is important to have a thick uterine lining when a fertilized egg arrives in the uterus. (3.1)

Describe the events that signify that pregnancy has begun. (3.2)

Describe where and the method by which nutrients and wastes are passed between the bodies of mother and fetus. (3.2)

Describe the special protective layers of membrane inside of which a fetus develops. (3.2)

Explain why it is important for the brain and the heart to be among the first organs to develop in an embryo. (3.3)

Discuss reasons why good maternal nutrition is so important during pregnancy. (3.3)

Discuss factors that may pose a risk for a developing fetus. (3.3)

Summarize the chapter by doing one of the following. Use a graphic organizer (such as a concept map), produce a poster, or write the summary to include the key chapter concepts. Here are a few ideas to use as a guide:

• Explain the physical and chemical conditions that are needed to sustain a pregnancy throughout the gestation period.

• Describe the process of sperm production.

• Compare and contrast puberty in males and females.

• Describe the process of fertilization and implantation.

• Explain what happens during gastrulation.

Prepare Your Own Summary

• What is the environment of a developing fetus? How might this environment influence pre-birth development?

• In your notebook, make a copy of the following diagram and label it.

Reviewing Key Terms

If you need to review, the section numbers show you where these terms were introduced.

1. The following terms are related to reproduction in males and females. Arrange them under one of three appropriate headings: male, female, both male and female.

   pituitary gland (3.1)   progesterone (3.1)
   FSH (3.1)   gonads (3.1)
   testosterone (3.1)   hormones (3.1)
   estrogen (3.1)   secondary sexual
   scrotum (3.1)   characteristics (3.1)
   follicles (3.1)   epididymis (3.1)
   oviduct (3.1)   prostate (3.1)
   vas deferens (3.1)   cervix (3.1)
   seminiferous tubule (3.1)

2. Arrange the following terms to describe the structure of a gastrula from outermost to innermost layer: mesoderm, ectoderm, endoderm. (3.2)

3. What is the difference between an embryo and a fetus? (3.2)

4. From the list of Key Terms at the beginning of this chapter, write ten terms that relate *only* to pregnancy. (3.2)

Understanding Key Concepts

Section numbers are provided if you need to review.

5. Sperm and egg cells have certain structural differences. (3.1)

   (a) State these structural differences.

   (b) Explain the advantage that each cell type has because of its special structure.

6. What are the components of semen?

7. As well as no longer producing eggs, what other changes occur at menopause in the female's monthly cycle? (3.1)

8. Describe the differences in mobility of egg and sperm and explain how each may reach the oviducts for fertilization. (3.1)

9. Describe the differences in the microscopic structures involved in the production of eggs and sperm. (3.1)

10. Outline all the structures through which a sperm cell passes on its route to fertilize an egg. (3.1)

11. How is the process of mitosis related to a fertilized egg? (3.2)

12. There are two sources of progesterone during pregnancy. (3.2)

    (a) Name the two sources.

    (b) Explain how progesterone is essential to the maintenance of a pregnancy.

13. Explain the purpose of gastrulation. (3.2)

14. An expectant mother sometimes does not realize she is pregnant for the first several weeks. How might this be a harmful situation for the developing embryo? (3.3)

15. Describe two hormonal changes that occur in the female's body just prior to the birth process. (3.3)

16. Why is the afterbirth appropriately named? Of what does it consist? (3.3)

Developing Skills

17. If a male reaches puberty at age 14 and continues to produce sperm until age 80, estimate the number of sperm he will produce in his lifetime.

18. If a female reaches puberty at age 13 and continues to produce eggs until age 50, estimate the number of eggs she will produce in her lifetime.

19. Which hormones are involved in the following pathways? What effect do they have on the structures shown?

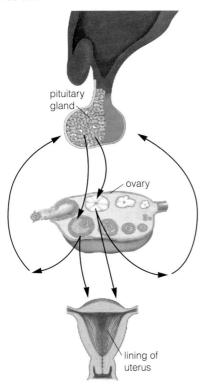

pituitary gland

ovary

lining of uterus

20. Make a copy of the following concept map of the male reproductive system and complete it.

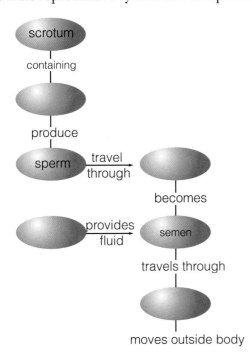

scrotum

containing

produce

sperm — travel through

becomes

provides fluid — semen

travels through

moves outside body

Problem Solving

21. Account for the large difference in the number of sperm produced, compared with the number of eggs produced in a similar time period.

22. A low rate of sperm cell production is the cause of one type of infertility. How might *in vitro* fertilization be used to help achieve pregnancy in a family with this problem?

23. Explain how a developing fetus obtains nutrients from its mother's bloodstream. What structures are involved?

Critical Thinking

24. Describe at least five changes a newborn baby undergoes immediately following delivery.

25. Infer some reasons why the mortality rate of sperm is so high, compared with that of eggs.

26. Identify some environmental factors that could influence pre-birth development. Explain how their effects are produced.

Pause&
══Reflect

1. Why do you think mammals are not able to produce offspring until they have reached a size that is close to that of an adult?

2. Look back at the entry you made in your Science Log when you first began studying this chapter. Find the drawing of the zygote as you pictured it would have looked at two days of development. Draw another picture based upon what you have learned. Compare your drawings.

3. Go back to the beginning of this chapter on page 78 and check your original answers to the Opening Ideas questions. How has your thinking changed? How would you answer these questions now that you have investigated the topics in this chapter?

CANADIAN RESEARCHERS DISCOVER
GENE FOR CYSTIC FIBROSIS

FIRST ARTIFICIALLY
CLONED MAMMAL

Opening Ideas...

- How would you feel if you saw a copy of yourself walking down the street? How might this happen?

- Do you think caffeine-free coffee beans could be harvested directly from a plant?

- How can a never-before-seen life form be created?

Science Log

People may use reproductive technologies for many different purposes. Think about what some of these purposes are and describe them in your Science Log. Add to your list as you read this chapter.

The photograph on this page shows Dolly, a sheep born in 1997. Take a close look. Dolly appears to be a normal, everyday kind of sheep, just like any other you would see on a farm. Dolly, however, is very special. She does not have a mother and father — at least, not in the usual way we think of parents. Dolly is the first artificially cloned mammal, a genetically identical copy of another sheep. She was produced by Dr. Ian Wilmut and his team of researchers in Edinburgh, Scotland. This event made people wonder

whether it will be possible to clone humans in the future.

Newspaper headlines of breakthroughs in biological research have become commonplace. What is behind these headlines, and what are we to make of them? How far removed are clones and other techniques of reproductive biology from our daily lives? In this chapter, you will learn about DNA and examine some of the methods, results, and applications of the rapidly changing field of biotechnology.

Technologies

Key Concepts

In this chapter, you will discover

- reproductive technology has a long history
- DNA contains the instructions for the characteristics of all living organisms
- reproductive technology may provide cures, treatments, and prevention of genetic diseases
- genetic engineering involves altering an organism's DNA
- reproductive technology raises a number of issues and concerns

Key Skills

In this chapter, you will

- analyze research findings and write a report
- infer uses of DNA research
- design and construct a scientific model
- design and conduct biological experiments
- assess the risks and benefits of reproductive technologies

Key Terms

- biotechnology
- selective breeding
- reproductive technology
- codon
- proteins
- amino acids
- gene
- mutations
- mutagenic agents
- genetic engineering
- transgenic
- recombinant DNA
- gene splicing
- genetic screening
- karyotype
- gene therapy
- genome
- Human Genome Project
- hybrid
- monoculture
- aquaculture
- bioremediation
- consortia
- inbreeding

"Wanted for Murder"

A person can be identified from a single strand of hair. Except for identical twins, every person's body contains unique genetic information. Thus, your DNA is like your fingerprint. Police can use DNA fingerprinting to identify criminals, based on samples (such as a hair) collected at a crime scene. Can you identify a murderer by using DNA evidence?

This is a photograph of a DNA fingerprint. Scientists used an electric field to separate tiny pieces of DNA according to size. The pieces of DNA are represented with dark bands.

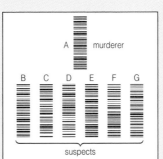

Sample A is the DNA fingerprint taken from a strand of hair. The hair was found on a murder victim, but it is not the victim's hair. Samples B through G are DNA fingerprints of hair taken from six suspects.

What to Do

1. Compare the DNA fingerprint of the murderer with those provided by six suspects.

What Did You Discover?

1. Out of the list of potential suspects, infer which one was the murderer.

2. Do you think this method is foolproof? Explain.

4.1 Biotechnology

Figure 4.1 Yogurt and cheese are products of biotechnology.

Have you eaten some yogurt or cheese today? These foods are produced by a simple kind of biotechnology. Other products produced by biotechnology are less obvious, but extremely important for many people. **Biotechnology** refers to various techniques that use living organisms to make products or provide services. It includes a wide variety of methods that can alter the normal genetic make-up of organisms, including viruses, bacteria, plants, or animals. The word makes some people anxious because they don't really know what biotechnology does — and this isn't surprising because it changes so quickly. However, biotechnology of one kind or another has been used for thousands of years. Modern biotechnology is more sophisticated than in the past, but its principles are still based on the natural properties of organisms.

An early example of genetic alteration can be seen in purebred dogs (see Figure 4.2). Breeding individuals with certain desired traits produces offspring with similar traits. This is called **selective breeding**. Since ancient times, humans have sought to alter the natural features of plant and animal species to suit various human needs.

Figure 4.2 Distinctive dog breeds, such as this tiny Chihuahua and enormous Great Dane, have been produced through selective breeding.

Biotechnology in the Classroom

Chymosin is a compound found naturally in the stomach of calves, where it helps them digest milk. It is used commercially in the production of cheese. This is an example of a simple form of biotechnology. In this activity, you will design and conduct an experiment to investigate the effect of chymosin on milk.

What You Need

chymosin (also called rennin or rennet)
milk
stirring rod
beaker (250 mL)
water bath
thermometer

What to Do

1. Design an experiment to determine the effect of chymosin on milk.

2. What are your experimental variables? What variables will you have to control?

3. Hypothesize what temperature would be optimal for your experiment.

4. Write out your experiment including: problem, hypothesis, procedure, observations, conclusions. **Note:** For tips on designing an experiment, turn to page IS-2.

5. Conduct your experiment and test your hypothesis.

What Did You Discover?

1. What was the effect of chymosin on milk?

2. Did your results support your hypothesis?

3. What changes could you make to improve your experimental procedure?

Extensions

4. Calves, like all mammals, depend on their mother's milk for the early part of their lives. How does chymosin help digest milk? What might happen to the milk if chymosin were not present?

5. What are some advantages of producing chymosin artificially?

Biotechnology Through the Ages

People began to practise biotechnology as early as 2000 B.C.E. Most of these early technologies were related to food production. Ancient art depicts seed banks, harvesting of cereal crops, and herding of domesticated animals, as shown in Figure 4.3. By selectively mating individual animals and plants with desirable characteristics, early farmers slowly created new genetic combinations. They practised, without realizing it, an early form of biotechnology, producing healthier and more productive crops and livestock.

Selective breeding of plants might have involved pollination by hand, and then covering the flowers so that no other pollen could fertilize the plant. Other biotechnologies included the use of micro-organisms in processes such as fermentation. Yogurt and cheese were produced with the help of bacteria and fungi. Bread and beer were made with the aid of yeast organisms. These methods are still used today.

Figure 4.3 Ancient biotechnology included domestication and selective breeding of animals.

Figure 4.4 The ancestors of strawberries were much smaller than the large, juicy varieties we cultivate today.

Early technologies did not involve conscious manipulation of the genetic material in living cells. Today, however, our knowledge of cell biology and DNA has developed into a specialized area of study, called **reproductive technology**. This includes methods of directly altering the genetic material in a cell's nucleus in order to obtain a desired outcome. These new techniques require detailed knowledge of the genetic material and use specialized tools. They hold the promise of increasing the world's food supply, producing new types of food, and uncovering new treatment of various diseases, including preventive measures for inherited genetic disorders. You will learn some of the possible applications of biotechnology later in this chapter. First, you need to know about the molecule that is fundamental to all life: DNA.

For much of human history, people did not know what makes heredity "work," or how traits get passed on from one generation to the next. We now know that genetic information is contained in

Cell

Chromosome

1868
Swedish chemist Johann Miescher collected material from the nuclei of certain cells to examine the properties of this material more closely. He called this material nuclein.

1882
German biologist Walther Flemming used more powerful microscopes to observe threadlike structures dividing within the cell nuclei of salamander embryos. These structures were chromosomes.

1928
British bacteriologist Fred Griffith carried out experiments to show that one bacterium can transfer an inherited trait to another bacterium.

1800s
The cell theory was established. It states that the cell is the basic unit of life, and that all cells come from other cells.

1850s
Gregor Mendel (an Austrian monk) discovered that inherited characteristics in pea plants are determined by distinct units — now recognized as genes.

1910
American geneticist Thomas Morgan noted that the inheritance pattern for eye colour in fruit flies followed the inheritance pattern of one of the chromosomes. He realized this could be explained if the gene for eye colour were located on that chromosome.

1944
American geneticist Barbara McClintock discovers that certain segments of DNA in corn plants can move to different parts of a chromosome. This process contributes to variation.

Figure 4.5 Major events in the history of biotechnology

the structure of deoxyribonucleic acid (DNA). This is the material chromosomes are made of. Study Figure 4.5. It shows some of the main scientific breakthroughs in history that eventually led to the discovery of DNA and its importance.

Check Your Understanding

1. When did humans begin to use biotechnology? What sorts of applications of biotechnologies were among the earliest?

2. Describe some of the potential benefits of biotechnology.

3. Explain the meaning of the term "selective breeding" and describe some of its uses.

4. Explain the relationship between biotechnology and reproductive technologies.

5. **Apply** Select one of the discoveries in the timeline below and find out more about it by doing library and/or Internet research. Produce a brief report on your findings.

Pause&
———Reflect

What sorts of features do people want to develop in a plant? Why? List some techniques that could be used to produce such features. Are these techniques natural? Do you think it is important to try to define what we mean when we say something is natural? Why?

1944
American bacteriologist Oswald Avery followed the experiments of Griffith and showed that inherited traits are carried by chromosomes.

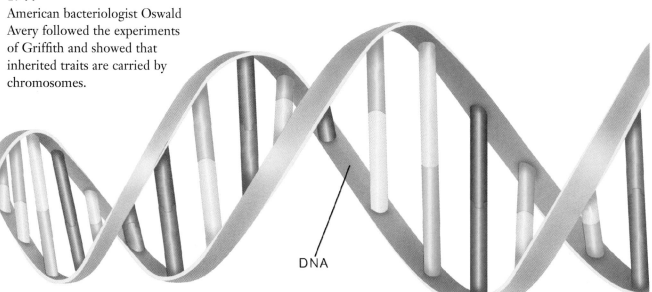

DNA

1953
James Watson and Francis Crick, at Cambridge University, used paper cutouts and a large model to figure out that DNA is shaped like a spiral staircase — a double helix.

1973
American biochemists Stanley Cohen and Herbert Boyer produced the first transfer of genes between species. They inserted genes from an African clawed toad into bacterial cells.

1993
Canadian scientist Dr. Michael Smith receives the Nobel Prize in Chemistry for his work in altering genes on chromosomes. This work led to the development of protein engineering.

1967
American scientists Har Gobind Khorana and Marshall Nirenberg discover the genetic code, finding which chemicals are encoded by each part of a gene.

1984
Alec Jeffreys of Britain develops DNA fingerprinting, a method that uses pieces of DNA to identify individual organisms.

1997
In Scotland, Ian Wilmut produces the lamb Dolly, the first artificially cloned mammal.

4.2 The Importance of DNA

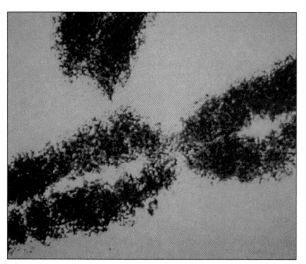

Figure 4.6 Chromosomes are formed from long strands of tightly coiled DNA.

Have you ever sent a coded message to someone? The person at the other end has to know the code in order to read the message. Cells also rely on coded information to tell them what to do. These instructions are contained in the molecules of DNA found in every cell.

DNA is called a nucleic acid because it is found in cell nuclei and is acidic. (In bacteria, where there is no organized nucleus, DNA forms a mass near the centre of the cell.) Which structures in the nucleus contain DNA? Recall from Chapter 1 that the chromosomes are also in the nucleus. The chromosomes are made of tightly coiled DNA, as shown in Figure 4.6. In the next investigation, you can actually collect some DNA by breaking open the nuclei of onion cells.

Figure 4.7 shows the structure of DNA. Study the information in the labels. Note especially how nucleotide base A is always bonded to T and C is always bonded to G. Note also that the order of these bases in a strand of nucleotides can vary infinitely. In the investigation on page 116, you will construct your own model of DNA in three dimensions.

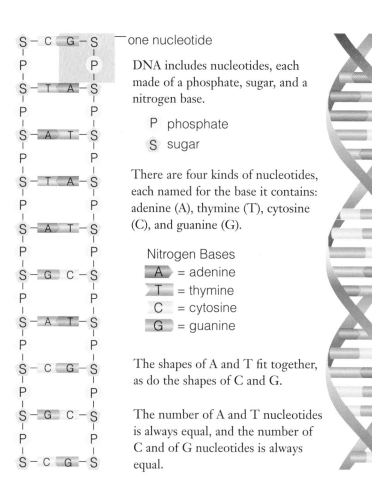

one nucleotide

DNA includes nucleotides, each made of a phosphate, sugar, and a nitrogen base.

P   phosphate
S   sugar

There are four kinds of nucleotides, each named for the base it contains: adenine (A), thymine (T), cytosine (C), and guanine (G).

Nitrogen Bases
A = adenine
T = thymine
C = cytosine
G = guanine

The shapes of A and T fit together, as do the shapes of C and G.

The number of A and T nucleotides is always equal, and the number of C and of G nucleotides is always equal.

Figure 4.7 DNA is made of many nucleotides. The ladder-like structure winds like a spiral staircase.

Extracting DNA from Onions

Although individual DNA molecules are too small to be seen even with a powerful microscope, you can collect enough DNA from tissues to see the extract with the unaided eye. DNA extraction for research is more complex than the procedure used here. The DNA that you will extract is not pure enough for research use.

Problem

How can you extract DNA from cells?

Apparatus

test tube rack
medicine dropper
glass stirring rod (small diameter)

Materials

capped test tube of onion mixture
meat tenderizer (powdered)
95% ethanol (cold)
flat toothpick

Procedure

❶ Add two toothpick scoops full of meat tenderizer to the onion mixture, cap the tube, and swirl gently to avoid foaming. The meat tenderizer contains papain, a substance that will help to separate the DNA from other parts of the cell.

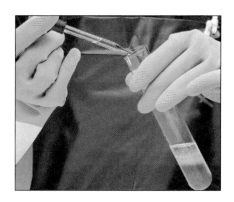

❷ Using the medicine dropper, slowly pour the cold alcohol down the inside of the test tube until it forms a layer of about 1 cm on top of the onion mixture. DNA is not soluble in alcohol and slowly separates out.

(a) Let the solution sit undisturbed for 2 to 3 min. *Do not shake the test tube.*

❸ Carefully spool the strands of DNA onto a glass rod. The DNA will be viscous and have the appearance of white mucous.

Analyze

1. In what area of the test tube contents did the mass of DNA gather?

Conclude and Apply

2. Do you think the DNA would look different, if it were from a different organism?

Extend Your Knowledge

3. Find and list some examples of how scientists might use DNA in medicine, agriculture, and forensic science.

Modelling DNA

Scientists James Watson and Francis Crick worked together to figure out the structure of DNA. In 1953, they presented their findings with a model made of wire and tin, as shown in the photograph. In this investigation, you will work with a partner to design and construct a three-dimensional model of a DNA molecule.

Challenge

Construct a model of DNA in three dimensions.

Materials

construction paper (6 colours; 2 sheets of each colour)
scissors
clear adhesive tape

Design Criteria

A. Your model must include the six colours of paper. Each colour will represent one of the following parts of DNA: phosphate, sugar, four nitrogen bases (A,T,C,G).

B. The nitrogen bases must be paired according to the rule: A pairs with T, and C pairs with G.

C. Your model must show the three-dimensional shape of DNA — a twisted ladder.

Plan and Construct

1. With your partner, decide on what shapes and colours you will use to represent each of the parts of your DNA model. How long will your DNA model be?

2. Brainstorm possible designs for your model. Make a list of your ideas.

3. Choose the best idea and sketch it. Include labels in your sketch. Then list the steps of how you will construct your model. Be specific.

4. Have your plan and sketch approved by your teacher. Then build your model.

Evaluate

1. Did your DNA model include all the parts that were outlined in your plan?

2. How did your model differ from those of other groups?

3. Did you have any problems in assembling your model? If so, how did you solve them?

4. How could you improve on your design?

5. What are some advantages of working with a partner? Did you have any difficulties? If so, what were they and how did you resolve them?

Extensions

1. Why do you think models are helpful to scientists?

2. Why do you think DNA is shaped like a twisted ladder or a double helix?

Proteins and DNA

The messages contained in DNA are spelled out in a code made up of three consecutive bases along one strand of DNA, as shown in Figure 4.8. Each segment of three consecutive bases is termed a **codon**. Figure 4.9 shows a more familiar example of a triplet code. One of the most important messages carried by DNA is instructions for making **proteins.** Protein molecules make up most of the structure of cells and tissues in plants and animals. They also include vital materials such as enzymes and hormones.

Each protein is a large molecule made up hundreds or thousands of smaller molecules known as **amino acids**. There are 20 different kinds of amino acids and they can be combined in many ways to make different proteins. One codon has instructions for making one amino acid. A **gene** is a segment of DNA with enough codons to produce all the amino acids to make one protein.

Computer **CONNECT**

Scientists from many countries assist each other in their work. In a spreadsheet, make a table listing all the names of the scientists mentioned in this chapter so far. State the country where they did their research, what their contribution was, and the approximate year of that work.

3. A codon recognizes a particular amino acid.

1. A codon is made of three consecutive bases, such as C-T-A.

2. DNA contains instructions for stringing together amino acids in a particular order. Therefore, the sequence of the codons is very important.

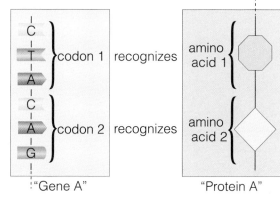

4. Amino acids are strung together to form proteins.

5. The number, order, and kinds of amino acids determine the structure and function of the protein.

7. The segment of DNA with the instruction to form protein A is called "gene A."

6. "Protein A" in this example is formed by two amino acids.

Figure 4.8 DNA is a series of codons. This sequence of codons provides instructions for assembling proteins.

In 1991, scientists discovered that the tips of chromosomes in cells become shorter each time the cell reproduces. After about 50 replications, certain cell types stop replicating. This may be what aging really is — the inability to replace old, worn-out, or damaged cells.

Figure 4.9 Airlines use a three letter code on baggage tags. There is a specific code for each airport in the world.

Mutations

Because DNA controls the characteristics of a cell, it must be copied before a cell reproduces (see Chapter 1). This is necessary because each new cell needs the same information as the original cell. Sometimes mistakes can occur during this process. Such errors are called **mutations**. For example, if a mistake occurs in the sequence of codons for assembling amino acids into a protein, a different protein or property of that protein may result. Do you think it will make a difference if a mutation occurs in a body (somatic) cell or in a reproductive cell (egg or sperm)?

Mutations can be inherited. They may be useful, harmful, or have no effect on the organism or cell in which they occur. A mutation in a body cell in a multicellular individual will have a much less drastic effect than a mutation in a reproductive cell or in an embryo, which can affect the development of the entire organism.

The most common causes of mutations appear to be **mutagenic agents** such as radiation, temperature extremes, or exposure to chemicals, such as pesticides. These agents alter the DNA code. As a result, a cell may produce the wrong protein, or no protein at all. This will alter the intended function of the cell. Other mutations cause cells to lose control of cell division processes. They divide rapidly and repeatedly, producing cancer.

Chromosome mutations usually occur after chromosomes are broken by a mutagenic agent. For example, a part of a chromosome can break and be lost. Some chromosome mutations are shown in Figure 4.10. Chromosomal mutations in reproductive cell often do not survive because the egg or sperm become incapable of fertilization. Consequently, most chromosomal mutations in reproductive cells are not passed on to offspring.

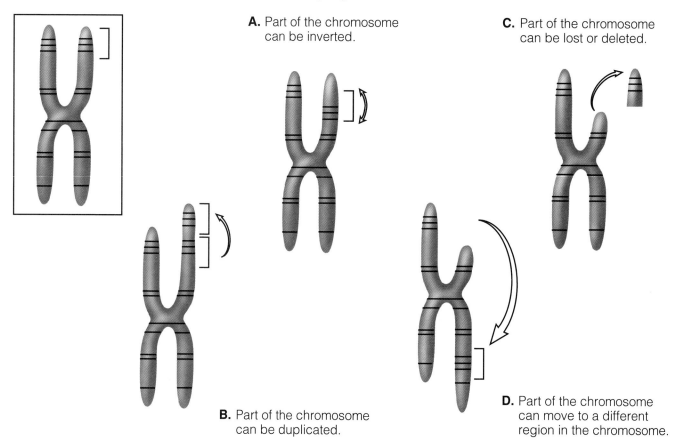

A. Part of the chromosome can be inverted.

B. Part of the chromosome can be duplicated.

C. Part of the chromosome can be lost or deleted.

D. Part of the chromosome can move to a different region in the chromosome.

Figure 4.10 Several types of chromosome mutations

Genetic Engineering

You have learned that new genetic combinations can be produced through selective breeding. As well, **genetic engineering** can be used to artificially combine genes in a cell. Scientists have learned how to take DNA from the cell of one organism and move it to another to produce a new combination. The result is a **transgenic** organism. The transferred DNA will produce changes in characteristics in the organism. For example, bacteria may be given a new gene. The bacteria can then make the protein coded by the new gene. The new protein may be human insulin or some other protein the bacteria do not normally produce.

Genetic engineering began in the early 1970s with work conducted on a bacterium called *Escherichia coli*. Many bacteria contain plasmids, small independent loops of DNA. Bacteria can exchange plasmids in conjugation, producing new combinations of DNA. Scientists took advantage of these features of bacteria to develop a new combination of genetic material, or **recombinant DNA**.

Scientists produce recombinant DNA by placing plasmids in a test tube together with fragments of DNA from another organism. These fragments contain specific genes, with which researchers want the plasmid to combine. Once plasmids and fragments are together, an enzyme is used to cut open the plasmid. The fragment then joins, or splices, into the plasmid. This technique is called **gene splicing.**

How are the DNA fragments obtained? Naturally occurring enzymes (called restriction enzymes) are used to cut strands of DNA at very specific places. Scientists have identified about 800 such enzymes, each of which cuts DNA strands at particular sites. Once a new gene has been spliced into a plasmid, the altered plasmids can be mixed with bacterial cells. The bacteria take up the plasmids and function with the new gene. For example, a gene for producing human insulin can be transferred into bacteria by means of this method.

One problem in genetic engineering is transferring engineered DNA into a host cell. Viruses have most often been used as "transporters." Another method uses a "gene gun," which fires microscopic metallic particles coated with engineered DNA into a host cell.

Why Would We Want "Designer Genes"?

Earlier in this chapter, selective breeding was described as a process for producing new varieties of animals and plants. On average, it takes 12 years to develop a new plant variety through selective breeding. An advantage of genetic engineering is that new varieties can be produced in as little as one year. Speed is not the only advantage, however. Genetic engineering allows scientists to give organisms genes from other species, which selective breeding cannot normally do.

Modern techniques allow us to make products that are useful in agriculture, medicine, and industry. In crop plants (such as corn, wheat, or rice) the goal is to create plants that produce more grain that is more nutritious, or that has resistance to disease-causing viruses, or drought. Livestock may be genetically altered to produce leaner meat, more milk or eggs, or to be more resistant to disease.

In medicine, a gene that is absent in a particular person may be supplied through genetic engineering. Selective breeding, of course, would not be useful for such cases. Think of reasons why this is so. Also, humans, as well as other organisms, may benefit by receiving essential products, such as hormones, that are produced artificially.

The Cloning Controversy

Think About It

News of the cloning of Dolly the sheep increased public awareness of the process of cloning. Cloning has many applications in the fields of agriculture, medicine, and forestry, but the possibility of human cloning has attracted the most attention.

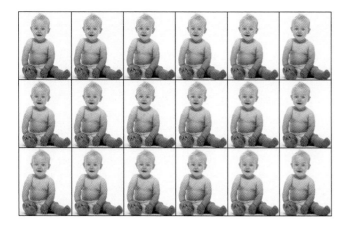

The idea of making genetic duplicates of certain individuals has been discussed for many years. Could this process be used to produce armies of super-soldiers or to make copies of great scientists or professional athletes? Will parents in the future be able to choose children from a catalogue? Decisions about what kinds of controls should be placed on this technology will have to be made in the near future.

Bioethics is the study of moral issues in the fields of medical treatment and research. Although there are many ways of analyzing bioethical issues, there are certain steps that are common to all discussions. In this investigation, you will consider the bioethics of cloning humans. What are the advantages and disadvantages of human cloning? Should there be any controls on experimentation? If human cloning becomes a reality, who should be allowed to do it and under what conditions? **Note**: For tips on issue analysis, turn to page IS-12.

What to Do

1. State what is involved in the cloning issue. This may be in the form of a question or a statement describing the dilemma, but it should summarize the problem briefly and clearly.

2. Identify who will gain or lose. Who has an interest in the outcome? Think of as many people or groups as possible.

3. Present possible solutions. There is always more than one solution to an ethical issue, so come up with as many solutions as you can.

4. Rank the solutions from best to worst. Choose the one that seems to make the most sense to you as an individual.

5. Explain why your choice seems best to you. What personal values are involved in your decision? Are you entirely happy with your decision? Why or why not?

Analyze

Choose one of the following ways to analyze this bioethical issue.

- Write out your analysis of the issue in the form of a magazine or journal article.

- Create a poem, song, play, or story that presents your analysis of the issue.

- Make a poster that shows your position on the issue and your reasoning.

Cloning

Cloning involves the production of identical copies, whether of molecules, genes, cells, or an entire organism. A simple way to make a clone is to take a cutting from a plant and put it in water, as you did in Chapter 1. When the cutting has grown roots, it can be potted and it will then produce a plant genetically identical to the original. Does this mean that parents and offspring will have an identical appearance? To answer this question, think about whether genes are the only determining factors in the final appearance of an organism. Study Figure 4.11. It describes how scientists are able to clone a mammal.

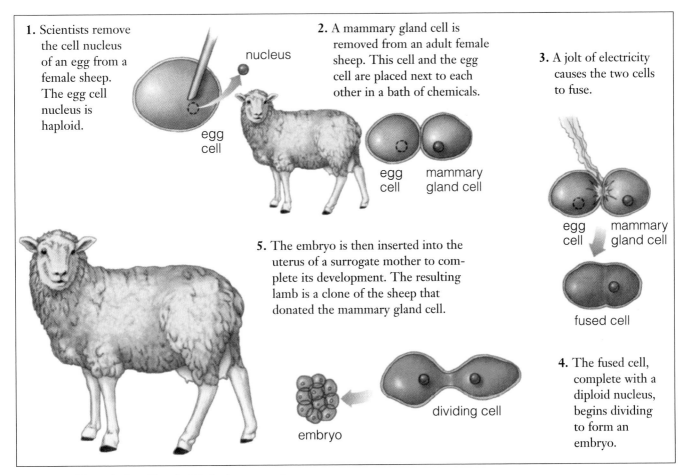

1. Scientists remove the cell nucleus of an egg from a female sheep. The egg cell nucleus is haploid.

nucleus
egg cell

2. A mammary gland cell is removed from an adult female sheep. This cell and the egg cell are placed next to each other in a bath of chemicals.

egg cell   mammary gland cell

3. A jolt of electricity causes the two cells to fuse.

egg cell   mammary gland cell

fused cell

5. The embryo is then inserted into the uterus of a surrogate mother to complete its development. The resulting lamb is a clone of the sheep that donated the mammary gland cell.

embryo   dividing cell

4. The fused cell, complete with a diploid nucleus, begins dividing to form an embryo.

Figure 4.11 The method used by scientists to clone mammals

Check Your Understanding

1. In what way is DNA a code?

2. Describe the purpose of DNA.

3. What is a gene?

4. What is the importance or significance of mutations?

5. **Thinking Critically** In what ways can transgenic organisms be used?

6. It is estimated that every human carries between five and eight harmful genes. Why do you think that more people are not born with inherited diseases?

4.3 Biotechnology and the Human Body

Figure 4.12 New techniques are being developed to diagnose and treat certain diseases.

Genetic research has come a long way in identifying and diagnosing human genetic disorders. There are about 3000 known diseases linked to genes and scientists are able to diagnose more than 200 of them. A genetic disease is caused by a defect in a person's DNA. Such a defect may result from a mutation or it may be due to missing or extra genes or chromosomes. This may lead to physical and physiological disorders.

How do researchers diagnose such disorders? Several genetic diseases can be identified simply by looking at a magnified image of a person's chromosomes. This is one type of **genetic screening**. A picture of a cell's chromosomes is called a **karyotype**. In the next investigation, you will use genetic screening to identify an abnormality in a human karyotype.

A technique called **gene therapy** allows scientists to replace defective genes with healthy ones. There are several methods for inserting genes into cells. One method uses an altered virus. A virus normally attacks cells by attaching to the cell's outer membrane and then pushing its own DNA into the cell. The viral DNA uses the host cell to make copies of itself. In an altered virus, scientists splice a healthy gene into the viral DNA, then let the virus transfer the gene into the patient's cells (see Figure 4.13).

Pause & Reflect

Do you think everyone should be tested for possible genetic disorders? Do you think none should be? Would you want to know if you had a genetic disease that may kill you before you turn 40? Think about these questions and write your thoughts about this complex issue in your Science Log.

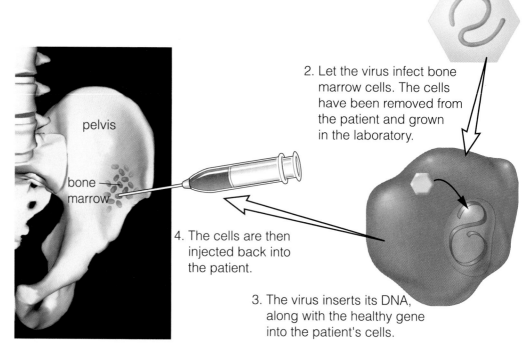

1. Insert the healthy gene into the DNA of the virus.

2. Let the virus infect bone marrow cells. The cells have been removed from the patient and grown in the laboratory.

3. The virus inserts its DNA, along with the healthy gene into the patient's cells.

4. The cells are then injected back into the patient.

Figure 4.13 A virus reproduces by inserting its DNA into a host cell, which makes copies of the virus. An altered virus can be used to insert a healthy gene into a cell to treat a genetic disorder.

Genetic Screening

To identify chromosomal disorders, a karyotype is prepared from a sample of tissue grown in a laboratory and then photographed under a microscope. Recall that normal humans have 23 pairs of chromosomes. One pair of chromosomes determines the sex of the person. The sex chromosomes are called the X and Y chromosome. Females have two X chromosomes (XX), while males have one X and one Y chromosome (XY). The X chromosome is considerably larger than the Y chromosome and contains more genetic information.

Problem

How can you identify a chromosomal disorder?

Materials

graphic of human chromosomes
scissors

Procedure

① Take the karyotype that is given to you by your teacher and cut out each of the individual chromosomes.

② Arrange the chromosomes in pairs. Use the size of the chromosomes and their distinctive banding patterns to match up the pairs of chromosomes, then arrange the pairs from largest to smallest. Chromosome number 1 is the largest and number 22 is the smallest. Place the sex chromosomes at the end of the sequence.

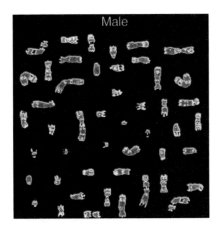

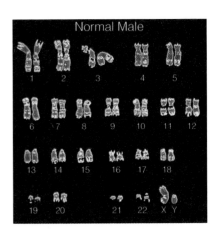

Analyze

1. How many chromosomes are shown in the karyotype?

2. What is the sex of the person?

3. What is unusual about this karyotype?

Conclude and Apply

4. Other abnormalities, such as having three copies of chromosome 13 or 15, cause major physical disorders in newborns. Why do you think these disorders result in such extreme effects?

Extend Your Knowledge

5. Amniocentesis is a procedure used to determine genetic disorders in a fetus. What is involved in this procedure? Why is it recommended for some pregnant women and not others? What are some benefits and risks associated with this procedure?

Genetic Disorders

Most genetic disorders are uncommon in the human population. Examples include cystic fibrosis, Down syndrome, Duchenne muscular dystrophy, Edward's syndrome, fragile X syndrome, hemophilia A, Huntington's disease, Klinefelter's syndrome, sickle cell anemia, spina bifida, Tay-Sach's disease, and Turner's syndrome. You may want to learn more about some of them.

What to Do

1. Select one of the genetic disorders mentioned above.

2. Find out its cause and effects and how it is detected.

3. Present your findings in a short report. Include diagrams and graphs to illustrate your report.

What Did You Discover?

1. How common is the genetic disorder that you investigated?

2. What new technologies have been developed to diagnose this disorder?

3. Is there any treatment for the disorder? If so, what is involved in the treatment?

Gene therapy using somatic cells can help a patient with an inherited disease. To avoid passing on a genetic disease to their offspring, however, defective genes would need to be located and altered in a patient's sex cells (sperm or egg). What are the risks associated with changing the reproductive cells of an organism? How might this type of therapy be abused? Some people have religious or ethical reasons for opposing such genetic procedures.

DidYou**Know**?

The first clinical use of gene therapy occurred in 1990. It involved a four-year-old girl who was missing a gene needed to help fight off many common infections. Samples of her white blood cells were grown in the laboratory and altered to include the missing gene, then transferred back into her bloodstream.

Figure 4.14 Dr. Lap-Chee Tsui of The Hospital for Sick Children discovered the gene responsible for cystic fibrosis. This information is vital in producing treatments and, potentially, a cure for the disease.

All of the genes found in a complete set of chromosomes make up a **genome**. By mapping the entire human genome, scientists expect to provide the ideal tool for diagnosing genetic disorders. The **Human Genome Project** was started in 1990 in the United States with the aim of locating approximately 100 000 genes that are found on one set (23) of human chromosomes. Work on this massive project now involves many nations. To speed up this task, scientists use DNA probes, short strands of "labelled" DNA that will attach to very specific genes. These probes can also be used to diagnose genetic diseases in people who have not yet shown symptoms. Techniques like this helped researchers find the gene responsible for cystic fibrosis, a disease that affects the pancreas and lungs (see Figure 4.14).

Making Human Proteins

It is not easy to replace faulty or missing genes. An alternative is to engineer bacteria to produce the product of the gene. For example, people with diabetes cannot produce their own insulin (a hormone that regulates the level of sugar in a person's blood). Diabetics were commonly treated with insulin taken from cows or pigs, but some patients may experience allergic reactions.

In 1978, the human gene for making insulin was transferred into bacteria. The insulin manufactured by the bacteria has the advantage of being human insulin, which decreases the possibility of an allergic reaction. The hormone can also be produced by bacteria in large quantities relatively inexpensively (see Figure 4.15). Bacteria are also used to produce human growth hormone (for the treatment of growth abnormalities) and interferon (a protein of the immune system).

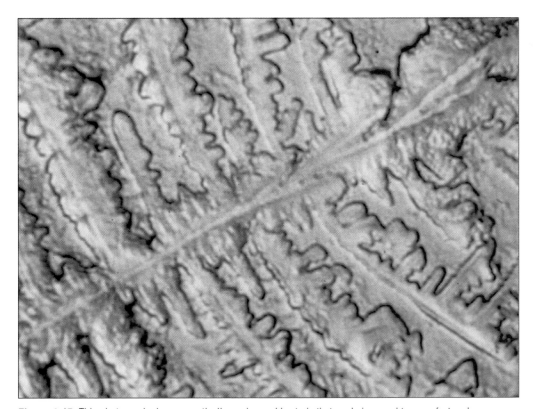

Figure 4.15 This photograph shows genetically engineered bacteria that are being used to manufacture human insulin.

Figure 4.16 This is Willow the goat, Canada's first transgenic livestock animal born in August 1998. Willow has a human gene in her body that allows her to produce a human protein in her milk.

Animals, as well as bacteria, can be given human genes (see Figure 4.16). Genetically modified, or transgenic, animals are produced by adding human genes to the fertilized eggs of the parents. The offspring grow up with a human gene. Usually, the gene product is a protein that can be collected in the transgenic animal's milk and then purified. Table 4.1 lists some proteins made using transgenic animals.

Table 4.1 Some Common Human Proteins Made Using Transgenic Animals

Product	Use	Animal
human lactoferrin	a good source of iron for babies	cow
antitrypsin	a compound to treat an inherited form of emphysema	sheep
factor VIII & IX	blood clotting factors used to treat hemophilia	sheep
human protein C	used to treat blood clots	pig

Bacterial cells cannot make large, complex proteins such as the ones listed in the table above. Making these proteins requires a number of steps that can occur only in the cells of a multicellular organism. An advantage of using mammals is that the proteins can be collected in the mammal's milk. The animal does not have to be killed to obtain the proteins. As well, the ability to produce human proteins can be inherited by the offspring of the transgenic animal.

Check Your Understanding

1. How can a karyotype be used to identify a genetic disease?

2. What is gene therapy and when is it used?

3. What is the objective of the Human Genome Project?

4. What are some of the human proteins that can be produced by genetically altered bacteria?

5. Why are some human proteins produced by transgenic cows, sheep, or pigs, rather than bacteria?

6. **Thinking Critically** Gene therapy may eventually lead to technologies that can alter human reproductive cells (sperm and eggs). Why are some people opposed to this?

4.4 Biotechnology in Agriculture

The New Crops

Farmers have always tried to improve their crop production. For example, a farmer might observe that one strain of wheat is more resistant to pests, while another has a greater rate of seed production. The farmer might then cross-pollinate the two strains by hand in order to create a new combined variety, or **hybrid,** with both characteristics (see Figure 4.18). This technique can be used only with closely related species.

Using modern biotechnology, however, cropbreeders can now select a specific genetic trait (gene) from one species and move it into the genetic code of a crop plant. This makes the job of breeding plants more effective in two important ways. First, it allows breeders to choose the particular genetic characteristics they want, which makes the process both faster and more specific than selective breeding. The second advantage is that biotechnology gives the breeders the alternative of using genes from unrelated species, including animals or micro-organisms as well as plants. For example, a wheat variety may contain a gene that allows the plant to resist a specific pest. The gene can be transferred to different species of plant.

Figure 4.17 Will there be enough food to support the growing human population?

Figure 4.18 First developed in 1867, triticale is a cereal grain produced by hybridizing wheat with rye. It is richer in protein than wheat and is used for human food and livestock feed.

Figure 4.19 These plants are not resistant to herbicides. How might they become resistant?

Figure 4.20 Selective plant breeding and genetic engineering were used to develop Canola. Derived from rapeseed plants, Canola oil and meal have superior nutritional qualities.

During the early 1990s, almost 86% (about 1600) of all genetically engineered crops in Canada were altered to be tolerant of herbicides. Herbicides are chemicals used to kill unwanted plants, or weeds, that grow with food crops (see Figure 4.19). However, herbicides can kill crop plants, as well. How can crop plants be protected from the effects of herbicides? They can be given a gene that allows them to function in the presence of the herbicide. What are the advantages of these crops? A farmer can spray such crops with herbicide at a concentration that will kill most weeds without damaging the crops. This means that the crops can be sprayed less often, which should be less costly for the farmer and safer for the environment. On the other hand, there are concerns that the genes for herbicide resistance might get into the weeds by natural cross-pollination with crops. This would produce weeds that are also resistant to herbicides.

Canola: A Canadian Success Story

Canada plays a leading role in plant biotechnology. An outstanding story in Canadian research and development is that of Canola, a term coined from the words "Canadian" and "oil." The ancestor of Canola is a plant called rapeseed. In ancient times, rapeseed oil was used in Asia and Europe in lamps, for cooking, and in foods. Today, its seeds contain a highly desirable oil used in shortening, salad oil, cooking sprays, and many other foods, as well as in printing ink, hydraulic fluids, and suntan lotion. Solid parts of the plant may be used as fertilizers and in feed for livestock, poultry, and fish.

Rapeseed has been grown in Canada (mainly in Saskatchewan) since 1936. It was in high demand during World War II as one of the most effective lubricants for metal engine parts. After the war, demand declined sharply and farmers began to look for other uses for the plant and its products. Edible rapeseed oil extracts were first put on the market in 1956-57, but not all of the characteristics of these products were considered acceptable. Rapeseed oil had a distinctive taste and a disagreeable greenish colour due to the presence of chlorophyll. It also contained a high concentration of erucic acid, suspected of causing cancer if ingested in large amounts. Feed meal from the rapeseed plants was not particularly appealing to livestock, due to high levels of sharp-tasting compounds called glucosinolates.

Canadian plant breeders took up the challenge to improve the quality of rapeseed. In 1968, Dr. Baldur

"Tough" Plants

What do you get when you cross a bacterium with a Canola plant? Sound like an old joke? Not to Canola farmers of the Canadian prairies. Canadian scientists in Saskatoon have found a bacterium that produces a protein that is toxic, not to people, but to the Canola plant's worst enemy: the fleabeetle. Using transgenics, scientists isolated the gene in the bacterium that produces the toxic protein and placed it in the DNA of Canola, creating a new kind of Canola. The plants now produce the same toxic protein as the bacteria. When the fleabeetles eat some of these new Canola plants, the protein kills them.

At the Plant Biotechnology Institute in Saskatoon and the Pacific Agriculture Research Centre in Vancouver, many crops including soybean, potato, and strawberry have been developed that are resistant to diseases and insects. For instance, there is a new tomato that contains an added gene that stops it from going too mushy as it ripens. Broccoli has also been engineered to contain more of its cancer-fighting ingredient.

Imagine that you are a transgenics scientist. Propose an idea for a genetically altered fruit or vegetable that most of us eat. Write a paragraph explaining why you think scientists should look for a gene to alter that crop.

Stefansson of the University of Manitoba used selective breeding to develop a low erucic acid variety of the plant. In 1974, another variety was produced with both a low-erucic acid content and a low level of glucosinolates.

Today, about 75% of the Canola crops planted in Alberta, Manitoba, and Saskatchewan are herbicide tolerant varieties. A variety developed in 1998 is considered to be the most disease and drought resistant variety of Canola to date. These recent varieties have been produced by gene splicing techniques.

Compared with sunflower, corn, olive, peanut, and other oils, Canola has the most favourable overall combination of saturated and unsaturated fats for a healthy diet. Its place in society seems assured for some time to come, thanks to the use of selective breeding and genetic engineering.

Although products such as Canola are a great success, the questions remain: Can the use of selective breeding and herbicide-resistant genes be a long-term solution to meet the growing demand for food production? Will genetically altered crops remain effective over a long period of time? Will there be side effects that harm the environment and other species?

The success of biotechnology may produce a situation where large parts of a country are planted with a single variety of a crop or a very limited number of varieties (see Figure 4.21). This practice is called **monoculture**. The lack of diversity makes crops prone to large-scale destruction by a single pest or disease to which the crops are not resistant.

INTERNET - CONNECT

www.school.mcgrawhill.ca/resources/

Conduct research on how Canadian scientists have developed cold-tolerant varieties of wheat, triticale, and rye. Visit the above web site. Go to **Science Resources**, then to **SCIENCEPOWER 9** to find out where to go next. Write a short report on how one of the crops mentioned above was developed.

Figure 4.21 Vast areas planted with a single type of crop are vulnerable to pests and disease.

The New Animals

With the decline of natural fish stocks in oceans and lakes, fish farming, or **aquaculture**, will become an increasingly important method of fish production. It is predicted that fish farming may provide 25% or more of Canada's fish harvest in the near future. Biotechnology is being used by the aquaculture industry. Scientists have added genes for disease resistance to some varieties of fish and growth hormone genes have been introduced into fish eggs to increase the size and growth rate of fish, as shown in Figure 4.22.

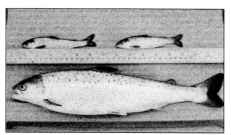

Figure 4.22 Salmon that are bioengineered to contain a gene for rapid growth can grow four to six times larger than salmon without the gene. The two fish at the top of this photograph do not contain the gene for rapid growth.

Some Canadian fish farms have problems operating during the winter, as subzero temperatures freeze Atlantic salmon and halibut. Researchers at Memorial University in Newfoundland have added an "antifreeze" gene into Atlantic salmon and halibut stocks (see Figure 4.23). The gene comes from a species of Arctic flatfish. It produces a protein that prevents the fishes' blood from freezing.

Hormones have also been used to increase the production of farm animal products. For example, Bovine Growth Hormone (BGH) is a hormone that is produced naturally in the bodies of cows. It controls both calf growth and milk production. Cows injected with this hormone can produce more milk than cows that do not receive hormone injections. In the 1980s, the gene for BGH was inserted into *E. coli* bacteria. These genetically engineered bacteria then produced the hormone like small factories. To be effective, BGH must be injected into the cow regularly. BGH was approved for use in the United States in 1994, but it continues to be controversial. Many people feel that the treatment is unnecessary, as milk production has continually exceeded demand. Consumers are concerned about possible

Figure 4.23 Researchers at Memorial University experiment with putting "antifreeze" genes into salmon eggs. In this photograph, the bright orange salmon eggs under the microscope are receiving some of these genes via the fine glass needle.

health risks. Farmers with small herds of dairy cattle are concerned that using the hormone might increase the chances of some types of infection in their cows. The increased costs of antibiotics, veterinarians, and nutritionists are more cost-effective on large-scale farm operations with many cows producing increased revenue. The large-scale use of BGH could mean farms with fewer than 50 cows would not be profitable.

In January 1999, the federal government did not approve the use of BGH for milk production in Canada. They stated that the continuing controversy and disagreements among researchers made approval unwise.

Pause& Reflect

Do you think you have the right to know what substances are in the food you eat, or how your food is produced? Would you buy milk produced by genetic engineering? Why or why not? Would you pay more for milk that was not produced in this way? Write your response in your Science Log.

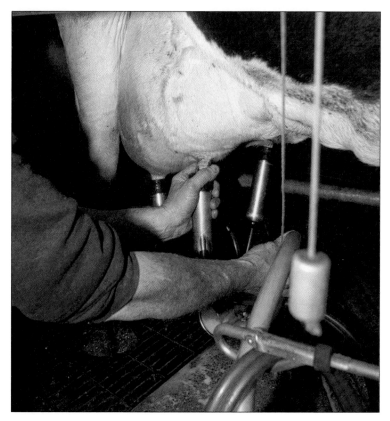

Figure 4.24 A cow can produce 10 to 25% more milk if it is rejected with Bovine Growth Hormone.

Check Your Understanding

1. In what two ways can biotechnology improve plant breeding?

2. What is the most common genetic manipulation of crop plants?

3. What is triticale and what advantage does it give?

4. What are some uses of Canola?

5. What are the advantages of Canola over its earlier form, rapeseed?

6. What are three types of genes that have been added to fish used for acquaculture.

7. **Thinking Critically** Give one reason why Bovine Growth Hormone has been approved for use in the United States, but banned in Canada.

8. Why is herbicide resistance so important to farmers?

4.5 Biotechnology in the Environment

One of the biggest environmental problems is how to clean up toxic wastes left over from years of carelessness or released into the environment by accident or negligence. Sometimes, soil or water that is contaminated with toxic material is removed from a site and then transported to a special facility for storage and treatment. This procedure is costly. Canada faces the possibility of having to spend millions of dollars for environmental clean-up. Across Canada, an estimated 1000 sites are contaminated with hazardous materials. Do you know the locations of toxic waste sites in your province? Can you think of a way these sites could be cleaned up economically without removing the toxic waste?

Bioremediation: Biotechnology Cleans Up the Environment

In the 1980s, scientists began to look for ways to use micro-organisms to break down the complex compounds in toxic waste. This process is called **bioremediation**. Bacteria, fungi, and other micro-organisms in the soil are decomposers. They use dead plants and animals as food (see Figure 4.25). In the process, the dead organisms are broken down into carbon dioxide, water, and other simple compounds.

Figure 4.25 Many bacteria, fungi and other micro-organisms live in the soil. These organisms break down dead vegetation and animals into nutrients that can be used by plants.

Different species of bacteria and fungi can decompose or break down almost anything — including chemicals that are toxic to humans. The trick is finding the right organisms to do the job. Some scientists began looking in the most toxic of the toxic waste sites for micro-organisms that, if they were not thriving, were at least able to survive in the hostile environment. Micro-organisms have been found that break down toxic compounds, such as methylene chloride, creosote, pentachlorophenol, and polychlorinated biphenols (PCBs). In many cases, the breakdown of complex compounds requires groups of different organisms, each responsible for one step in the process of decomposition. These groups of micro-organisms are called **consortia**.

Figure 4.26 Some micro-organisms can survive in this toxic environment. Why do you think they live here?

Bioremediation involves injecting micro-organisms into the ground along with nutrients that will help them grow. In other cases, only oxygen or nutrients are needed to nourish the micro-organisms that are already in the soil. Bioremediation has proven to be very effective, often costing only one-fifth the price of previous clean-up methods. It also has the advantage of treating the contamination without causing a major disturbance to the area and with a minimum of intervention. However, the technology is not yet perfect. To be able to use these micro-organisms effectively and safely, a better understanding of how they function in their natural habitat is needed.

Problems with Pesticides

Think About It

Chemical pesticides are poisons used to kill a variety of different organisms that damage crops. It has been estimated that without these chemicals, food prices would increase 30 to 50%. However, even with the extensive use of pesticides, pests damage or destroy half the world's food supply. The targets of these chemicals (usually insects) reproduce quickly, and in many cases they develop a resistance to the chemicals. This means that more toxic or different pesticides must be used in an attempt to keep ahead of the pest's ability to adapt.

A farmer sprays chemical pesticides to control pests.

Part 1

Disadvantages of Chemical Pesticides

- Many chemical pesticides are extremely toxic and persistent.
- Some do not break down easily and can remain in the environment for long periods of time.
- Persistent pesticides can harm endangered wildlife such as bald eagles, peregrine falcons, and brown pelicans.
- It is estimated that two million people are poisoned and 10 000 die each year from pesticides.
- Pesticides contaminate groundwater, rivers, and lakes.
- Many pesticides contribute to cancer, birth defects, genetic diseases, and long-term health problems.

What to Do

1 Based on the list above, what characteristics would you want a pesticide to have?

2 How might biotechnology be used to create less harmful pesticides? Explain your reasoning. (If you have difficulty, read the next section.)

Part 2

A Possible Solution to Chemical Pesticides

An example of a pesticide developed by biotechnology is the engineered bacterium *Bacillus thuringiensis* (Bt). These soil bacteria produce a toxin that is lethal to certain insects but apparently harmless to humans and other vertebrates.

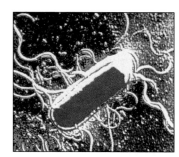

The bacterium *Bacillus thuringiensis* is commonly used as an insecticide.

What to Do

Research Bt pesticides at your local library and/or the Internet.

Analyze

1. In what ways do the new bacterial pesticides meet your description in Part 1 of the "ideal" pesticide? In what ways have the bacterial pesticides fallen short of the ideal?

2. Which characteristics of insects give them the ability to develop resistance to pesticides?

3. Which other group of organisms has developed resistance to the chemicals we have used to control them? Do they have some of the same characteristics that have helped insects survive? Explain.

4. Predict other ways that biotechnology may be used to protect our food supplies.

Oil Spills and Bioremediation

One of the first attempts at large-scale bioremediation occurred off the coast of Alaska in 1989 after the oil tanker *Exxon Valdez* ran aground, releasing 42 million L of crude oil. The oil spread down the coast of Alaska and killed thousands of animals. Biologists reported that 33 000 sea birds, 146 bald eagles, and 980 sea otters had been found dead. Oil covered 1600 km of shoreline and workers used everything from steam to towels to try to remove the oil (see Figure 4.27). To remove oil trapped beneath and between rocks, oil-eating bacteria were spread on the shoreline, with nitrogen and phosphorus fertilizers to aid their growth. The project had some success and caused less disturbance to the environment than other methods.

Figure 4.27 About 4 million t of oil are released into the ocean every year. Oil spills are extremely harmful to the environment, and their clean-up is very costly.

With its long coastlines, Canada can benefit from the use of bioremediation on oil spills. Between 1976 and 1987, over 300 significant oil spills occurred off Canada's east and west coasts. In December, 1988, an oil barge off the coast of Washington State spilled 875 t of oil, which drifted up the west coast of Vancouver Island. The spill was responsible for the death of 46 000 shorebirds.

Word **CONNECT**

Most new discoveries are protected by agreements called *patents*. What is a patent? Why do you think patenting a newly "invented" life form, such as a bacterium that breaks down oil or a herbicide-resistant wheat, is controversial?

Oil Spill Bioremediation

Scientists are increasingly using bacteria to break down spilled oil. Few bacteria are capable of using oil as a nutrient, and finding suitable bacteria is an important scientific activity. Bacteria are found in almost all soils, but the types of bacteria vary with the soil conditions. In this activity, you will sample soil from different places and design an experiment to investigate bacterial breakdown of oil.

What to Do

1. Predict where you would find soil that contains bacteria capable of breaking down oil.

2. Design an experiment to compare soil samples from a variety of locations.

3. What will be your experimental variable? What variables will you control?

4. What will be the most effective way of showing your results?

5. Write out your experiment, including the following headings: problem, hypothesis, procedure, observations, conclusions.

6. Conduct your experiment and test your hypothesis.

What Did You Discover?

1. What areas contained bacteria that were capable of breaking down oil? Why do you think the bacteria were found there?

2. If your experiment did not provide any conclusive results, suggest why.

Extension

3. Scientists using bacteria to break down oil often spray fertilizer on the mixture of bacteria and oil. Why do they do this?

Heavy Metal Biotechnology

Heavy metals, such as mercury, copper, zinc, and lead, are pollutants that can result in damage to the nervous, circulatory, digestive, and reproductive systems of humans and other organisms. The metals are released into the environment by industrial and mining activities, urban storm-water run-off, and the leaching of rocks and soil by acid rain. Removing heavy metals from soil or water is a difficult task. Micro-organisms may prove useful in gathering heavy metal pollutants. Certain bacteria, fungi, and algae can use various metals in the soil or rocks to produce energy. These micro-organisms have been used by the mining industry to separate copper and other metals from their surrounding impurities. However, these technologies are still being developed to make them more efficient and economical.

One solution may come from the Brassica family of plants, which include crops such as cabbage, mustards, and radishes (see Figure 4.29). Members of this family can concentrate heavy metals in their roots. These plants are so effective that the metals can compose up to

Figure 4.28 Heavy metals, such as mercury, can be lethal to many organisms such as fish. The metal can accumulate in body tissues, magnifying its concentration as it goes up the food chain.

30% of the dry weight of their roots. Using biotechnology, the plants can be genetically altered to take up specific metals from the soil. Some aquatic plants have the same potential. However, the plants do not remove the metals. They merely concentrate them. The plants must be harvested and then disposed of safely to remove the pollutants.

Figure 4.29 These cabbage plants can be used to clean heavy metals from the soil. How is this possible?

Species Preservation

The loss of biodiversity (variety of species) is a major concern today. For example, overfishing, pollution, and global climate change threaten to reduce the diversity of marine life throughout the world. The oceans contain a multitude of different organisms that have unique biochemical characteristics. These organisms provide many opportunities for solving a variety of medical problems. Some examples of marine life that are potentially medically useful are:

- a bacterium that lives with sponges and sea squirts and produces chemicals that kill certain viruses
- a compound from a deep-sea bacterium that can be used to inhibit the HIV virus that causes AIDS
- many sponges and corals that make chemicals that reduce the inflammation and pain of acute asthma, arthritis, and injuries
- other marine organisms that produce antibiotics and antibodies.

As these examples show, research of little-known plant and animal species could provide solutions to a wide variety of medical problems that still face the world today.

Figure 4.30 Certain compounds found in sharks can be used in the treatment of cancer.

Biotechnology can also be used to preserve certain endangered species. Some rare animal species must be bred in captivity in various zoos and wildlife preserves to increase their numbers. A major concern of captive breeding is the problem of **inbreeding**. Mating two closely related individuals can increase the chances of genetic diseases in their offspring. Furthermore, the offspring from such matings are less genetically variable than those from matings of non-related parents. Recall the genetic advantage of sexual reproduction explained in Chapter 2. Genetic variability increases the chance of offspring survival, when environmental conditions change. How can biologists ensure that the offspring of captive-bred animals will be as genetically diverse as possible? The solution is to use DNA fingerprinting. With this technique, biologists can not only identify individuals, but also determine how closely related they are. Then they can pair unrelated individuals to produce the offspring. This is really a type of selective breeding done to maintain genetic variation in the population.

What happens when the mating between two endangered animals is not successful? Many of the procedures used to help human couples who have fertility problems have also been used with animals. One early step in discovering why a female cannot become pregnant is to analyze the semen of her partner. Most males produce millions of sperm each day; however, not all the sperm are healthy enough to fertilize an egg. What might make one sample of semen less able to fertilize an egg than another? You will conduct an assessment of the fertility of two male animals — a tiger and a cheetah — in the next investigation.

Biotechnology used in captive-breeding programs may help to increase numbers of endangered species in zoos and reserves, but the goal of such programs is to return endangered species to their natural habitats. This means that there must be enough suitable habitat remaining in the wild to support these plants and animals. The discovery of biomedically important plants and animals may help to identify habitat in need of preservation.

Assessing Breeding Potential

Think About It

Imagine you are assisting Dr. Karen Goodrowe, head reproductive physiologist at the Metro Toronto Zoo. The zoo is considering either Tonghua, a male tiger, or Chuma, a male cheetah, for an international breeding program. Your job is to assess and recommend which of the two animals will be the best candidate for the program.

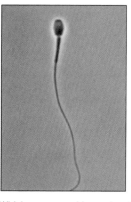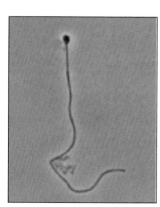

Which sperm would you classify as normal and which as abnormal? What criteria did you use to make your classification?

Data for Samples of Sperm Taken From Two Endangered Cats

Variable	Tiger (Tonghua)	Cheetah (Chuma)
percent sperm moving actively	95	75
percent normal sperm	80	28
sperm concentration (millions/mL)	125	5

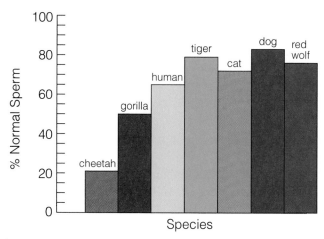

Percent normal sperm in selected mammals

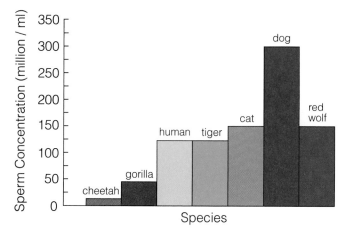

Normal sperm concentration in selected mammals

What to Do

1 Compare the percentage of actively moving sperm for each animal. Record which has the highest percentage. How might this influence successful fertilization?

2 Compare the percent of normal sperm in each cat's sample to the percent of normal sperm for the cat's species. Is either animal above or below the normal amounts?

3 Compare the sperm concentration for each cat to the normal sperm concentration for its species. Do both animals have enough sperm to fertilize an egg?

Analyze

1. Write a report for Dr. Goodrowe recommending which animal is likely to be more successful in the breeding program. Use the results of your analysis to support your conclusion.

2. Based on your investigation, what conclusions can you draw about the relative ability of each cat to reproduce?

Across Canada

Sara Iverson

January is seal-milking time for Dr. Sara Iverson of Halifax's Dalhousie University. She heads for Sable Island off the coast of Nova Scotia. This windswept sandy spit is home to one of the world's largest colonies of mammoth grey seals. From Sable Island, mammoth grey seals roam as far as Newfoundland and the Gulf of St. Lawrence. However, when it's time for their pups to be born, they always return to the island of their birth. Mammoth grey seals, like humans, are mammals and feed their offspring milk. Seal milk is very rich: 60% fat, compared with 4% fat in human milk. The hungry seal pups gorge themselves on milk, gaining up to 60 kg in about two weeks. If humans ate such a diet, their arteries would clog and they would develop heart disease. Yet seals never have heart trouble. Does seal milk contain a special ingredient that protects against heart disease? Could an understanding of seals' bodies help prevent heart disease in humans? These are among the many questions Sara and her colleagues hope to answer.

Sara Iverson, left, with her husband and fellow researcher Don Bowen and colleague Jo-Ann Mellish take a small sample of milk from a mother seal.

Where Do We Go From Here?

Biotechnology is a good example of how science, technology, society, and the environment interact. The food you eat, the treatment of disease, the well-being of your children, and the environment in which you live will all be determined by what happens in this field. This chapter contained some examples of discoveries and innovations that have not yet been approved by society as a whole. Many factors will influence the future of biotechnology. Decisions that you and others will make depend on a clear understanding of the science and technology involved, as well as on people's most deeply held beliefs.

Check Your Understanding

1. What is bioremediation?

2. Where do scientist look for organisms that can break down toxic wastes?

3. What bacterium is used as a pesticide?

4. How can plants be used to remove heavy metals from the environment?

5. How is biotechnology used to determine the genetic diversity of endangered species?

6. **Apply** What are some of the advantages of using *in vitro* fertilization for breeding programs in zoos?

7. **Thinking Critically** Why are pesticides harmful to birds at or near the top of the food chain?

Now that you have completed this chapter, try to do the following. If you cannot, go back to the sections indicated.

Describe how early forms of biotechnology were used to produce food. (4.1)

Describe the structure of a DNA molecule. (4.2)

Explain the importance of proteins in the structure and function of living things. (4.2)

Explain how the formation of proteins is determined by DNA. (4.2)

Describe the causes and possible effects of mutations. (4.2)

Describe how DNA can be transferred from one organism to another. (4.2)

Explain cloning and some of the bioethical issues that arise from this technology. (4.2)

Explain karyotype and how it can be used to diagnose genetic disorders. (4.3)

Describe gene therapy and explain its possible applications. (4.3)

Explain the Human Genome Project and why it is important for our understanding of human genetics. (4.3)

Explain transgenic organisms and why such organisms are important. (4.3)

Explain why the formation of herbicide-resistant crops is important to Canadian agriculture. (4.4)

Describe how Canola was formed and the various uses of this crop. (4.4)

Describe how the addition of specific genes into fish has aided acquaculture. (4.4)

Describe the risks and benefits of using Bovine Growth Hormone. (4.4)

Explain what bioremediation is and what its purpose is. (4.5)

Describe the hazards of using pesticides and how these hazards might be overcome by biotechnology. (4.5)

Describe the effects of oil spills on natural ecosystems and the use of bioremediation in clean-up efforts. (4.5)

Explain the importance of biodiversity and describe some of the ways that biotechnology is being used to protect endangered species. (4.5)

Prepare Your Own Summary

Summarize the chapter by doing one of the following. Use a graphic organizer (such as a concept map), produce a poster, or write the summary to include the key chapter concepts. Here are a few ideas to use as a guide:
- Explain biotechnology and how it is different from previous technologies.
- Explain why the new technologies are used.
- Describe how the new technologies accomplish their objectives.
- Copy the diagram into your notebook and label it.

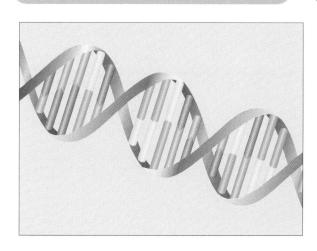

Reviewing Key Terms

If you need to review, the section numbers show you where these terms were introduced.

1. In your notebook, match the description in column A with the correct term in column B.

A	B
• the molecule that controls life	• bioremediation (4.5)
• a transgenic goat	• gene (4.2)
• three DNA bases	• somatic (4.2)
• not a sex cell	• DNA (4.1)
• the sequence of bases on a set of chromosomes	• hormone (4.3)
• a section of DNA that makes a protein	• clone (4.2)
• a genetic duplicate	• herbicide (4.4)
• a molecule that controls bodily functions	• transgenic (4.2)
• a chemical that kills weeds	• codon (4.2)
• an organism that contains the gene of a different species	• toxic (4.5)
• using micro-organisms to clean up pollution	• Willow (4.3)
• a deadly chemical	• genome (4.3)
	• amino acid (4.2)
	• inbreeding (4.5)

2. What is genetic engineering? (4.2)

3. What are the different types of mutations and how can they affect an organism? (4.2)

4. What is recombinant DNA? (4.2)

Understanding Key Concepts

Section numbers are provided if you need to review.

5. Some parts of a cell cannot be used for DNA fingerprinting. What part of a cell must be present? (4.2)

6. Explain the relationship between DNA, genes, and chromosomes. (4.2)

7. What are the names of the four nucleotides found in a molecule of DNA and which ones pair with each other? (4.2)

8. What is a DNA molecule made of? (4.2)

9. Describe the process of taking a piece of DNA from one organism and putting it into a bacterium. (4.2)

10. How can a karyotype be used to determine the gender of a person? (4.3)

11. What are the advantages of having bacteria produce human proteins such as insulin? (4.3)

12. What are two advantages of using biotechnology to alter crop plants? (4.4)

13. Why does monoculture pose a problem? (4.4)

14. What are the advantages of bioremediation over other forms of cleaning up toxic waste? (4.5)

15. How can researchers determine whether or not two animals are too closely related to breed? (4.5)

Developing Skills

16. Make a Venn diagram (two overlapping circles) showing the relationship between selective breeding and genetic engineering. In the overlapping area of the circles, write the things the two have in common. In the areas that do not overlap, write the things that are different.

17. Copy the following diagram and label the corresponding bases (A, T, C, or G) in the right side of the DNA molecule.

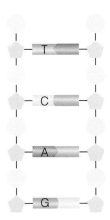

18. The human genome contains approximately 3 000 000 000 bases. If each of the bases (A, T, C, or G) is like a letter in an instruction manual, how many pages long would that manual have to be? Hint: Count the number of letters on five randomly selected lines of this textbook. Determine the average number of letters per line. Count the number of lines on each page and calculate the number of pages that would be required.

Problem Solving

19. Dolly the sheep was cloned at an agricultural research station. What would be the advantages of using cloned animals in farming?

20. Describe how DNA can be used to solve crimes.

21. Herbicide-resistant genes are usually selected to resist specific herbicides. Why would it be advantageous for a company to produce both the genetically altered seed and the herbicide?

22. Factories sometimes release toxic wastes in very low concentrations. Explain why these wastes may still be dangerous to people and other organisms.

Critical Thinking

23. Defend or reject this statement: "The functions of human liver cells are controlled by DNA, but the growth of plant leaf cells is not."

24. The gene for Human Growth Hormone has been added to bacteria, which produce the hormone in quantity relatively cheaply. What problems might this create?

25. Work on the Human Genome Project is very expensive and involves many of the best scientists in the world. However, many people believe the project is a mistake. Why do you think this is so?

26. Where would you look for an "anti-freeze" gene for fish?

27. Why is it important to prevent contamination of DNA extract?

Pause & Reflect

1. Did any of the technologies described in this chapter make you feel uncomfortable? Do you think that biotechnology should be controlled? If so, how?

2. How can governments control biotechnology when it is changing so quickly?

Ask an Expert

Brown eyes, curly hair — these and other characteristics are traits determined by your genes. Your genes carry hereditary information passed on to you by your parents' DNA. Genes determine many characteristics, including ones that can cause serious health problems. David Macgregor understands a great deal about the field of genetics. He translates his technical knowledge into practical information for patients who want to know how their personal genetic make-up may affect them and their family.

Q What sort of patients do you counsel?

A We see patients of all ages for many different reasons. People who have a family member with a genetic disorder often come to us to find out if they might develop that disorder or pass it on to a future generation. If an adult has been diagnosed with a disease that can be hereditary — early-onset breast cancer, for example — we may meet with other members of the extended family who might be at risk for the disease. That helps relatives decide if they want to be tested to see if they carry the gene.

Sometimes we see patients because they have growing children who have a health or developmental problem that doctors have not been able to diagnose. We help a geneticist assess the family and the medical information to see if the problem could have a genetic cause.

Q How do you figure out the chances of a particular disorder?

A First, I get information from the patient. When I meet with a couple who are thinking of having a child, I ask about each family's medical history and who in the family has a suspected genetic

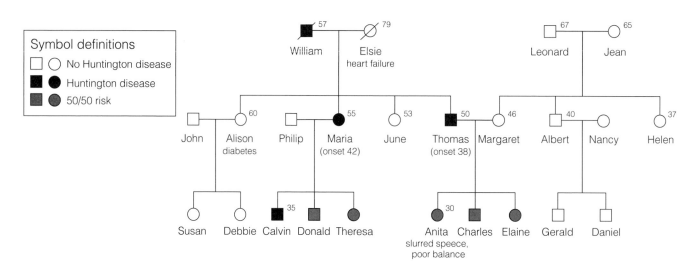

Symbol definitions
- ☐ ○ No Huntington disease
- ■ ● Huntington disease
- ▦ 50/50 risk

William 57
Elsie 79
heart failure

Leonard 67
Jean 65

John | Alison 60
diabetes
Philip | Maria 55
(onset 42)
June 53
Thomas 50 | Margaret
(onset 38)
Albert 40 | Nancy
Helen 37

Susan | Debbie | Calvin 35 | Donald | Theresa
Anita 30 | Charles | Elaine | Gerald | Daniel
slurred speece,
poor balance

Huntington's disease is a condition characterized by impairment of the nervous system. Symptoms do not appear until adulthood. Each child of an affected parent has a 50/50 chance of developing the disease (individuals marked in red). This happens because the child receives half of its genetic information from one parent and half from the other. Long before symptoms appear, tests can be done to find out if a person has the Huntington gene. However, many people prefer not to know whether they have the gene.

disorder. Those facts and the pattern in how the disorder is inherited help me determine the chances that this couple's child would have that disorder.

Q What sort of genetic disorders are we talking about?

A Down syndrome, cystic fibrosis, spina bifida, Huntington's disease, to name just a few. If someone in the family has one of these disorders, a child in a future generation is sometimes, but not always, more at risk for it. My job is to figure out whether the odds of this couple having a child affected by the disorder are higher than the odds are for other couples. I explain the risk and give parents the information they need to make informed decisions about family planning, further testing, and so on.

Q What kind of tests can be done?

A A blood test is one example. Looking at the DNA extracted from a blood sample, a technologist can tell if that person is a carrier of a disease, such as sickle cell anemia or cystic fibrosis. If the expectant parents are both carriers, one or both of them may decide to have another test, amniocentesis. During amniocentesis, a doctor withdraws some amniotic fluid from the mother's uterus. Using the cells in that fluid, technicians analyze the DNA of the fetus to determine the presence or absence of the disease.

Amniocentesis is also a choice for pregnant women over the age of 35, whose babies are more likely to have chromosome problems. Technologists look at the chromosomes of fetal cells from the amniotic fluid. An extra copy of chromosome 21 means the baby will have Down syndrome; an extra chromosome 18 indicates Edwards' syndrome, and so on.

Q What happens when the test results come back?

A We give the patient as much information as we can. Sometimes the results are very reassuring. Other times, the results mean facing some difficult decisions. A large part of my job is just to listen and help the patients deal with their situation. We review their options and provide support, but never make their decisions for them.

Q How important is knowledge of genetics in your work?

A It is essential. What I learned doing my Bachelor of Science degree in genetics and my Master's degree in genetic counselling isn't enough, though. Advances in technology and research occur almost every day. New genes are discovered, new tests developed. I attend lectures and read medical journals to keep up with the changes.

Science isn't the whole story in my job, though. I spend a lot of time each day talking with people and helping them cope. That's as important to me as the science.

EXPLORING Further

Making Choices

A genetic counsellor can provide scientific information about the chances that a child will inherit a particular genetic disorder from his/her parents. This is an estimate of the risk that a disorder will be present and does not mean that the child will or will not have the disease. What other factors would help prospective parents in deciding whether or not to have children? For instance, what is the severity of the genetic disorder in question? Would special accommodations have to be made to care for a child with a certain genetic disorder? Some genetic disorders are evident at birth while others establish themselves later in life.

What factors would you consider important in deciding whether or not to have children if you or a family member were affected with an inherited disorder? Whom would you consult for information — another family member or counsellor, individuals with children affected by a genetic disorder, for example? How would you weigh, or assess, the information provided by these individuals? Prepare an outline of your position on this issue. Discuss the various options with members of your class.

A SIMULATION

Genetically Altered Foods

Think About It

Tomatoes have a relatively short shelf life. The tomatoes that you buy in supermarkets are nearly always harvested before they are ripe. Thus, they arrive in stores before they have begun to deteriorate. However, tomatoes that are harvested early do not have the same delicious taste as do vine-ripened ones.

In 1994, a new genetically altered tomato was developed that would remain ripe seven to ten days longer than normal tomatoes. Therefore, farmers could allow tomatoes to ripen on the vine because they would remain fresh during transport to supermarkets.

Genetic engineering of certain species of plants and animals can make food production and processing easier and more profitable. However, many people are concerned about the genetic manipulation of our food supplies. They cite potential problems such as:

- the development of new allergies in humans
- "counterfeit" freshness
- unpredictable gene interactions
- diminished nutritional quality
- environmental problems caused by altered organisms
- ethical issues associated with transgenics

In response to concerns such as these, a public commission has been organized to study whether the genetically altered tomatoes should be allowed into Canada.

Plan and Act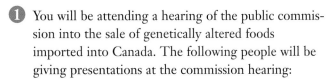

1 You will be attending a hearing of the public commission into the sale of genetically altered foods imported into Canada. The following people will be giving presentations at the commission hearing:

The Minister of Agriculture
A health food store owner
The owner of a large grocery store chain
A consumer
An environmentalist
A lawyer
A farmer
A scientist

2 What do you think each person's point of view might be before the commission hearing?

3 Your teacher will give your group the role of one of these people. As a group, discuss the issue, gather information, and formulate your point of view. One group member will make the presentation.

4 As a class, prepare a commission report summarizing the various positions and setting forth formal recommendations regarding the sale of genetically altered tomatoes in Canada.

Analyze

In a debriefing session after the simulation, consider the following questions:

1. What information, if any, do you think was missing from the presentations?

2. What other points of view, if any, might have been included in the commission hearing?

3. Did the participants seem to think that the risks of importing genetically altered tomatoes outweighed the benefits, or vice versa?

4. Was it difficult to reach a consensus in terms of commission recommendations? Explain your answer.

5. Did your group feel comfortable with its role and with the commission's recommendations? Explain your answer.

Secret Faces

Artificial codes, such as written language, braille, bar codes, sign language, and Morse code, have been used throughout human history. In this unit, you learned how the genetic code is responsible for determining how an organism is built and what physical traits it will have to distinguish it from other organisms of the same species. In this project, you will have the opportunity to put these two ideas together.

Challenge

In a small group, create a secret code that can be used to identify any person in a crowd, based on a set of facial or other physical features. Make a poster to present and explain your code.

Materials

art supplies and/or computer (for transmitting the code)
drawing paper and markers (for the poster)

Design Criteria

A. Your code should be based mainly on the facial features of the people in your class (other characteristics, such as approximate height and gender, can be used as well). You can use a written, pictorial, or gesture-based code, or a different system of your own.

B. Your code should have a set of rules, simple enough to learn and use easily, but not so obvious that the code can be guessed without knowing the rules.

C. Your poster should include the rules for your code and the symbols or code words that represent the different physical traits. Also include a brief explanation of how the code should be executed and interpreted. You could use a sketch or photograph of a face, with labels that help explain your code.

Plan and Construct

1. In your group, brainstorm on the facial features and other physical traits that can be used to identify a person in your class. Include as many as you can, as well as the possible varieties of each one.

2. After brainstorming, choose about ten to fifteen traits that can be used to identify someone readily. Some traits might only have one possibility. For example, eyeglasses are present or absent. Other traits, such as hair colour, might have more than one possibility.

3. Decide on a code system. You may want to research some well-known codes to help you generate ideas. Develop the code symbols, words, or gestures for your code. Record these in a table or chart. Give your code system a name.

4. Write out the rules of how to use and read your code. Each group member should learn the code and use it to see if it works. Fix any "bugs" in your code, or expand your code to make it more specific.

5. Prepare your poster. Be prepared to present or demonstrate your code system to the class.

Evaluate

1. To test your code system, one person in your group is secretly given the name of a student in the class who is to be identified. He or she should use the code that your group developed to "tell" the others in the group who it is. Did it work? How quickly did the group members guess?

2. Teach the class the code. Is your code too complicated for other students to understand easily how to use it?

3. Consider the codes developed by the other groups. How were they similar? How were they different? Which one worked the fastest? Which one was the easiest to learn? Now that you have seen other codes, how might you change yours to make it better?

4. Think about whether your code would reflect family resemblances. Could you use it to guess whether two unknown subjects might be closely related?

Now that you have completed Chapters 1, 2, 3, and 4, you can assess how much you have learned about reproduction by answering the following questions. Before you begin, you may find it useful to return to each Chapter at a Glance and to each Chapter Review.

True/False

In your notebook, indicate whether each statement is true or false. Correct each false statement.

1. Organs are the basic units of structure and function in all organisms.

2. Most mammals can reproduce asexually.

3. Meiosis can occur only in somatic cells.

4. Birds, like frogs, reproduce through external fertilization.

5. Canola is a crop plant that has been developed in the last 30 years.

6. Genetic engineering and selective breeding both involve direct manipulation of the DNA molecule.

Completion

In your notebook, complete each statement with the correct term or phrase.

7. Skin and bone cells undergo ▓▓▓▓▓ to repair injured tissue.

8. Moulds can reproduce asexually through reproductive cells called ▓▓▓▓▓ .

9. Fertilization occurs when male and female ▓▓▓▓▓ meet and join to produce a zygote.

10. Estrogen affects the uterus by causing a ▓▓▓▓▓ of its lining.

11. Chromosomes are made of a compound called ▓▓▓▓▓ and are found in a cell's nucleus.

12. ▓▓▓▓▓ are short sections of DNA that contain the instructions for the individual characteristics of an organism.

Matching

13. In your notebook, copy the descriptions in column A. Beside each number, write the term from column B that best fits the description. A term may be used once, more than once, or not at all.

A	B
• making a copy of the cell's DNA	• mitosis
• chromosomes align across the middle of the cell	• insulin
• threads of fungal filaments	• hyphae
• the process that doubles the number of chromosomes in a nucleus	• mutation
• an animal that contains both male and female gonads	• estrogen
• a spontaneous error that occurs during chromosome replication	• anaphase
• chemical messengers in the body	• hermaphrodite
• stimulates egg cell development	• metaphase
• a hormone that regulates blood sugar	• hormones
	• replication
	• conjugation
	• testosterone

Multiple Choice

In your notebook, write the letter of the best answer for each of the following questions.

14. All living things
    (a) take in nutrients
    (b) respond to changes in surroundings
    (c) eliminate wastes
    (d) all of the above
    (e) a and c only

15. The cell organelle that holds the master instructions to assemble proteins is the
    (a) nucleolus
    (b) mitochondrion
    (c) ribosome
    (d) nucleus
    (e) vacuole

16. The formation of a new individual with identical genetic information as the parent is called
    (a) unicellular reproduction
    (b) regeneration
    (c) *Acetabularia* reproduction
    (d) asexual reproduction
    (e) sexual reproduction

17. Which one of the following is not a flower part?
    (a) stamen
    (b) spore
    (c) pistil
    (d) sepal
    (e) stigma

18. Which condition is not necessary for external fertilization to occur?
    (a) both parents travelling to the same location
    (b) a watery environment
    (c) the production of many eggs
    (d) the sperm and eggs must be of the same species
    (e) all of the above are necessary for external fertilization to occur

19. Which statement below is true about sexual reproduction?
    (a) only one parent is required
    (b) less energy is require than for asexual reproduction
    (c) genetic variability increases
    (d) reproduction occurs by mitosis
    (e) all of the above are true

20. Changes in the levels of which hormones start the birth process?
    (a) FSH and oxytocin
    (b) Oxytocin and progesterone
    (c) Estrogen and LH
    (d) Progesterone and FSH

21. How many chromosomes are found in a human somatic cell?
    (a) 11
    (b) 23
    (c) 34
    (d) 46

22. The organisms used in bioremediation are
    (a) producers
    (b) consumers
    (c) decomposers
    (d) autotrophs

23. The purpose of DNA replication is
    (a) to make a cell grow larger
    (b) to replace old, worn out DNA
    (c) for growth and repair of an organism
    (d) for organizing extra DNA parts into useful form

Short Answer

In your notebook, write a sentence or a short paragraph to answer each of the following questions.

24. What event is taking place in the diagram below? Briefly describe what is occurring in each of the steps shown.

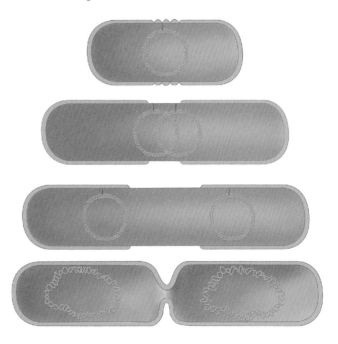

25. Briefly explain how you could experimentally determine which of the cell organelles controls cell function.

26. What is the purpose of mitosis?

27. Why must the number of chromosomes in sex cells be reduced?

28. At menopause, estrogen levels drop.
    (a) Describe the effect on the ovarian follicle.
    (b) Describe the effect on the uterine lining.

29. In the male, over 300 million sperm may be produced at one time, compared with a female's production of only one egg approximately every 28 days. Suggest an explanation for this difference.

30. Why is Canola oil considered to be better for you than other oils such as peanut or corn oil?

31. Why are heavy metals dangerous?

32. Infer how a change in an amino acid sequence could affect the cell or organism in which it occurs.

33. Suggest three advantages for cloning a food crop or food animal. Suggest three disadvantages. Explain.

Problem Solving

Show complete solutions for all problems that involve equations and numbers. Use the GRASP problem-solving model or a model suggested by your teacher.

34. During germination, the young plant parts inside the seed begin to grow. Explain why water is one of the most important requirements for germination to begin?

35. How does sexual reproduction reduce the chance that individuals of a species will be killed by a disease?

36. Suggest some of the problems that could arise in the developing fetus if the mother is inadequately nourished. Name a specific substance that is needed for the development of a skeleton. What do you think could happen if the supply of that substance was inadequate?

37. What technique was used to develop the dog breeds shown in the photograph below? Why would people want to develop certain varieties of animals or plants? What is required to maintain these varieties?

38. Oil spills in the arctic can be much more damaging to the environment than oil spills that occur in more temperate areas. Can you explain why the natural processes that break down oil occur more slowly in the Arctic?

39. How many chromosomes are present in a somatic cell of an animal with a haploid number of 38?

40. A mutation that results in faster growth of a plant could be advantageous. Explain why.

41. Suggest some reasons for human infertility. What are some possible treatments?

Critical Thinking

42. Propose a theory that explains why bacteria, protists, fungi and some invertebrates reproduce most often asexually, while most vertebrates never reproduce this way. How could you test your theory?

43. Seeds are an important food source for birds and many small animals. Where is the "food" stored in a seed, and why do seeds need a food source?

44. In Chapter 3, you learned that there is a relationship between survival rate for females and the number of offspring produced.
   (a) What is that relationship?
   (b) Suggest reasons for that relationship.

45. One of the stated objectives of zoos and wildlife preserves is the protection of endangered species. However, many people believe that keeping animals in captivity is wrong. Is it better to let animals become extinct in their natural habitat or to save them in the basically unnatural habitat of zoos and preserves?

Applications

46. As part of a research team, you have been asked to develop a new variety of grass that only has to be mowed once or twice a year. How would you approach this problem? What investigations would you carry out?

47. What is a hybrid plant? Research how horticulturists and botanists produce hybrids, for what reasons, and how hybrids reproduce.

48. What is a transgenic animal? Describe how transgenic animals can be used to produce human products?

Atoms and Elements

The science of aerodynamics enabled the Wright brothers to build and fly the first airplane in 1903, but they used only very basic materials for their pioneering craft. To build a modern airplane, which can carry passengers safely at hundreds of kilometres per hour, requires a highly sophisticated science of materials.

For most of human history, scientists were able to construct only simple mental models to explain the nature of matter. In recent times, however, far more complex and accurate theories have been developed. The properties of many unusual metals are now so well understood that manufacturers in the aerospace industry know exactly which metals, in which combinations, to use for light yet strong airframes and for high-quality electrical wiring in electrical control systems. The industrial refining of carbon-based fuels, and the chemistry of their combustion in turboprop and jet engines, are also of crucial importance to the design of modern aircraft.

How did the modern scientific understanding of matter develop? What technologies, in Canada and around the world, have arisen as a result of this scientific development? How does the study of chemical substances in laboratories translate into practical uses for these substances? In this unit, you will discover some of the answers to these questions, as you follow the observations, inferences, and models of atomic and chemical structure that link ancient Greek philosophy to modern nuclear chemistry.

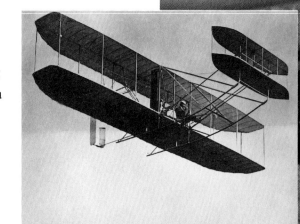

Unit Contents

5 Properties and

Opening Ideas...

- Does a glass of milk have more in common with a glass of water or with a steel girder?

- Is melting ice the same kind of change as burning paper?

- How do scientists know the formula of water is H_2O?

Science Log

In your Science Log, show what you think the particles of a pure substance, such as water, look like. Then make a sketch to illustrate your understanding of a mixture of water and, for example, salt. Finally, what do you think happens when a substance like water is involved in a chemical change? As you study this chapter, you will learn about substances, their composition, and the changes they may undergo.

The chemistry laboratories we see in modern films and television programs often look like the laboratory in the large photograph above. But much of what we know about matter today was discovered in laboratories that were far less advanced or complex, with simple equipment, as in the small sketch. Some early chemists had private sources of funding, so they could hire metalworkers and glass blowers to make specialized equipment. Many were poor, however, and used whatever materials were at hand to make their own equipment. Even with this homemade equipment, they were able to make

important discoveries to further the understanding of matter.

It is important to realize that balances, beakers, and other laboratory equipment are *technology* — tools that help us control or manipulate matter so we can observe its properties and behaviour. The *science* of chemistry lies in making the observations and interpreting the results.

In this chapter, you will explore properties of matter and changes in matter by using the science of chemistry to observe and explain. You will also learn some facts about matter that scientists have discovered and some theories that they have developed to explain these facts.

Changes

Key Concepts

In this chapter, you will discover

- how matter is described and classified
- what changes in matter show that a physical or a chemical change has occurred
- why there are different types of mixtures
- who contributed to the development of chemistry as a science and to our understanding of matter
- how simple tests and careful measurements of certain properties help to identify pure substances

Key Skills

In this chapter, you will

- perform investigations using appropriate safety and disposal procedures
- make quantitative and qualitative observations of chemical substances
- distinguish between physical and chemical properties and changes
- perform tests to identify hydrogen, oxygen, and carbon dioxide
- use an electric current to decompose water

Key Terms

- particle theory of matter
- scientific model
- heterogeneous
- homogeneous
- solution
- mechanical mixture
- physical change
- chemical change
- physical property
- density
- combustibility
- chemical property
- precipitate
- qualitative physical property
- quantitative physical property
- solvent
- solute
- alloy
- suspension
- colloid
- Tyndall effect
- compound
- philosopher
- alchemist
- electrolysis
- law of conservation of mass
- law of definite proportions
- Dalton's atomic theory
- element
- atom

What's in the Bag?

How can you tell when a chemical change is taking place?

What You Need

resealable plastic sandwich bag
empty camera film canister with close-fitting lid
scoopula with about 2 mL baking soda
enough "white" vinegar to fill the canister
50 mL water   paper towel

What to Do

1. Pour 50 mL of water into the open bag. The bag should now stand up by itself.

2. Using the scoopula, tap a *few* grains of solid baking soda into the water. Mix the bag *gently* until all of the solid has dissolved. Add a *few* more grains, and mix again. Continue adding the solid until it no longer dissolves.

3. Fill the canister with vinegar. Put on the lid tightly. Wipe off any spilled vinegar. Carefully lower the canister into the bag. Squeeze as much air out of the bag as you can, and then seal it.

4. Working through the walls of the bag, carefully snap the lid off the canister so the vinegar can mix with the solution. Look for any changes in the bag's appearance.

What Did You Discover?

1. List the starting materials, and describe their properties. (Remember, any feature that can be used to describe or identify matter can be called a property.)

2. Note what happened to the starting materials, and describe any changes that you observed in them and in the bag. Also note any new materials that were produced.

5.1 Exploring the Nature of Matter

Questioning, sceptical, persistent, honest — these are characteristics of a good scientist. A good scientist also respects the body of knowledge that has been built up over the centuries through the work of other scientists. Our knowledge of chemistry includes facts and observations about matter, laws that summarize patterns of behaviour in matter, and theories that explain the patterns of behaviour. For example, you may recall the **particle theory of matter** from your earlier studies. This theory is summarized below.

The Particle Theory of Matter

* All matter is made up of extremely tiny particles.
* Each pure substance has its own kind of particle, different from the particles of other pure substances.
* Particles attract each other.
* Particles are always moving.
* Particles at a higher temperature move faster on average than particles at a lower temperature.

Skill
P O W E R

For more information about scientfic models, turn to page 595.

The particle theory of matter is one example of a **scientific model**. Scientific models help scientists to picture, in an imaginative way, processes in nature that cannot simply or directly be seen. For example, in the particle theory of matter, the individual particles would be far too small and fast-moving to be observed directly. But you can use the first two parts of the theory to imagine how particles might make up substances that can be seen, and the other three parts to explain properties like the cohesiveness of matter and how it behaves when temperature changes occur.

Pause&
Reflect

Based on the particle theory, draw simple sketches in your Science Log to illustrate the following:

* evaporation of water from a puddle
* solidification of hot liquid lava on a mountainside
* a cold lake
* a hot bath

Figure 5.1A In gases, the particles have enough energy to overcome attractive forces that would hold them together.

Figure 5.1B The particles of a liquid do not have enough energy to overcome all attractive forces, but they do have enough energy to move around each other.

Figure 5.1C Solids are made up of particles that do not have enough energy to move from one place to another.

In your earlier studies of science, you have likely learned that matter can be classified according to its state: a solid, a liquid, or a gas. As well, you may have learned that it can be classified according to one of its properties: **heterogeneous** or **homogeneous**. Lastly, you may have been introduced to the idea of classifying matter according to its composition: a mixture or a pure substance. Figure 5.2 shows one way to classify matter, using some of these ideas.

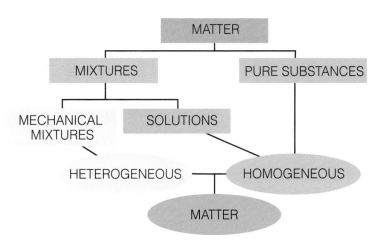

Figure 5.2 Read the chart from top to bottom. How is matter classified? Can you see what the different colours mean?

What the Particle Theory of Matter Explains

Many of the classification systems that have been developed by scientists are based on theories. The particle theory of matter explains why pure substances are always homogeneous — because each pure substance contains its own unique kind of particle. In contrast, mixtures contain at least two kinds of particles. If the particles are uniformly scattered, the mixture is a homogeneous **solution**. If the particles are not uniformly scattered, the mixture is a heterogeneous **mechanical mixture**.

The classification chart in Figure 5.2 is based on the particle theory. It is important to realize, however, that there is more than one way to classify matter. In this unit, you will see other ways that chemists classify thousands of different pure substances and the millions of different mixtures containing them.

Changes in Matter

Every kind of matter has properties. Some of these properties, such as the strength of the ice on a pond or the smooth surface of writing paper, can be useful. Others, such as the taste of strongly chlorinated water, can be unpleasant.

Properties can be used to identify the kind of matter. Properties can and do change, however. Ice may melt and lose its ability to support skaters. Paper may burn and become useless for writing. Chlorinated water, left overnight, may lose its unpleasant taste.

Chemists classify changes in matter into two categories: physical changes and chemical changes. During a **physical change,** no new substance is formed. New properties may appear, but the particles of the starting substance or substances are not changed. Ice melting is an example of a physical change. The new properties are temporary, for a change of state can be reversed. The liquid water can easily be converted into solid ice again.

The unpleasant taste of the chlorinated water is also the result of a physical change. The taste is caused by chlorine

Figure 5.3 This hockey player can move quickly over the ice because the ice melts under the pressure of the skate blades and reduces friction. The melted ice resolidifies quickly on the sheet of ice.

Figure 5.4 How is the change shown in this picture different from the change shown in Figure 5.3? Which change is physical, and which is chemical? How do you know?

dissolved in the water. If the solution stands overnight, it separates and most of the dissolved chlorine escapes. The chlorine particles still exist, with all of their properties unchanged, but they are now dissolved in the surrounding air instead of being dissolved in the water.

In contrast, a **chemical change** always causes at least one new substance, with new properties, to be formed. A chemical change may be difficult or impossible to reverse. Burning paper is an example of a chemical change. The smoke that escapes and the black solid that is left behind cannot be recombined again to form paper — the change cannot be reversed.

Science Inquiry

A Classification Puzzle

Classification is just as important to chemistry students as it is to professional chemists. This activity will help you brush up on your classification skill by classifying several samples of matter according to the system in Figure 5.2.

What You Need

8 vials containing unidentified mixtures or pure substances (provided by your teacher)
Appendix D: Properties of Common Substances (page 564)

What to Do

1. Copy the table below to record your observations and inferences. Give your table a title.

Vial Number	Observations	Probable Classification	Reasons for Classification	Probable Identity

2. Your teacher will give you eight vials that contain unidentified samples. Three vials will contain mechanical mixtures, three will have pure substances, and two will have solutions. Inspect the contents of each vial visually. *Do not open the vials!* Record your observations.

3. Examine the following list: calcium carbonate (chalk, crushed), carbon (graphite), copper (II) sulfate (bluestone), glycerol (glycerine), iron (filings), rock salt, sugar, vegetable oil, water, zinc (mossy). The vials contain only materials

in this list, but some vials may contain two of the materials.

4. Using your observations, classify each sample as homogeneous or heterogeneous. The heterogeneous samples are mechanical mixtures. Determine a probable identity for each substance in each mechanical mixture using observation and Appendix D. Record your ideas.

5. You now have five vials that are unidentified. These vials contain homogeneous materials. Using Appendix D and your observations, find the three pure substances. Determine a probable identity for each pure substance, and record your ideas.

6. The remaining two vials contain solutions. Again use your observations and Appendix D to determine a probable identity for each substance in each solution, and record your ideas.

What Did You Discover?

1. How are solutions different from mechanical mixtures? What similarities do they have?

2. Which vials contained materials that were difficult to classify? Why?

Extension

3. Examine some bottles and jars in your refrigerator at home. Classify what the bottles and jars contain as mixtures or pure substances. Which seem to be more common?

Properties: Chemical or Physical?

In building a craft like a space shuttle, NASA's aerospace engineers need to know everything about the materials used in its construction and how the materials might change. For example, will they melt in extreme heat, become brittle in the cold, or react with other materials? Understanding changes in matter depends on knowing the properties of matter. Chemists classify the properties to gain a better understanding of matter. Table 5.1 shows three properties of two pure substances: hydrogen and helium.

Table 5.1 Properties of Helium and Hydrogen

Property	Helium	Hydrogen
colour	colourless	colourless
density	low (0.18 g/L)	very low (0.09 g/L)
combustibility	does not burn	burns explosively

Any property that can be observed or measured without forming a new substance is a **physical property.** The colour of both helium and hydrogen can be observed without touching or changing either one. Therefore colour is a physical property. As you will recall from earlier studies, **density** is the amount of matter that occupies a certain space — it is the mass per unit volume of a substance. Density can be measured without forming a new substance, so density is also a physical property.

Suppose that you had two balloons: one filled with hydrogen, and the other filled with helium. How could you tell which was which? If you could see inside the balloons, both gases would be colourless, so you could not distinguish the gases by colour. Both balloons would float in air, since both gases have a low density. It would be very difficult for you to detect any difference in how well they floated, however, so knowing their densities would not help you much.

What if you unsealed each balloon and held a match to its neck? Only one gas would burn explosively, causing a new substance with entirely new properties to be formed: liquid water. The gas in the other balloon would not burn at all. The ability of a substance to burn in air is called **combustibility**.

Any property that describes how a substance reacts with another substance when forming a new substance is a **chemical property**. Combustibility is therefore a chemical property. Hydrogen burns in air, so it has the property of combustibility. Helium does not burn in air, so it does not have the property of combustibility. Knowing that something is not combustible is just as important as knowing that it is.

Tools of Science

To survive the fierce heat of re-entering Earth's atmosphere, the space shuttle uses a system of heat-resistant tiles. Made from silica and ceramic bonding materials, these tiles can be removed from an oven at 1200°C and put straight into cold water without cracking.

Figure 5.5 How could you tell if these balloons contained hydrogen or helium?

INVESTIGATION **5-A**

Chemical or Physical Change?

Physical changes do not alter the composition of matter, but chemical changes do. Without careful testing, you cannot always know for certain that a chemical change has occurred and a new substance has formed. You can, however, observe an experiment and look for evidence to make an inference about the kind of change. This is what you will do here.

Problem

What observations indicate that a chemical change has taken place?

Safety Precautions

- Wear your safety glasses and an apron.
- Always report spills of any chemical to your teacher.
- Handle all chemicals with care as they may be toxic, irritant, or corrosive.
- Hydrochloric acid is a caustic liquid. If any gets on your skin or clothes, rinse it off immediately with plenty of running water and tell your teacher.
- Copper (II) sulfate is a poison and an irritant. Wash your hands after using this chemical.
- Wash your hands thoroughly at the end of this investigation.

Part 1

Procedure

1 Make a table like the one below. Give your table a title. Keep it for Parts 2 to 8.

2 In this part of the investigation, photographs are used to show the experiment, as the chemicals involved are poisonous. If you do perform this part, be very careful when handling the chemicals and wash your hands thoroughly when done.

3 Observe and record the physical properties of each starting substance before mixing the substances together.

4 Record what happens after the substances are mixed. Underline key observations, which indicate that a chemical change may have taken place.

5 Record whether you think a physical or chemical change has taken place.

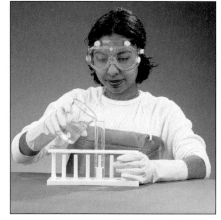

Pour 2 to 3 mL of lead (II) nitrate solution into a clean dry test tube.

Pour about the same quantity of potassium iodide into a second test tube.

(Photos for Part 1 continue on next page.)

Part of Investigation	Starting Substance	Physical Properties	Changes After Mixing (state, temperature, colour, quantity)	Physical or Chemical Change

Carefully pour the contents of one test tube into the other.

What do you see right away?

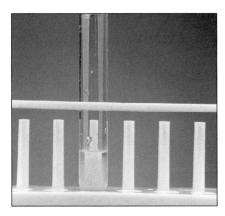
What do you see after a few minutes?

Depending on the time available, your teacher may ask you to do only a few parts of the rest of the investigation and share your findings with classmates who have done different parts.

Part 2

Apparatus
test tube
test tube rack
scoopula

Materials
dilute hydrochloric acid
calcium carbonate

Procedure

1. Pour about 4 to 5 mL of dilute hydrochloric acid into a clean, dry test tube. Record your observations in the table from Part 1. Hint: If a quantity is described as "about", you do not have to measure it. You can use an approximate amount. To approximate the volume of a substance, look at the test tube you will be using. If the opening is about 1 cm in diameter, then a depth of 1 cm corresponds to a volume of about 1 mL.

2. Use your scoopula to obtain a pea-sized sample of calcium carbonate. Record your observations.

3. Carefully add the calcium carbonate to the hydrochloric acid. Record your observations.

4. Dispose of the materials as directed by your teacher.

Part 3

Apparatus
test tube and stopper
test tube rack
scoopula

Materials
copper (II) sulfate
distilled water

Procedure

1. Using your scoopula, obtain a few crystals of copper (II) sulfate (read as "copper two sulfate"). Record your observations in the table from Part 1.

2. Pour about 5 mL of distilled water into a clean, dry test tube. Record your observations.

3. Add the copper (II) sulfate to the water, place a stopper in the test tube, and gently shake the test tube. Record your observations.

4. Save the test tube and the liquid in it for Parts 4 and 5 of this investigation.

Part 4

Apparatus

eye dropper
evaporating dish
ring clamp
wire gauze
Bunsen burner

Materials

liquid from Part 3

Procedure

1. Use an eye dropper to place two drops of the liquid from Part 3 in the evaporating dish. Record your observations in the table from Part 1.

2. Place the evaporating dish on the ring clamp and wire gauze. Heat it *gently* over a low Bunsen burner flame. **CAUTION:** Keep your face away from the liquid. It will spit as it dries.

3. Wash the evaporating dish when it is cool.

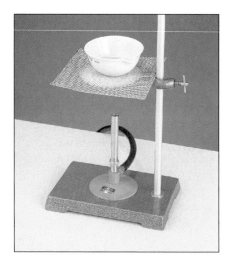

Part 5

Apparatus

test tube
test tube rack
tongs

Materials

liquid from Part 3
steel wool

Procedure

1. Examine the test tube and liquid from Part 3. Record your observations in the table from Part 1. Place the test tube in the rack.

2. Examine the steel wool, and record your observations. Using the tongs, pick up a piece of steel wool small enough to fit in the test tube.

3. Add the steel wool to the liquid in the test tube. Record your observations.

4. Dispose of the materials as directed by your teacher.

Part 6

Apparatus

test tube
test tube rack
scoopula

Materials

dilute hydrogen peroxide solution

manganese dioxide

Procedure

1. Pour 2 to 3 mL of hydrogen peroxide solution into a clean dry test tube. Record your observations in the table from Part 1.

2. Use your scoopula to obtain a small sample of manganese dioxide. Record your observations.

3. Carefully add the manganese dioxide to the hydrogen peroxide. Record your observations.

4. Dispose of the materials as directed by your teacher.

Part 7

Apparatus

test tube, test tube rack

Materials

dilute hydrochloric acid
2 cm piece of magnesium ribbon
steel wool

Procedure

1. Pour 4 to 5 mL of dilute hydrochloric acid into a clean, dry test tube. Record your observations in the table from Part 1. Clean the magnesium ribbon with the steel wool.

2. Carefully add the magnesium ribbon to the hydrochloric acid. Record your observations of the magnesium ribbon and what happens.

3. Dispose of the materials as directed by your teacher.

Part 8

Apparatus

3 test tubes   test tube rack
2 stoppers   scoopula

Materials

distilled water
calcium oxide
ammonium nitrate

Procedure

1. Pour about 4 mL of distilled water into each of three clean test tubes. The level of the water should be the same in all the test tubes. You will add substances to two of the test tubes. The third test tube will act as a control.

2. Using your scoopula, obtain a sample of calcium oxide. Record your observations in the table from Part 1.

3. Add the calcium oxide to one of the test tubes. Put a stopper in the test tube, and gently shake the test tube. Record your observations.

4. Clean the scoopula, and dry it thoroughly. Use it to obtain a similar quantity of ammonium nitrate. Record your observations.

5. Add the ammonium nitrate to the second test tube of water. Put a stopper in the test tube, and gently shake the test tube. Record your observations.

6. Compare the three test tubes, and record any differences.

7. Dispose of the materials as directed by your teacher.

Analyze

1. Compare your table with a classmate's table, and discuss the similarities and differences.

Conclude and Apply

2. What physical changes took place? What evidence supports your inference?

3. What chemical changes took place? What evidence supports your inference?

4. Describe what happens when potassium iodide is added to lead (II) nitrate. (A solid that is formed during a chemical change and settles out of solution is called a **precipitate**.)

5. What did you see when you added manganese dioxide to hydrogen peroxide? What might be happening? Explain your reasoning.

Extend Your Knowledge

6. Make a copy of the table below, and give your table a title. With a partner, review this chapter so far. Look for an example of a chemical change that fits each observation. Record the chemical changes in the second column. Now look for an example of a physical change that fits each observation. Record the physical changes in the third column.

Observation	Example of Chemical Change	Example of Physical Change
Bubbles are produced.	mixing baking soda and vinegar	water boiling
There is a colour change.		
The starting material is used up.		
Heat is produced or absorbed.		
A solid (precipitate) forms.		

7. Compare the observations listed in the first column of the table above with the kinds of changes you observed in this investigation. How are they similar? How are they different? Explain why it is difficult to make a list of simple rules that will let you classify a change as physical or chemical.

Word CONNECT

Have you encountered words like "ductility," "malleability," and "viscosity" before? If you have, can you write accurate definitions for them? Try to do so now, using a regular or science dictionary if you think you need help.

Table 5.2 classifies the chemical and physical properties that are most interesting to chemists. Note that physical properties are often further classified as either qualitative or quantitative. A **qualitative physical property** is a characteristic of a substance that can be described but not measured. A **quantitative physical property** is a characteristic of a substance that can be measured numerically.

Table 5.2 Classification of Properties

Chemical	Physical	
	Qualitative	Quantitative
reacts with water	colour	melting temperature
reacts with air	texture	boiling temperature
reacts with pure oxygen	taste	density
reacts with acids	smell	viscosity
reacts with other pure substances	state	solubility
toxicity	crystal shape	electrical conductivity
stability	malleability	heat conductivity
combustibility	ductility	

Copper reacts with substances in air to form a green coating that artists call *patina*.

Gold has the property of malleability, so it can be hammered into thin sheets and different shapes.

Sulfur will react with oxygen to form a new substance, sulfur dioxide.

Iron melts at the extremely high temperature of 1535°C.

Figure 5.6 The physical properties of different substances

A solid that is ductile can be stretched to form a wire.

Density by the Numbers

Chromium and silver are two metals with fairly similar appearances. Suppose that you had a sample of each and wanted to decide which was which. Since they have different melting points, you might decide to try melting one of the samples. Unfortunately the melting point of chromium is very high: 1907°C! Even silver has a melting point of 961°C. These temperatures are too high to achieve safely or practically in a laboratory. What about trying another property, density? A 1 cm cube of silver always has a mass of 10.5 g, while a 1 cm cube of chromium always has a mass of 7.2 g. Density can be a much more practical way to identify the samples.

Figure 5.7 Silver (left) and chromium (right) look very similar. How could you tell them apart?

You may have already met density as a qualitative concept, in the particle theory of matter. Density is also very useful as a quantitative physical property to measure. It is the same for any sample of a particular substance in solid or liquid form (except for very slight variations caused by temperature differences). Since different substances usually have different densities, measuring density can be a good way to identify them. You can look up the densities of various substances in Appendix D: Properties of Common Substances (page 564).

In order to measure density, you need to know that it is mathematically defined by the formula

$$\text{Density} = \frac{\text{Mass}}{\text{Volume}} \qquad \text{or} \qquad D = \frac{m}{V}$$

You can interpret this formula by saying that density measures how much mass is crowded into a given space. For example, a chunk of silver has a volume of 2.00 cm³ and a mass of 21.0 g. The density of silver is therefore

$$D \text{ (silver)} = \frac{21.0 \text{ g}}{2.00 \text{ cm}^3}$$

$$= 10.5 \text{ g/cm}^3$$

Substance X

Imagine that you are a chemical assayer (someone whose job is to identify chemical substances) who has been given a sample of what is claimed to be a "new metal," substance X. In fact, you suspect that this metal is not new at all, but a disguised sample of a very common metal. The pressure is on you to make a correct identification, because a new metal could be an extraordinarily valuable resource. As a first step, you decide to determine the density of the substance. If it matches the density of any of the metals in the table below, you could focus on that particular metal for further tests.

Densities of Some Common Metals

Metal	Density (g/cm^3)
lead	11.3
nickel	8.9
iron	7.9
tin	7.3
aluminum	2.7

Science Inquiry ACTIVITY

What You Need

unidentified metal cuboid (provided by your teacher)
ruler, marked off in centimetres and millimetres
balance
Appendix D: Properties of Common Substances (page 564)

What to Do

1. Use the balance to find the mass, in grams, of your mystery sample.

2. Carefully measure and record, in centimetres, the length, width, and height of the sample. You will need to be accurate to the nearest 0.1 cm. Use these measurements to calculate the volume of the sample.

3. Divide the mass by the volume to find the density.

What Did You Find Out?

1. Is the density of your sample close to any of the densities in the table? Which one?

2. What other properties might help you to determine the identity of the sample? Check Appendix D: Properties of Common Substances.

Skill
P O W E R

For tips on measuring mass and volume, turn to page 583.

STRETCH Your Mind

Many panels in the body of a modern car are not made from metal but from a kind of plastic called Kevlar™. This material was developed to have similar rigidity properties to steel, but to be much less dense, reducing the overall weight of the car and thus making the car more fuel-efficient. As an added bonus, plastic panels can be moulded to almost any desired shape. This is one reason why modern cars have smoothly curved lines. Usually, the chassis (the central "skeleton") of a car is still made from steel, however. Try to think of two reasons why.

How Much? How Dense?

Although lead is much more dense than iron, if you have a larger sample of iron than of lead, it will probably be heavier. Figure 5.8 should help you to explain this.

In Figure 5.8, think of the formula for density as rearranged into the form

$$\text{Mass} = \text{Volume} \times \text{Density} \qquad \text{or} \qquad m = V \times D$$

For the iron bar, a larger volume more than makes up for the smaller density.

Model Problems

Example 1: A softball has a mass of 360 g and a volume of 270 cm³. Find its density.

Given
Mass, m = 360 g
Volume, V = 270 cm³

Required
Density, D, in g/cm³

Analysis
Use the formula $D = \dfrac{m}{V}$, which gives density in g/cm³.

Solution

$D = \dfrac{m}{V}$

$\quad = \dfrac{360 \text{ g}}{270 \text{ cm}^3}$

$\quad = 1.33 \text{ g/cm}^3$

Paraphrase
The density of the softball is 1.33 g/cm³.

Example 2: The density of nickel is 8.9 g/cm³. What is the volume of 500 g of nickel?

Given
D = 8.9 g/cm³
m = 500 g

Required
Volume, V, in cm³

Analysis
Solve the formula $D = \dfrac{m}{V}$ for V. Multiply both sides by V to give $DV = \dfrac{m\cancel{V}}{\cancel{V}}$.

Now divide both sides by D to give $V = \dfrac{m}{D}$.

Since mass is in grams and density is in g/cm³, volume will be in cm³.

Skill
P O W E R
For help with numerical problem solving, turn to page 603.

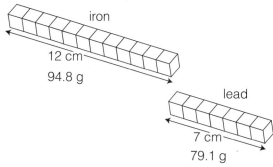

Figure 5.8 Compare the different-sized metal samples above. Each 1 cm cube of iron weighs less than a 1 cm cube of lead, but the bar of iron has more cubes than the bar of lead.

Math CONNECT

Here are some data about seven metal samples:
Sample A: 51 g, 4.5 cm³
Sample B: 22 g, 3.0 cm³
Sample C: 70 g, 6.2 cm³
Sample D: 27 g, 10.0 cm³
Sample E: 48 g, 5.4 cm³
Sample F: 54 g, 7.4 cm³
Sample G: 17 g, 1.5 cm³
Make a graph of these data with mass as the vertical axis and volume as the horizontal axis. Which samples could be of the same metal? Hint: Try drawing straight lines on your graph through the point (0, 0).

Skill
P O W E R
For help with graphs, turn to page 587.

Skill
P O W E R

For help with SI units,
turn to page 574.

Math CONNECT

1. A one-dollar coin has mass 7.0 g and volume 0.78 cm³. What is its density?

   The loonie is made from an alloy (a mixture of different metals). Suggest some metals from which you think the loonie might be made.

2. Coal (or carbon) has a density of 2250 kg/m³. How much volume (at the minimum) would a 20 kg bag of coal take up? Why might you expect the actual volume of the bag to be more than this?

Skill
P O W E R

For help with powers of
10, turn to page 574.

Pause&
Reflect

Did you notice that the density of iron measured in kg/m³, is 1000 times greater than its density measured in g/cm³? In your Science Log, write two reasons why you would usually want to measure density in units of g/cm³, rather than kg/m³.

Solution

$$V = \frac{m}{D}$$

$$= \frac{500 \text{ g}}{8.9 \text{ g/cm}^3}$$

$$= 56 \text{ cm}^3$$

Paraphrase

A 500 g sample of nickel has a volume of 56 cm³.

Example 3: What is the mass, in kilograms, of a 1.0 m³ block of iron? Write down the density of iron, in units of kg/m³.

Given

$V = 1.0 \text{ m}^3$
$D = 7.9 \text{ g/cm}^3$ (from the table on page 166)

Required

Mass, m, in kg
Density, D, in kg/m³

Analysis

First notice that your units do not match. Convert volume into cm³ to give mass in grams; then convert mass into kilograms.

Use the formula $D = \frac{m}{V}$.

Solve this formula for m (in grams) by multiplying both sides by V: $DV = \frac{m\cancel{V}}{\cancel{V}} = m$

Finally, for the density in kg/m³, use the formula $D = \frac{m}{V}$, with m in kg and $V = 1.0 \text{ m}^3$.

Solution

$V = (1.0 \times 1.0 \times 1.0) \text{ m}^3$
$\quad = (100 \times 100 \times 100) \text{ cm}^3$
$\quad = 1\,000\,000 \text{ cm}^3$

(In scientific notation:
$\quad = (10^2 \times 10^2 \times 10^2) \text{ cm}^3$
$\quad = 10^6 \text{ cm}^3$

$m = DV$
$\quad = 7.9 \text{ g/}\cancel{\text{cm}^3} \times 1\,000\,000 \cancel{\text{cm}^3}$
$\quad = 7\,900\,000 \text{ g}$
$\quad = 7900 \text{ kg}$

$m = DV$
$\quad = 7.9 \times \text{g/}\cancel{\text{cm}^3} \times 10^6 \cancel{\text{cm}^3}$
$\quad = 7.9 \times 10^6 \text{ g}$
$\quad = 7.9 \times 10^3 \text{ kg}$

$D = \frac{7900 \text{ kg}}{1.0 \text{ m}^3}$
$\quad = 7900 \text{ kg/m}^3$

$D = \frac{7.9 \times 10^3 \text{ kg}}{1.0 \text{ m}}$
$\quad = 7.9 \times 10^3 \text{ kg/m}^3)$

Paraphrase

The mass of 1.0 m³ of iron is 7900 kg. The density of iron in these units is 7900 kg/m³.

Can You Ever Be Sure About Changes?

Remember that physical properties can be determined without altering the identity of the sample. Chemical properties involve a chemical change, however. If a sample of matter breaks down or reacts with another substance, a new substance will be produced. You will not have your original sample.

As you have discovered, it can be difficult to decide if a change is physical or chemical. Here is a rule that can help you: If you make two or more of the following observations, then a chemical change has *probably* taken place.

• Heat is produced or absorbed.
• The starting material is used up.
• A new colour appears.
• A starting colour disappears.
• A material with new properties forms.
• Gas bubbles form in a liquid.
• Grains of solid precipitate form in a liquid.

Why does the rule say *probably*? You cannot be sure that a chemical change has occurred unless you are certain that a new substance has been formed; and you cannot be certain that a new substance has been formed unless you do careful tests both before and after the change. Observing changes in properties can be used to make a reasonable inference, but changes in properties can be misleading.

Check Your Understanding

1. Use the particle theory to distinguish between a pure substance, a solution, and a mechanical mixture. Give one example of each.

2. Classify each of the following as a pure substance, a mechanical mixture, or a solution.
   (a) soil
   (b) perfume
   (c) baking powder
   (d) hair spray
   (e) glass cleaner

3. Which of the following are physical changes, and which are chemical changes?
   (a) Sugar dissolves in water.
   (b) A steak is well cooked.
   (c) The filament of a light bulb glows when an electric current flows through it.
   (d) A piece of chalk is crushed.
   (e) A plant grows into a shrub.

4. **Apply** Water and gasoline are both clear liquids at room temperature. Describe one physical property and one chemical property that might be used to distinguish between them.

5. **Thinking Critically** State two quantitative physical properties that change when antifreeze is dissolved in water.

5.2 Mixtures

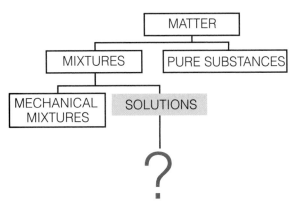

Figure 5.9 How do you think solutions can be further classified?

Mixtures make up most of the matter in the world around us, and solutions are one kind of mixture. The word "solution" makes many people think of a liquid like one of those in Figure 5.10. All are transparent and colourless, yet they are very different in composition.

Explaining the Properties of Solutions

Particles in a solution are very tiny — too tiny to be seen with the best optical microscope. The substance that dissolves a solute to form a solution is called the **solvent.** The **solute** is the substance that dissolves in the solvent.

STRETCH Your Mind

When most people think of solutions, they think of a solid solute dissolved in a liquid, usually water.

Solutions that involve other states of matter are possible. Give an example of each solution below.

• gas dissolved in a gas

• gas dissolved in a liquid

• liquid dissolved in a liquid

• solid dissolved in a liquid

• solid dissolved in a solid

Figure 5.10A
Salt water (solid sodium chloride dissolved in water)

Figure 5.10B
Soda water (gaseous carbon dioxide dissolved in water)

Figure 5.10C
White vinegar (liquid acetic acid dissolved in water)

Every solution retains some properties from its solute and some properties from its solvent. For example, the solution in Figure 5.10A still tastes like salt and still looks like water, but other properties seem to be lost. The salt is no longer solid, and the water is no longer tasteless. These new properties *might* make you might think that a new substance has been formed. Is the dissolving of salt in water a chemical change? The answer is no.

It is true that some properties change during dissolving. If you heat the salt water, however, the water boils away but the salt does not. The solution separates, leaving the solid salt behind. If you shake soda water, most of the carbon dioxide will bubble out of the solution. If you distil vinegar, the liquid acetic acid will separate from the water it is dissolved in. Dissolving is therefore a

Word CONNECT

All of the liquids in Figure 5.10 are called *aqueous* solutions because water is the solvent. ("Aqueous" comes from the Latin word *aqua,* meaning "water.") Aqueous solutions are always transparent, but they are not always colourless. Think of beverages such as lime Kool-Aid™. If the solute is coloured, the solution will be coloured, too. Make a list of coloured aqueous solutions you know.

physical change because it can be reversed by methods based on differences in physical properties.

All of the liquid solutions mentioned above (salt water, soda water, and vinegar) are transparent as well as homogeneous. The particle theory of matter explains that the solutes are present as separate, individual particles, which are too small to see. Thus all we can see is the solvent. Since the solvent is water, a transparent pure substance, the entire solution looks homogeneous.

Transparency is a property of a homogeneous mixture. Lack of transparency may be a sign of a heterogeneous mixture. For example, smog is hard to see through. A close look at Figure 5.11 shows that smog is a "non-solution." Since you can see some of its separate parts, smog is heterogeneous and therefore classified as a mechanical mixture.

Transparency or the lack of it, however, is not a sure guide for distinguishing solutions from mechanical mixtures. Some of the most important solutions that people make are nontransparent solids. For example, Wood's metal is made by melting four pure substances — bismuth, lead, tin, and cadmium — and mixing the hot liquids. Wood's metal also has a surprising new property, however. Its melting point is only 70°C, and it softens at even lower temperatures. Novelty stores sometimes sell spoons made from Wood's metal. The spoons soften and bend when placed in a hot drink. A more important use is in automatic sprinkler systems that activate if a fire occurs. A soldered joint of Wood's metal blocks the flow of water through the sprinkler heads. This joint melts if the temperature gets too high, and the water is released.

Alloys are homogeneous mixtures of one or more metals, so Wood's metal is an example of an alloy. Alloys are tremendously important metal solutions. Adding small amounts of other substances dramatically changes the properties of a pure metal. For example, pure iron is relatively soft and easily rusts, but the addition of a small amount of carbon makes steel, which is much stronger. If nickel and chromium are also added, the result is stainless steel, which resists rust.

Another common application of alloys is the manufacture of coins. Pure nickel was used to make the five-cent coin when it was first introduced in 1922, hence it was called a "nickel". Today the nickel coin is made using an alloy called cupronickel, which consists of about 75% copper and 25% nickel. There is more copper in a nickel than nickel!

Gold is too soft to be used in pure jewellery. Instead, an alloy is used, such as gold and copper ("yellow gold"). Both components make an important contribution to the properties of the alloy. The gold adds its beautiful colour and lustre, and resistance to chemical change. The copper adds hardness. Figure 5.12 shows how the composition of the alloy can be varied to suit its use.

Figure 5.11 Smog is heterogeneous because you can see its separate parts.

Math CONNECT

1. Use the information in Figure 5.12 to figure out the mathematical relationship between the percentage of gold in the alloy and the karat of the gold. What percentage of gold would there be in an 18-karat gold piece?

2. Pure gold has a density of 19.3 g/cm³, and pure copper has a density of 8.9 g/cm³. Copper is therefore much less dense. What would you expect the density of genuine 12-karat gold to be?

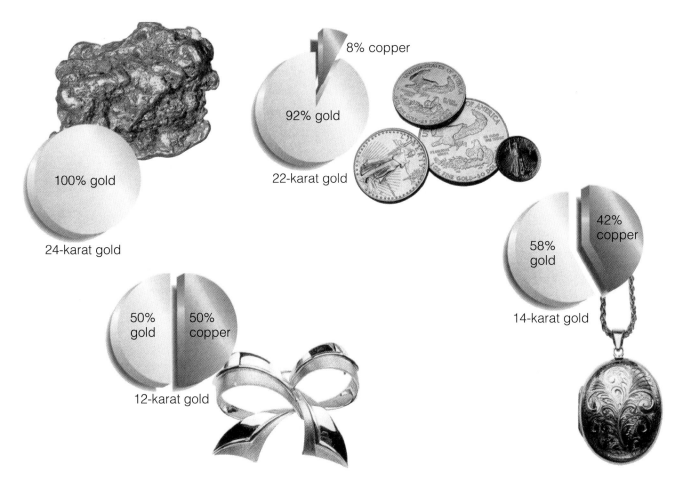

Figure 5.12 The circle graphs show the percentages of gold and copper found in the different "gold" objects.

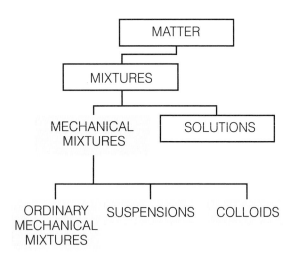

Figure 5.13 Classifying mechanical mixtures

Mechanical Mixtures

Mechanical mixtures, unlike solutions, are heterogeneous. This means that you can see the different particles in them. Mechanical mixtures can be further classified into three types, based on the size of the particles. (See Figure 5.13.)

In an ordinary mechanical mixture, the different parts are big enough to see, and they stay mixed. They do not settle out or separate on their own. For example, speckled rocks such as granite are classified as ordinary mechanical mixtures.

In a **suspension**, the particles may be seen with the unaided eye or through a low-power microscope. If a suspension is left undisturbed, gravity will eventually cause the suspended particles to separate. For example, the active ingredient in Milk of Magnesia is not very soluble in water, so the product is a suspension. This is why the bottle must be shaken before the product is used. Another example of a suspension settling out is the sediment deposited by a river when the flow of the river decreases.

The smaller the suspended bits, the more slowly they separate. Allowing a suspension to separate naturally can sometimes take a lot of time. Technology is used to speed up the separation of a suspension. For example, filtration will clarify muddy water in a hurry. Technology is also used to stop a suspension from separating. Emulsifying agents can keep the components of a suspension mixed together indefinitely.

Emulsifying agents are only one way to prevent suspensions from separating. For example, milk straight from a cow is a natural suspension. It quickly separates into two layers. Homogenization uses high-speed agitation to break the particles of fat into droplets that are so tiny, they can remain suspended without settling. The motion of the water particles in the rest of the milk is enough to keep the tiny fat droplets mixed in the suspension.

Figure 5.14 This island in the Fraser river in British Columbia has formed from sediment that separated out from the river.

Outside Link ACTIVITY

Keep It Together!

Emulsifying agents make our life easier. Without them, we would have to spend a lot more time shaking the products we use. Try this activity to find out how well one emulsifying agent works.

What You Need

cooking oil and vinegar
jar with tight-fitting lid
dishwashing liquid (not dishwasher detergent)
watch or clock with second hand or counter

What to Do

1. Place a small amount of cooking oil and an equal amount of vinegar in the jar and seal the lid tightly. Shake the jar thoroughly. Time how long it takes before the two liquids separate. Record the time.

2. Shake the suspension harder; then shake the suspension longer. Can you make the suspension last longer? How long? Record the time it took for the liquids to separate in each of your trials.

3. Add two drops of dishwashing liquid. Shake the jar thoroughly again. How long does the suspension last now? Record the time.

4. Leave the mixture overnight and inspect it in the morning. Record your observations.

What Did You Discover?

1. What did you learn about keeping a suspension from separating? Which substance acted as an emulsifying agent?

2. Did you form a permanent suspension?

Extensions

3. Look on the labels of liquid food products. Which contain emulsifying agents? What could happen if the emulsifying agent was not present?

4. Look on the labels of personal care products. Which contain emulsifying agents? What could happen if the agent was not present?

5. Many salad dressing recipes call for raw egg yolk. What do you think the egg yolk contributes to the dressing? Find out why many home economists are advising people to use mashed cooked egg yolk instead of raw egg yolk in salad dressing recipes.

Figure 5.15 Which mixture above must be a colloid? Why? Which mixture must be a solution? Why?

If the suspended particles are small enough, gravity will not cause them to separate. This type of mechanical mixture is called a **colloid**. Like solutions, there are several kinds of colloids that involve different states of matter. For example, jelly is a colloid that consists of a solid and a liquid. Whipped cream, another colloid, consists of a gas and a liquid. Other examples of colloids include mayonnaise, paints, glues, butter, and milk.

Colloids, although heterogeneous, have a homogeneous appearance, and are on the dividing line between solutions and heterogeneous mixtures. The particles in a colloid are too small to be seen using an optical microscope, but they are larger than the particles in a solution. A beam of light is scattered by the particles in a colloid, but not by the smaller particles in a solution. The scattering of light by colloid particles is called the **Tyndall effect,** and it is used to distinguish between a colloid and a solution.

Check Your Understanding

1. Classify each of the following as a solution, a mechanical mixture, a suspension, or a colloid.

    (a) Raisin Bran™ cereal

    (b) paint thinner

    (c) paint

    (d) nail polish remover

    (e) shaving cream

    (f) oil and vinegar salad dressing

2. (a) Name three different alloys.

    (b) Is an alloy a homogeneous mixture or a heterogeneous mixture?

    (c) Why are alloys sometimes used rather than pure metals? Give an example to illustrate your answer.

3. Distinguish between a solution, a suspension, and a colloid. Give one example of each. (Do not choose examples from question 1.)

4. **Apply** Your teacher has just given you two stoppered test tubes that have been shaken. You are told that one contains milk, and the other contains chalk and water. How can you decide which is which?

5. **Thinking Critically** How could you distinguish experimentally between the following three solutions without tasting them?

    (a) alcohol dissolved in water

    (b) salt dissolved in water

    (c) carbon dioxide dissolved in water

5.3 Compounds and Elements

Look at the highlighted section of Figure 5.16. "Compound" comes from the same root word as "compose," meaning make up or put together. **Compounds** are pure substances that are made up of two or more elements chemically combined together. They can be broken down into elements again by chemical means.

Exactly what are elements? This section shows how our knowledge of elements has shifted from earlier ideas to the ideas that scientists accept today.

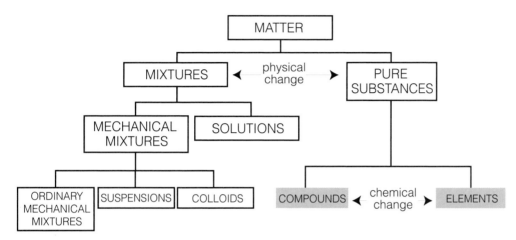

Figure 5.16 So far your attention has been focused on the mixtures side of this table. But chemists also know that pure substances can be further classified into two types: elements and compounds. What do you think the labelled arrow between compounds and elements means?

Shifting Views of the Elements

From very early times, scholars called **philosophers** (thinkers) wondered why matter behaves as it does. Philosophers manipulated matter in their minds, but they did almost no "hands-on" research or experimentation. Figure 5.17 shows what ancient Greek philosophers thought about matter.

In Europe, this view of the elements lasted as late as the early seventeenth century, since most scholars still believed that wisdom came from thinking not from experimenting. They also believed that only the knowledge recorded by the ancient philosophers was valid, and that this "approved" knowledge could not and should not be challenged.

The philosophers' view of the elements was not the only view, however. Hands-on investigations of matter were carried out for many centuries by people known as **alchemists**. Part pharmacist, part mystic, alchemists practised their craft all over Europe and the Middle East. Their view of the elements included a very strong belief that some elements could be changed into others — in particular, that "base" (meaning lower value) metals, such as lead, could be changed into gold. Alchemists developed many useful procedures, such as distillation, and probed the properties of many materials. They were secretive about their findings, however. Many invented their own shorthand symbols and secret codes so nobody else could share their findings.

Did You Know?

People used gold, silver, copper, iron, and other metals to make jewellery and tools and to decorate pottery long before these metals were identified scientifically as elements. The technologies used by these people in the past were highly advanced.

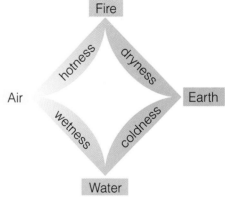

Figure 5.17 According to the Greek four-element theory, all matter consisted of some combination of just four elements, and everything in the physical world could be explained using these four elements.

Collect the Elements

For several centuries, the alchemists laboured to understand seven metals that we recognize today as elements, although they did not use the term as we do today. These metals are gold, silver, copper, mercury, lead, tin, and iron. In this activity, you will find out as much as you can about these elements.

What to Do

1. Start an "element collection" with the seven metals of the alchemists. Write the name of each element on an index card, or choose another way to record what you learn. You may want to use a computer program.

2. Use print and electronic resources to research these elements. Record the information you find, such as when each element

was discovered, major physical properties, major chemical properties, and major uses. Add any new information you learn about these elements throughout the unit.

3. As a class, choose one other element for each student to research. By the end of the unit, be prepared to report on your "special" element through a medium of your choice: for example, a poster, a video presentation, or an oral presentation with pictures.

4. Add cards for other elements you meet in this unit.

5. If you need help with conducting research, turn to Appendix B: Using Resources and the Internet Effectively, on page 560.

The currently accepted view of the elements began to develop in the early seventeenth century. A new attitude toward knowledge was beginning to gain favour at that time. Sir Francis Bacon (1561–1626) made a very important contribution with his use of a scientific method to investigate the physical world. In 1620 Bacon published a book arguing that science should be built on the basis of experimental evidence rather than philosophical speculation only.

Robert Boyle (1627–1691) made an important contribution soon afterward when he expressed scepticism about the four-element theory of the ancient philosophers. In 1661 he published *The Skeptical Chymist*, in which he wrote, "I mean by elements, certain simple unmingled bodies…." As well, Boyle recognized that elements could be combined to form compounds. Although he did not identify which materials he believed to be elements and which he believed to be compounds, his description was widely accepted at the time and laid the groundwork for our modern definition.

Bacon's ideas about scientific method and Boyle's ideas about elements led to a widespread search for elements using this new approach to investigating matter.

DidYou**Know**?

Robert Boyle was one of the founders of The Royal Society of London for the Advancement of Science. Since his time, the Royal Society has acted as a clearing house for knowledge — a place where scientists can share their experimental results and continue to build new knowledge. Today the Royal Society also undertakes projects when there is a special need. For example, current projects include researching methods to rehabilitate tropical rainforests that have been damaged by cutting or burning.

TEACHER DEMONSTRATION

Testing for Gases

One of the chemist's tools for investigating matter is a set of standard tests that will positively identify different substances. In this investigation, which your teacher will demonstrate, you will learn about the standard tests for three gases. Two of the gases are elements (oxygen and hydrogen), and one is a compound (carbon dioxide).

Problem

How can different gases be identified by using standard tests?

Safety Precautions

Some gases are highly explosive. Follow your teacher's directions for observing this demonstration safely.

Apparatus

3 gas-collecting jars

Materials

samples of oxygen, hydrogen, and carbon dioxide
limewater
wooden splints

Procedure

1 Your teacher will prepare a small supply of each gas and safely collect each gas in a labelled jar.

2 Your teacher will then use the following methods to test each gas safely.

(a) Light a long wooden splint. Tip the jar containing hydrogen, and hold the burning splint near the mouth. You will hear an explosive "pop." This is the standard test for hydrogen.

(b) Relight the splint if necessary; then blow it out gently so that the tip continues to glow. Lower the glowing splint into the jar containing oxygen. The glowing splint will burst into flame. This is the standard test for oxygen.

(c) Relight the splint if necessary. Invert the jar containing carbon dioxide, and hold the burning splint under it. The carbon dioxide will smother the flame.

(d) Other gases will also smother a flame, so another test is needed to confirm that the gas is carbon dioxide. Place a few drops of limewater (a solution of calcium hydroxide) into the jar, cover the jar, and shake it. The limewater will turn milky. This is the standard test for carbon dioxide.

Analyze

1. How can you tell by physical properties that the three gases are not the same? Hint: Why must one jar be upside down at the beginning?

2. How can you tell by chemical properties that the three gases are not the same?

Conclude and Apply

3. (a) One of the gases is used in fire extinguishers. Which one?

(b) Another gas was used for many years to float transportation balloons. Which one? Why is this gas not used today?

(c) Another gas is used to assist the breathing of many patients in hospitals. Which one?

Give reasons for your answers.

The Development of a Modern View of the Elements

One of the standard tests you just learned is for detecting a compound, carbon dioxide, while the other two tests are for detecting elements. Part of the exciting story of the elements is how scientists learned to take matter apart by ordinary chemical means until it would not break down any farther. In this way, they were able to determine if a substance was an element or a compound.

Through the seventeenth and eighteenth centuries, scientists worked with matter by heating, burning, mixing, and cooling. Antoine Lavoisier (1743–1794) was a pioneer in the field, defining elements as pure substances that cannot be decomposed (broken down) into simpler substances by means of a chemical change. This is still part of the definition we use today. Lavoisier identified 23 known pure substances as elements.

Figure 5.18 Marie-Anne Lavoisier was invaluable to her husband's research. She read the scientific articles in English and translated the articles she thought would interest her husband.

One of Lavoisier's most successful techniques as an experimenter was his careful measurement of mass. He emphasized the importance of measuring the mass of all the substances involved in a chemical change, which is essential for making sound inferences about what is happening to the substances.

By the nineteenth century, there was a new way to investigate matter. Allesandro Volta had invented the "voltaic pile" — a device we would now call a battery. The voltaic pile was not nearly as convenient as today's dry cells, but it delivered a reliable supply of electric current. Almost immediately, scientists began using this new tool, first passing electricity through water. They discovered that hydrogen and oxygen gases were produced, while the water level fell slightly. They inferred that some of the water had been decomposed into hydrogen and oxygen.

The English chemist Humphry Davy (1778–1829) experimented to find out whether substances other than water could be decomposed by using electric current. Once he figured out that he had to start with either a liquid mineral or at least a solution of a mineral, he succeeded in isolating potassium, sodium, magnesium, calcium, strontium, and barium within a two-year period from 1806 to 1807. Davy's assistant, Michael Faraday, named this method **electrolysis**.

In Investigation 5-C, you will have the chance to repeat Lavoisier's observations. Then, in Investigation 5-D, you will use an electrical power source to decompose water, as nineteenth-century scientists did.

Mass and Chemical Change

The greatest challenge when investigating mass during a chemical change is collecting everything: all the starting materials and all the products. Lavoisier was one of the earliest chemists to use this "balanced" view of chemical changes. What Lavoisier observed during his experiments is what we now call the **law of conservation of mass**: In a chemical change, the total mass of the new substances is always the same as the total mass of the original substances. Resealable bags make it a lot easier for you to observe this law than it was for Lavoisier.

Problem

What happens to mass during a chemical change?

Safety Precautions

Handle the chemicals with care. If there is a spill, inform your teacher.

Apparatus

balance

Materials

sodium carbonate solution
calcium chloride solution
resealable plastic sandwich bag
empty film canister with close-fitting lid

Procedure

1. Pour the sodium carbonate solution into the plastic bag, to a depth of about 1 cm.

2. Pour the calcium chloride solution into the film canister until the canister is nearly full. Close the lid tightly.

3. Put the canister into the bag, and seal the bag tightly.

4. Using the balance, measure and record the mass of the bag and its contents.

5. Working through the walls of the bag, carefully snap off the lid of the canister so the two liquids mix.

6. Measure and record the mass of the bag and its contents again.
   Wash your hands when you have completed this investigation.

Analyze

1. Did a chemical change take place? How do you know?

2. What was the mass of the bag and its contents before and after mixing? Do your observations agree with the law of conservation of mass?

Conclude and Apply

3. Compare this investigation with the Starting Point Activity. Which observations are similar? Which are different?

4. Suppose that you had measured the mass of the bag and its contents in the Starting Point Activity before and after mixing. What do you think you would have observed?

Extend Your Knowledge

5. Early scientists believed that combustion was caused by the escape of a material they called "phlogiston." Why do you think they believed this?

6. Consult reference material to find out more about the phlogiston theory. How was it finally disproved, and by whom?

Decomposing Water with Electricity

In this investigation, you will duplicate what nineteenth-century scientists did when they passed electricity through water, and find out first-hand what they learned about the composition of water. Do you think equal amounts of oxygen and hydrogen will be produced, or would you expect more of one gas or of the other? Write down your prediction.

Problem

How does electrolysis help us understand elements?

Safety Precautions

Hydrogen is explosive. Either conduct the test for hydrogen under your teacher's supervision, or have your teacher conduct the test for you.

Apparatus

600 mL beaker
400 mL beaker
2 test tubes
2 carbon rods for electrodes
2 wire leads with alligator clips
6 V power source
stirring rod

Materials

sodium sulfate
water samples: distilled water, mineral water, tap water
wooden splints

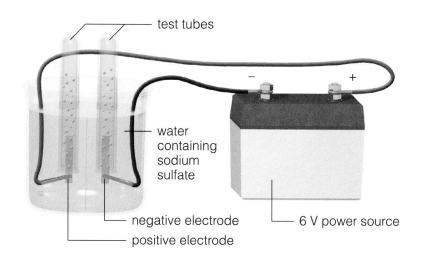

test tubes

water containing sodium sulfate

negative electrode

positive electrode

6 V power source

Procedure

1 Your teacher will arrange you 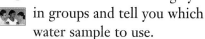 in groups and tell you which water sample to use.

2 Describe the tests for hydrogen and oxygen in your notes. If you need to review these tests, refer to Conduct an Investigation 5-B. If you know the chemical formula of water, write it in your notes, as well.

3 Pour about 500 mL of your water sample into the 600 mL beaker. Record which type of water you used.

4 Add a small amount of sodium sulfate (about the size of a peanut), and stir to dissolve.

5 Pour the solution into a 400 mL beaker until the beaker is about three-quarters full.

6 Place the two carbon rods in the water on opposite sides of the 400 mL beaker. The rods must not touch.

7 Fill a test tube from the rest of the solution, put your thumb over the open end, turn the tube upside down, and dip it into the

water so that the end (with your thumb still covering it) is completely immersed. Now carefully take your thumb away, and put the open end over one of the electrodes. Repeat for the second test tube and electrode.

8 Use an alligator clip to attach a wire to one carbon rod. Attach the other end of the wire to the positive terminal on your power supply. Connect the other rod to the negative terminal in the same way. Observe and record what happens in the test tubes.

9 When one of the test tubes is almost full of gas, disconnect a wire from the power source to stop the electric current. Estimate and record the volume of gas in the other test tube.

10 Light a wooden splint. Lift out the test tube that is full of gas, and conduct the test for hydrogen. Record what happens.

11 Blow out the flaming splint so it is glowing. Lift up the other test tube, and let the water drain. Test for oxygen, and record what happens.

Wash your hands when you have completed this investigation.

Analyze

1. Which connection was made to the electrode where most gas was collected? Was this gas oxygen or hydrogen?

2. How did the volume of hydrogen gas collected compare with the volume of oxygen gas collected? What might you infer about the composition of water?

Conclude and Apply

3. The chemical formula of water is H_2O. Does there appear to be a relationship between the chemical formula of water and the volumes of the gases formed?

4. Check with other groups who used different water samples. Were their results any different from yours? What does this tell you about the composition of different kinds of water?

5. Since you did not measure exactly the amount of sodium sulfate added to the water, it is reasonable to assume that different groups added different amounts. Compare the relative volumes of the gases you collected with the relative volumes other groups collected. Do the results support the claim that adding sodium sulfate to water does not change the quantities of hydrogen and oxygen produced?

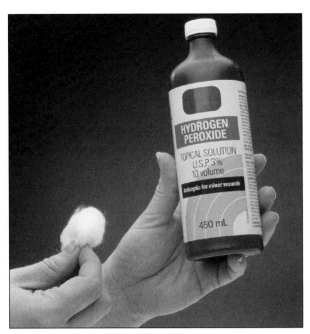

Figure 5.19 Hydrogen peroxide is an antiseptic, so it will kill bacteria in a cut. Water will only clean the cut.

Lavoisier's emphasis on measuring mass inspired the French scientist Joseph Proust (1754–1826). He performed numerous experiments to decompose compounds into elements and to measure the mass of each element. After Proust had tested several compounds, he began to notice a pattern. This pattern is now called the **law of definite proportions**: Compounds are pure substances that contain two or more elements combined together in fixed (or definite) proportions.

Pure water, for example, always contains the elements hydrogen and oxygen combined together in the following proportions: 11% hydrogen and 89% oxygen by mass. These proportions hold true no matter where the water is obtained. Hydrogen peroxide, which is very different from water, contains the same two elements but in different proportions: 6% hydrogen and 94% oxygen. These proportions hold true for every sample of hydrogen peroxide.

Because pure substances have constant composition, they also tend to have constant, unvarying properties. So we can identify an unknown substance by measuring a property and comparing our value to known values. For example, you might determine the density or melting point of an unknown metal and compare this value to the value found in a scientific table, like Appendix D (page 564).

Today there is usually no need to separate out a pure substance in order to identify it. Many tests have been developed to identify unknown substances, whether they are in pure form or part of a mixture. You already know some of these tests, such as the tests for oxygen, hydrogen, and carbon dioxide. You will learn about other tests as you continue with this unit.

Word CONNECT

You have used compounds, such as hydrochloric acid and carbon dioxide, in some of your investigations. Make a list of all the substances you think might be compounds, from your work in this chapter. Try to figure out how they got their names. For example, carbon dioxide is probably made of carbon and oxygen, but what does the "di" mean? (Hint: Sometimes water is referred to as dihydrogen oxide.) Jot down your ideas, and check them as you learn more about how compounds are named.

Check Your Understanding

1. How were the activities of early philosophers different from the activities of alchemists? Compare these two groups with modern scientists.

2. In your own words, write out the two laws mentioned in this section.

3. What is electrolysis? Draw a labelled sketch of the apparatus needed to electrolyze water.

4. **Apply** Air contains some carbon dioxide, but you exhale more carbon dioxide than you inhale. How would you design an experiment to confirm this statement?

5. **Thinking Critically** Why is publishing experimental details and results a vital part of the experimental method? How do you think the development of the World Wide Web will affect scientific publishing? Will the effects all be for the good of science?

5.4 Atomic Theory: Explaining Chemical Facts and Laws

Figure 5.20 John Dalton

In earlier studies, you used the particle theory of matter to explain your observations of matter. It cannot explain everything you have just learned about pure substances, however. It cannot, for example, explain what happens in the electrolysis of water. The properties of the compound, water, are different from the properties of the elements that make it up, hydrogen and oxygen. Thus the particles of water must be very different from the particles of hydrogen and the particles of oxygen. Since the particle theory of matter does not distinguish one particle from another, a more powerful theory is needed. John Dalton (1766–1844) introduced a new way of talking about and explaining chemical facts and laws in his atomic theory.

Dalton's Atomic Theory

- All matter is made up of small particles called atoms.

- Atoms cannot be created, destroyed, or divided into smaller particles.

- All atoms of the same element are identical in mass and size, but they are different in mass and size from the atoms of other elements.

- Compounds are created when atoms of different elements link together in definite proportions.

As you can see, **Dalton's atomic theory** is based on a scientific model that is different from the model used in the particle theory. Dalton's model uses the idea that elements are different because their "particles" (atoms) are different. The model in the particle theory does not use this idea. This leads to a more accurate definition of the word "element", which is the one you should try to remember:

An **element** is a pure substance made up of one type of particle, or **atom**. Each element has its own distinct properties and cannot be broken down into simpler substances by means of a chemical change.

The Difference Between Laws and Theories

In science, *laws* do not explain anything. They just *describe* and *summarize* what happens. *Theories* are imaginative ways to *explain why* something happens. When you explain something, you use different terms than the terms you would use to describe it. In science, the terms used in theories are discussed and criticized at length. Scientists spend a lot of effort trying to convince others of their theories.

In the Science Inquiry Activity on the next page, you will have the opportunity to see for yourself how Dalton's atomic theory can give an explanation of the laws about forming compounds discovered by Lavoisier and Proust. This explanatory power made Dalton's theory very convincing for other scientists of his time.

Explaining with Dalton's Atomic Theory

In this activity, your group will explain some chemical facts and laws by using Dalton's atomic theory. Remember that when you develop an explanation, it has to convince other people. Within your group, practise giving convincing explanations; then try your explanations on another group.

What You Need

collection of element cards from "Collect the Elements" activity (page 176)
four points from Dalton's atomic theory

What to Do

1. From your collection of element cards, choose two elements for your group to compare. Use Dalton's atomic theory to explain the differences between the two elements, using at least two of their properties.

2. Pick one of the elements you used in step 1. Assume that it will combine with another element to form a compound. (Ask your teacher for some help here, or use your element cards for ideas.) According to the law of definite proportions, the compound will always have the same proportion of each element by mass. Develop an explanation of this law based on Dalton's atomic theory.

3. Suppose that one of your elements enters into a chemical reaction with another pure substance, forming one or more substances. Use Dalton's atomic theory to explain why this reaction would conform to the law of conservation of mass.

Chemists in Dalton's time had performed the electrolysis of water experiment you have done (page 180). They also had the experimental technology to measure the mass of the hydrogen and oxygen that results when water is decomposed. In modern experiments, we find that the mass of oxygen is about 89% of the total mass of the electrolysis products, while the mass of hydrogen is about 11%. Dalton's leap of genius was to focus attention on the "relative" masses of the products: that is, how the masses relate to each other, or their ratio.

Dalton theorized that the ratio of mass of each individual atom would have to be the same as the mass ratio of the observed decomposition products. Thus, using the modern data, the ratio of the masses of oxygen and hydrogen atoms would be 8 to 1. Hydrogen was the lightest element known at the time, so Dalton gave it an atomic mass of 1. The atomic mass of oxygen would be 8, on this scale. In fact, Dalton was assuming that water contains equal numbers of oxygen and hydrogen atoms, which is different from our modern understanding, but the principle on which he based his calculation was sound.

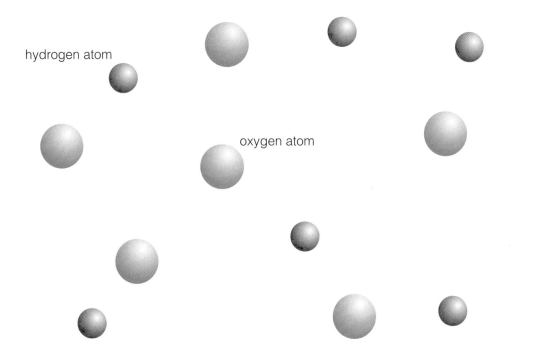

hydrogen atom

oxygen atom

Figure 5.21 Water as Dalton might have pictured it, with equal numbers of smaller hydrogen and larger oxygen atoms.

Pause&
Reflect

According to Dalton's theorizing, the formula for water would be HO. How did it get to be H_2O, one of the most familiar landmark formulas in chemistry? That is a long and interesting story, and you may have suspected it has to do with the volume ratio of hydrogen to oxygen in the electrolysis experiment. It took chemists quite a number of years to work out the problem, but try this. What would have to be changed in Dalton's reasoning if you assume a formula of H_2O instead of HO? (Hint: The change would require that the relative mass of oxygen be 16 instead of 8.)

Nobody can put a single atom on a balance to find its mass, of course. The basic idea of relative mass of atoms is still used today, although it is a more complex idea now. Later in this unit, you will discover more about the "mass number" of each of the elements.

In his *New System of Chemical Philosophy*, published in 1808, Dalton provided relative masses for 20 elements to support his atomic theory. He also showed 17 examples of how the theory explained the formation of compounds. There were several cases of compounds containing the same two elements but having very different properties. For example, there were two compounds that contained only carbon and oxygen, but the elements were present in different mass ratios.

When Dalton found such compounds, he assumed the atoms were combined in equal numbers in one of them (the same assumption he made about hydrogen and oxygen in water). For the other, he assumed there were twice as many atoms of either the first or the second element, depending on the mass ratio for the experimental data. Table 5.3 shows an example.

Table 5.3 Carbon-Oxygen Compounds: Mass Ratios for Data

Compound	Mass Ratio of Carbon to Oxygen
A	1 : 1.33
B	1 : 2.66

When Dalton was measuring and working with experimental data about the ratios of elements, such as carbon and oxygen, he was establishing chemical facts and laws. As soon as he shifted to imagining how the atoms would combine, and what their relative masses would be, he was theorizing.

STRETCH Your Mind

Table 5.3 is based on Dalton's report about the mass ratios in experimental data for two compounds of carbon and oxygen, using modern experimental data. On the basis of Dalton's atomic theory, infer the number of carbon and oxygen atoms in compound A and compound B.

The Story So Far...

To keep track of the history of the scientific achievements in the search to understand matter, it will help if you can see all of the main events at a glance. This activity suggests one way to make a time line to summarize the events. You may wish to make one like this, or make another of your own design.

What You Need

a large sheet of paper
pens or pencils in three colours: black, blue, and red
ruler

What to Do

1. Along the bottom edge of the paper, draw a number line that starts at 1600 and ends at 2000. Divide the line into four equal centuries; then divide each century into ten equal decades.

2. Starting in the bottom left corner, just above the number line, use the black pen to draw a horizontal line that stretches across the lifetime of Francis Bacon. Below this line, use blue pen to print Bacon's full name and dates of birth and death. Above this line, use red pen to print Bacon's main contribution to our understanding of chemistry.

3. Move up a little, and draw a new horizontal line to mark Robert Boyle's lifetime. Again, use blue pen to print his full name and dates of birth and death below the line, and red pen to print his main contribution above it.

4. Continue in this way until you have recorded the contributions of all the chemists mentioned in this chapter. Your finished time line will resemble a staircase.

5. Store your time line so you can use it again in Chapter 7.

Dalton's atomic theory gave chemists a great deal to think about. It provided a quantitative basis for thinking about the structure of matter and it stimulated a lot of discussion and experimentation, enabling scientists to explain the structure and behaviour of elements and compounds more accurately. You will explore more about these matters in the next chapter.

Check Your Understanding

1. Summarize the experimental evidence that supports the following statements made by Dalton in his atomic theory:

   • All matter is made up of small particles called atoms.

   • Atoms cannot be created, destroyed, or divided into smaller particles.

2. Why was Dalton's atomic theory important? How did it stimulate further research and promote speculation about the structure of atoms?

3. **Apply** What would be the result if 5.0 L of hydrogen were burned with 2.0 L of oxygen in a closed container?

4. **Thinking Critically** When fire burns a log of wood, the mass of the ashes left behind is much less than the mass of the original log. Is this an exception to the law of conservation of mass? Explain.

Now that you have completed this chapter, try to do the following. If you cannot, go back to the sections indicated.

Outline some safety procedures you should follow when performing experiments with or disposing of hazardous chemicals. (5.1)

Summarize the main points of the particle theory of matter. (5.1)

Distinguish between a physical change and a chemical change, and give one example of each type of change. (5.1)

List observations that indicate a chemical change has taken place. (5.1)

Distinguish between chemical properties, quantitative physical properties, and qualitative physical properties. Give some examples of each type of property. (5.1)

Given any two of mass, volume, or density, calculate the third. (5.1)

Given an example of a solution, describe its components in terms of a solute or solutes and a solvent. (5.2)

In your own words, define the term "alloy" and list two different examples of alloys. (5.2)

Distinguish between a mechanical mixture, a suspension, and a colloid. State one example of each. (5.2)

Sketch a diagram showing how the Tyndall effect can be used to distinguish between a solution and a colloid. (5.2)

Define the word "compound" and list three examples of compounds. (5.3)

Define the word "element" and list three examples of elements. (5.3)

Describe the tests you would perform to identify each of the following gases: oxygen, hydrogen, and carbon dioxide. (5.3)

Summarize the contributions to chemistry of each of the following: Sir Francis Bacon, Robert Boyle, Marie-Anne Lavoisier, and Antoine Lavoisier. (5.3)

In your own words, state the law of conservation of mass. (5.3)

Draw a labelled sketch of the apparatus used to electrolyze water. (5.3)

In your own words, state the law of definite proportions. (5.3)

List the main points of Dalton's atomic theory. (5.4)

Distinguish between laws and theories. (5.4)

Prepare Your Own Summary

Summarize this chapter by doing one of the following. Use a graphic organizer (such as a concept map), produce a poster, or write the summary to include the key chapter concepts. Here are a few ideas to use as a guide:
• Make up a chart to show how matter is classified.
• Outline the key points in the particle theory of matter. Use the theory to explain the classifications of matter you identified in your chart.

• What properties does matter have, and what changes can it undergo?
• What did you learn about elements and compounds?
• Which laws were identified in this chapter? Why are they important?
• What did you learn about atoms and how atoms can be used to explain some chemical facts and laws?

CHAPTER 5 Review

Reviewing Key Terms

If you need review, the section numbers show you where these terms were introduced.

1. Write a sentence using the words "mass" and "density" to compare the following. (5.1)
   (a) the water in a cup with the water in a swimming pool
   (b) the water in a cup with the wood from a maple tree

2. What is the difference between each of the following terms?
   (a) a heterogeneous (mechanical) mixture and a homogeneous mixture (5.1)
   (b) a qualitative property and a quantitative property (5.1)
   (c) a colloid and a suspension (5.2)
   (d) an element and a compound (5.3, 5.4)

3. What is an inference? What is the relationship between facts, inferences, and a theory? Illustrate your answer in terms of a detective trying to solve a crime. (5.4)

Understanding Key Concepts

Section numbers are provided if you need to review.

4. Think of a pure substance such as salt or sugar. If the substance undergoes a physical change, will there be a change in its chemical properties? If the substance undergoes a chemical change, will there be a change in its physical properties? Explain. (5.1)

5. Some of the properties of pure water are listed below. Which properties are qualitative, and which are quantitative? (5.1)
   (a) Pure water is a very poor conductor of electricity.
   (b) The volume of a sample of water is 26.8 mL.
   (c) The normal boiling point of water is 100 °C.
   (d) Small depths of water are transparent to light.

6. State three examples of physical properties that would not help to identify a pure substance. (5.1)

7. Think of a substance commonly found in the home, and write down three of its physical properties. See if a classmate can identify the substance from its properties. (5.1)

8. What is the difference between a physical property and a chemical property? Give one example of each property to describe oxygen gas. (5.1)

9. Which of the following are physical properties and which are chemical properties? (5.1)
   (a) Lead is a relatively soft metal.
   (b) Copper wires are good conductors of electricity.
   (c) An iron nail rusts.
   (d) Milk of Magnesia neutralizes excess stomach acid.

10. What key information would enable you to distinguish between a physical change and a chemical change? State three indicators of chemical change. (5.1)

11. Classify each of the following as a physical change or a chemical change. (5.1)
    (a) frying an egg
    (b) percolating coffee
    (c) letting paint dry
    (d) toasting bread
    (e) letting cement set
    (f) growing a plant

12. Classify each of the following samples of matter as an element, compound, solution, suspension, mechanical mixture, or colloid. (5.1, 5.2, 5.3)
    (a) egg   (g) 18-carat gold
    (b) mercury   (h) hair conditioner
    (c) ketchup   (i) $2 coin
    (d) detergent   (j) compost
    (e) fog   (k) copper
    (f) sand   (l) muddy water

13. What is the Tyndall effect? What use is made of it? (5.2)

14. (a) Describe the test for oxygen gas.

   (b) How is the test for hydrogen different from the test for oxygen?

   (c) Carbon dioxide will put out a burning splint, but this alone does not confirm the presence of the gas. Why not? Describe the test for carbon dioxide. (5.3)

15. Describe the similarities and differences between the particle theory of matter and Dalton's atomic theory. (5.1, 5.4)

Developing Skills

16. The five most abundant elements (by mass) in Earth's crust are

oxygen	50%
silicon	26%
aluminum	7%
iron	5%
calcium	3%

   Construct a pie chart showing these percentages. Remember to include a category for "other elements."

17. Some chemicals in your home are hazardous. Examine a variety of materials and prepare a short report identifying which have a WHMIS hazard symbol on the label and what the hazard is.

18. Make a concept map for pure substances that contains the following terms: atom, element, compound, molecule.

19. Briefly name the scientists identified in this chapter who contributed to the concept of elements. Summarize, in a sentence or two, the contribution of each.

Problem Solving

20. Suppose that your teacher has just given you three test tubes. You are told that one is a solution of calcium chloride, another contains a suspension of calcium carbonate, and the third contains water to which a little milk has been added. How could you identify the contents of each test tube?

21. Natalia gently dropped an object weighing 15.8 g into an open container that was full of ethanol. The volume of ethanol that spilled out was equal to the volume of the object. Natalia then found that the container and its contents weighed 10.5 g more than the container full of ethanol only. The density of ethanol is 0.789 g/cm^3. What is the density of the object? (Hint: You will need to work out how much the spilled ethanol weighed.)

22. One of the problems in recycling empty containers is that they must be sorted so similar materials can be processed together. How might you use the property of density to separate a mix of plastic and glass bottles and metal cans?

Critical Thinking

23. Describe a physical change that is not easily reversed.

24. All aqueous solutions are clear. Why?

25. Bubbling a gas through water that is then displaced is a common method of collecting gases. What physical property of a gas is necessary for this method to be effective?

Pause& Reflect

1. What difficulties would arise if materials were classified by appearance rather than composition?

2. What is the difference between philosophy and science?

3. Which of the following scientists do you think best deserves the title "the father of modern chemistry": Sir Francis Bacon, Robert Boyle, Antoine Lavoisier, or John Dalton? Briefly state your reasons.

Meet the Elements

Opening Ideas...

• Ancient statues and ornaments were made using gold and silver rather than a cheaper metal. Why?

• Why do advertisements encourage you to recycle aluminum cans more than any other container?

• What properties of gold make it so valuable? How did the nickel coin get its name, and is that name still appropriate?

Science Log

In your Science Log, write why you think some elements, such as gold and silver, have been known for centuries, while others were only discovered in the twentieth century. Aluminum is one of the more abundant elements in Earth's crust, and it is a relatively cheap metal today. In the nineteenth century, however, aluminum was more expensive than gold. What chemical property could account for these facts?

The alchemist lifts a solid, waxy, white lump from a jar of water. The lump gives off a puff of smoke and then bursts into flame. Plunging the lump back into the water douses the flame; exposing the lump to fresh air brings the flame back to life. Is this eternal fire?

We call the waxy, white solid "phosphorus" (from the Greek word meaning "bringer of light"). Its discovery in 1669 brought the number of known elements up to 14. It was the only element discovered during the seventeenth century.

In the eighteenth century, the pace of discovery quickened, for identifying a new element was a sure path to scientific fame. Another 18 elements were identified by 1800, and chemical research became so competitive that some over-eager chemists neglected safety precautions and died while conducting experiments.

The research continued, however, and 50 more elements were discovered in the nineteenth century. Interpreting this rapidly growing body of knowledge was difficult. For example, most of the new elements were metals with similar properties: shiny, silvery grey in colour, and good conductors of heat and electricity. Thus it was not always easy to prove that what seemed to be a new metal actually was a new element.

In this chapter, you will learn about properties that can be used to identify the elements. You will also see how some elements are related to each other according to their properties. You will learn more about metals, their chemical reactivity, and some of the processes used to obtain them. Finally, you will learn how patterns of properties can be used to organize the elements in a format known as the periodic table.

Key Concepts

In this chapter, you will discover

- how to write symbols for the elements
- what a chemical formula represents
- what elements make up Earth's atmosphere, hydrosphere, and crust
- how metals are extracted from minerals
- how families of elements in the periodic table illustrate patterns of physical and chemical properties

Key Skills

In this chapter, you will

- perform a simple laboratory test that can be used to identify certain metals
- build molecular models
- compare the reactivity of various metals by observing chemical reactions
- obtain pure copper from an aqueous solution by means of electrolysis
- determine the effect of hardening and heat treatment on metal

Key Terms

- element symbol
- chemical formula
- molecule
- atmosphere
- hydrosphere
- reactivity
- metals
- non-metals
- metalloids
- metallurgy

- mineral
- ore
- modification
- tempering
- smelting
- chemical family
- periodic table
- group
- period

Identifying Metals

The "alchemist's flame" also has a role in modern chemistry. The brilliant colours you will see in this flame test can reveal metals in the compounds or mixtures that contain them.

Safety Precautions

Your teacher may demonstrate this activity. If you do the activity yourself, carefully review the safety precautions on page ixx before you begin.

What You Need

Bunsen burner, heat resistant pad, Q-tips™
aqueous solutions of the following compounds: barium chloride, calcium chloride, potassium chloride, sodium chloride

What to Do

1. Make a table like the one below to record the results of the tests. Give your table a title.

Compound	Colour of Flame
barium chloride	

2. Put the Bunsen burner on the heat resistant pad, light it, and adjust the air supply to produce a hot flame with a blue cone.

3. Dip one end of a Q-tip™ into one of the solutions, then hold the saturated tip so it is just touching the blue cone of the flame. You may need to hold the Q-tip™ in this position for as long as 30 s. Record the colour of the flame.

4. Repeat step 3 for the other solutions, and record the colours of the flames.

What Did You Discover?

1. How do you know that the colour of the flame is due to the metals and not to something else in the solutions?

2. If you saw a fireworks display that was green, what metal would be present?

6.1 Symbols for the Elements

Suppose that you had to write out every mathematical calculation in full, like this:

Four thousand three hundred and seventy-eight divided by two thousand one hundred and eighty-nine equals two.

Would you find this shorthand version easier to interpret?

4378 ÷ 2189 = 2

The first chemist to report a new element had the right to name it. For example, the chemist Marie Curie discovered the element polonium and named it after the country of her birth, Poland. (You will discover more about Marie Curie's work in the next chapter.)

Uranium was named after the planet Uranus. Einsteinium was named after the physicist Albert Einstein. Since it would be very difficult and time consuming to write names like these over and over again, a system of **element symbols** was developed.

The Invention of Chemical Symbols

The explosion of chemical knowledge during the nineteenth century could have led to mass confusion, since the names of the elements came from many different sources. In 1817, however, the system of chemical symbols that we use today was first proposed by the Swedish chemist Jons Jakob Berzelius (1779–1848). Eventually this system was accepted all around the world. It was accepted not only because it provided symbols for all the known elements, but also because it showed how to create symbols for any new elements that might be discovered later. The activity opposite will help you understand how this international system works.

Although every language has its own way of saying and spelling the names of the elements, the symbols that are used to represent the elements are the same throughout the world (see Table 6.1). Even in Japan and China, students learn symbols based on our alphabet rather than their own.

Table 6.1 The International Symbol for Hydrogen

Language	Name of Element	Symbol for Element
English	hydrogen	H
French	hydrogène	H
German	wasserstoff	H
Italian	idrogeno	H
Portuguese	hidrogênio	H
Spanish	hidrógeno	H

DidYouKnow?

With the help of her husband Pierre, also a chemist, Marie Curie discovered the element radium. She invented the term "radioactivity," and she was the first scientist to be awarded two Nobel prizes. The element curium, discovered in 1944, was named in her honour.

DidYouKnow?

The history of chemistry is filled with tales of nearly simultaneous discovery. For example, the English scientist Joseph Priestley (1733–1804) and the Swedish researcher Karl Wilhelm Scheele (1742–1786) discovered oxygen at about the same time. Priestley published first and got all the credit for its discovery, however. The name "oxygen" was suggested by the French chemist Antoine Lavoisier (1743–1794).

Inferring Symbols for Elements

Unlike the naming of the elements, the system used for determining the symbols follows a set of rules. In this activity, you will find out what these rules are by examining the symbols for certain elements.

What You Need

Appendix D: Properties of Common Substances
your collection of element cards from Chapter 5, section 5.3.

What to Do

1. Kal's body mass is 50 kg. Most of it (48 kg) is made up of just four elements: hydrogen (H), oxygen (O), carbon (C), and nitrogen (N). The symbols for these elements are in the parentheses.

   (a) What rule do you think Berzelius used to create these symbols? Write it down. Call it "Rule 1."

   (b) Kal's body contains less than 1 g of the element iodine. Use Rule 1 to infer the chemical symbol for iodine. Use Appendix D: Properties of Common Substances to check your inference.

2. About 1 kg of calcium is distributed throughout Kal's bones, teeth, and blood.

   (a) If you used Rule 1 to work out a symbol for calcium, what would the symbol be?

   (b) What element already has this symbol?

   (c) Refer to Appendix D. What is the actual symbol for calcium?

   (d) Infer the rule that was used to create the symbol for calcium. Write it down. Call it "Rule 2."

3. Several element names begin with "b."

   (a) The element boron can be used to make silicon computer chips conduct more electricity. Boron's symbol is B. Is this symbol based on Rule 1 or Rule 2?

   (b) Infer likely symbols for barium, beryllium, bismuth, and bromine. Which rule did you use? Explain why. Check your ideas in Appendix D.

   (c) In 1947 chemists in Berkeley, California manufactured a new element and named it berkelium. Refer to Appendix D. What is the symbol for berkelium?

   (d) Infer the rule that was used to create the symbol for berkelium. Write it down. Call it "Rule 3."

4. The seven metals known to the ancients were called by their Latin names for centuries: *argentum* for silver, *aurum* for gold, *cuprum* for copper, *ferrum* for iron, *hydrargyrum* for mercury, *plumbum* for lead, and *stannum* for tin.

   (a) Infer possible symbols for these metals. Use Appendix D to check your inferences.

   (b) Infer which metal was probably used for water pipes in ancient times. Explain how its name helped you make your inference.

5. The hair-thin wire in a light bulb is made of an element with two official names. Most of the world knows it as tungsten, but it is called wolfram in its country of discovery. Refer to Appendix D. Which name was used to create this element's symbol?

What Did You Discover?

1. Look at the rules you wrote in the activity. Use these rules, and anything else you learned, to write a paragraph about how elements are given symbols.

Extensions

2. Add symbols on your element cards from Chapter 5. Add to your collection any new elements you wish or any your teacher suggests.

3. Find out about tungsten's key properties. Then write an advertisement trying to sell it. Use its symbol in your advertisement.

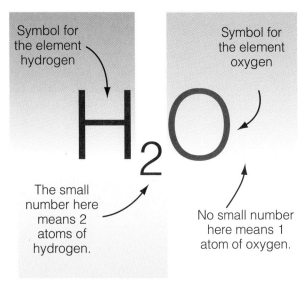

Symbol for the element hydrogen

Symbol for the element oxygen

H_2O

The small number here means 2 atoms of hydrogen.

No small number here means 1 atom of oxygen.

Figure 6.1 Anatomy of a chemical formula

Word **CONNECT**

Dalton and others of his time used the terms "compound particles" and "compound atoms" when theorizing about what happens to atoms when elements combine. The Italian physicist Amedeo Avogadro (1776–1856) introduced and used extensively the term "molecule." Where does the word "molecule" come from, and what did it originally mean? Check print or electronic sources to find out. You will learn more about molecules in the next chapter.

Understanding Formulas for Compounds

Pure hydrogen is a gas at room temperature; so is pure oxygen. Burning hydrogen in oxygen, however, produces a familiar compound: water. You may already know that the shorthand H_2O represents the formula for water.

A **chemical formula** uses symbols and numerals to represent the composition of a pure substance. For example, the chemical formula for water represents

- the composition of pure water wherever it is found

The law of definite proportions tells us that every pure substance has a fixed and definite composition. According to the chemical formula H_2O, water must always contain two atoms of hydrogen for each atom of oxygen, whether the water is in a glass or a lake.

- the composition of a molecule of water

A **molecule** is the smallest independent unit of a pure substance and is generally a cluster of atoms bonded together. The formula H_2O tells us that a water molecule is made of three atoms: two hydrogen atoms and one oxygen atom. These three atoms stay linked together regardless of how many times the water is melted, boiled, or frozen.

solid   liquid   gas

Figure 6.2 Regardless of state, all water molecules have exactly the same formula, just as the law of definite proportions predicts.

As you know, water molecules can be decomposed by electrolysis. This is because the added energy tears the H_2O molecules apart. Unless there is added energy, as in electrolysis, the atoms remain fixed or locked in their own independent molecules.

Interpreting Chemical Formulas

In this activity, you will find out more about chemical formulas and what they can tell us about different substances.

Part 1

Formulas for Molecular Compounds

Think About It

Many compounds are made of molecules. Examples include water, carbon dioxide, propane, and glucose (sugar). Interpret the formulas for these compounds by using the first line of this table as a guide.

The Composition of Four Compounds

Name of Compound	Formula of Molecule	Elements Present	How Many Atoms of Each?
water	H_2O	hydrogen, oxygen	2 atoms H, 1 atom O
carbon dioxide	CO_2		
propane	C_3H_8		
glucose	$C_6H_{12}O_6$		

What to Do

Based on the table above, how many atoms, in total, are present in the following molecules?
(a) one water molecule
(b) one carbon dioxide molecule
(c) one propane molecule
(d) one glucose molecule

Part 2

Formulas for Nonmolecular Compounds

Think About It

Not all compounds are made of molecules. For example, sodium chloride (table salt) does *not* contain independent salt molecules. The following representative

model shows part of a salt crystal. It shows the position of the atoms in the salt crystal, but it does not show what the crystal actually looks like. Examine the model carefully to see how the two elements are arranged.

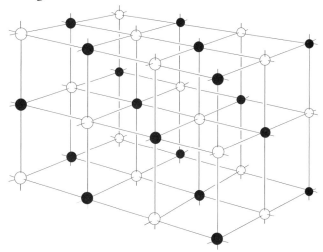

The symbol for sodium is Na. The sodium atoms are black in this model. The symbol for chlorine is Cl. The chlorine atoms are white.

What to Do

1 Count the total number of atoms of each element that are represented in the model.

    (a) How many sodium atoms are represented?

    (b) How many chlorine atoms are represented?

2 Complete the following statements.

    (a) The model has 1 Na atom for every ▇ Cl. (Choose 1, 2, 3, or 6.)

    (b) The model has 1 Cl atom for every ▇ Na. (Choose 1, 2, 3, or 6)

    (c) The ratio of Na to Cl in the model is ▇. (Choose 1:1, 1:2, 1:3, or 1:6.)

3 The compound represented in the model is sodium chloride.

    (a) Write a formula that shows every Na and Cl in the model.

    (b) Repeat part (a) for a model that is twice as big.

CONTINUED

(c) The formula for sodium chloride is normally written as NaCl. Is this an accurate description of the compound? Explain.

(d) Do you see any sign of independent molecules with the formula NaCl? Explain your answer.

Part 3
Formulas for Molecular Elements

Think About It

Many elements exist as molecules under ordinary conditions. For example, the air you inhale with every breath is mostly a mixture of two compounds and two elements. These are listed in the table below.

Some Components of Air

Name of Gas	Compound or Element?	Made of Molecules?	Formula	Number of Atoms per Molecule
water vapour	compound	yes	H_2O	3
carbon dioxide			CO_2	
oxygen		yes	O_2	
nitrogen	element	yes		2

Oxygen and nitrogen exist as diatomic molecules in the air. Diatomic molecules are molecules made up of two atoms of the same element. Hydrogen is another example of a diatomic molecule.

What to Do

The first line in the table is complete. Copy the table and fill in the missing information in the other three lines.

Part 4
Building Model Molecules

Think About It

The following diagram represents molecules of hydrogen, oxygen, water, ammonia, methane, and carbon dioxide.

What to Do

Build your own models for each of these molecules. You may use the model components provided by your teacher, or you may create your own model kit using materials such as coloured mini-marshmallows and toothpicks.

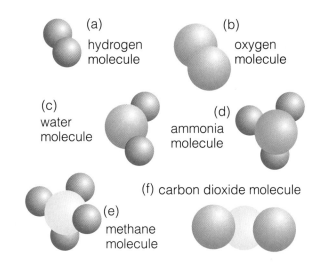

(a) hydrogen molecule

(b) oxygen molecule

(c) water molecule

(d) ammonia molecule

(e) methane molecule

(f) carbon dioxide molecule

Check Your Understanding

1. (a) Today the system of chemical symbols that we use is international. Explain what this statement means, and why it is important.

   (b) Give an example to demonstrate the international nature of chemical symbols.

2. (a) Give an example of a symbol for a metallic element.

   (b) Give an example of a symbol for a non-metallic element.

   (c) Give an example of symbols used to represent a molecular formula.

3. The formula for hydrogen peroxide is H_2O_2.

   (a) Which elements are present in hydrogen peroxide? How many atoms are in each molecule?

   (b) Define the terms "molecule" and "diatomic molecule."

4. Only 13 elements were known before 1600: antimony, arsenic, bismuth, carbon, copper, gold, iron, lead, mercury, silver, sulfur, tin, and zinc. Phosphorus was added to the list in 1669.

   (a) List these elements, one to a line.

   (b) With the help of Appendix D (page 564), write the symbol for each element beside its name.

5. In the eighteenth century, 18 elements were discovered. Their symbols are Co, Pt, Ni, H, N, Cl, Mn, O, Mo, Te, W, U, Zr, Ti, F, Sr, Be, and Cr.

   (a) List these symbols, one to a line.

   (b) Use Appendix D "in reverse" to write the name for each element beside its symbol.

6. Consider the lists you made in questions 4 and 5.

   (a) What is the total number of elements in the two lists?

   (b) How many of these elements are metals? (Hint: Consult Appendix D.)

   (c) Express the number of metallic elements as a percentage of the total number of elements in the list.

6.2 Elements on Planet Earth

You saw in Chapter 5 that early scholars imagined a universe made of four basic "elements": air, water, earth, and fire. We now know that fire refers only to the energy given off by burning, so it is not made of matter. Air, water, and earth are made of matter, but they are not elements in the scientific sense. In this section, you will look more closely at these three substances to see what chemical elements each contains.

Air: Elements in the Atmosphere

The term **atmosphere** usually refers to a gaseous envelope surrounding a planet. Table 6.2 shows the composition of the atmosphere that surrounds Earth.

Table 6.2 Percentage Composition of Dry Air

Name of Gas	Chemical Formula	Percentage by Number of Molecules
nitrogen	N_2	78.03
oxygen	O_2	20.99
argon	Ar	0.94
carbon dioxide	CO_2	0.04

Note: Neon, helium, krypton, and xenon are also found in dry air, in trace amounts.

Three of these gases go through interesting cycles that are essential to life on our planet. A cycle is a "return trip" for a substance. It goes through a sequence of steps or processes and then comes back to its starting point. You may remember these cycles from your earlier science studies.

Oxygen is so reactive that it cannot exist for more than a fleeting instant as an uncombined atom. The oxygen in the atmosphere is therefore in the form of diatomic O_2 molecules. Nearly all living cells depend on oxygen to release energy through cell respiration (see Figure 6.3).

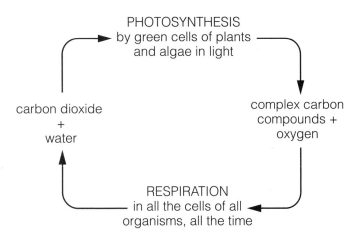

PHOTOSYNTHESIS
by green cells of plants
and algae in light

carbon dioxide
+
water

complex carbon
compounds +
oxygen

RESPIRATION
in all the cells of all
organisms, all the time

Figure 6.3 The oxygen/carbon dioxide cycle

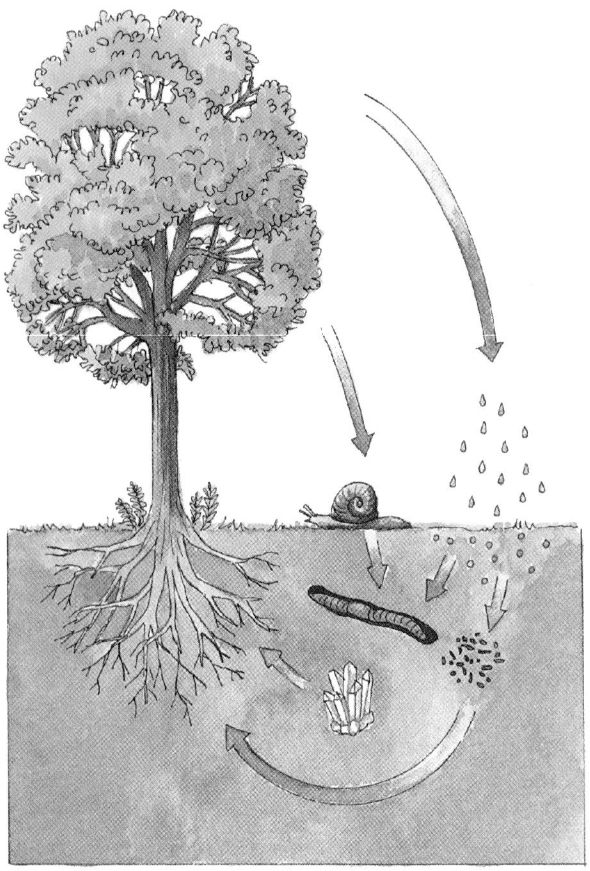

The nitrogen gas in the atmosphere consists of N_2 molecules. This element is vital to life. Every protein in your body contains nitrogen atoms that cycled through the atmosphere at some time (see Figure 6.4).

Gaseous argon consists of single, uncombined Ar atoms. Argon is unreactive and is not involved in a cycle.

The carbon in our atmosphere is present in carbon dioxide (CO_2) molecules, which also contain the element oxygen. Plants and plant-like organisms use CO_2 to make

Figure 6.4 The nitrogen cycle

the food we depend on (see Figure 6.3) and then release O_2 back to the atmosphere.

Dry air does not contain any hydrogen at all. However, air is seldom truly dry. It contains a variable percentage of water vapour — more on a hot humid day above a lake, less above a desert. Thus air does contain the element hydrogen in H_2O molecules. These molecules are cycled back and forth between the atmosphere and Earth (see Figure 6.5).

INTERNET CONNECT

www.school.mcgrawhill.ca/resources/

The element lead is a solid, yet the air in Mexico City contains enough lead compounds to be toxic. Many large Canadian cities used to have toxic levels of lead in the air, but now there is very little lead, if any. Find out more about how these compounds get into the air and what is being done to reduce their levels. Go to the web site above. Go to the **Science Resources**, then to **SCIENCEPOWER 9** to know where to go next.

Water: Elements in the Hydrosphere

Earth is sometimes called "the big blue marble" because water dominates its surface. Even land that seems dry may have water lying or flowing beneath it. Much of what appears to be land in Canada's North is actually "sea ice": solid water floating on the Arctic Ocean. Together, all of this water makes up the **hydrosphere**, a nearly continuous layer of water lying on or just under Earth's crust.

Figure 6.5 The water cycle

DidYou**Know**?

In the seventeenth century, people began to burn coal in ever-increasing amounts to provide energy for industrial and domestic use. In the nineteenth century, we began to burn petroleum, as well. The result has been a gradual increase in the carbon dioxide content of our air. Many scientists now think that this extra CO_2 may be causing increased global temperatures, an effect called global warming. What effect could global warming have on the polar icecaps?

Figure 6.7 As seen from space, the oceans are Earth's most dominant feature. The atmosphere is barely noticeable. If Earth were as small as an orange, the atmosphere would be thinner than the orange's skin.

Figure 6.6 Canada's only true desert ecosystem is located in British Columbia, beside Lake Okanagan.

Pause&
Reflect

Take out your collection of element cards from Chapter 5, section 5.3. Add the symbols and/or formulas for the elements and compounds you have met so far in Chapter 6. (For example, give oxygen the element symbol "O" and the formula "O_2.") As you find new elements or compounds, add them to your collection. Make sure that you understand what each symbol stands for. Look for any pattern to where certain element symbols appear in compound formulas, on the right or on the left.

DidYou**Know**?

Copper is the most abundant metal found in an uncombined form. In Canada, deposits are found in most of the provinces and territories. Most of the world's uncombined copper occurs in the Lake Superior region.

Pure water is made of H_2O molecules, so it has twice as many hydrogen atoms as oxygen atoms. Water found in nature, however, is seldom, if ever, pure in the chemical sense because it contains numerous dissolved substances. Water animals, such as fish, depend on dissolved oxygen gas (O_2) for cell respiration. Water plants, such as sea weed, use dissolved carbon dioxide gas (CO_2) to make food.

Evaporating sea water leaves a solid residue, natural sea salt, that contains compounds such as sodium chloride ($NaCl$), potassium chloride (KCl), and calcium chloride ($CaCl_2$). These compounds come from the rocks and soil that make up the continents. Even mineral compounds that are nearly insoluble appear in the oceans because runoff from millions of years of rain has washed them into the oceans. That is why ocean water tastes salty.

Earth: Elements in the Crust

Earth's crust is our planet's outermost layer of solid rock. Figure 6.9 lists the principal elements in the crust. Notice that the most abundant element is oxygen. How is this possible? After all, oxygen is a gas.

The reason is that oxygen atoms are very reactive. When one atom of oxygen combines with a second atom of oxygen, the result is O_2, the molecule that makes up oxygen gas. But many other elements are also reactive. Their atoms can react with atoms of oxygen to form a variety of solid mineral compounds. For example, oxygen combines with the element silicon to form the compound that makes up most sand. Oxygen also combines with the element iron to form a red compound we call rust.

Only a few metallic elements, including gold, silver, platinum, and copper, exist in nature uncombined with other elements. Most others react in differing degrees. How strongly an element reacts is an important chemical property, known as its **reactivity**. In the next investigation, you will be able to compare the reactivity of different metals.

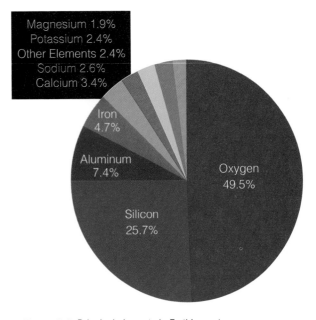

Figure 6.9 Principal elements in Earth's crust.

Figure 6.8 Oxygen combines with iron to form a compound that will eventually rust through the body of this car.

Comparing the Reactivity of Metals

You can compare the reactivity of different metals by carrying out a test that works in the following way. The most reactive metals will produce hydrogen gas when placed in cold water. Slightly less reactive metals will need hot water to produce hydrogen, while the least reactive metals in this investigation will require acid. (How will you know that a gas is produced, and that it is hydrogen? Recall the standard tests you learned in Chapter 5, page 177.)

Problem

What evidence do you need in order to compare the reactivity of metals?

Safety Precautions

- Wear your safety glasses and an apron.
- Always report spills of any chemical to your teacher.
- Handle all chemicals with care.
- Dilute hydrochloric acid is very corrosive. If any gets on your skin or clothes, rinse it off immediately with plenty of running water, and tell your teacher.

Apparatus

6 test tubes
test tube rack
heat source
test tube holder
boiling water bath

Materials

distilled water
dilute hydrochloric acid
samples of the following metals:
aluminum, calcium, iron, lead,
magnesium, zinc
wooden splints
masking tape

Procedure

① Make a table like the one here to record your observations. Give your table a title.

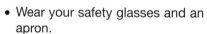

Metal	Cold Water	Hot Water	Dilute Hydrochloric Acid
aluminum			
calcium			**CAUTION:** Do not do this test.
iron			
lead			
magnesium			
zinc			

② Use masking tape to label each test tube with the name of a metal you will be testing. Pour 5 to 10 mL of distilled water into each test tube.

③ Add a small sample of each metal to its labelled test tube. Record your observations in the table.

④ If a gas is produced, make a positive identification using the standard test for hydrogen. (Don't forget, those could just be air bubbles!) Think about this: If any sample of metal reacts with cold water, why would you need to test it further?

CONTINUED

5 Your teacher will set up a boiling water bath. Place any test tubes containing metals that did not react with cold water into the boiling water bath for a few minutes. If any of these metals react with hot water to produce a gas, test to see if the gas is hydrogen and record your observations in your table. Why don't you need to test such metals in acid?

6 Use a test tube holder to remove the test tubes from the hot water bath. Carefully pour out the water from the test tubes containing metals that did not react. Allow the test tubes to cool for a minute.

7 Add about 5 mL of dilute hydrochloric acid to the test tubes containing metals that did not react with either hot or cold water. Record your observations. **CAUTION:** Do not do this test with calcium.

Wash your hands thoroughly after completing this investigation.

Analyze

1. Rank the metals you tested from most to least reactive. What criteria and observations did you use to do this?

2. Did any metal(s) not react in your experiments? Which ones? What does this tell you about them?

Conclude and Apply

3. Sodium is a more reactive metal than calcium, has a density that is less than water's, and melts at 98°C. What problems would you anticipate in trying to put out a fire if sodium was involved?

4. What relationship do you think there is between the date of discovery of a metal and how reactive it is?

5. How would chemical reactivity affect the extraction and use of metals?

6. Explain why copper is often used as a roofing material for large buildings. Why do you think iron is only used for temporary roofing?

7. Copper is also used for water pipes, but in Roman times lead was used for plumbing. What makes both these metals suitable for this use? What makes lead unsuitable?

Different Kinds of Elements

Most of the metals in the investigation you just completed are probably familiar to you. **Metals** are one kind of element, and they have certain properties in common. Metals conduct electricity and heat. They can be hammered into sheets and stretched into wires — physical properties called *malleability* and *ductility*. (These properties were mentioned in Chapter 5.) Metals have a shiny appearance or lustre, and all of them, except mercury, are solids at room temperature.

Figure 6.10A Mercury

Non-metals, such as oxygen and sulfur, differ from metals in several ways. At room temperature, some are gases, some are solids, and one (bromine) is a liquid. The non-metals that are solid are brittle, they cannot be stretched into wires, and they are not very shiny. Non-metals do not conduct electricity or heat very well, either.

Figure 6.10B Bromine

Some elements, such as silicon, have properties that lie "in between" metals and non-metals. These elements are called **metalloids**, and they are in between because they can have properties of both metals and non-metals.

Table 6.3 compares the properties of the three different kinds of elements.

Figure 6.10C Silicon and microprocessor chips

Table 6.3 Properties of Metals, Non-Metals, and Metalloids

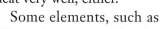
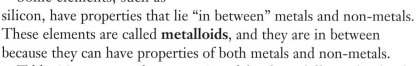

	State	Appearance	Conductivity	Malleability and Ductility
Metals	• solids at room temperature, except for mercury (a liquid)	• shiny lustre	• good conductors of heat and electricity	• malleable • ductile
Non-Metals	• some gases at room temperature • some solids • only one liquid (bromine)	• not very shiny	• poor conductors of heat and electricity	• brittle • not ductile
Metalloids	• solids at room temperature	• can be shiny or dull	• may conduct electricity • poor conductors of heat	• brittle • not ductile

Among the principal elements in Earth's crust (see Figure 6.9), the only non-metal is oxygen. Even when it is cooled to its liquid state, oxygen does not conduct electricity, and solid oxygen is very brittle. Silicon is the only metalloid found among the principal elements in the crust. In its most common compound, it appears as silicon dioxide (SiO_2). Although silicon can be made to conduct electricity, its properties lie in between those of metals and non-metals.

Metalloids are few in number. Non-metals are more numerous, but metals are the most numerous of these three kinds of elements. The most abundant metal in Earth's crust is aluminum — it is even more abundant than iron. Yet aluminum did not come into use for cooking utensils or building materials until many centuries after the first pure iron was beaten into a useful device. Why did it take so long? You will find out in the next section.

Check Your Understanding

1. Use four physical properties to compare metals, non-metals, and metalloids.

2. Describe the cycles for oxygen and carbon dioxide, for nitrogen, and for water. Be sure to indicate how each of these substances returns to the atmosphere.

3. List the chemical compounds in the hydrosphere, and write a sentence that explains the role of each compound.

4. Write a paragraph on how you can conduct a test to compare the reactivity of metals in the laboratory. Why is the test for hydrogen so important?

5. **Apply** The following list of metals is in alphabetic order, with the date of discovery of each metal shown in parentheses. Arrange these metals in order from least to most reactive.
   • aluminum (1825)
   • chromium (1797)
   • lead (prehistoric)
   • nickel (1751)

6.3 The Science and Technology of Metallic Elements

Go back to Figure 6.9 (page 200). If you subtract the amount of oxygen (non-metal) and silicon (metalloid), you can see that metals occur in about one quarter of Earth's crust. Almost all the metals are locked up in compounds, however, except the metals that are not very reactive. Early human progress was in large part the story of how we discovered the materials in Earth's crust and refined them to get the metals out.

This section is about **metallurgy**: the science and technology of retrieving metallic elements and making them as useful as possible. Metallurgy includes three major processes: extraction, modification, and alloying.

Extraction

Few metals are found pure in nature, so most must be extracted from minerals. A **mineral** is a solid pure substance that occurs naturally in Earth's crust. The names of mineral compounds that contain metallic elements often end in "ite."

Minerals usually occur as veins, grains, or chunks embedded in a rocky **ore** (see Figure 6.11). The metallic element is extracted from the ore in two main stages, as shown in Figure 6.12.

Figure 6.11 Can you see the minerals within these ore samples?

Concentration involves eliminating as much rock as possible from the ore so that the remaining mixture contains as much mineral as possible.

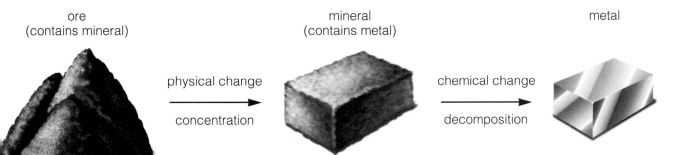

ore
(contains mineral)

physical change

concentration

mineral
(contains metal)

chemical change

decomposition

metal

Figure 6.12 Concentration and decomposition

Decomposition involves breaking down the mineral compound by a chemical change, discarding unwanted materials, and releasing the desired metal in a nearly pure form.

Tools of Science

Technology can help greatly in locating mineral deposits. Small differences in Earth's magnetic field, caused by large mineral deposits, can be detected using a *magnetometer*. Other clues can be obtained from the density of rock. A machine called a *seismograph* records vibrations travelling through different rock densities. Some minerals, such as uranium, can be detected using a *Geiger counter* that registers the radioactive emissions released.

Figure 6.13 Blacksmiths modify the properties of metals with physical methods. This kind of technology was practised for thousands of years before any scientific explanation was available.

Modification

In metallurgy, **modification** refers to altering the properties of a pure metal *without* using a chemical change. For example, a blacksmith can change the properties of plain iron by physical methods such as beating, heating, and sudden cooling (see Figure 6.13). This process is known as **tempering**.

Alloying

As you learned in Chapter 5, the properties of a metal can also be altered by mixing elements together to produce an alloy. Some striking changes can be made by using this process.

Extracting Metal from Ore

Heat and electricity are the two energy sources that drive the chemical changes required to extract metal from its ore. The use of heat for this purpose is called **smelting**. For example, smelting is commonly used to separate iron from the oxygen that is chemically united with it in the two compounds magnetite (Fe_3O_4) and hematite (Fe_2O_3). These two iron oxide ores are found in Canada.

To make a concentrate from iron ore that contains magnetite, heavy-duty magnets are used to attract the mineral grains, leaving most of the ground-up rock behind. If the ore contains hematite (which is not magnetic), a method called froth flotation is used (see Figure 6.14). Both methods produce a mineral-rich concentrate.

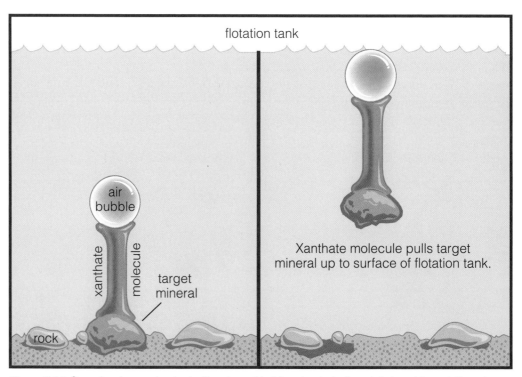

Figure 6.14 Ground-up iron ore is mixed with water and frothing chemicals; then air is forced through the wet mixture. The bubbles that form have a filmy surface that sticks to hematite but not to rock. As the bubbles rise, they float the grains of hematite to the surface.

The concentrate is mixed with limestone and coke (nearly pure carbon), and the mixture is heated strongly in huge furnaces. Examine Figure 6.14 to trace the process that decomposes the minerals and releases nearly pure iron.

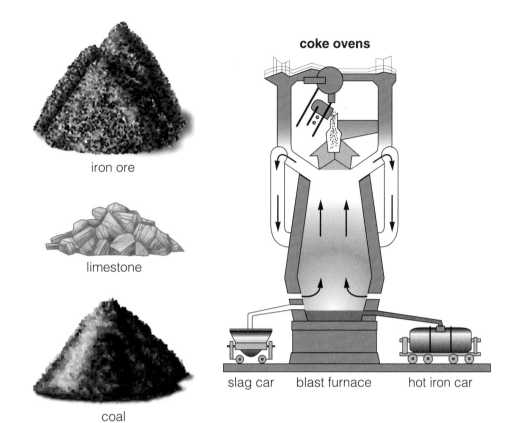

coke ovens

iron ore

limestone

coal

slag car   blast furnace   hot iron car

Figure 6.15 The iron smelting process

Many other metals are extracted from their ores by similar smelting technology. Nickel was first identified near Sudbury, Ontario in 1856. Thomas Edison (1847–1931) used a magnetometer to detect nickel deposits, and in 1901 he began drilling in the area. He wanted to find a source of nickel to use in a battery he had invented. He sank a number of shafts at Falconbridge but hit quicksand at a depth of about 25 m and eventually gave up. In 1916 a new drilling program discovered ore just 5 m below the quicksand. Today the mines at Falconbridge are among the largest producers of nickel in the world. New developments of nickel, copper, and cobalt at Voisey's Bay in Newfoundland will further increase Canada's market share of these important metals.

Copper and nickel are often found together. British Columbia, Ontario, Québec, and Manitoba together produce copper exports worth almost $3 billion. Copper is the metal of choice for electrical wires because it is a better conductor than any other metal except silver, which is usually too expensive.

In early 1848, a man named James Marshall was building a sawmill by a river near Coloma, California. His work was almost complete when he saw something glint in the sun. It was a piece of gold about half the size of a pea. From 1849 onward, thousands of amateur miners (the original "forty-niners") followed their dream to become rich using only a pick, a shovel, and a gold pan. In doing so, they brought about the greatest mass movement of people the world had ever known. Most of the miners did not strike gold, but they did settle the West Coast region of the U.S.A., and many moved north into British Columbia.

Gold was produced in Canada as early as 1823 on the Chaudière River in Québec. Most of the gold recovered in early mines made use of its high density.

This is effective for coarse gold particles but not for fine flecks, especially if they are trapped in rock. In this case, the ore is ground and concentrated by froth flotation. A cyanide solution is added to the concentrated ore to dissolve the gold. Zinc dust is added to the solution to make the gold precipitate out. The cyanide leaching process was developed in Scotland in 1888 and was quickly adopted in Canada. As a result of the new process, world production of gold doubled in the next ten years.

Until it was discovered that uranium can be exploited as a nuclear fuel, this unusual metal had few uses (for example, it was used as a high-priced clothes dye). After the Second World War, the demand for uranium increased dramatically. The first modern plant in North America opened at Eldorado in the North West Territories in 1952. Today Canada is the largest producer of uranium in the world, with annual sales worth about $600 million and production over 12 000 t each year. About 85 percent is exported, mostly to the United States.

Figure 6.16 A huge truck dumps uranium ore onto a metal grid called a "grizzly," which acts as a coarse sieve.

Coal is another key export for Canada, which is the world's fourth largest exporter (mostly to Japan and South Korea), with almost 80 million tonnes being produced every year. Nearly all Canada's coal mines are surface mines, and most are in Saskatchewan, Alberta, and British Columbia. Coal is a heterogeneous mixture formed from the remains of plant life and transformed over millions of years by pressure and heat into a compact solid. It is the most abundant fossil fuel in the world and is essential for the manufacture of steel. It is also used in the smelting of iron (as you have seen).

Smelting technology depends on intense heat to extract metallic elements from their mineral compounds. Electrical technology is also used by metallurgists to extract metals. You are already familiar with the technology used in electrolysis from your investigation of the electrolysis of water in Chapter 5. In Investigation 6-C, you will use electrolysis to model extracting a metal (copper) from one of its compounds (copper chloride) in solution. Then, in Investigation 6-D, you will learn about the problems of extracting a remarkable metal — aluminum.

Extracting a Metal by Electrolysis

In this investigation, you will use electricity to decompose a copper-containing mineral. As the electrolysis proceeds, observe any colour changes carefully.

Problem

Can copper be extracted from a compound using electrical energy?

Safety Precautions

Copper (II) chloride is toxic and an irritant.

Material

copper (II) chloride solution

Apparatus

400 mL beaker
2 carbon rods for electrodes
2 wire leads with alligator clips
6 V power source

Procedure

1. Pour about 100 mL of copper chloride solution into the beaker.

2. Place the two carbon rods in the solution on opposite sides of the beaker. The rods must not touch.

3. Use an alligator clip to attach a wire to one carbon rod. Attach the other end of the wire to the positive terminal on your power supply. Connect the other rod to the negative terminal in the same way.

4. Leave the power connected for a few minutes, and record any changes you see.

5. Carefully smell the beaker by taking a breath away from the apparatus and then wafting the air over the beaker toward your nose. Note and record the presence of any odour.

6. Disconnect one wire from the power supply. Record the appearance of each carbon rod and identify which terminal it was connected to on the power supply.

7. Return the contents of the beaker to your teacher for safe disposal.
   Wash your hands thoroughly after completing this investigation.

Analyze

1. What evidence did you observe to show that copper was produced during electrolysis? Which terminal was connected to the rod where you observed the copper?

2. What evidence would support the claim that a gas was generated during this electrolysis? What do you think the gas might be?

Conclude and Apply

3. Think about whether the electrolysis would have worked if you had used dry copper chloride powder instead of copper chloride solution. What would you have to do to confirm your ideas? (You might wish to review what you know about electrolysis from the discussion of Davy's work in Chapter 5.)

The Story of Aluminum

Think About It

Aluminum is an extremely useful material because of its unusual properties. Its excellent thermal conductivity and malleability make it an ideal material for baking foil. Curiously, aluminum's great reactivity actually makes it a *good* roofing material: a thin, tough coating of aluminum oxide forms instantly and protects the rest of the metal from the rain and wind.

The great reactivity of aluminum also explains why so many years passed between the scientific discovery of the element and the development of technology to extract large amounts at a reasonable cost. What happened during these years is an interesting and complex story, summarized in the table below.

Year and Country	Historical Development
1807 England	Humphry Davy (1778–1829) infers the existence of a previously unknown element in a sample of clay. Even with electrolysis, however, Davy cannot isolate the new element. Available methods can only produce the white compound this element forms with oxygen. Davy names the new compound *alumina*.
1825 Denmark	Hans Christian Oersted (1777–1851) mixes the compound aluminum chloride with a mercury-potassium alloy and heats the mixture strongly. This high-risk process produces a tiny lump of metal of the pure metallic element we now call aluminum. But the sample is too small to permit an investigation of its properties.
1827 Germany	Friedrich Wöhler (1800–1882) mixes aluminum chloride with pure metallic potassium and heats the mixture strongly. This produces pure aluminum, but the grains are extremely small and immediately form a coating of alumina (aluminum oxide). Wöhler still cannot determine the metal's properties.
1845 Germany	Wöhler finally produces grains of aluminum large enough to test for the metal's physical properties. Aluminum's low density is recognized.
1855 France	The newborn baby of Napoleon III (1808–1873) is given an aluminum rattle. The emperor is given a set of aluminum cutlery, which is reserved for honoured guests. The emperor is eager to outfit the French army with equipment made of this wonderfully light metal, but the price is too high. The race is on to produce aluminum more cheaply.
1859 France	So far, aluminum has been produced only by heat-based smelting processes. Henri Deville (1818–1881) improves the existing smelting technology and brings the metal's price down, but it is still too expensive to be practical.

Deville was not the only person who was trying to develop a new extraction technology. By 1860 every metallurgist knew that a fortune was waiting for anyone who could invent a less costly way to refine aluminum. Everyone who tried faced the same set of problems, however:

- A coating of aluminum oxide (Al_2O_3) always forms on the surface of pure aluminum. If you scrape the coating off, another layer forms immediately.

- Aluminum oxide is strongly bound and very difficult to decompose, so smelting aluminum requires extremely high temperatures, expensive ingredients, and dangerous materials.
- Electrolysis is often a practical way to decompose strongly bound compounds, but electrolysis works only on liquids, either pure substances or solutions.
- Aluminum oxide is a solid. Melting it is not practical, and the solid powder does not dissolve in water, alcohol, or any other common liquid.

What was the answer? Use an uncommon liquid. But what liquid was uncommon enough to dissolve alumina? Amazingly two young chemists, working thousands of miles apart, solved the problem in almost exactly the same way at almost exactly the same time.

In 1886 both Charles Martin Hall in the United States and Paul Louis Héroult in France hit upon the idea of using hot melted cryolite (aluminum sodium fluoride, Na_3AlF_6) as a solvent for powdered aluminum oxide. This idea was far from obvious, for cryolite is an uncommon mineral that melts at just under 1000°C. Melted cryolite does dissolve aluminum oxide, however. Applying a strong electric current to this hot solution decomposes the oxide. Pure liquid aluminum collects at the bottom of the container, where it can be drained off and allowed to cool.

What to Do

Answer the following questions. Discuss what you think, and why, with a partner or a group of classmates.

1 Who do you think discovered aluminum? Give reasons for your opinion.

2 Napoleon III was not a scientist. Why is the French emperor's name included in the table of historical developments?

3 Few major discoveries are made by someone working entirely alone. Hall had two mentors.

(a) Professor Frank Jewett of Oberlin College continued to encourage Hall's research even after the young scientist graduated. Jewett himself had studied in Germany, where he had met Friedrich Wöhler. What influence might Wöhler and Jewett have had on Hall's work?

(b) Hall's older sister, Julia, had also studied chemistry at Oberlin. What influence might she have had on Hall's work?

4 Every researcher needs a laboratory and equipment. Think carefully as you read the following information, and give reasons for your opinion in each case.

(a) Héroult had access to a well-equipped laboratory. Hall made his discoveries in a shed in his parents' backyard. Which researcher had the advantage?

(b) Héroult had access to a furnace. Hall had to build his own. Why was a furnace needed? Which researcher had the advantage?

(c) Héroult borrowed a generator to produce electric current. Hall had to make his own batteries. Why was a current needed? Which researcher had the advantage?

5 On February 23, 1886, Hall produced the world's first sample of aluminum extracted by electrolysis. Julia Hall was out of town that day, so Charles demonstrated the procedure for her the next day.

(a) From a scientific viewpoint, why must scientists be able to duplicate their findings?

(b) What practical purpose is served by demonstrating a new process for an educated, well-informed witness?

(c) Why might someone in Hall's position have to be careful about who was allowed to witness the new process? Explain why Julia was a good choice.

Extend Your Knowledge

1. In Investigation 6-C, you electrolyzed copper (II) chloride ($CuCl_2$). You used an aqueous solution. How do you know it was the $CuCl_2$ that decomposed, rather than the water?

2. How is the Hall-Héroult process similar to the one you used to extract copper? How is it different?

3. How many times a week do you use aluminum? Make an estimate, and then check it by keeping an aluminum journal. Note every time you use an aluminum-lined juice box, eat food that is cooked or wrapped in aluminum, or ride in a vehicle that contains aluminum. Where else do you encounter aluminum?

Canada and Aluminum

Once the Hall-Héroult process was perfected, two problems still had to be solved before large-scale production of aluminum could begin:

- how to concentrate the ore from which most commercial aluminum is extracted
- how to produce electricity cheaply enough to make electrolysis practical and aluminum affordable

The first problem was solved by Karl Joseph Bayer in 1888. He cooked bauxite for two days with sodium hydroxide and then filtered it to eliminate impurities. This produced a good concentrate for electrolysis.

The second problem was monetary rather than scientific. Bauxite was (and still is) mined mainly in South America; but electricity could not be produced cheaply enough near the bauxite mines. Amazingly it proved to be far cheaper to transport the bauxite to places where electricity was more economical — places such as Canada.

Canada has no significant bauxite mines, but our hydroelectric resources can be used to produce electricity at a lower cost than nearly anywhere else on Earth. Some other countries refine more aluminum than Canada, but we refine far more than we use and export the rest. The sale of aluminum earns valuable income for our country and provides jobs, not only for those who work in the factories, but also for those who teach, nurse, and run stores in the towns where the factories are located.

Modification of Metallic Properties

An alloy is always harder and stronger than a pure metal. An alloy is also easier to melt and more resistant to electricity, which may not always be desirable. Fortunately there is another way to make metals harder and stronger, without melting, without adding another metal, and without chemical change. This is modification. In the following investigation, you will see for yourself how modification can change the properties of a metal object.

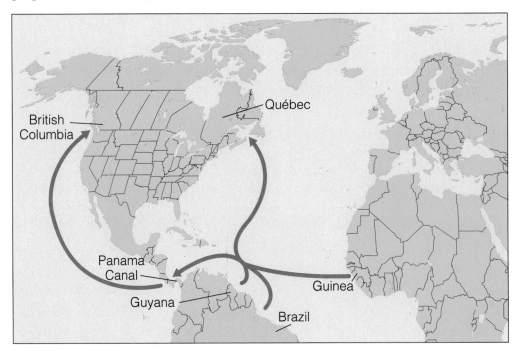

Figure 6.17 Concentrated bauxite ore is transported by sea from mines in Brazil, Guyana, and Guinea to British Columbia and Québec.

INVESTIGATION 6-E

Modifying Metallic Properties

Blacksmiths use hardening and heat treatment to shape horseshoes and other metal objects, in a process called tempering. In this investigation, you will demonstrate how these methods affect a smaller metal object — a paper clip.

Problem

How do hardening and heat affect the properties of a metal?

Safety Precautions

- Handle hot objects with care.
- Keep hair and loose clothing away from the flame.

Apparatus

Bunsen burner
heat resistant pad
utility tongs
100 mL beaker

Materials

3 metal paper clips
cold water

Procedure

1 Take one of the paper clips, and bend it so you have almost a straight metal wire.

2 Bend the wire carefully at one point to make roughly a right angle. Now bend the wire at the same point, at a right angle in the other direction.

3 Count the number of times you can bend the wire before it breaks. Record the number.

4 Straighten a second paper clip. Bend it as you bent the first one, but only half the number of times you took to break the first one.

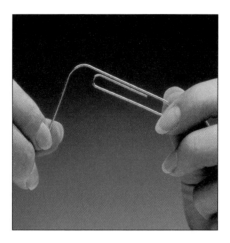

5 Hold the second paper clip in your tongs, and heat it in a Bunsen burner flame until it is glowing. Heat it for about 10 s more, and then hold it in the air to cool slowly. Place it on the heat resistant pad to leave it to cool to room temperature. You will use this wire again in step 8.

6 Half fill the beaker with cold water. Using the third paper clip, repeat step 4. Heat this paper clip so it glows for about 10 s, and then quickly put it into the cold water. Let it cool for about 1 min.

7 Retrieve the wire from the water, and count the number of right-angle bends you can make before it breaks. Record the number.

8 Use the wire from step 5. Count the number of right-angle bends you can make before this wire breaks. Record the number.

   Wash your hands thoroughly after this investigation.

Analyze

1. You compared the flexibility of a metal wire that was heated and allowed to cool slowly with the flexibility of another that was cooled rapidly. Which treatment resulted in a wire that was hard and brittle? Which treatment resulted in a wire that was more flexible?

2. Write a short paragraph, explaining the effect that hardening and heating can have on a metal.

So far in this chapter, you have learned about three different classes of elements and the properties of the elements within each class. Like most large groups, these classes of elements can be divided even further into smaller groups, which share more specific or specialized properties. In the last section of this chapter, you will find out how elements are further classified and organized.

Check Your Understanding

1. Distinguish between a mineral and an ore. Briefly describe the two main stages involved in extracting a metal from its ore. Which stage involves a chemical change? Which stage involves a physical change?

2. What does the term smelting mean? State two metals that are extracted by smelting.

3. Name the mineral that contains aluminum. Why is this mineral mixed with another compound before it is electrolyzed?

4. Name the elements that are present in alumina, hematite, and magnetite.

5. **Apply** Aluminum is a more abundant metal in Earth's crust than iron, but iron is less expensive. Explain.

6. **Thinking Critically** Read through this newspaper report about chocolate manufacture, and then answer the questions that follow it.

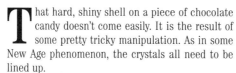

Truffles without tears

That hard, shiny shell on a piece of chocolate candy doesn't come easily. It is the result of some pretty tricky manipulation. As in some New Age phenomenon, the crystals all need to be lined up.

If you don't believe it, try melting some chocolate and dipping something into it. More than likely, you'll end up with something pretty ugly.

That's because the chocolate is out of temper.

Tempering chocolate is something best left to pastry chefs, candy makers, and the truly obsessed.

The problem is that a bar of hard chocolate gets its crisp structure and glossy shine from having the cocoa fat crystals aligned in a particular formation. When the crystals melt, the formation is lost. The chocolate forms crystals and solidifies again when it cools. But it's unlikely that it will go back to that perfect arrangement.

There are four primary crystalline arrangements for fat, and only one (called beta-prime) is the correct crystal for tempered chocolate.

In fact, it is true of almost all fats. That's one reason melted butter that solidifies never looks as smooth and waxy as it did when it came out of the package. (The other is that the water and milk solids have fallen out of emulsion, but that's another story.)

Fortunately, chocolate makers have learned how to realign the melted crystals. The process is called tempering. Traditionally, it's done by what is called the "tablier" method: Chocolate is melted to 31 to 32°C and then two thirds of it is poured out on a cold table. It is worked back and forth with a spatula until it cools slightly to a temperature of about 27°C, which encourages the creation of those beta-prime crystals.

At this point, the cooled part is added back to the rest of the melted chocolate and the whole is mixed until all the chocolate cools in lock-step with the beta-prime crystals.

The Los Angeles Times February 24, 1999, (Extract from article by Russ Parsons)

(a) Where else in this section have you seen the term "tempering"? Which material was being discussed?

(b) In Investigation 6-C, you used mechanical force and heat to change the physical properties of a metal. How was this similar to the process described in the newspaper article? How was it different?

6.4 Families of Elements

In chemistry, the term **chemical family** is used to describe a group of related elements. For example, copper, silver, and gold all belong to the same chemical family. These three elements are often referred to as coinage metals, even though few countries use them to make coins nowadays.

Less than a century ago, gold coins worth $5 and $10 were common currency in Canada. Until 1967 Canada's one-dollar coins were made of silver. Although the Royal Canadian Mint still produces a special "silver dollar" every year, the one-dollar coin we use every day is not made of silver. It can be exchanged for a dollar's worth of goods, but the metal in the coin itself is worth very little. Similarly, Canadian quarters and dimes were made of nearly pure silver until 1967, and pennies were made of nearly pure copper. Today our quarters and dimes contain metal that is worth far less than the face value of the coins.

Canada's use of copper, silver, and gold for coinage followed thousands of years of tradition. Most of the earliest civilizations made their coins from these same three metals. The reason why this tradition lasted so long is the same as the reason why modern chemists refer to the coinage metals as a family. Despite their different colours, these elements share several common properties.

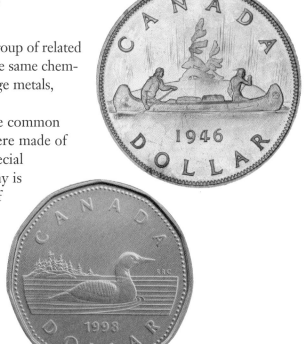

Figure 6.18 The silver in a silver dollar minted before 1967 was worth one dollar, if not more. But the metal in the "loonie" we use today is worth less than its face value.

Figure 6.19 These Roman coins, which are almost 2000 years old, are made from copper, silver, and gold — the coinage metals.

Patterns of Properties in a Chemical Family

As in human families, the members of a chemical family are not identical. Yet they do have certain features in common.

Scan the table below, and answer the questions that follow it.

Property	Aluminum (Al)	Copper (Cu)	Gold (Au)	Iron (Fe)	Silver (Ag)
effect of acid on cleaned, bare, pure metal	reacts with acid; hydrogen gas released	unreactive with most acids	unreactive with most acids	reacts with acid; hydrogen gas released	unreactive with most acids
compound formed with oxygen?	readily	not readily	not readily	readily	not readily
malleability	very malleable	very malleable	highly malleable	malleable	very malleable
electrical conductivity	very good	second best of all metals	excellent	good	best of all metals

What to Do

Use the word "pattern" in your answers to the following questions.

1. The coinage metals — copper, silver, and gold — are considered to be a chemical family. List three arguments to explain why.

2. (a) List arguments in favour of including aluminum in the family of coinage metals.

   (b) List arguments against including aluminum.

3. (a) List arguments in favour of including iron in the family of coinage metals.

   (b) List arguments against including iron.

4. Do you think aluminum belongs to the same chemical family as iron? List arguments for and against.

The Need for Better Classification

By the 1850s, chemists had identified a total of 58 elements, and nobody knew how many more there might be. Thanks to Berzelius' invention of chemical symbols, it was easy to communicate about the elements. Thanks to Volta's invention of the battery, it was easy to classify elements into three classes: metals (which conduct electricity readily), non-metals (which do not conduct it at all), and metalloids (which conduct it a little). These classes — the metals especially — were too large for convenient study, however.

The idea of chemical families was helpful for obvious families like the coinage metals, but most family relationships were far from obvious. Properties such as density and electrical conductivity were not enough by themselves to use as a basis for classification. Thanks to Dalton, nineteenth-century chemists knew that relative atomic mass was the one property that distinguished every element from all the others. According to Dalton's atomic theory, each element had its own kind of atom with a specific atomic mass, different from the atomic mass of any other elements.

By the 1860s several scientists were trying to sort the known elements according to atomic mass. The one who did it best was the Russian chemist Dmitri Mendeleev (1834–1907).

Mendeleev Builds a Table

Mendeleev made a card for each known element. On the card, he put data similar to the data you see in Figure 6.21. (Figure 6.21 shows modern values for silicon, rather than the ones Mendeleev actually used, but his values were surprisingly close to these.)

Figure 6.20 Dmitri Ivanovich Mendeleev was born in Siberia, the youngest of 17 children.

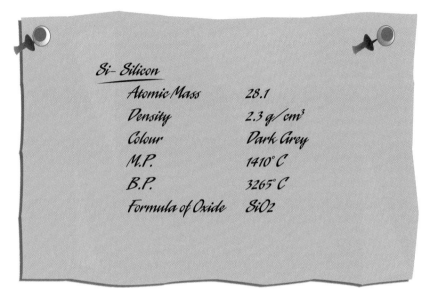

Si– Silicon

Atomic Mass	28.1
Density	2.3 g/cm³
Colour	Dark Grey
M.P.	1410° C
B.P.	3265° C
Formula of Oxide	SiO2

Figure 6.21 This is the kind of information that Mendeleev wrote on his property cards.

Mendeleev pinned all the cards to the wall, in order of increasing atomic mass. Day after day, he stared at the wall, moving elements around and looking for patterns in their properties. In the next activity, you will model Mendeleev's method.

Mendeleev "played cards" for several months, arranging the elements in vertical columns and horizontal rows. When he arranged the elements in order of increasing atomic mass, he found that the properties of the elements repeated at definite, or periodic, intervals. The eighth element in his arrangement (sodium) had properties similar to the first (lithium), and the fifteenth element (potassium) had properties similar to the eighth. Therefore the first, eighth, and fifteenth elements made up a chemical family. Because of these periodic intervals, the pattern he discovered became known as the **periodic table**.

Keep in mind that not all of the elements had been discovered, so Mendeleev's table was a very imaginative idea. It caught on quickly because of its usefulness in making predictions. Mendeleev left gaps in his table, blank spaces predicting the existence of elements not yet found or even suspected by other chemists. He even predicted properties of these unknown elements, which spurred on other scientists to prove or disprove his predictions.

Chemical Solitaire

In this activity, you will arrange element cards in groups according to their atomic mass and other properties.

What You Need

sheet of property cards for fictional elements (provided by your teacher)
scissors

What to Do

1. Cut the sheet into separate cards.

2. Examine the cards to find the atomic mass for each element.

3. Line up the cards in order of increasing atomic mass.

4. Scan the cards to look for properties that are similar enough to justify grouping certain cards together. Record your first arrangement on a piece of paper.

5. Now look from group to group. Is there a better way to arrange the cards than the way you did in step 4? If so, record your new arrangement.

6. Share your arrangements with one or two other students. Record any other arrangements you come up with.

What Did You Discover?

1. Which cards probably represent metallic elements? Which probably represent non-metallic elements? Give reasons for your opinions.

2. Which elements are solids? Which are liquids? Which are gases? Explain how you know.

3. Which of your arrangements do you think is the best? Why?

Extensions

4. How long did it take you to classify these elements? Mendeleev had to classify 63 elements. How long do you think it took him?

5. Where do you think Mendeleev got the data he wrote on his cards? (Hint: Do you think he performed all the experiments himself to get the data?)

INTERNET CONNECT

www.school.mcgrawhill.ca/resources/

There are a number of sites that can provide information about elements and their properties, and some historical background. Go to the web site above. Go to **Science Resources**, then to **SCIENCEPOWER 9** to know where to go next.

How did Mendeleev's table make it possible for him to predict the properties of other, still undiscovered, elements? By carefully examining the properties of the elements as they appeared in his periodic sequence, he was able to infer what might be the properties of any "missing" elements in the same family. Two examples, gallium and germanium, are famous for having been discovered shortly after Mendeleev predicted their existence and physical properties — a remarkable example of experimental evidence confirming scientific theory.

Over the years, Mendeleev's basic periodic table has become one of the foundations of modern chemistry. The following investigation gives you a gradual introduction to the structure of the modern periodic table — a very important idea for classifying chemical data. You will study the periodic table in more detail in Chapter 7.

Meet the Modern Periodic Table

Part 1

Every Element Has Its Own Number

Think About It

Mendeleev had noticed a periodic relationship between increasing atomic mass and chemical properties of elements. He published two versions of his periodic table, one in 1869 and one in 1871. His work provided a logical organization for a huge amount of data about the elements, but no one could explain why the elements showed their amazing periodicity.

By about 1915, chemists and physicists had developed models of atomic structure, and it became more and more clear that atomic structure was the key to explaining the periodicity of chemical properties. The periodic table was therefore reorganized with a focus on atomic structure, rather than simply

on atomic mass. The changes were surprisingly few. The resulting modern periodic table is based on a special number for each element, called its atomic number. This number is related to the atomic structure of the element, in ways you will learn about in Chapter 7. For now, notice that the atomic number gives a unique definition to each element.

The periodic table below is simplified so you can concentrate on the format. It shows you the general shape of the modern periodic table and includes symbols for the elements, which are arranged in order of their atomic number. As well, it also indicates which elements are gases and which are liquids.

H																		He
Li	Be			liquid	gas							B	C	N	O	F		Ne
Na	Mg											Al	Si	P	S	Cl		Ar
K	Ca	Sc	Ti	V	Cr	Mn	Fe	Co	Ni	Cu	Zn	Ga	Ge	As	Se	Br		Kr
Rb	Sr	Y	Zr	Nb	Mo	Tc	Ru	Rh	Pd	Ag	Cd	In	Sn	Sb	Te	I		Xe
Cs	Ba	La	Hf	Ta	W	Re	Os	Ir	Pt	Au	Hg	Tl	Pb	Bi	Po	At		Rn

A simplified view of part of the modern periodic table

What to Do

1 An element's position in the periodic table is determined by its atomic number. The numbering system begins with hydrogen (H), atomic number 1, in the upper left-hand corner and moves from left to right. The numbers skip any blank space in between, so helium (He) has atomic number 2. The numbers then jump back to the left again, so lithium (Li), atomic number 3, is next.

Make a copy of this simplified periodic table and record these atomic numbers on it.

2 Infer and record the atomic numbers for beryllium (Be) and boron (B), then do the same for the rest of this horizontal row, from carbon (C) to neon (Ne).

Analyze

Which element in each pair below has the larger atomic number? Explain how you know.

(a) carbon (C) or silicon (Si)

(b) silicon (Si) or phosphorus (P)

(c) beryllium (Be) or sodium (Na)

CONTINUED

Part 2

Every Element Is Part of a Group

Think About It

The correct name for each vertical column in the periodic table is a **group**. What we have been calling "chemical families", such as the coinage metals, are located in the same group. Some groups are given special names because they form a family of elements with especially strong relationships. You will be examining some of these groups immediately after this investigation.

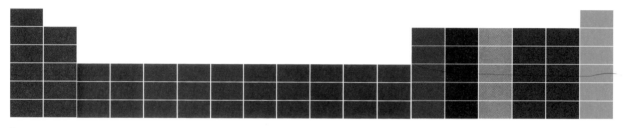

How groups appear in the periodic table

What to Do

Combine information from the simplified periodic table in Part 1 and the diagram above to answer the following questions.

① There are actually 18 groups in the periodic table, as you can see by counting across the top of the diagram. For this introductory investigation, only eight of the groups are coloured, just to suggest the idea of what groups are. Locate the elements in the second group from the left in your simplified periodic table.

② Record the symbols for these elements in a vertical list. Which element in the list has the largest atomic number?

③ Which element would you expect to have the greatest atomic mass? Why?

④ Which element would you expect to have the greatest density? Why?

Analyze

1. List the symbols, and as many names as you can, of the other elements that are found in the same group as the elements below.

    (a) aluminum (Al)

    (b) potassium (K)

    (c) lead (Pb)

2. Locate the elements copper (Cu), silver (Ag), and gold (Au) on your simplified periodic table. Are they in the same group? Is this what you expected? Explain your answer.

3. Like gold, the element platinum (Pt) is often called a "precious metal." Locate platinum in your simplified periodic table. Is platinum in the same group as gold? Is this what you expected? Explain your answer.

Part 3

Every Element Is Part of a Period

Think About It

The horizontal rows of the periodic table are called **periods**. You probably noticed the big empty spaces in the middle of Periods 1, 2, and 3. (The periods are numbered starting at the top. There are seven periods, although these simplified diagrams show only six.) There is a reason for these spaces. It would not make sense simply to put helium (He) right next to hydrogen (H) in Period 1, just because a space is available. Helium belongs in the group having similar chemical properties — the group with neon (Ne), argon (Ar), and so on. The table has to be wide enough, and flexible enough, to allow for this periodic feature which is its basis. The empty spaces are not like the ones Mendeleev left because the elements were unknown. These modern empty spaces have a very important function.

How periods appear in the periodic table

What to Do

Combine information from the simplified periodic table in Part 1 and the diagram above to answer the following questions.

1 Record the symbols of the elements in Period 2 (the second row) so they are stretched out horizontally across a page. Place the symbols of the elements in Period 3 (the third row) directly beneath them, as they appear in the table.

2 Most of the elements are solids at room temperature. In your simplified periodic table, elements that are liquids at room temperature are marked like this: ◊. Circle all of the liquids on your periodic table. Do any of them appear in Period 2 or Period 3?

3 Elements that are gases at room temperature are marked like this: ♀. Mark all of these on your periodic table with a highlighter. You will find gases in both Period 2 and Period 3. For each gas in Period 2, is there a corresponding gas underneath it (in the same group) in Period 3? Period 4? Period 5?

Analyze

1. If one element in a group is a gas, do all of them have to be gases? Explain in terms of what periodicity means. (Hint: Is the state of a substance at room temperature a chemical property or a physical property?)

2. The elements in the group that is second from the right have a very pronounced family resemblance. They are called the halogens.

   (a) The groups in the periodic table are numbered from left to right, from 1 to 18. What is the group number for the halogens?

   (b) Find iodine (I) in Period 5. Tellurium (Te) appears immediately to the left of iodine, yet the atomic mass of tellurium is slightly greater than that of iodine. This is one of the most famous "reversals" in the periodic table, and it was known to Mendeleev. Write a short paragraph explaining, in your own words, why Mendeleev would have made this reversal in the sequence of elements according to atomic mass.

Three of the halogens —
chlorine (Cl), bromine (Br),
and iodine (I) — derive
their names from Greek
words that describe one of
their properties. Chlorine
comes from *chloros*,
describing the greenish-
yellow colour of the gas.
(You may also recall the
word "chlorophyll" from
your earlier science studies. What colour is
chlorophyll?) *Iodeides*
means violet-coloured,
which describes the
vapour of iodine. Look up
bromine in a dictionary.
Which Greek word is it
derived from? What could
you guess about bromine
vapour?

DidYou**Know**?

Only nine natural elements
have been discovered in
the twentieth century.
Since the discovery of
atomic energy in the
1930s, however, chemists
have actually created
several elements. Since
these elements do not
occur in nature, they are
often called "artificial" or
"synthetic elements." Use
one of the web sites you
found on page 218 to
learn more about them.

Characteristics of Some Interesting Groups

At the left-hand and right-hand sides of the periodic table, you will find groups that demonstrate the periodic feature of the table in a striking way. The alkali metals (Group 1) react rapidly when exposed to air and water. For example, sodium (Na) reacts with water to produce hydrogen, and, as you know, hydrogen is extremely flammable. This reaction is so intense that the hydrogen can explode. Sodium is usually stored in kerosene to keep the water vapour in the air away from it, because it is so violently reactive.

Locate sodium on your simplified periodic table, and notice the other elements in this group. It may surprise you to find hydrogen, a gas, in the same group as solid metals. The reason has to do with atomic structure, as you will learn in Chapter 8. You know already that hydrogen is extremely reactive (like the other elements in Group 1). In fact, it is so reactive that it cannot exist in nature as an atom, but exists as a diatomic molecule.

The alkali metals are the most reactive metals. The halogens, which were mentioned earlier, are the most reactive non-metals. Notice the position of the halogens near the right-hand side of the periodic table (Group 17). Fluorine (F) is so reactive that it will etch glass, and indeed it is used (with great care!) to decorate glass panels and sculptures. Chlorine (Cl) causes serious respiratory problems if it is inhaled, and bromine (Br) causes very serious and painful skin burns. Amazingly sodium (a highly reactive alkali metal that can damage human tissue) reacts with chlorine (a highly reactive halogen that will also damage human tissue) to produce sodium chloride, which we consume in our food every day. What a chemical change! You will learn why such changes occur as you continue with this unit.

At the extreme right-hand side of the periodic table is Group 18, the noble gases. (This group was entirely missing from Mendeleev's table.) They were called "noble" because they are chemically calm. Calmness was thought to be a characteristic of people of the noble classes in historic times. As you will learn in Chapter 7, the noble gases can be excited by electricity to produce interesting colours in discharge tubes, but they are not changed *chemically* when they do so.

Check Your Understanding

1. Which three metals are called the "coinage metals"? Name one chemical prop-erty and one physical property you used in order to group them as a "family".

2. Use your simplified periodic table to locate the element selenium (Se) and answer the following questions.

   (a) What is the physical state of selenium at room temperature: solid, liquid, or gas?

   (b) What is its group number in the table?

   (c) What is its period number in the table?

3. How is Mendeleev's periodic table different from the modern periodic table? How is it similar?

4. What do we mean by a "family" of elements? Name the three special "families" that were discussed near the end of the section, and state one characteristic of each.

5. **Thinking Critically** Mendeleev's periodic table did not include the group we now know as the noble gases. What might be the reason?

Now that you have completed this chapter, try to do the following. If you cannot, go back to the sections indicated.

Write the names and symbols of the first 20 elements in the periodic table. (6.1)

Interpret a chemical formula in terms of the elements present in the molecule and the number of atoms combined together. (6.1)

State the molecular formulas of some common gases. (6.1)

Write the names and chemical formulas of the four most abundant gases in dry air. (6.2)

Distinguish between Earth's atmosphere and hydrosphere, and identify elements that are found in both. (6.2)

Perform chemical tests to rank the reactivity of metals, and identify the gas that is displaced from water by reactive metals. (6.2)

Given the physical properties of an unknown element, identify it as a metal or a non-metal. (6.2)

List the three major processes that make up the study of metallurgy. (6.3)

Distinguish between a mineral and an ore. (6.3)

Define the terms "concentration" and "decomposition" as they apply to the extraction of an element from its ore. (6.3)

Identify the two energy sources that are used to extract metals from their minerals. (6.3)

Identify the key steps in the production of iron from its ores. (6.3)

Draw and label a diagram showing the electrolysis of a copper (II) chloride solution. Identify the electrode where copper is formed. (6.3)

Summarize the key discoveries that led to the commercial process for refining aluminum. (6.3)

Identify the reason why Canada is a major producer of aluminum. (6.3)

Describe the benefits of recycling aluminum products. (6.3)

Describe how the properties of a metal can be modified by hardening and heat treatment. (6.3)

Define the term "family" as it relates to elements in the periodic table. (6.4)

Distinguish between atomic mass and atomic number. (6.4)

Distinguish between a period and a group in the periodic table. (6.4)

Identify the following families in the periodic table: alkali metals, halogens, noble gases. (6.4)

Use the periodic table to predict trends (such as density, melting point, and boiling point) of the elements within a given family. (6.4)

Prepare Your Own Summary

Summarize this chapter by doing one of the following. Use a graphic organizer (such as a concept map), produce a poster, or write the summary to include the key chapter concepts. Here are a few ideas to use as a guide:

• How are symbols used to represent chemical elements and their compounds?

• Which are the most abundant elements found in Earth's atmosphere, hydrosphere, and crust?

• What chemical reactions would you perform to compare the reactivity of different metals?

• Summarize the physical properties of metals, non-metals, and metalloids.

• Describe how an iron ore might be discovered, concentrated, and smelted.

• Describe how bauxite is concentrated and electrolyzed to obtain pure aluminum.

• Explain the organization of elements in the periodic table. Show how the periodic table can be used to predict the physical properties of elements.

6 Review

Reviewing Key Terms

If you need review, the section numbers show you where these terms were introduced.

1. For each of the following, an element name and symbol are given. Identify the correct pairs, and rewrite any that are incorrect (6.1)
   (a) nitrogen, Ni (c) sodium, S (e) neon, Ne
   (b) potassium, P (d) fluorine, F (f) carbon, Ca

2. What information is represented in a chemical formula? (6.1)

3. Describe properties that are typical of each type of element: metal, non-metal, metalloid. (6.2)

4. Which elements are often referred to as coinage metals? (6.4)

5. Write the name and symbol of:
   (a) a metal and a non-metal that are liquids at room temperature
   (b) a metal and a non-metal that are solids at room temperature
   (c) several gaseous elements (6.4)

Understanding Key Concepts

Section numbers are provided if you need to review.

6. Each of the following symbols is incorrect. Identify the rule for writing symbols that has been broken. (6.1)
   (a) c (carbon)   (c) cU (copper)
   (b) CA (calcium)   (d) Cob (cobalt)

7. Name the elements that are present in each of the following compounds. State the number of atoms of each element that are present in one molecule. (6.1)
   (a) N_2H_2, used as a rocket fuel
   (b) $CaCO_3$, present in antacid tablets
   (c) Ca_3P_2, used in emergency signal lights
   (d) $Na_2S_2O_3$, used in photography

8. Name four elements that have been known since ancient times. Write their chemical symbols. (6.1)

9. At a mine, would the mineral or the ore be present in the larger quantity? Explain. (6.3)

10. What are the main stages that are involved in the refinement of a metallic element? (6.3)

11. Which element is more reactive, aluminum or iron? Which element is more durable? Explain. (6.3)

12. Name an element that will
    (a) react with cold water
    (b) react with dilute hydrochloric acid but not with hot water
    (c) not react with dilute hydrochloric acid (6.2)

13. What properties of aluminum make aluminum foil useful for baking food? (6.3)

14. What is coke? How is it used in the manufacture of iron? (6.3)

15. (a) How did Mendeleev organize the elements in his periodic table?
    (b) In this chapter, you read about two elements that were unknown but predicted by Mendeleev. Name these two elements. (6.4)

16. Why is the modern periodic table one of the foundations of modern chemistry? (6.4)

Developing Skills

17. Research lung diseases, such as asbestosis and silicosis, that used to be common among miners. Find out what safety procedures are in place in modern mines to reduce the occurrence of lung diseases.

18. Write biographies of Charles Hall and Paul Héroult, the inventors of the electrolytic production of aluminum. Look for similarities in their lives.

19. The following table shows the average of the high and low prices of gold (in U.S. dollars) from 1983 to 1997.

1983	$442	1988	$440	1993	$366
1984	$357	1989	$386	1994	$383
1985	$313	1990	$385	1995	$384
1986	$382	1991	$374	1996	$391
1987	$445	1992	$345	1997	$325

(a) The average of the high and low prices of gold during the year may not be the best estimate of the average price during the year. Why not?

(b) Plot the data as a bar graph.

(c) Why do you think the price of gold changes? In which years was the price high?

(d) Do you think the price of oil might have changed in the same ways that the price of gold changed? How would you find out?

Problem Solving

20. Think about the following metals:

   aluminum   copper   lead

   steel   tungsten   mercury

   Which of these metals might be used for the objects below?

   (a) saucepans

   (b) electrical cables

   (c) hot water pipes

   (d) the roof of a building

   (e) the filament of an incandescent bulb

   (f) the metal framing for a building

21. A typical copper ore in Canada contains about 2 percent of the metal. If the annual production of mined copper is about 700 000 t, how much ore must be mined annually?

22. (a) If one kilogram of aluminum is needed to make 70 beverage cans, what is the mass (in grams) of each can?

   (b) Mass an empty beverage can. Is there a difference between your calculated and measured values? Explain.

Critical Thinking

23. Transportation is the largest single market for aluminum.

   (a) Name several applications of aluminum in transportation.

   (b) Which properties of aluminum make it particularly useful in this sector?

24. Why is the body of a car often made using steel, which rusts, but never using aluminum, which does not corrode easily?

25. Should Canadian resources be owned and developed by Canadian-owned companies? What are some of the advantages and disadvantages of a "Canada only" approach to resource development?

26. Canada is the world leader in the production of uranium. What are some of the advantages and disadvantages of dominating the production of a given material?

Pause & Reflect

1. If you want to prepare hydrogen gas in the laboratory, you should not add a very reactive metal to an acid. Why?

2. For each person who is employed to mine an ore, many other people are employed in related industries. Name some of the industries that are related to the mining of ores containing iron.

3. How is the Canadian production of metals and minerals linked to the economies of other nations?

4. How do you benefit from minerals that are mined in provinces other than your own?

Opening Ideas...

- What can the colours of a firework tell you about the inside of an atom?

- How can you tell the age of an Egyptain mummy?

- What do television sets, X-rays and nuclear power plants have in common?

Science Log

In your Science Log, write down what you know about the inside of an atom. Then draw sketches to illustrate what you think an atom might look like. As you study this chapter, you will learn about the particles that make up an atom and the work of the men and women who contributed to our understanding of the atom. You will find that learning about the atom will help you understand how to use the periodic table.

In prehistory, people had only one source of light — the Sun. Today we enjoy a mind-boggling variety of lighting technology. The coloured sparks of a fireworks display inspire "oohs" and "aahs." We light our homes with incandescent bulbs containing tungsten filaments and with fluorescent tubes containing mercury vapour. We illuminate our businesses with neon lights and our highways with sodium vapour lamps.

The earliest cars lit their way with kerosene lamps hung on the sides. These lamps were replaced with a more complex system, which involved water dripping onto calcium carbide. The resulting chemical reaction released acetylene gas, which burned with an intensely bright light. (Acetylene torches are still used for metalwork.) Halogen headlights are standard equipment on most cars today, but a new "high-intensity discharge" headlight technology, involving both xenon gas and metallic salts, may soon become the standard.

Tungsten, neon, mercury, sodium, calcium, xenon, halogens — you already know these as the names of elements or groups of elements. Each emits light in its own special pattern or mixture, which produces a distinctive colour: the brilliant red shine of neon, the violet glow of mercury, the warm orange radiance of sodium, the penetrating glare of modern car headlights. Earlier you learned that flame tests can identify an element. This is not all that the light given off by an element can do. To a trained eye, an element's light can reveal the internal structure of its atoms.

Structure

Key Concepts

In this chapter, you will discover

- how scientists discovered electrons and protons by experimenting with tubes similar to the tube in a television set or a computer monitor

- how radioactivity was discovered, and how it was used to probe the structure of atoms

- why different models of the atom were suggested as a result of new technology and new experiments

- how the structure of the atom explains the position of elements in the periodic table

- why atoms of the same element may have different masses

Key Skills

In this chapter, you will

- use a spectroscope to observe the spectrum of various light sources

- perform simple experiments and collect observations to make inferences about the internal structure of a closed box

- determine the number of electrons, protons, and neutrons in an atom, and draw a sketch of an atom given its atomic number and mass number

- use your model-building and presentation skills to explore the development of models of the atom

Key Terms

- spectrum
- gas discharge tube
- anode
- cathode
- cathode ray
- electron
- proton
- subatomic particle
- X-ray
- radioactivity
- alpha particle
- beta particle
- gamma ray
- nucleus
- electron cloud
- nuclear medicine
- neutron
- nuclear energy
- electron shell
- Bohr-Rutherford model
- atomic number
- mass number
- atomic mass unit (u)
- isotope

Starting Point ACTIVITY

Elements and Colours

When you aim a diffraction grating or a hand-held spectroscope at a light source, you can produce a **spectrum**, or banded pattern of colours. Do different light sources produce different spectra?

What You Need

hand-held spectroscope
variety of light sources, including sunlight, ordinary light bulb, and fluorescent lamp

CAUTION: Do not aim the spectroscope directly at the Sun.

What to Do

1. Aim your spectroscope at a well-lit window or a laboratory source of white light. Look for the rainbow-like spectrum. This may require some practice! Make a labelled sketch, and list the colours in order.

2. Aim your spectroscope at an ordinary light bulb and a fluorescent lamp. Make labelled sketches of each, listing the colours in order. Are the spectra continuous (the colours change smoothly) or interrupted (black spaces between the coloured bands)?

What Did You Discover?

1. Which of the light sources you observed gave off the most complete spectrum? Why might the others be interrupted?

2. (a) What colours make up the light from a fluorescent lamp? Explain how you know.

   (b) What colour does the light from a fluorescent lamp appear to be when viewed without a spectroscope?

3. The light from an ordinary light bulb is given off by a tungsten filament. How could spectrum patterns help you tell the difference between the light given off by glowing tungsten and the light given off by the sodium in a street lamp?

7.1 Probing the Atom

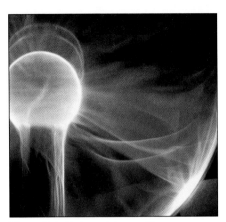

Figure 7.1 Under certain conditions, gases can conduct electricity quite easily.

During the nineteenth century, many chemists worked on determining the properties of known elements and discovering new elements to fill in the gaps Mendeleev had left in his periodic table. While this important work was going on, other scientists became more and more interested in the way electricity interacts with matter.

As you learned from the electrolysis tests you performed in Chapters 5 and 6, electricity causes decomposition when it is passed through liquids, such as water, and compounds in solution, such as copper chloride. You saw that metals conduct electricity very well. Electricity goes right through them without making any apparent change. The spectacular spark you see in a lightning storm shows that gases, too, can conduct electricity. There is an electrical discharge that makes the air glow. This discharge is often violent enough to be frightening, or powerful enough to set fires. You will learn more about what causes lightning, and other aspects of electricity, in the next unit. In this chapter, however, you will focus on how electricity was used to learn more about the atom.

Modelling the Atom

As you work through this chapter, you will encounter many of the scientists whose work led, step by step, to our modern understanding of atomic structure. Later in this chapter, you will have the opportunity to use your model-building and presentation skills to recreate their breakthroughs.

Gases do not conduct electricity as well as metals under normal conditions. It takes an extremely big electrical discharge to make those violent lightning sparks you can see in a storm. In 1821, however, Humphry Davy (whose work with electrolysis you read about in Chapter 5) found that air conducts electricity better if it is trapped and its pressure is reduced.

Other scientists followed up on Davy's discovery. They trapped air and other gases in small **gas discharge tubes** made of glass and equipped with electrodes that were connected to a power source. One electrode, called the **anode**, was positively charged. The other electrode, called the **cathode**, was negatively charged. By removing some of the air in the tube with a crude vacuum pump, the scientists reduced the pressure inside the tube. The trapped gases began to glow when the power source was activated. They could not get the pressure low enough to see any other effects, however, because of the poor quality of the vacuum pump. It was not until about 30 years after Davy's discovery that better technology became available.

How Did Technology Change Our View of the Atom?

Sometimes science shows the way for technological discoveries, and sometimes new technology stimulates scientific discoveries. The technological achievement that did the most to change our view of the atom was the improvement of the gas discharge tube. In 1855, Heinrich Geissler (1814–1879), an expert German glass blower and mechanic, introduced a new gas discharge tube, which had a much improved vacuum pump.

The apparatus that Geissler invented actually had two parts. Figure 7.2 shows only one part — a tightly sealed glass tube with electrodes embedded at each end. The other part was a powerful pump, capable of producing a very strong vacuum. Figure 7.3 shows what happened when an experimenter attached the electrodes to a high-energy source of electricity and began pumping air out of the tube.

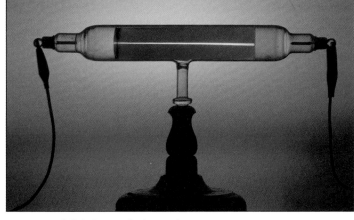

Figure 7.2 A Geissler gas discharge tube.

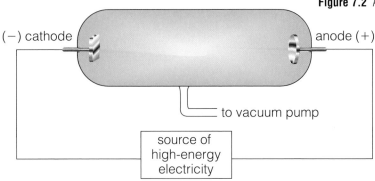

The air pressure inside the tube is only 0.5 percent (or $\frac{1}{200}$) of the air pressure outside.

The tube's strong glass walls keep it from collapsing as the pressure difference builds up. The remaining air glows with a blue colour.

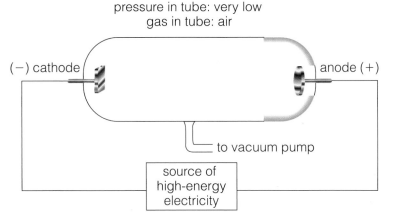

As more air is pumped out, very few molecules remain. The air inside the tube stops glowing, but the part of the glass tube opposite the cathode begins to glow with a green colour.

Figure 7.3 This simplified view of a gas discharge tube shows only the tube.

Today gas discharge tubes are not just a historical curiosity — you probably have one in your home. The picture tube of your television set is a gas discharge tube. It has a cathode (called an "electron gun") at the back and a screen at the front coated with fluorescent materials. Fluorescent substances give a visible glow when struck by certain kinds of invisible rays, in this case the beam of electrons. Electromagnets control the direction of the electrons so that the beam sweeps across the screen, making 525 lines of tiny dots in $\frac{1}{30}$ second. These dots are perceived by you as a continuous picture.

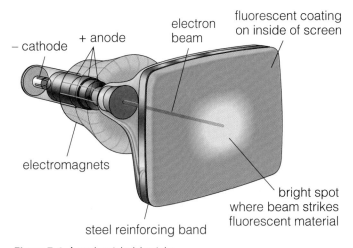

Figure 7.4 A modern television tube

Once scientists had easy access to well-made pumps and discharge tubes, many began to investigate the movement of electricity through gases. This flow diagram summarizes what they learned.

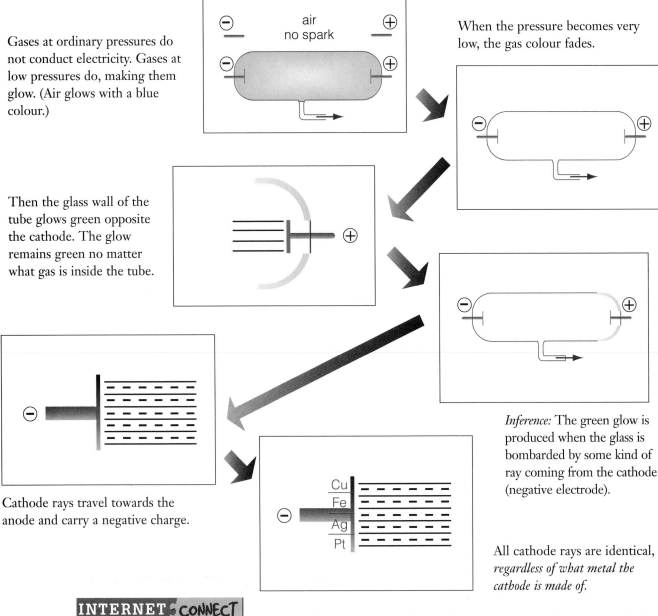

Gases at ordinary pressures do not conduct electricity. Gases at low pressures do, making them glow. (Air glows with a blue colour.)

When the pressure becomes very low, the gas colour fades.

Then the glass wall of the tube glows green opposite the cathode. The glow remains green no matter what gas is inside the tube.

Inference: The green glow is produced when the glass is bombarded by some kind of ray coming from the cathode (negative electrode).

Cathode rays travel towards the anode and carry a negative charge.

All cathode rays are identical, *regardless of what metal the cathode is made of.*

INTERNET • CONNECT

www.school.mcgrawhill.ca/resources/
If you have ever seen a "neon" sign, then you have seen a gas discharge tube. The colour of the sign depends on what gas is inside the tube. Find out what colour is given off by a tube that contains neon gas. What gas glows a pale violet-blue? When was the neon tube invented? Where did the first neon sign appear? Answer these questions and learn more about neon signs by going to the web site above. Go to the **Science Resources**, then to **SCIENCEPOWER 9** to know where to go next.

Scientists now knew that **cathode rays** came from the cathode and travelled through the gas discharge tube towards the anode, and inferred that they carried a negative charge. The last discovery in this flow diagram puzzled researchers a great deal. In Chapter 6, you saw that energizing metal atoms by heating them produces flames of different colours — even when the atoms are part of a compound. Nineteenth-century scientists had assumed that the kind of metal in the cathode also should affect cathode rays. It did not, however. So the atoms of different metals must all have something in common — something negatively charged.

Crookes' Corpuscles

In the 1870s, British scientist William Crookes (1832–1919) conducted many experiments with discharge tubes he designed himself. The experiment in Figure 7.5 is just one well-known example. The iron cross blocks the rays. Looking at the path of the rays, which electrode must they be coming from, the cathode or the anode? What does this tell you about their charge?

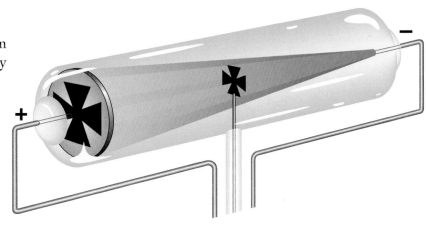

Figure 7.5 Crookes is best known for this experiment. What is making the glass glow? Why is one part of the glass not glowing?

In another experiment (see Figure 7.6), Crookes mounted a tiny pinwheel inside a custom-made discharge tube. When the electric current was switched on, the pinwheel began to spin, much like a windmill in a strong breeze. To Crookes, this meant that the cathode rays must have mass as well as motion. Other scientists quickly accepted his idea that cathode rays are made of fast-moving "corpuscles" — minute bits of matter. Just how tiny they are was investigated by the next great scientist to enter the story.

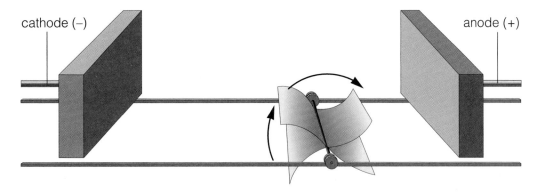

Figure 7.6 From this cleverly designed experiment, Crookes inferred that cathode rays must be made of matter.

The search for what we now call the "electron" culminated in the work of British scientist Joseph John Thomson (1856–1940). Starting in 1894, Thomson worked with a new version of Crookes' apparatus to investigate how these electrically charged corpuscles would move in an electric field, and to figure out how small they might be. In the next investigation, you will follow the experimental path Thomson took, and see for yourself what he was able to infer.

Figure 7.7 J.J. Thomson, "the father of the electron"

Chasing the Electron

Think About It

How could you use gas tube technology not just to produce cathode rays but also to steer them around? What might this tell you about the charge and the mass of the individual particles? (Remember, the lighter a particle, the easier it is to change the direction of the particle.)

What to Do

1 Diagram A shows a basic discharge tube, Thomson's experimental starting point. Compare it with Geissler's earlier gas discharge tube in Figure 7.3.

    (a) How is this discharge tube similar to Geissler's device?

    (b) How is it different?

2 Study diagram B.

    (a) In which of these directions do the rays travel?

        • from the anode to the cathode

        • from the cathode to the vacuum pump

        • from the source of electricity to the cathode

        • from the cathode to the anode

    (b) Your answer to part (a) is an example of an inference. What evidence supports your inference?

    (c) What does the slit in the anode do to the rays?

3 To make it easier for you to see what Thomson added to the apparatus, some of the labels in diagram B have been deleted in diagram C.
    (a) Describe the new equipment.

    (b) How does the second source of electricity differ from the first?

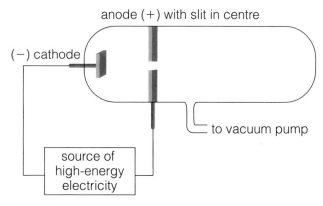

Diagram A

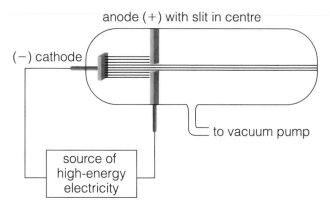

Diagram B

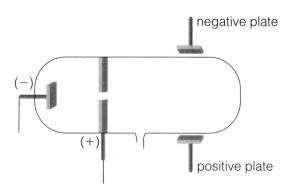

Diagram C

4 Only one of the following diagrams shows what happens when both electrical circuits are switched on. Which do you think predicts the outcome correctly: diagram D, E, or F? Give reasons for your choice.

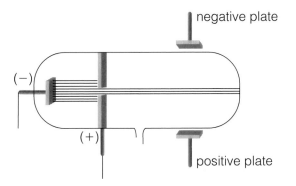

negative plate

(−)

(+)

positive plate

Diagram D

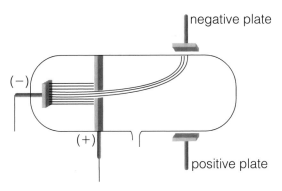

negative plate

(−)

(+)

positive plate

Diagram E

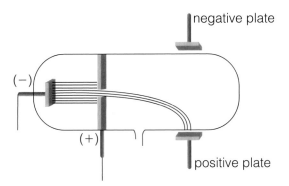

negative plate

(−)

(+)

positive plate

Diagram F

Analyze

1. Draw a simple sketch to show what you think would have happened if Thomson had exchanged the two plates (that is, positive plate above, negative plate below). Give reasons for your answer.

2. Draw a simple sketch to show what you think would have happened if Thomson had slid the two plates to the left, closer to the anode.

3. Earlier scientists had concluded that cathode rays carried a negative charge. Did Thomson's experiment support this conclusion?

4. By measuring the path of the cathode rays very carefully, Thomson was able not only to confirm the rays' negative charge, but also to work out a relationship between the charge and the mass of the "corpuscles." He showed that either they had far more charge than any other particles then known, or they were much smaller. Amazingly it turns out that they have barely $\frac{1}{2000}$ the mass of a single hydrogen atom. How does this differ from Dalton's picture of the smallest particles of matter?

Thomson's Inference About the Proton

By now, it was clear that the atom has negatively charged parts that can be made to move. Scientists agreed to call these tiny, negatively charged bits of matter **electrons**. Atoms usually have no charge, however. They are electrically neutral. Thomson inferred that the atom must possess something with a positive charge to balance the negatively charged electrons.

In 1886 the German physicist Eugen Goldstein (1850–1930) had detected rays travelling away from the anode of a discharge tube that was filled with hydrogen gas. Thomson conducted similar experiments and concluded that these anode rays must be made of positive particles. Thomson called these particles **protons**. Here is what Thomson inferred about electrons and protons:

- All atoms contain both protons and electrons.
- All protons are identical. All electrons are identical. Electrons differ from protons, however.
- An electron has a negative charge. A proton has a positive charge.
- An electron has the same amount of charge as a proton, even though the charges are opposite in kind.
- A proton has much more mass than an electron.

From Science to Technology: The Electron Microscope

You have read about the electron microscope in Unit 1. This technology is actually a direct descendant of the gas discharge tube. Electromagnets are used to control the direction and intensity of a powerful beam of electrons.

The electron microscope was developed to fill a need. By 1900 the compound light microscope had reached its limit, a magnification of about 2000 with skilled operation. Realizing that electrons could be used as the basis for a more powerful microscope, Albert Prebus and James Hillier, two graduate students at the University of Toronto, built the first useful electron microscope in 1938.

Depending on the type of electron microscope, a focussed beam of electrons may either pass straight through a prepared specimen (this is known as "tunnelling") or bounce off it ("scanning"). In either case, the result is an altered electron pattern, which can be displayed on a monitor as an image magnified up to 800 000 times.

It is unlikely that Thomson himself would have thought of using his findings in this way. But the scientific practice of building on knowledge by communicating research results allowed other scientists to see how the electron could be used to probe the atom of which, as Thomson discovered, it is a part.

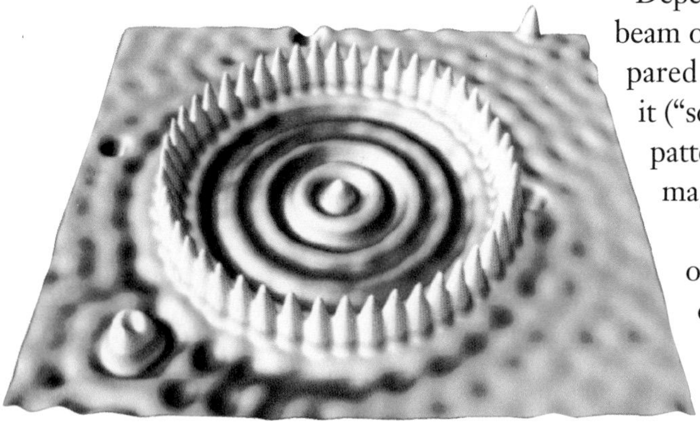

Figure 7.8 This electron microscope image shows individual atoms as "dimples."

DidYou**Know**?

Thomson is sometimes called "the father of the electron." When he published his results in 1897, however, he was still referring to the cathode ray particles as corpuscles. It was not Thomson, but another scientist, G. Johnstone Stoney, who invented the name "electron" in 1891 to describe a unit of charge in electrolysis experiments. A third scientist, George Fitzgerald, argued that this electron and Thomson's corpuscle were really the same thing.

The Divisible Atom

In 1803, Dalton had pictured the atom as a tiny indivisible sphere, like a very tiny billiard ball. By Thomson's time, it was clear that atoms could be torn apart by high-energy electricity; therefore atoms were divisible, after all. Protons and electrons came to be called **subatomic particles** because they were smaller than atoms.

Thomson pictured the atom as a composite of these subatomic particles (see Figure 7.9). His muffin-like model was a major step forward in our understanding of atomic structure. It was soon revised, however, by Thomson's own students.

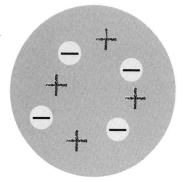

Figure 7.9 In Thomson's model, the negative electrons are like raisins embedded in a doughy framework of positive charge. With a little effort, you can pull the electrons out, just like you can pull the raisins out of a muffin.

Figure 7.9 compares Thomson's model to a muffin, but Thomson himself compared his model to a popular English dessert of the time, plum pudding (or "plum duff"). Thus some books refer to it as the plum pudding model.

Check Your Understanding

1. The discovery of the electron gave scientists their first clue that atoms are divisible. How was the electron discovered, and what are its properties?

2. What is a gas discharge tube? Sketch and label the essential features of a typical gas discharge tube.

3. Describe the modifications William Crookes made to his discharge tubes and the conclusions of his experiments.

4. How was the proton discovered? What are its properties?

5. **Apply** Identify as many applications that rely on electrons as you can.

6. **Thinking Critically** Do you think a television could be made that relied on moving protons rather than electrons? Explain the reasons for your answer.

Where do science and science fiction meet? In 1932 a new and comparatively rare particle, the positron, was discovered. Positrons are not components of the atom, but they have the same mass as an electron and a positive charge like the proton. Just seven years later, a young science fiction writer named Isaac Asimov imagined this particle as the basis for "positronic brains" in robots. He suggested that these brains would have a hard-wired moral code, which he called the "Three Laws of Robotics." Research the positron, robots that have actually been built, and Asimov's three laws at your local library or on the Internet. How do you think positronic brains could work in practice? How might real robots benefit from the three laws?

7.2 The Bohr-Rutherford Model

In Chapter 5, you saw that scientific models help to picture structures or processes that cannot directly be seen. In the case of the atom, direct observation is out of the question, but a good model can give a satisfactory explanation of what can be observed indirectly, and of what scientists of the time can infer from these observations. For example, Dalton's atomic model was a good one when he developed it, but Thomson's model was based on almost a century of further scientific research and interpretation. In this section, you will follow the development of a further model, which changed Thomson's model just as Thomson's had changed Dalton's.

Build a Mental Model

In the study of atomic structure, mental models depend on inferences. Making inferences and constructing mental models requires practice and good reasoning skills.

In this activity, you will construct a mystery box and make your own mental model of what is inside it. Then you will challenge a partner to collect evidence, make inferences, and make a mental model about what is inside.

What You Need

cardboard box, the size of a shoe box
objects to place inside box
adhesive tape
thin, stiff wire

What to Do

1. Design a mystery box. Keep in mind that:
   - a simple but creative mystery box is better than one that is too complicated
   - your box may not contain any liquid that could spill or any object that could decompose, such as food
   - your design must allow for simple tests or experiments, such as probing with a thin wire or shaking

2. Construct your box. You can
   - put in one or two objects that can move and make noise when the box is tilted
   - tape a few objects to the inside of your box

Science Inquiry  ACTIVITY

3. Make a mental model of the inside of your box. Your mental model must be based on the inferences you think your partner can make about it.

4. Seal your box, and exchange boxes with your partner.

5. Perform simple tests to determine what is inside your partner's box. Make a table like the one below to record what you did and what you can infer about the internal structure of the box. Give your table a title.

Tests Conducted on Box	Observations and Evidence Collected	Inferences Made Based on Evidence

6. Put your inferences together to create a mental model of the internal structure of the box. Then make a sketch to describe your model.

What Did You Discover?

1. Compare your mental models with your partner's. How similar are they? Which inferences could account for the differences between them?

2. Which test yielded the most useful evidence?

3. In your own words, define the term "inference."

Mysterious Radiation: X-Rays

As scientists learned more about matter, they also began to learn more about new kinds of radiation. In 1895 German scientist Wilhelm Konrad Roentgen (1845–1923) discovered a new, invisible but highly penetrating form of radiation, the **X-ray**, almost by accident.

Roentgen had been studying the effects of cathode rays, using as a detector a crystal known to glow (fluoresce) under ultraviolet light. To see the effect better, he darkened the room and wrapped his cathode ray tube in cardboard. When he turned on the tube, a bright glow on the other side of the room caught his attention. It came from a sheet of paper coated with the fluorescent material, but this paper was not in the path of the tube. He observed the effect even when the paper was placed in the next room. The mysterious radiation "X" could penetrate both cardboard and walls!

The medical profession began to use X-rays just a few months after their discovery. A number of X-ray tube operators were over-exposed and died before the effects of X-rays on living tissues were properly understood. What precautions are taken by X-ray technicians today?

Modern medicine would be very different without X-rays. Because they penetrate the soft tissues of the body but are stopped by bones and other concentrated tissue masses, X-rays can be used to probe the internal structure of the human body. Soon after Roentgen's discovery, however, another discovery was made which would help to reveal the internal structure of the atom.

Radioactivity: A New Kind of Probe

French chemist Henri Becquerel (1852–1908) knew of Roentgen's work and, in 1896, was doing research of his own into X-rays. He had inferred that there might be a link between fluorescence and X-rays, because Roentgen's fluorescent paper had glowed when exposed to X-rays. Knowing that sunlight is a good source of ultraviolet light, Becquerel wondered if substances exposed to sunlight would give off X-rays as well as the usual fluorescence. He put samples of crystals, some containing uranium, on well-wrapped photographic plates, then exposed them to the Sun for several hours to see if X-rays would penetrate the light-proof paper and expose the film. One cloudy day, he put his samples away in a drawer. Imagine his surprise when he later found that some of the films had been exposed, even in darkness.

Becquerel reasoned that X-rays could not have been responsible for exposing the films, because there was no ultraviolet light to trigger them. He had discovered a *new* kind of ray, a "self-generated" form of radiation that came from the uranium-bearing samples. Testing showed that pure uranium also emitted these rays. Marie Curie (1867–1934) took a great interest in this new discovery and invented the term **radioactivity** to describe the emission of these rays by certain substances.

The discovery of radioactivity led to three types of experiments:

- searching for other radioactive elements
- exploring the composition of the rays
- using the rays to probe atomic structure

Figure 7.10 Even inside a dark drawer, Becquerel's uranium sample was able to take its own picture. The rays penetrated the light-proof wrapping around the photographic plates that were stored in the same drawer.

Searching for Radioactive Elements

During the 1890s, uranium was used to make a yellow dye that was in great demand for fashionable garments. The principal source of uranium was an ore called pitchblende. To everyone's surprise, pitchblende proved to be even more radioactive than pure uranium. Curie hypothesized that pitchblende must contain a *second* radioactive element. With the help of her chemist husband Pierre, she set out to test this hypothesis. You can trace their long and difficult experimental journey in Figure 7.11.

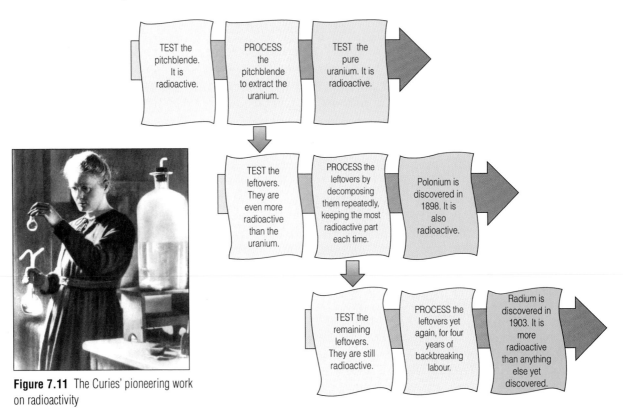

TEST the pitchblende. It is radioactive.

PROCESS the pitchblende to extract the uranium.

TEST the pure uranium. It is radioactive.

TEST the leftovers. They are even more radioactive than the uranium.

PROCESS the leftovers by decomposing them repeatedly, keeping the most radioactive part each time.

Polonium is discovered in 1898. It is also radioactive.

TEST the remaining leftovers. They are still radioactive.

PROCESS the leftovers yet again, for four years of backbreaking labour.

Radium is discovered in 1903. It is more radioactive than anything else yet discovered.

Figure 7.11 The Curies' pioneering work on radioactivity

Exploring the Composition of Radioactivity

Meanwhile, in 1895, a New Zealander named Ernest Rutherford arrived in England to study with Thomson. In 1898 the news of radioactivity stimulated Rutherford, who by then was teaching at McGill University in Montréal, to begin an extensive research program. He performed many experiments and discovered that radioactivity included three types of radiation. Rutherford named them **alpha particles**, **beta particles**, and **gamma rays**, after the first three letters of the Greek alphabet. Figure 7.13 summarizes their individual properties. In 1908 Rutherford won the Nobel Prize in Chemistry for these discoveries. By then, he had returned to England to continue his work with Thomson.

Figure 7.12 Rutherford thought deeply about radioactivity during his time in Montréal.

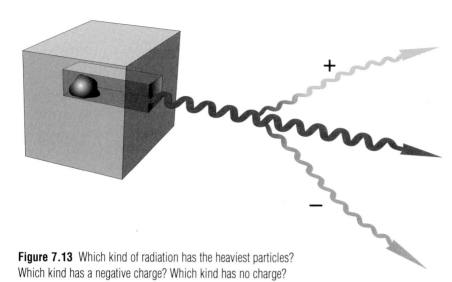

beta particles:
• made of matter
• same mass as one electron
• same negative charge as one electron

gamma rays:
• made of energy
• no mass
• no charge

alpha particles:
• made of matter
• four times the mass of one proton
• same positive charge as two protons

Figure 7.13 Which kind of radiation has the heaviest particles? Which kind has a negative charge? Which kind has no charge?

Probing the Atom with Radioactivity

In 1909 Rutherford designed an experiment to probe the atom by using alpha particles as atomic bullets. To make the "gun," Rutherford placed polonium in a lead container with a narrow opening. A beam of alpha particles was "shot" through this opening at a thin sheet of gold foil (see Figure 7.14).

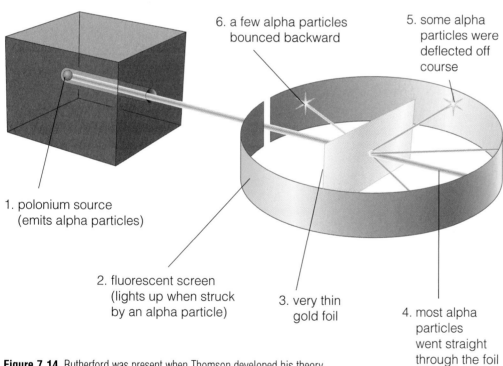

6. a few alpha particles bounced backward

5. some alpha particles were deflected off course

1. polonium source (emits alpha particles)

2. fluorescent screen (lights up when struck by an alpha particle)

3. very thin gold foil

4. most alpha particles went straight through the foil

Figure 7.14 Rutherford was present when Thomson developed his theory about the electron and proton. Thus he had no reason to doubt Thomson's muffin model of the atom — until he observed what you see here.

Pause & Reflect

Have you ever done an experiment that "didn't work"? Speaking later about the results of the gold foil experiment, Rutherford said, "It was quite the most incredible event that has ever happened to me in my life. It was almost as incredible as if you fired a 15-inch [38 cm] shell at a piece of tissue paper and it came back and hit you." Rutherford knew, however, that experiments always provide useful information, even if the results are not what you expect, so he developed a model to explain what he actually observed.

In your Science Log, note what you think Rutherford *expected* to see, according to Thomson's model.

First, Rutherford observed that most alpha particles passed straight through the gold foil as if it were made of empty space. He had expected this, because he knew there must be relatively large distances between atoms. Secondly, however, he was astonished to see that a few alpha particles rebounded from the foil much as a ball rebounds from a solid wall. Why do you think Thomson's "muffin model" of the atom could not account for this second observation?

Rutherford's Model of Atomic Structure

What model of atomic structure could explain the second, surprising result? To find out, trace the line of reasoning shown in Figure 7.15.

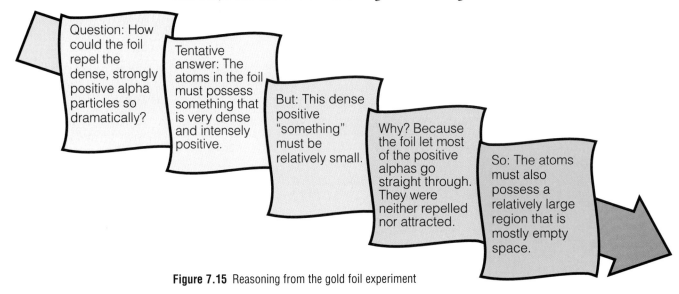

Question: How could the foil repel the dense, strongly positive alpha particles so dramatically?

Tentative answer: The atoms in the foil must possess something that is very dense and intensely positive.

But: This dense positive "something" must be relatively small.

Why? Because the foil let most of the positive alphas go straight through. They were neither repelled nor attracted.

So: The atoms must also possess a relatively large region that is mostly empty space.

Figure 7.15 Reasoning from the gold foil experiment

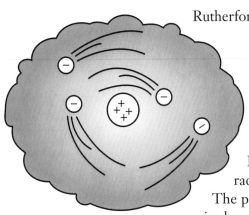

Figure 7.16 Rutherford's nuclear model

Rutherford concluded that the metal atoms in the foil must contain:

- a **nucleus** — a tiny core that is very small in volume, dense compared to the rest of the atom, and intensely positive
- an **electron cloud** — "envelope" that is very large in volume, light compared to the nucleus, and negatively charged

From Science to Technology: Nuclear Medicine

During her research into radioactivity, Marie Curie suffered a severe radiation burn from carrying a vial of uranium chloride in her pocket. The power of radioactivity to penetrate the human body was thus recognized very early, but it took much more research before the beneficial side of this phenomenon emerged. **Nuclear medicine**, the controlled application of selected radioactive elements, is now a key feature of the diagnosis and treatment of cancer, as well as other serious diseases.

Of the three types of radioactivity, gamma rays are the most useful in medicine. They are much more penetrating than alpha or beta particles, and easier to detect.

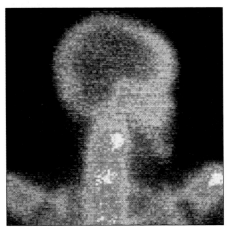

For example, when radioactive technetium (mixed with a phosphorus compound) is injected into the bloodstream, it is carried directly to the bones. There the technetium nuclei release gamma rays, which are detected by a *gamma ray camera*. The resulting image can be used to diagnose bone abnormalities, such as cancer or osteoporosis, at a much earlier stage than with X-ray images (see photograph).

Nuclear medicine can also be used for certain kinds of therapy. For example, the body concentrates iodine (which is not normally radioactive) in the thyroid gland. This means that thyroid tumours can be treated using a radioactive form of iodine. The radioactive iodine releases beta particles directly into the diseased area, minimizing damage to the cells in other parts of the body.

Inferring the Neutron: Where Is the Missing Mass?

Rutherford's scattering experiment also told him something unexpected about the mass of the nucleus of a gold atom. Gold has 79 protons in its nucleus, but their total mass accounts for less than half the mass that Rutherford calculated for the nucleus. He reasoned that protons were not alone in the nucleus and inferred that the nucleus must also contain additional, uncharged (or "neutral") particles. Each of these **neutrons** would have roughly the same mass as a proton, but no charge at all.

Rutherford's inference was not confirmed until the 1930s. We now know that neutrons are important in atomic structure. They counteract repulsion between the protons, which, being so intensely positive, would otherwise fly apart. In the next section, you will learn about the role of neutrons in the periodic table.

From Science to Technology: Nuclear Power

Late in 1938, an aunt-and-nephew team of Austrian scientists, Lise Meitner (1878–1968) and Otto Frisch (1904–1979) took a winter holiday in Denmark. Both had already left their home country because it was by then controlled by Nazi Germany, and they were Jewish. This was a time when the possibility of **nuclear energy** — releasing energy from the nucleus of an atom — was one of science's "hottest topics."

In Einstein's famous equation $E = mc^2$, E stands for energy, m for mass, and c for the speed of light. In SI units, c is a large number — about 3×10^8 m/s — so squaring it gives a colossal number. In theory, this means that a very small amount of matter can be converted into a very large amount of energy. But what method could be used to achieve this conversion? This was the question that kept Meitner and Frisch entertained during their holiday.

On a long walk in the snowy woods, they discussed the latest scientific news. One of Meitner's colleagues had recently used neutrons to bombard uranium. The results were puzzling. The large uranium nucleus had broken up into two different elements: barium and krypton. Meitner and Frisch thought they had a way to account for this.

The conversation grew livelier. The two became so excited that they sat down there and then, on a snowy log. Using accurate atomic masses from Meitner's memory, and a scrap of paper from Frisch's pocket, they worked out how much mass is lost during the disintegration of the uranium nucleus. Then they calculated how much energy could be released.

Later Meitner and Frisch published a paper describing the energy potential of the process they had termed "nuclear fission." By then, much of the world was at war. Meitner decided to stay in Sweden, a neutral country, but Frisch went to the U.S.A. There, like many other refugee European scientists, he worked on the top secret "Manhattan Project," which developed the world's first nuclear bomb. Once the war was over, the science and technology the project had accomplished were applied to develop nuclear reactors for the generation of electrical energy. You will learn more about these reactors in Chapter 12.

Math CONNECT

Write out the speed of light in expanded form. How many zeros do you have to write? Now square it, and write the answer in expanded form. Can you get the answer all on one line?

Figure 7.17 This nuclear power plant, in Pickering, Ontario, provides a sizable fraction of Ontario's electricity.

Bohr Describes Electron Arrangements

Despite all the evidence in favour of Rutherford's model, it immediately ran into considerable opposition. The "nuclear atom" certainly explained the results of the gold foil (alpha particle) experiment, but it did not agree with what was already known about electricity. As other scientists argued, every previous experiment dealing with electric charge had shown that objects with opposite charges attract each other. Why did the negative electrons not spiral into the positive nucleus and "crash" there?

In 1912 a promising young Danish scientist named Niels Bohr (1885–1962) arrived in Manchester, England, to study with Rutherford. It was Bohr who, in 1913, explained why electrons do not spiral into the nucleus.

Bohr began by assuming that the nuclear model was essentially accurate as far as it went, but was incomplete. He avoided experiments that involved bombarding atoms with radioactivity. Instead, he decided to go back and take a closer look at the light emitted by atoms in a gas discharge tube. Like many earlier researchers, he decided to focus on the element with the simplest atom — hydrogen.

In the Starting Point Activity for this chapter, you saw that light can be analyzed (broken down) with a spectroscope. Bohr used a spectroscope to analyze the light emitted by glowing hydrogen atoms. Figure 7.18 shows what Bohr saw: the visible hydrogen spectrum consists of just four narrow lines. Why are there only four bright lines? Why is there so much empty space with no light at all? Bohr realized that the answers to these questions could also explain why electrons stay in fixed orbits, and he inferred a model that compared the atom to the solar system.

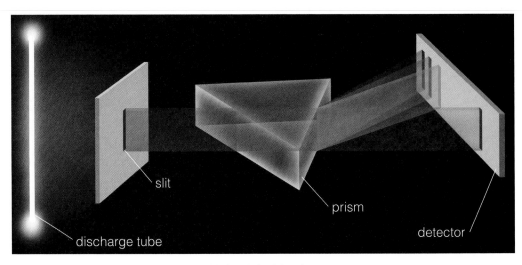

Figure 7.18 The spectrum of hydrogen was Bohr's "window" into the atom.

Bohr's model compared the nucleus to the Sun, and the electrons to the planets. The Sun exerts an enormous gravitational pull on the planets, but they do not spiral inward and crash. Why? Because they revolve at just the right speed to remain in their orbits. Similarly, the atom's positive nucleus exerts a strong force of attraction on the negative electrons. The electrons do not spiral inward and crash, however, because they are moving rapidly in fixed regions around the nucleus. These regions are three-dimensional and sphere-like. For this reason, they are called **electron shells**. Another way to imagine Bohr's model is to think of nesting dolls. Each doll represents an electron shell, with the smallest doll at the centre representing the nucleus.

Bohr concluded that the location of a hydrogen atom's single electron depended on how much energy it was given. More energetic electrons could occupy more distant shells, or energy levels. The four spectral lines of hydrogen told Bohr exactly how far away from the nucleus these shells would be. Eventually Bohr's idea was extended to bigger atoms, as Figure 7.20 shows.

Figure 7.19 Electron shells can be compared to dolls that nestle inside each other.

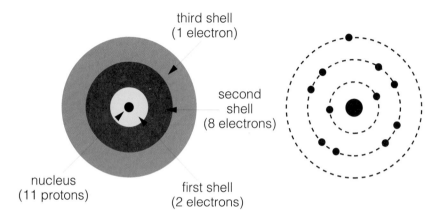

third shell
(1 electron)

second shell
(8 electrons)

nucleus
(11 protons)

first shell
(2 electrons)

Figure 7.20 Anatomy of an atom. These two models look different, but both describe the same sodium atom. Which model would you find easier to use?

The picture of the atom that emerged from the work of Rutherford and Bohr, with a central nucleus and electron shells, is often called the **Bohr-Rutherford model** of atomic structure. It is certainly not the last word on atomic structure, and in almost a century since their work, much has been added to scientists' models and theories of atomic structure. The Bohr-Rutherford model can be called the first "modern" view of the atom, however, and it is still of great use in understanding the chemistry of the elements today.

How could Bohr be sure that the orbits of electrons are fixed? The farther out an electron is from the nucleus, the faster it has to go and the more energy it needs. Putting electricity through hydrogen gas gives the electrons more energy, so they can "jump" from shells that are close to the nucleus to shells that are farther out. In a very short time, though, all the electrons fall back into their old shells, giving up the energy. The energy that is given up is the glow in the discharge tube. Remember that the spectrum of this glow has only four bright lines. If you assume that a hydrogen electron can release energy in only a few fixed amounts, how can you relate these energy amounts to the lines in the spectrum? Why does the "shells" model explain these fixed energy amounts better than a model in which the electrons spiral in to the nucleus? (Hint: The nearer to violet the colour, the higher the energy, and the farther the electron has "jumped.")

Summarizing Atomic Structure

The term "atomic structure" includes two ideas: parts and arrangement. This activity will help you recall what you now know about atomic structure.

What to Do

1. Copy and complete the following table to summarize what you know about the parts of an atom.

	Electron	Proton	Neutron
Charge	negative		
Mass		heavy	about same as proton
Location	electron cloud		nucleus

2. To summarize what you know about the arrangement of the parts, copy the following diagram and fill in the blanks.

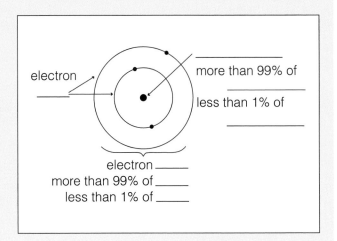

Check Your Understanding

1. Give an example of a radioactive element that occurs naturally.

2. What three kinds of experiments followed as a direct result of the discovery of radioactivity?

3. How is the spectrum of hydrogen atoms different from a continuous spectrum? How did Bohr use the hydrogen atom spectrum to develop a new model for the atom?

4. **Thinking Critically** List as many technologies as you can that depend on understanding atomic structure. Write a paragraph for two of these technologies, assessing the benefits and drawbacks they offer to society.

5. **Thinking Critically** Rutherford studied for his undergraduate degree in New Zealand, did graduate studies to get a Ph.D. at Cambridge University in England, did further research at McGill University in Montréal, and then returned to England, to Manchester University. Do you think all this moving around was a disadvantage or an advantage to Rutherford as a scientist?

6. **Apply** You probably recall how to draw a food chain to show how energy is passed through an ecosystem. Use information from this section to draw a theory chain to show how inspiration was passed through the scientific world.

7.3 A New Basis for the Periodic Table

In Chapter 6, you saw how Mendeleev constructed his periodic table, using chemical properties and atomic mass as his guiding principles. Sometimes, however, he found that he had to choose between these two principles. When this happened, he was guided by the chemical properties of an element, even if he had to place the element out of order of increasing mass. Mendeleev's genius was being able to see that sometimes the masses just did not "fit"; but he lacked the detailed model of atomic structure that could have explained why.

In the activity on page 246, you will look more closely at some of Mendeleev's "reversals." Since the simplified periodic table you were using in Chapter 6 is insufficient for your work in this activity, you will use the more complete version of the table, found on page 562. Notice a few important additions for each element, including the name, the atomic number, and the atomic mass. Also, the groups and periods are numbered. You will examine and use other features of this more complete periodic table later.

By 1913 Rutherford's deeper understanding of the nucleus and Bohr's model of electron shells provided the opportunity to explain the apparent inconsistencies in the periodic table. You will discover, in this section, that the key to the puzzle turned out to be the neutron — the "missing mass" in the atom.

A New Basis for Ordering the Elements

The sequencing of elements in the periodic table was put on a firm footing as a result of a discovery by Henry Moseley (1887–1915), who came to work in Rutherford's laboratory in 1910. By 1913 Moseley had discovered a very regular pattern in the way different elements respond to X-rays. This pattern gave chemists the evidence they needed to make important inferences about the atomic nucleus of each element.

Moseley's regular pattern was obtained by placing elements into an X-ray tube, one after the other, as they appeared in the periodic table of the time. From the patterns of the wavelengths of the X-rays produced, he was able to see that Mendeleev had been correct in placing cobalt before nickel, and tellurium before iodine, in spite of the atomic mass "reversals" required. He was also able to see whether elements were missing in the periodic sequence.

Chemists assumed that the response of each element to X-rays was the result of an interaction with the most massive part of the atom, rather than with the electrons. (Do you see how they would infer this?) The regular increase in the pattern suggested a regular increase in something that was present in the nucleus. Chemists inferred that an increasing number of protons was responsible.

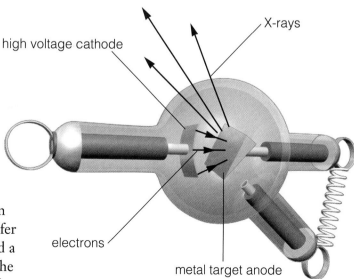

Figure 7.21 Moseley's X-ray apparatus

high voltage cathode

X-rays

electrons

metal target anode

Odd Couples

In some places in the periodic table, you can find neighbouring pairs of elements which, if you go only by their atomic mass, look as though they are in reverse order, with the heavier element first. In this activity, you will examine some of these reversals, or "odd couples."

What You Need

Appendix C: Periodic Table (page 562)

What to Do

1. Find Te and I in Period 5.

   (a) What do you notice about their atomic masses?

   (b) If Mendeleev had used only atomic mass to sequence the elements, tellurium would have been placed with bromine and the other halogens in Group 17. Use electronic and print resources to find out if tellurium has the properties of a halogen.

2. Locate nickel and cobalt in Period 4.

   (a) What is their order from left to right: Ni–Co or Co–Ni?

   (b) If Mendeleev had positioned these elements strictly according to atomic mass, what order would they have been in?

3. Recall from Chapter 6 what you know about the noble gases (Group 18).

   (a) Find the atomic mass of argon, and then go to the next element, potassium (K). You will need to look in Group 1 to find it. What do you notice about the atomic mass of these two elements?

   (b) If the periodic table were organized strictly by atomic mass, argon and potassium would switch places. What properties of argon make it out of place in the alkali metals? Why is potassium out of place in the noble gases?

What Did You Discover?

Write a short paragraph, stating, in your own words, why the periodic table is not organized by atomic mass alone.

Word CONNECT

Look up "argon" in a dictionary, and find out about the Greek word it comes from. Why is "argon" a good name for an unreactive gas?

Figure 7.22 Henry Moseley did not have a chance to see the important consequences of his work in the development of chemistry as a science. In 1915, he left Rutherford's Manchester laboratory to serve as a soldier in World War I. He was killed in the British storming of Gallipoli, one of the war's bloodiest battles.

With this thinking, the number of protons in the nucleus of the atom for each element became highly significant in understanding periodicity. The number of protons came to be called the **atomic number** of each element. The modern periodic table is built on the concept of atomic number.

Atomic Number, Mass Number, and Atomic Structure

The atomic number of an element provides information about its atomic structure. For example, the atomic number of fluorine is 9, indicating that there are nine protons in the nucleus. According to our model of atomic structure, there must then be nine electrons in a fluorine atom, too.

In section 7.1, you learned that an atom includes neutrons as well as protons and electrons. Neutrons play an important part in holding the nucleus together and in keeping the protons from flying apart.

On its own, the atomic number does not tell us the number of neutrons in an atom. Chemists use another number, called the **mass number**, to give the *total* number of protons and neutrons. By subtracting the atomic number from the mass number, you can work out the number of neutrons. The proper notation for writing about the structure of an atom uses the chemical symbol with both the mass number and the atomic number, so that fluorine, for example, can be represented like this:

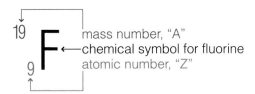

mass number, "A"
chemical symbol for fluorine
atomic number, "Z"

The mass number is sometimes labelled as "A", and the atomic number as "Z", in this notation. Can you now work out how many neutrons there are in a fluorine atom?

Atomic Mass Units

The mass number for an element does not appear anywhere in the periodic table. The atomic mass does, however. Look at the periodic table on page 562 to find the atomic mass of lithium. You will see that it is given as 6.941, which is not a whole number, as a mass number would be. In fact, you can see that most of the atomic masses in the table are given in decimalized amounts. (The exceptions, which are in Period 7, are in parentheses. This is because they are estimates for synthetic elements.)

The atomic masses in the periodic table are stated in **atomic mass units (u)**. Atomic mass units are not units for the measurement of mass in the same way that grams are units for the measurement of the mass of an object placed on a balance. Remember, when Dalton first proposed atomic masses in the nineteenth century, he was imagining the masses of atoms *relative to each other*. Thus relative atomic mass is a ratio. Dalton used hydrogen as the starting unit, with an atomic mass of 1, and other atomic masses were expressed in relation to it. For example, a relative atomic mass of 6 on Dalton's scale means that the atom is six times as heavy as a hydrogen atom.

Modern atomic mass units are also ratios. The modern periodic table is based on a standard that defines one atomic mass unit as $\frac{1}{12}$ the mass of a $^{12}_{6}C$ atom. Thus all atomic masses are defined relative to the mass of this particular carbon atom. For example, a proton has a relative atomic mass of about 1 u, and an electron is much, much lighter — about $\frac{1}{2000}$ $\left(\frac{1}{1837}$ to be exact$\right)$ of the proton's mass. The relative atomic mass of a neutron is about the same as that of a proton — about 1 u.

IUPAC (the International Union of Pure and Applied Chemists) has developed a system of temporary "names" for elements that have been predicted to exist in theory but either have not yet been discovered or have been discovered so recently that no "proper" name has been internationally agreed on for them. The system uses Latin words, based on the atomic numbers of these elements. Each name puts together three of the following Latin words:

nil=0   un=1   bi=2   tri=3   quad=4

pent=5 hex=6 sept=7 oct=8 enn=9

For example, unnilquadium (chemical symbol Unq) literally means element 104. This element is now named rutherfordium (symbol Rf) to honour the work of Ernest Rutherford.

All the elements up to 109 have now been named. Notice on your periodic table, however, that the last four elements, recently discovered by scientists in Germany and in Russia, are still unnamed and have symbols Uun, Uuu, Uub, and Uuq. Can you see why they have these symbols? There are predictions that element 115, though not yet discovered, should be relatively stable. What temporary name would be assigned to this element?

Introducing Isotopes

Why are relative atomic masses decimals, and not simple whole numbers? Dalton's original model of an atom assumed that all of the atoms of each element were the same. According to the model of atomic structure we have been developing, this would mean that each atom of an element would have the same number of protons, electrons, and neutrons as every other atom of the element. Thus the atomic mass of every atom of an element would be the same.

In the early twentieth century, scientists studying radioactivity found that some substances had different atomic masses, yet they had identical chemical properties. Scientists inferred that they must be different atomic forms of the same element. This phenomenon was also found among much lighter, non-radioactive elements. For example, there are two forms of the element lithium. They have the same chemical properties, but their physical properties differ, leading to the conclusion that they are atoms of the same element, but somehow different in structure.

These two forms of the lithium atom — "light" and "heavy" — are called **isotopes** of lithium. "Isotope" comes from the Greek words for "same place." Both isotopes of lithium occupy the same place in the periodic table. Both have the same atomic number and the same number of electrons. They do not, however, have the same number of neutrons. As a result, the two isotopes differ in mass number and in relative atomic mass.

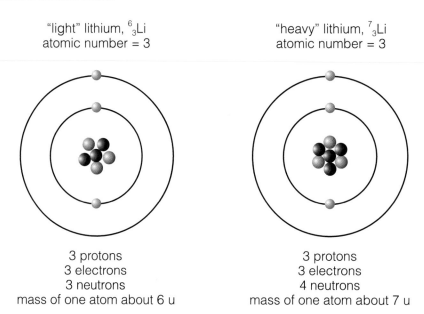

"light" lithium, $^6_3$Li
atomic number = 3

"heavy" lithium, $^7_3$Li
atomic number = 3

3 protons	3 protons
3 electrons	3 electrons
3 neutrons	4 neutrons
mass of one atom about 6 u	mass of one atom about 7 u

Figure 7.23 Isotopes of lithium

Lithium's atomic mass in the periodic table is 6.941 u, or 6.9 u to one decimal place. It is not 6.0 u — what it would be if every lithium atom were "light" lithium, or lithium-6. Nor is it 7.0 u — what it would be if all lithium atoms were the "heavy" form, lithium-7.

The atomic mass for lithium that is shown in the periodic table is calculated on the basis of what is called a "weighted average." This average is closer to 7 u than to 6 u, reflecting the fact that there is a very high percentage of the isotope lithium-7 in nature and a much lower percentage of lithium-6. Do you see why?

Most elements have different forms, or isotopes, that have different atomic masses but the same chemical properties. The same system of weighted averages used for lithium produces the atomic masses given in the periodic table for these elements. The investigation on page 250 will help you relate atomic mass to numbers of neutrons for two elements with different isotopes, helium and tin.

From Science to Technology: Carbon Dating in Archaeology

One example of a useful isotope is carbon-14, or $^{14}_{6}C$, which is a rare form of carbon with six protons and eight neutrons in the nucleus. Carbon-14 is very slightly radioactive — not enough for it to be dangerous but enough for its atoms to throw off beta particles steadily and turn into nitrogen-14 atoms ($^{14}_{7}N$).

It takes about 5600 years for half of the atoms in a sample to turn into nitrogen. If you know what the natural level of carbon-14 in the environment is, and if you find an ancient wooden artifact with only half this level, you can deduce that the artifact must date from about 3600 B.C.E., since the wood it was made from was last alive then. An older artifact or relic would have less carbon-14, and a more recent one a bit more. You can go back about 50 000 years (farther back than written history) before carbon-14 levels get too small to measure accurately. This technique is called *carbon dating*, and it is extremely important for archaeologists.

Figure 7.24 This reconstructed Egyptian funeral boat has been carbon-dated at approximately 3000 B.C.E.

Copy and complete the atomic mass of lithium.

	Lithium-7	Lithium-6
The atomic mass of one atom of the isotope is . . .	7.02 u	6.02 u
The percentage of atoms with this atomic mass in a natural sample is . . .	92.4%	7.6%
A 1000-atom sample of natural Li would have . . .	_____ atoms with a mass of 7.02 u	_____ atoms with a mass of 6.02 u
The total mass of each isotope (to the nearest 10 u) would be . . .		

1. What is the total mass of all 1000 atoms in the sample (to the nearest 10 u)?

2. What is the average mass of each atom in the sample?

3. Compare your average mass with the atomic mass of lithium that is shown in the periodic table.

Inferring the Number of Neutrons

Think About It

Imagine that you have analyzed a natural sample of helium gas. All of the atoms have two protons, therefore they all have two electrons. All have the same atomic number, so they all occupy the same place in the periodic table. You have detected two distinctly different isotopes, however.

What to Do

❶ Copy the following table into your notebook. Give your table a title.

	"Light" Helium	"Heavy" Helium
Atomic Number	2	2
Number of Protons	2	2
Number of Electrons	2	2
Mass of One Atom of Isotope	3 u	4 u
Number of Neutrons	1	

Isotopes of helium

(a) What method was used to infer the number of neutrons in one atom of "light" helium? Explain.

(b) Use this method to infer the number of neutrons in one atom of "heavy" helium. Record this number in your table.

(c) Write the proper notation for the two isotopes.

❷ Another student conducted similar research for tin. Unfortunately some of the data for tin were wiped off the hard drive during a power failure. The table below shows the data that are left. Copy the table into your notebook, and give it a title.

(a) Fill in the gaps in the table. (There are enough data left for you to do this.)

(b) How many isotopes of tin did the student identify?

(c) What is the atomic mass of tin according to the periodic table?

(d) Do you think there is much of isotope A in an average sample of tin? Explain.

Extend Your Skills

Build three-dimensional models of the two isotopes of helium. At craft stores, you can find transparent plastic spheres to represent the electron shells. The nucleus can be made of beads and suspended with wire. Be sure that an outside observer can count all the subatomic particles. If another atom approached your models, could it react to the difference between the two isotopes? Explain your answer.

	A	B	C	D	E	F	G	H	I	J
Atomic Number		50	50	50			50			
Number of Protons				50			50	50		
Number of Electrons					50				50	50
Mass of One Atom of Isotope	112 u	114 u		116 u	117 u		119 u		122 u	124 u
Number of Neutrons	62	64	65			68		70		

Isotopes of tin

Modelling the Atom

You have read about many scientists so far in this chapter. Each of these scientists advanced the understanding of atomic structure in some way.

Challenge

Your teacher will divide you into groups and assign each group one of these scientists: John Dalton, William Crookes, J.J. Thomson, Ernest Rutherford, Marie Curie, Niels Bohr, Henry Moseley.

Your challenge is to put together a presentation about your scientist. The main part of your presentation will be a model of either the scientist's theory of the atom or a key experiment. Your presentation should also include some drawings or photographs, as well as a role-play interview with the scientist.

Materials

materials to make models: for example, plasticine, metal foil, plastic spheres, drinking straws or pipe cleaners, marshmallows (different colours and sizes), spherical objects (wide range of sizes), raisins

materials to make drawings, or mount and display photographs: for example, white paper, construction paper, cardboard, coloured felt pens or pencils

Design Criteria

A. Your model should be detailed enough to show the key features of the scientist's picture of the atom or experiment.

B. Most importantly, it should be dynamic. For example, for Thomson's theory of the atom, your model should allow you to show what might happen to an atom in the cathode of an electrified discharge tube.

C. Your model should illustrate the strengths and weaknesses of the scientist's work.

Plan and Construct

1 In your group, discuss your scientist's role in the story of the atom, under three headings:
  • what his or her initial questions were

  • how he or she answered these questions, with a model of the atom or a key experiment
  • what new questions the scientist's work raised

2 Decide on the features that your model will include. Draw plans for your model (you will probably need more than one plan if your model is to be dynamic), and choose your materials.

(a) Divide your group into two teams, which will work together closely. The first team will construct the model according to the plans, test it to make sure it will effectively demonstrate the scientist's ideas, and run the demonstrations during the presentation.

(b) The second team will plan the presentation, based on the finished model.
  • One person from the presentation team will take the role of the scientist and narrate the presentation.
  • A second person will play a science journalist and prepare questions to ask the scientist.
  • You can use drawings, posters, or other visual materials to enhance your presentation, and cue cards to help with the spoken part.
  • Remember to use your ideas from step 1 in your presentation.

3 Give the presentation, either "live" or filmed with a video camera. At the end of the presentation, conduct a "one-on-one" interview between the scientist and the journalist. After the interview, invite members of the audience to ask further questions of the scientist, if you wish.

Evaluate

1. Which group got across the scientist's key ideas most effectively? Which group gave the clearest picture of the questions answered by the scientist and the new questions raised by his or her work?

2. How well did your model demonstrate your scientist's work? What aspects of your model could you improve?

Atomic Number and Chemical Reactivity

You have seen that atomic number is the best way to order the periodic table. The chemical properties of the elements, especially how reactive they are, can also be understood in terms of atomic number. Atomic number is a key predictor of chemical reactivity because it determines the arrangement of the electrons in their shells. So you can use the periodic table, which is organized by atomic number, to make predictions about the chemical properties of the elements. In Chapter 8 you will be able to make some predictions about some of the elements you met in Chapter 6.

Across Canada

Cobalt-60, a radioactive isotope of the metallic element cobalt, can be used in the treatment of cancer. Canada led the world in this life-saving application, and Dr. Sylvia Fedoruk was one of its pioneers. She was chief medical physicist for the Saskatchewan Cancer Foundation for 35 years, and during this time she helped pioneer one of the world's first nuclear medicine scanning machines.

Sylvia was born in Canora, Saskatchewan. As a teenager, she loved sports, including hockey, basketball, volleyball, track, and curling. She has remained active in athletics, and in 1986 she was inducted into the Canadian Curling Hall of Fame. Sylvia has also been active in public life. From 1988 to 1994, she served as Lieutenant-Governor of Saskatchewan. She has promoted causes such as environmental conservation and excellence in education.

When Sylvia Fedoruk entered physics, there were few women in the field. When she became Saskatchewan's Lieutenant-Governor, she was the first woman in that office. What is her advice to young women of today? "Set personal goals. Dream of doing better than you ever thought you could. If you dream of accomplishing the impossible, you can!"

Sylvia Fedoruk

Check Your Understanding

1. What were Mendeléev's reversals? How did Henry Moseley explain them?

2. What is an atomic mass unit (u)? What are the approximate masses of the subatomic particles, expressed in atomic mass units?

3. What are isotopes? Explain how the existence of different isotopes of an element would affect the element's relative atomic mass in the periodic table.

4. For each of the following isotopes, identify the name of the element and the number of protons, neutrons, and electrons.
   (a) $^{35}_{17}Cl$ (b) $^{238}_{92}U$ (c) $^{56}_{26}Fe$

5. Take out your collection of element cards from Chapter 5 (page 176) and add cards for the new elements you have met in this chapter. Also add to your cards information about isotopes, or about applications to technologies.

6. **Thinking Critically** Could carbon dating be used to estimate the age of a skeleton? How could an archaeologist date some grass seeds or a stone axe-head found with the skeleton?

CHAPTER at a glance

Now that you have completed this chapter, try to do the following. If you cannot, go back to the section indicated.

Draw a labelled sketch of a continuous spectrum, and list the colours of the spectrum in order. (7.1)

Draw a labelled sketch of a discharge tube, and outline how discharge tubes were important in discovering electrons. (7.1)

Summarize the experimental evidence that suggested electrons are particles with charge and mass. (7.1)

Outline the events leading to the discovery of radioactivity and the isolation of some radioactive elements. (7.2)

Summarize the properties of alpha, beta, and gamma radiation. (7.2)

Draw a labelled sketch of Rutherford's gold foil experiment, and describe the observations he made. (7.2)

Describe Rutherford's model of the atom. Give reasons why the model was known to be incomplete. (7.2)

Sketch diagrams to illustrate models of the atom suggested by Dalton, Thomson, Rutherford, and Bohr. (7.1, 7.2)

List the names and summarize the work of the scientists identified in this book as contributing to our understanding of atomic structure. (7.1, 7.2, 7.3)

Distinguish between the terms "atomic number" and "atomic mass." State the basis for the organization of the modern periodic table. (7.3)

Given the atomic number and mass number of a particular isotope, state the number of protons, electrons, and neutrons present in its atoms. (7.3)

Outline how carbon dating can be used to identify the age of an ancient object made from wood. (7.3)

Prepare Your Own Summary

Summarize this chapter by doing one of the following. Use a graphic organizer (such as a concept map), produce a poster, or write the summary to include the key chapter concepts.
- Summarize the experiments leading to the discovery of the electron and some of its properties.
- Outline how radioactivity was discovered and why this led to a better understanding of the structure of atoms.
- Summarize key features of the three principal atomic models discussed in this chapter and the experimental evidence leading from one model to the next.
- Describe the organization of elements in the periodic table, and explain how the data shown for each element can be used to determine the number of subatomic particles present in its atoms.

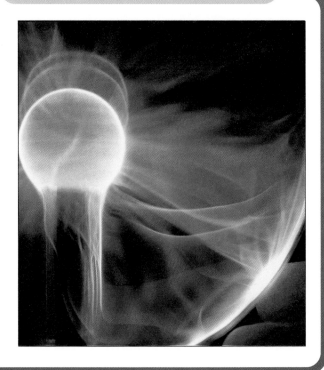

Reviewing Key Terms

If you need review, the section numbers show you where these terms were introduced.

1. How is the gas discharge tube related to some advertising display lights and the tube in a television set? (7.1)

2. What are cathode rays? How can they be made visible? Which type of radioactive emission is similar to cathode rays? (7.1)

3. Distinguish between the terms "evidence" and "inference," giving examples from Rutherford's gold foil experiment. (7.2)

4. What are some of the properties of alpha rays, beta rays, and gamma rays? (7.2)

5. How did Henry Moseley find a way to determine the atomic number of an element? (7.3)

Understanding Key Concepts

Section numbers are provided if you need to review.

6. What is the evidence that electrons are a part of all matter? (7.1)

7. How was Rutherford's experiment similar to your activity with the mystery box? (7.2)

8. When Rutherford shot alpha particles at thin gold foil, he discovered that some of the alpha particles rebounded directly back in the direction of the source. What conclusions concerning atomic structure was Rutherford able to draw? (7.2)

9. Describe at least two difficulties with Rutherford's model of the atom. (7.2)

10. Explain why the atomic masses of most elements are not whole numbers. (7.3)

11. Naturally occurring isotopes of both rubidium and strontium are found with the same mass number, 87. Explain how this is possible. (7.3)

12. There are ten stable isotopes of tin. State at least two ways in which atoms of these isotopes would be alike. (7.3)

Developing Skills

13. Plot a graph for the first 20 elements, showing the relative atomic mass on the y-axis and atomic number on the x-axis. What periodic trend is illustrated? Comment on any exceptions.

14. Construct a concept map for the Bohr-Rutherford model, including atomic number, mass number, electron shells, and neutrons.

15. Research has shown that protons and neutrons are composed of smaller particles called "quarks." Find out more about these particles, and write a brief report.

16. Most hydrogen atoms do not contain a neutron in their nucleus. Deuterium is a naturally occurring isotope of hydrogen that contains one neutron. Heavy water consists of atoms of deuterium instead of hydrogen bonded to oxygen. Find out why heavy water is used in the CANDU (Canadian Deuterium Uranium) reactor at Pickering, Ontario, and write a short report.

17. Extend your time line from Chapter 5 (page 186) to show the development of theories about atomic structure.

Problem Solving

18. Use a periodic table to determine the atomic number of chlorine. Two isotopes of chlorine exist with mass numbers 35 and 37.

    (a) How many neutrons are present in each isotope?

    (b) If you sampled 100 atoms of chlorine, 75 might be chlorine-35 and the rest chlorine-37. What would be the average mass of a chlorine atom from this sample?

19. A particular isotope of magnesium (atomic number 12) has a mass number of 24. If an ion of this isotope has the same number of electrons as an atom of argon, how many protons, neutrons, and electrons will it have?

20. If the mass of a neutron were half its actual mass, and the mass of an electron were twice its actual mass, would the mass of a single calcium-40 atom be increased or decreased, and by roughly how much? (Assume the mass of a proton is unchanged.)

Critical Thinking

21. The tube that Geissler invented was, and still is, known by several names: gas discharge tube, Geissler tube, cathode ray tube, and Crookes tube. Explain how one device could have so many names, all of them in some way appropriate.

22. If the Thomson model of the atom had been correct, how would the results of Rutherford's gold foil experiment have been different?

23. Why did Rutherford use alpha rays rather than beta rays in his experiment to investigate atoms?

24. Copy the diagram below and add labels to identify the different parts of the apparatus. Also add arrows to illustrate what happens when the two electrode plates are connected to a power supply. Which scientist first conducted this experiment?

25. If an element contains two or more naturally occurring isotopes, is it a pure substance?

26. How could carbon dating be used to estimate the age of an Egyptian mummy? (Hint: Think about the different kinds of organic material in this type of artifact.)

Pause & Reflect

1. How are science and technology related? Provide one example from this chapter where a technology had to be invented before further scientific progress could be made, and another example where progress in science led to a new technology.

2. "The scientific method is often described as logical and systematic."

   "The path to scientific understanding sometimes takes wrong turns and may occur by accident with an unexpected discovery."

   Comment on these statements, illustrating your answer with examples from the text.

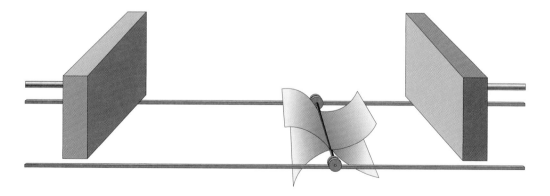

Chemical Bonding

Opening
Ideas...

- How are sugar and salt alike? In what ways are they different?

- Why is the formula of water H_2O?

- What are plastics?

Science
Log

In your Science Log, write down everything you have learned so far about the elements fluorine, neon and sodium, including properties, number of electrons, and where they appear in the periodic table. Think about possible chemical reactions between these elements, and write down any compounds you think they might form.

What is the athlete in the photograph doing? If you answered that she is quenching her thirst, you would be right; but this is not all she is doing. She is replacing water and ions that her body has lost through perspiration. If lost water is not replaced, the human body can become dehydrated. Dehydration, with its accompanying loss of ions, can cause tiredness, nausea, and dizziness. The liquid in the bottle is a "sport" drink, made from water that contains ions as well as carbohydrates and sugars to replenish energy.

Sodium chloride (table salt) and potassium chloride are common sources of ions. Sugar may look a lot like salt, but it does not form ions in solution. Why do some substances contain ions while others do not?

You might have difficulty distinguishing sugar from salt, but you would have no difficulty distinguishing either of these substances from the bottle containing the drink. The plastic material that makes up the bottle has very different properties from either sugar or salt. To understand these properties, and the properties that describe all other materials, you need to know how the atoms and molecules that make up different substances are bonded together. This chapter is about chemical bonding.

Key Concepts

In this chapter, you will discover

- how ions form, and how ionic bonding occurs
- how bonding occurs in substances that do not have ionic bonds
- why substances with different types of bonding have different properties
- how chemicals play an important role in your life

Key Skills

In this chapter, you will

- perform tests to identify ionic substances and non-ionic substances
- use the periodic table to predict different types of bonding between atoms
- investigate the properties of different plastics

Key Terms

- alkaline earth metals
- stable octet
- ion
- ionic compound
- ionic bond
- valence electrons
- crystal lattice
- molecular compound
- covalent bond
- graphite
- diamond
- polymer

Now That's Energy!

When a chemical reaction takes place, energy is transferred and a new substance is formed. Watch what happens in this activity. Think about the properties of the substances involved and the energy transformation that occurs.

What You Need

new non-electronic flash bulb
spent non-electronic flash bulb

What to Do

1. Examine the new flash bulb. Write a description of its properties.

2. Watch as your teacher uses a flash bulb. Write what you observe.

3. Your teacher will ask a student to touch the flash bulb. Note the student's observations.

4. Now examine the spent flash bulb, and describe the properties you observe.

What Did You Discover?

1. How did the properties of the flash bulb compare before and after use?

2. What evidence did you observe that told you energy was involved? What forms of energy were involved?

3. Explain why you might infer that a chemical reaction took place.

8.1 Explaining Chemical Families

The model of atomic structure that you developed in Chapter 7, sometimes called the Bohr-Rutherford model, can be extended to develop a model of how chemical compounds form. In the Starting Point Activity, you saw another example of what you learned in Chapter 5: when elements form compounds, their chemical properties are changed. The filament of the flash bulb was made of the element magnesium. When the flash bulb was set off, magnesium combined with oxygen to form the compound magnesium oxide, in a chemical reaction that also generated the heat and light you observed. The properties of the compound are quite different from those of the elements, which is what you would have expected from your earlier studies.

A model of compound formation will have to explain why the chemical properties of any compound are different from those of the elements forming it. This may seem like a very complicated task, but it is made easier by analyzing families of elements to explain their similarities. This is an important first step toward developing a model of compound formation.

In the activity opposite, you will build on the Bohr-Rutherford model to examine the arrangement of electrons in the atoms of each of the first 20 elements in the periodic table. Using that many elements will allow you to consider the chemical properties of four families, in particular. Of special significance is the number of electrons in the outer shell of each element, because when atoms move around and bump into each other, their outer shells of electrons are what come into contact. Figure 8.1 shows some of the shell diagrams on which the activity is based.

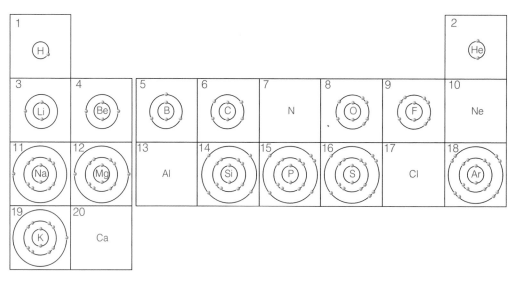

Figure 8.1 The first 20 elements, with electron shells

The Outer Electrons

Shell diagrams are a way of representing atoms based on the Bohr-Rutherford model, and they are helpful in understanding how substances react chemically. In this activity, you will look at the first 20 elements in the periodic table, drawing shell diagrams for some of them.

What to Do

1. Look at the simplified periodic table below. Notice that there are only two elements, hydrogen and helium, in Period 1. This is because the first Bohr shell has room for only two electrons: hydrogen has one electron in this shell, and helium has two. What are the atomic numbers of these two elements?

2. Now look at Period 2. Most of the elements in this period have a full first shell (two electrons) and a partly filled second shell. The last element, neon, has both the first and second shells filled. Count the number of elements in Period 2. How many electrons can the second shell contain?

3. Now look at Figure 8.1 opposite, which shows the first 20 elements, with shell diagrams for most of them. Copy this table carefully into your notebook. Begin filling in the missing shell diagrams, as far as atomic number 10 (neon).

4. Look at the next row of the table, which shows the Period 3 elements. It begins with sodium and ends with argon (atomic number 18). Draw the missing shell diagrams in this row also.

5. Potassium and calcium complete the 20 elements you are studying. Draw the shell diagram for calcium in the last space of the table.

What Did You Discover?

1. How many electrons will the outer electron shell hold in the first period? How many will the outer shells in the second and third periods hold?

Extension

3. Notice the "staircase" at the right of the simplified periodic table below. The elements to the left of this staircase are metals (with the exception of hydrogen), and the elements to the right are non-metals. Lying on the staircase, and marked in red, are the metalloids, which you learned about in Chapter 6. Try to identify a pattern in the number of electrons in the outer shells of these elements. As you read about the gain and loss of electrons, later in this section, try to think about why this pattern might occur.

$_1$H																	$_2$He
$_3$Li	$_4$Be											$_5$B	$_6$C	$_7$N	$_8$O	$_9$F	$_{10}$Ne
$_{11}$Na	$_{12}$Mg											$_{13}$Al	$_{14}$Si	$_{15}$P	$_{16}$S	$_{17}$Cl	$_{18}$Ar
$_{19}$K	$_{20}$Ca												$_{32}$Ge	$_{33}$As			
														$_{51}$Sb	$_{52}$Te		
															$_{84}$Po	$_{85}$At	

Outer Electrons and Groups of Elements

You can see from the shell diagrams in the last activity that the elements in each group show some differences. The atomic mass increases as you go down a group, and so too does the number of electron shells. For example, in Group 2, calcium has a higher atomic mass and more electron shells than magnesium or beryllium, and the radius of a calcium atom is larger. In spite of these differences, all the elements in the groups you have studied do have one thing in common: the number of electrons in the outer shell is the same.

Table 8.1 illustrates this idea using four groups: halogens, noble gases, alkali metals, and a group you have not yet studied, the **alkaline earth metals** (Group 2). These groups are displayed in a special format to help you compare electron arrangements. Refer to Table 8.1 frequently as you read the rest of this section.

Table 8.1 Electron Arrangements of Four Families

Halogens (very reactive)	Noble Gases	Alkali Metals (very reactive)	Alkaline Earth Metals (fairly reactive)
	2 He	3 Li	4 Be
9 F	10 Ne	11 Na	12 Mg
17 Cl	18 Ar	19 K	20 Ca
35 Br	36 Kr	37 Rb	38 Sr
53 I	54 Xe	55 Cs	56 Ba
85 At	86 Rn	87 Fr	88 Ra

The Noble Gases: A Stable Outer Shell

Chemists find the noble gases interesting because they are so unreactive. As you will find out, unreactivity can be a very useful property.

Figure 8.2A The earliest light bulbs burned out rapidly, as oxygen in the air reacted with the glowing filament.

Figure 8.2B Modern light bulbs are filled with the unreactive gas argon.

Consider an ordinary light bulb. If the slightest leak allows air to get inside the glass covering, the filament will burn out in a bright flash of light and the bulb will go dark. Exposure to oxygen makes the tungsten filament burn. This is because tungsten's outer shell of electrons is affected by oxygen's outer shell, especially when tungsten is hot. If oxygen is excluded, however, tungsten cannot react. Modern light bulbs are usually filled with argon, an unreactive gas, to keep the tungsten filament from burning out.

Argon is a noble gas. The high-intensity discharge (HID) headlights that you read about at the beginning of Chapter 7 contain another noble gas: xenon. Xenon's role in HID headlights is quite different from argon's role in light bulbs, however. The new headlights are actually gas discharge tubes, which have no filament. Instead, they work like the discharge tubes that Crookes and Thomson used to study atoms. The headlight is filled with low-pressure xenon, and the inside surface of the glass is coated with metallic salts. As the current arcs through the tube, it energizes the xenon atoms and causes them to glow with an intense ultraviolet light. This light energizes the metallic salts which, in turn, glow with their own bright blue light.

Numerous laboratory experiments have confirmed that all noble gases are chemically "stable." This means that they are highly unlikely to take part in a chemical change. In fact, only the very largest noble gas atoms can be made to react chemically at all. Even when they do react, their compounds soon decompose, allowing the noble gas to separate into single atoms again.

Based on these and other observed properties, chemists have reasoned that the electron arrangement of the noble gas atoms must be exceptionally stable. For example, helium has only two electrons in total. The shell that holds them has room for only two, so it is full. When a helium atom bumps into an atom of another element, its outer shell is unchanged.

The same is true for all the other noble gases. Their outer shells have eight electrons instead of two, but these outer shells are unchanged when they collide with other atoms, even if the other atoms are usually reactive. This arrangement — eight electrons in an outer shell — is often called a **stable octet**. The stable octet is an important concept because it can also help to explain why the halogens and the alkali metals are so unstable or reactive, and what happens when they do react.

Think about this question as you read:

> Where can a fluorine atom get the extra electron it needs to make a stable octet?

As you saw in Table 8.1, all halogen atoms have seven outer electrons, regardless of their mass, number of shells, or total electrons. Halogen atoms react vigorously with nearly everything. Even the least reactive halogens are extremely corrosive and harmful.

Figure 8.3B Most swimming pools have chlorine gas bubbled into them to kill germs.

Figure 8.3A Tincture of iodine (an alcohol solution) was once used to kill germs on cuts. Unfortunately the iodine also killed the surrounding cells.

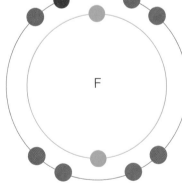

Figure 8.4 This is how fluorine's electron shells would appear if fluorine could gain one electron.

Fluorine is so reactive that the first person to isolate it, Henri Moissan, in 1886, won a Nobel Prize. Nearly four decades passed before safe methods for producing large amounts of fluorine were developed. This project involved massive spending and intensive effort by many scientists.

From these examples of halogen reactivity, we can infer that an outer shell with seven electrons is unstable. Take a close look at fluorine's electron arrangement, however. Notice how closely the shells resemble those of neon. What if fluorine could somehow acquire one more electron? Then fluorine's outer shell would have a stable octet, as pictured in Figure 8.4.

STRETCH Your Mind

Fluorine, at the top of Group 17, is more reactive than chlorine, just below it. The more electron shells a halogen atom has, the less reactive it is. Can you explain why?

The Alkali Metals: One Electron Beyond Stability

Now think about this question as you read:

How can a sodium atom get rid of its "extra" electron to become chemically stable?

The arrangement of outer electrons in the alkali metals group differs considerably from the arrangement in the halogen group. Regardless of atomic radius or number of electron shells, all alkali metals have one outer electron. Alkali metals react vigorously with many other substances (see Figure 8.5), which suggests that the electron structure they have in common must be unstable. In Chapter 6, you saw how reactive sodium is.

Figure 8.5A Freshly cut sodium is bright and shiny, but only while stored in oil.

Figure 8.5B After a few minutes' exposure the surface of the sodium has dulled because the sodium atoms have reacted with oxygen from the air.

Figure 8.5C When a small lump of sodium is dropped into water, a vigorous reaction takes place.

The most reactive alkali metal atoms are the largest ones. Since sodium has almost the same number of electrons as neon and fluorine, however, it is easier to compare these three elements. At first glance, the electron shells of sodium do not seem much like those of neon. Neon's outer shell has eight electrons, while sodium's has only one electron. What if sodium could get rid of that one electron? Figure 8.6 pictures how sodium's electron shells would look if this happened.

In Figure 8.6, sodium's almost empty outer shell (the red line) is now completely empty. The next shell inward (the blue line) has become the new outer shell, and it has eight outer electrons — the same stable octet as neon. Therefore sodium would be chemically stable if it could shed an electron.

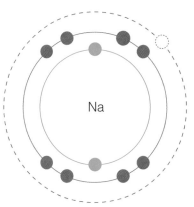

Figure 8.6 This is how sodium's electron shells would change if sodium could lose one electron. The old outer shell is shown by the broken red line.

The Alkaline Earth Metals: Two Electrons Beyond Stability

The arrangement of the outer electrons of the elements in Group 2 is similar to that of the alkali metals in Group 1. There are two electrons beyond a stable octet in calcium, for example. Regardless of atomic radius or number of electron shells, all the alkaline earth metals have this same structure. They react fairly vigorously with a number of substances, but not as vigorously as the alkali metals. For example, magnesium reacts with water but less vigorously than sodium does, even though they are both in the same period.

As with the alkali metals, the most reactive metals in Group 2 are the largest ones. Notice that two electrons must be given up to achieve a stable octet. In a reaction between calcium and fluorine, for example, two fluorine atoms would need to be available to give up two electrons to each calcium atom.

Magnesium, which you saw in the Starting Point Activity, is also an alkaline earth metal. You will learn more about magnesium's reaction with oxygen in the next section as you further develop your model of compound formation.

Check Your Understanding

1. (a) Why is the outer shell of electrons thought to be the most important for determining chemical properties?

   (b) Why are the noble gases generally unreactive?

2. Briefly describe the uses made of some noble gases mentioned in this section.

3. Why are the alkali metals and the halogens so reactive?

4. Take out your collection of element and compound cards from Chapter 5 (page 176), and add to them the new information about reactivity and applications you have learned about in this section.

5. **Thinking Critically** List some of the physical properties of sodium, and then of chlorine. Are the physical properties of sodium chloride (table salt) an average of the properties of the elements it contains? Explain.

6. **Apply** Compare the uses of argon, xenon, and magnesium in lighting technologies. In which technologies is chemical reactivity, or the lack of it, important?

8.2 Ionic Compounds

In the previous section, you were asked to think about the two questions below. Do you see how each question suggests an answer to the other one?

How can a sodium atom get rid of its "extra" electron to become chemically stable?	Where can a fluorine atom get the extra electron it needs to make a stable octet?

The answers to these two questions are an important part of your model of compound formation. The fluorine atoms can gain the electrons they need for stable octets from the sodium atoms. The sodium atoms will lose the electrons they need to lose in order to have stable octets. This process of electron rearrangement explains the formation of the compound sodium fluoride.

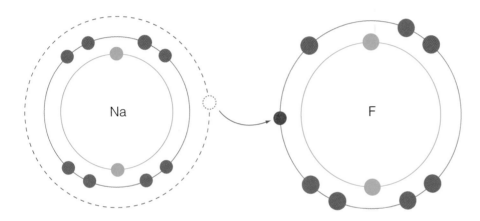

Figure 8.7 One electron has been transferred to fluorine's outer shell from sodium's outer shell. Both atoms now have a stable electron arrangement, like neon's.

The sodium will no longer have its original properties, however, and neither will the fluorine. The electron rearrangement leaves the fluorine with a slight negative charge and the sodium with a slight positive charge. There is no longer an equal number of electrons and protons in each atom. Instead of two elements, the atoms now form a compound — sodium fluoride, or NaF, which is a key ingredient in toothpaste. You met a very similar compound, NaCl, in Chapter 6, on page 195.

Table 8.2 shows that other alkali metal and halogen combinations also form one-to-one compounds. This bonding pattern is a result of the atomic structure of the elements involved. In this section, you will use your new understanding of atomic structure to predict bonding patterns for many other element combinations.

The alkaline earth metals have a slightly different bonding pattern with the halogens. Two halogen atoms are required to permit the electron rearrangement so that one of the alkaline earth metals can achieve a stable octet. Can you make a table to show the bonding pattern for the first three alkaline earth metals with the same four halogens?

Table 8.2 Bonding Pattern Between Alkali Metals and Halogens

	Fluorine	Chlorine	Bromine	Iodine
Lithium	LiF	LiCl	LiBr	LiI
Sodium	NaF	NaCl	NaBr	NaI
Potassium	KF	KCl	KBr	KI

The Formation of Ions

When an atom gains or loses electrons, the atom is no longer neutral. It has become an **ion**, meaning a particle or group of particles with a positive or negative charge. Recall that atoms are neutral because they contain equal numbers of positive and negative charges. A sodium atom contains 11 protons and 11 electrons. If it loses one electron, it has 11 protons but only 10 electrons, so the ion is positive. You can show this neatly by writing the chemical symbol for sodium with a single plus sign next to it: Na^+.

Fluorine atoms must gain one electron to complete a stable octet. When fluorine gains an electron from sodium, it has 10 electrons but only 9 protons, so the ion has a negative charge and its symbol is F^-.

Your model for compound formation now includes a way to understand how **ionic compounds** are formed. The positive ions and negative ions attract each other after the electron rearrangement happens. This attraction is called an **ionic bond**. The attraction is not only strong but also the same in all directions. It extends from one ion to the next throughout an ionic compound.

You can use your model to predict which elements in the periodic table will form ionic compounds. The most efficient way to do this is to use the concept of families, or groups, of elements. Identify the number of electrons in the outer shell of the elements in a group by using the Bohr-Rutherford model, as you did in the activity on page 259. The electrons in the outer shell are called the **valence electrons**. They are the atom's most loosely bound electrons and are therefore available for compound formation. If the number of valence electrons is low for one group but high for another, you can predict that an ionic compound will form readily. (Can you see why the noble gases are a special case?) For example, the alkali metals all have one valence

Figure 8.8 You can move electrons, too! Just try brushing or combing your hair — can you hear a crackling sound? In Chapter 9, you will find out how electrons cause situations like this.

electron, and the halogens all have seven valence electrons. You know that sodium and fluorine actually form an ionic compound, sodium fluoride; whenever you can observe what your model predicts, you can be more confident about your model. What would you predict about the bonding of an alkaline earth metal (Group 2), with two valence electrons, to a halogen?

In the Starting Point Activity, you observed a chemical reaction between magnesium and oxygen. Two electrons are transferred from the magnesium to the oxygen to form the compound magnesium oxide (MgO). The ions in this compound have the symbols Mg^{2+} and O^{2-}. How can the concept of valence electrons explain this?

When metals and non-metals react, the total number of electrons transferred from positive ions must equal the total number received by negative ions because electrons must be conserved. You can use this concept to predict the formula of any ionic compound, no matter how complex it is. For example, you saw in Chapter 6 that aluminum readily combines with oxygen to form an ionic compound called aluminum oxide. Aluminum atoms have three valence electrons, so they form Al^{3+} ions. Oxygen will form O^{2-} ions. How can you use this information to explain the formula Al_2O_3? Draw a shell diagram of the five atoms involved to show the electron transfers.

A Strong Attraction

The ions in ionic compounds fit together in a regular repeating pattern called a **crystal lattice**. Figure 8.9 shows how this regular pattern gives a sodium chloride crystal its characteristic shape, as you saw in Chapter 6. The strong forces between ions make ionic compounds hard, and ionic solids are not electrical conductors because the ions are not able to move. When an ionic solid is dissolved in water or heated above its melting point, however, the ions are free to move, and they conduct electricity.

In effect, a sodium chloride crystal behaves like one large structure. Although we usually write the formula of sodium chloride as NaCl because it consists of equal numbers of Na$^+$ and Cl$^-$ ions, there is no single NaCl particle.

Figure 8.9 When crystals of sodium chloride are carefully formed, they are cubic.

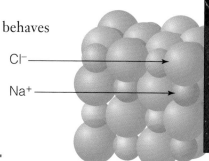

Cl$^-$

Na$^+$

Check Your Understanding

1. Explain the term "valence electron."

2. Use the periodic table to answer the following questions.

   (a) How many valence electrons does calcium have?

   (b) How many valence electrons does phosphorus have? How many electrons does it need to form a stable octet?

3. List three properties of ionic compounds.

4. Why are ionic compounds non-conductors of electricity when they are solid but good conductors when they are melted?

5. When an ionic compound is named or its formula is written, what sort of element is placed first? What is the charge on its ion?

6. **Apply** Compare the electrical conductivity of a metal with that of an ionic compound. How is it the same? How is it different?

7. **Thinking Critically** Element Q is a metal with two valence electrons and element X is a non-metal with three valence electrons.

   (a) What ions would you expect Q and X to form?

   (b) What is the formula of the ionic compound they form?

8.3 Molecular Compounds

Word CONNECT

The prefix "co-" usually changes a word to suggest "shared" or "sharing." Which chemical term do you think the term "covalent" comes from? The second half of the term "covalent" comes from a Latin word meaning "strength." Can you see why? (Hint: Think about reactivity.)

You have already seen in Chapter 6 that not all substances are ionic. Your model for compound formation can now be extended to include non-ionic or **molecular compounds**. Unlike ionic compounds, molecular compounds are made up of uncharged atoms. How can the atoms remain uncharged when they combine to form new compounds?

In ionic compounds, the model tells you that metal and non-metal atoms bond by *swapping* electrons. To extend the model, imagine that non-metals atoms can combine with each other by *sharing* their electrons. Remember that the number of valence electrons lets you calculate how many electrons an atom needs to form a stable octet. For example, oxygen has six valence electrons, so it requires two more. If two oxygen atoms each share two of their electrons with the other atom, a stable molecule, O_2, is formed. (You may remember this diatomic molecule from Chapter 6.) This electron-sharing arrangement is called a **covalent bond**, and Figure 8.10 shows how your model, expanded to include the formation of covalent bonds, applies to some familiar molecular compounds in addition to H_2 and O_2.

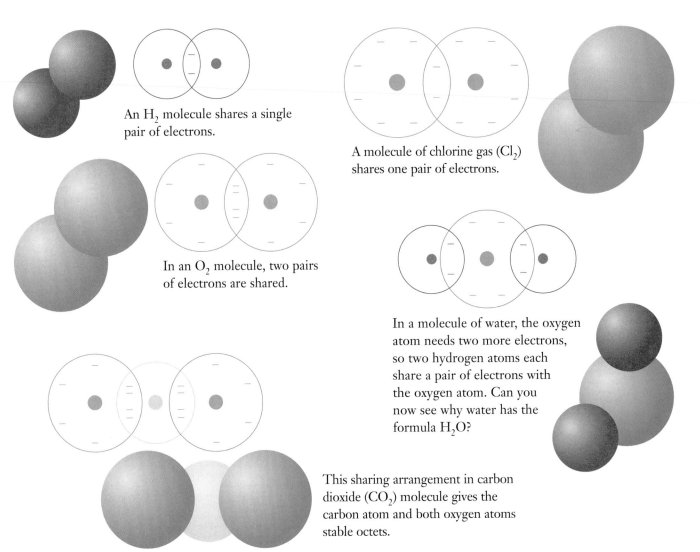

An H_2 molecule shares a single pair of electrons.

A molecule of chlorine gas (Cl_2) shares one pair of electrons.

In an O_2 molecule, two pairs of electrons are shared.

In a molecule of water, the oxygen atom needs two more electrons, so two hydrogen atoms each share a pair of electrons with the oxygen atom. Can you now see why water has the formula H_2O?

This sharing arrangement in carbon dioxide (CO_2) molecule gives the carbon atom and both oxygen atoms stable octets.

Figure 8.10 Sharing outer electrons in some molecular compounds

What Is the Difference?

What is the difference between an ionic bond and a covalent bond? Covalent bonds between different atoms vary in strength, as do ionic bonds between different ions. In general, however, the strength of covalent bonds is about the same as the strength of ionic bonds. The key difference is the attraction between molecules. An ionic compound behaves like one large structure, with each ion surrounded by ions of opposite charge. This means that strong attractions extend throughout the crystal. Most molecular compounds do not form large structures. Although the *bonding* between *atoms* is strong, the *attraction* between *molecules* is weak.

When you melt or vaporize a molecular compound, you must supply enough energy to overcome the attraction between the molecules. Because this attraction is weak, most molecular compounds have relatively low melting and boiling points. The weak attraction between molecules explains their relative softness, as well. Finally, because molecular compounds have no ions or free electrons, they are always poor electrical conductors, even when in a liquid state. In the activity below, and in the next investigation, you will explore these differences in properties between ionic and molecular compounds.

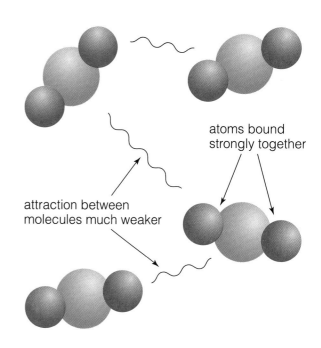

atoms bound strongly together

attraction between molecules much weaker

Figure 8.11 In molecular compounds like water, the attraction between molecules is much weaker than the bonding of the atoms in each individual molecule.

Which Forces Are Stronger?

You can compare the attraction between ions (in an ionic compound) with the attraction between molecules (in a molecular compound).

What You Need

pan balance
salt crystals, NaCl (an ionic compound)
ethyl alcohol, C_2H_5OH (a molecular compound)
2 beakers (100 mL)

What to Do

1. Place some salt crystals in a beaker on one side of the pan balance.

2. Place an equal mass of alcohol in another beaker, on the other side of the balance.

3. Write a hypothesis about what will happen, based on what you know about ionic and covalent bonds.

4. Leave the balance for about 15 min, and then observe to see if there is any change. Record your observations.

What Did You Discover?

1. What happened to the balance after a short time?

2. What could you infer had happened?

3. How can you relate your observations to what you know about ionic and molecular compounds?

Comparing Ionic and Molecular Properties

In this investigation, you will examine a number of substances to find out which are ionic and which are not. You will then conduct some further tests to compare their properties.

Safety Precautions

If you are using an older model conductivity tester with two separate electrodes, you should be extremely careful to keep them well separated while you perform your tests.

Problem

How do the properties of ionic and molecular substances compare?

Apparatus
conductivity tester
wire gauze
ceramic evaporating dish
8 small beakers (100 mL)
Bunsen burner
scoopula
magnifying lens
stirring rod
ring clamp
8 labels

Materials
400 mL distilled water
sodium iodide, NaI
copper nitrate, $Cu(NO_3)_2$
magnesium chloride, $MgCl_2$
graphite (carbon)
paraffin wax, $C_{25}H_{52}$
sucrose, $C_{12}H_{22}O_{11}$
starch (long molecule based on sucrose)

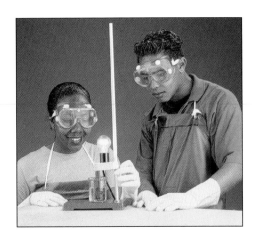

Substance	Solubility in Water	Conductivity Test	Ionic? (yes/no)	Appearance	Odour	Texture	Relative Melting Point
sodium iodide							
copper nitrate							
magnesium chloride							
graphite							
paraffin wax							
sucrose							
starch							

Procedure

① Make a table like the one above. Give your table a title.

② Based on information from the periodic table and what you already know, which of these substances do you think might be ionic?

③ Label each beaker with the name of one of the substances to be tested. Pour about 50 mL of distilled water into each beaker. Label one beaker "Control."

④ Test the "Control" beaker with the conductivity tester, and record your results.

⑤ Use the scoopula to add a small quantity of sodium iodide (about the size of a peanut) to the beaker with the appropriate label. Use a stirring rod to dissolve the solid. Note whether the solid dissolves completely.

(a) Test the solution with the conductivity tester, and record your results.

(b) Record whether or not the solid is ionic.

⑥ Repeat step 5 for each of the other substances.

⑦ Examine a small sample of each substance using a magnifying lens. Briefly describe the shape of the grains.

(a) Carefully smell each compound. In your table, describe any odour.

(b) **CAUTION:** You must wear protective gloves for this test. Test the texture of each substance by rubbing a small sample between your thumb and forefinger. Use words like "soft," "waxy," "brittle," and "granular" to record your observations.

(c) Wash your hands thoroughly when you have completed this step.

⑧ Choose one solid that you think is ionic and one solid that you think is not ionic.

(a) Place a small sample of each into a ceramic evaporating dish. Put the samples on opposite sides of the dish, separate from each other. Use a retort stand, wire gauze, and a small iron ring clamp to hold the dish.

(b) Heat evenly with a Bunsen burner until one of the substances melts. In your table, record the relative melting point for this substance as "low" and for the other substance as "high."

(c) After the evaporating dish has cooled down, clean it and put it away. Be careful when you put away the ring clamp. It can remain hot longer than the other equipment.

Analyze

1. (a) Which compounds used in this activity are ionic?

   (b) In which part of the periodic table do the elements in ionic compounds occur?

2. (a) Which compounds are molecular?

   (b) In which part of the periodic table do their elements occur?

3. (a) In general, are ionic compounds soluble in water?

   (b) In general, are molecular compounds soluble in water?

   (c) Did you find any compounds that were exceptions to your answers for parts (a) and (b)?

Conclude and Apply

4. Make a general statement comparing the appearance of ionic compounds and molecular compounds.

5. Do ionic compounds tend to have an odour? Do molecular compounds tend to have an odour?

6. In general, which type of substance is harder, ionic or molecular?

7. Share your results on relative melting points with others in your class who tested different compounds. Which type of compound has the higher melting point?

8. Summarize some general properties of ionic and molecular compounds.

Carbon: An Element with Disguises

You have already seen that ionic compounds form large structures because they have ions in regular positions, with strong forces that join one ion to the next throughout a compound. Usually molecular compounds are formed as small molecules, but sometimes covalent bonds that extend from one atom to the next throughout a substance can form giant molecules with important properties. You may well be holding an example of one of these substances right now.

Graphite contains carbon atoms that are linked together with strong covalent bonds to form hexagons (six-sided figures). The hexagons form sheets with very weak forces between the planes. As a result, the sheets or planes can slip past one another, making graphite an excellent lubricant. When mixed with clay, graphite can be rolled into a rod to make pencil "lead." As well, electrons can move between planes of carbon hexagons. This movement means that carbon (in the form of graphite) is the only non-metal, non-metalloid element that conducts electricity.

Another, much rarer form of carbon is **diamond**. Diamond is formed from graphite in geological processes that involve extreme pressure. Pencil lead has properties very different from those of diamond because the carbon atoms are joined together in different ways.

In diamond, each atom forms four covalent bonds with other carbon atoms to create a three-dimensional network of atoms (see Figure 8.13). Even a tiny diamond contains about 10^{20} (one hundred billion billion) atoms bonded together with no weak links. Because of these strong bonds that extend throughout the crystal, diamond is the hardest known natural substance. It should not surprise you that a very high temperature, 3550°C, is required to melt diamond. The beauty of a cut diamond is related to its crystal properties, but these properties give diamond many practical uses, too.

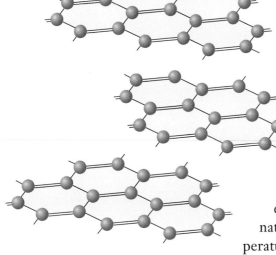

Figure 8.12 In graphite, carbon atoms bond together in sheets.

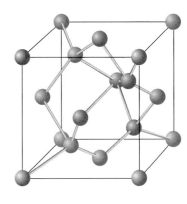

Figure 8.13 Covalent bonding between carbon atoms produces the giant structure present in diamonds.

Blades, drills, and grinding tools may have a diamond coating to handle really tough jobs (see Figure 8.14). Not only is diamond hard, but it also has a greater ability than most metals to conduct heat. Consequently, the drilling or cutting process can be faster, and the life of the tool prolonged. A very thin film of diamond can be deposited on the surface of an object. These diamond films are used in electronics to make stronger, heat-conducting silicon wafers. Imagine a razor blade with a diamond film edge or a glass surface that is chemically resistant and can never be scratched. What other uses can you think of for diamond films?

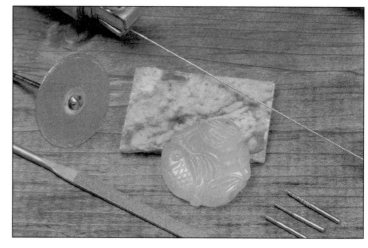

Figure 8.14 Diamonds are a stoneworker's best friend.

More Giant Structures: Polymers

Plastics, and many fibres used for clothing, are made of giant molecules called **polymers**. A polymer is made of many small repeating "sub-molecules" called monomers. A polymer is like a string of beads, but there would have to be thousands of beads to have the same number of monomers that are present in most polymer chains. In Unit 1 of this book, you learned about a naturally occurring, highly complex polymer: DNA. You also identified the monomers of this polymer. Can you now see what they are?

Many of the commonest manufactured polymers are based on the monomer ethylene (C_2H_4, also known as ethene). This simple molecule is at the heart of complex manufacturing processes, as pictured in Figure 8.15.

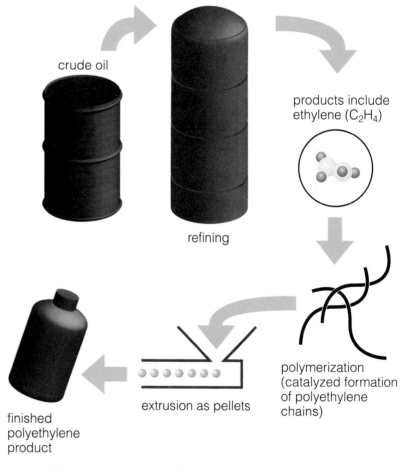

crude oil

refining

products include ethylene (C_2H_4)

polymerization (catalyzed formation of polyethylene chains)

extrusion as pellets

finished polyethylene product

Figure 8.15B The manufacture of polyethylene

Figure 8.15A The plastic products you use are made of polymers. Many of them are based on a chemical commonly called ethylene.

Polymer Properties and Uses

Think About It

In Canada, about 40 percent of all manufactured polymers are used in packaging. In this investigation, you will identify a number of different polymers used for containers around your home, and you will describe their properties.

Materials

a variety of plastic containers:

polyethylene (PETE) 2 L soft drink bottle or water bottle

high density polyethylene (HDPE) crinkly store bag or bleach bottle

polyvinyl chloride (PVC) vegetable oil bottle or window cleaner bottle

low density polyethylene (IDPE) grocery bag or garbage bag

polypropylene (PP) margarine tub, microwave food tray, or ketchup bottle

polystyrene (PS) packing materials or disposable cup

What to Do

1 Make a table like the one below.

Polymers Used in Packaging

Polymer	Logo	Typical Containers	Properties
polyethylene			

2 Examine the plastic containers your teacher has provided. For each container, find the logo that identifies the polymer used in its manufacture. Use the logo to identify the polymer in the table, and add the container to the list of typical containers.

3 Record the properties of each polymer. Is it relatively flexible or rigid? Can it be deformed, or will it break, stretch, crack, tear, or shatter? Does it appear to be resistant to corrosion? How well does it conduct heat? Is it transparent or opaque? Describe any other properties you can think of.

Analyze

1. Analyze the properties of each polymer, and relate them to its use. Identify the properties that you think were most important when the manufacturer wanted a container for

   (a) cooking oil

   (b) shampoo

   (c) headache or vitamin pills

Conclude and Apply

2. Toothpaste tubes are made of plastic, but the identifying logo is usually missing. What properties are desirable in a toothpaste tube, and which polymer might it be made from?

3. Describe the contents of a container made using each of the following materials: glass, plastic, and metal. For each container, describe the advantages and disadvantages of the material it is made from, considering the contents of the container. Could substitutions have been made? For example, could plastic have been used instead of metal, or glass instead of plastic?

Extend Your Skills

4. Plastics and other materials can have a wide variety of properties. Look about your home, and identify one item made from each of the following materials: metal, plastic, wood, glass, and paper. Which properties were important when the manufacturer decided to make each item?

5. In your kitchen, you may have three different "wraps": plastic film, wax paper, and aluminum foil. The properties of each wrap determine how it is used. Make a table to compare the properties and uses of each wrap.

Slimy Connections

One of the ways a chemist can change the properties of a polymer is to make chemical bonds between different polymer chains. This process is called cross-linking. In this activity, you will observe how the properties of polyvinyl alcohol change when another chemical is added to produce cross-linking. Before you begin, predict what you think will happen to the properties of a polymer if cross-links are formed between polymer chains.

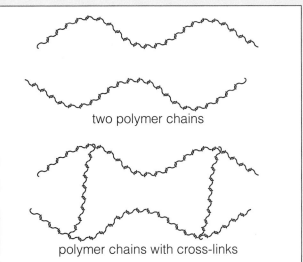

two polymer chains

polymer chains with cross-links

What You Need

50 mL polyvinyl alcohol solution
5 mL sodium borate solution
disposable cup
stirring rod
food colouring (optional)
paper towel
plain paper
water-soluble marker

What to Do

1. Place about 50 mL of polyvinyl alcohol solution into a disposable cup. Add a few drops of food colouring, if desired, and stir. Describe the properties of the solution.

2. Pour about 5 mL of sodium borate solution into the cup while stirring. Record what happens to the mixture.

3. Put your slime on a sheet of paper towel. Pick it up, and describe what happens when you let it ooze between your fingers.

4. Next try stretching the slime quickly, and note how it behaves differently.

5. On a piece of paper, write your name backward with a water-soluble marker. Press the slime onto the paper for only half a second. (The slime will stick to the paper if it is left too long.) What do you observe?

6. Dispose of your slime as your teacher directs. Wash your hands thoroughly after completing this activity.

What Did You Discover?

1. What evidence suggests that the sodium borate solution produced cross-links between polyvinyl alcohol chains?

2. Are the cross-links strong or relatively weak bonds? Explain.

Check Your Understanding

1. What is a covalent bond? Which types of atoms generally combine using covalent bonds?

2. List four properties of many molecular compounds.

3. How is graphite the same as diamond? How is it different? Explain some uses of the two forms in terms of their properties.

4. Distinguish between a monomer and a polymer.

5. Name three different polymers, and suggest a use for each one.

6. **Thinking Critically** A student describes a molecule as the smallest particle of a molecular compound that retains all the properties of the compound.

   (a) Is this true for chemical properties?

   (b) Is this true for physical properties?

   Explain your answers.

7. **Thinking Critically** Polyethylene can be made in a high density form (HDPE) or a low density form (LDPE). Briefly outline an experiment you could perform to distinguish between these two forms.

8.4 Chemicals in Your Life

You have seen how atoms, molecules, and ions combine chemically to make new substances. In this section, you are going to look at the ways we use these substances.

Chemicals in Farming

If you had been alive in Canada 150 years ago, you would have probably been living on a farm. Even 50 years ago, over 20 percent of Canadians worked and lived on farms. Today the farm population is about 2.5 percent, feeding a much larger population and producing food exports for the rest of the world. One reason for this change is mechanization. A farmer with a tractor and other machines can do the work that used to require dozens of farm hands. Another reason is chemicals, which can be used to produce crops with higher yields and less spoilage.

Figure 8.16 The wise use of chemicals helps to keep food costs down.

Plants need nitrogen in order to form proteins and nucleic acids, such as DNA. Some plants, such as peas and beans, obtain their nitrogen through certain soil bacteria. Most plants absorb nitrogen compounds from the soil, however, and a chemical fertilizer may increase their yield. One commonly used fertilizer is ammonia, NH_3, which is composed of molecules that contain 82 percent nitrogen by mass. Ammonia is a gas at atmospheric pressure, but it is easily liquefied at higher pressure. In its liquid form, it is injected below the surface of the soil. Nitrogen fertilizers can also be applied in solid form, similar to the granules in a typical lawn fertilizer. Ammonium nitrate, NH_4NO_3, is a common example of a solid fertilizer. It is an ionic compound that is very soluble in water, so the granules are coated to allow them to dissolve over a longer period of time.

Tools of Science

In Alberta, some farmers use tractors that monitor the soil every few metres. On-board software uses laboratory soil analysis data to calculate the *exact* quantity of fertilizer needed for each specific square metre of soil.

Figure 8.17 Chemical fertilizers are an essential part of modern farming.

Plants must also absorb phosphorus, a key element for managing the energy they need to grow and reproduce. Many phosphorus compounds are not very soluble in water, so they would be poorly absorbed by plants. These compounds can be treated chemically to make other phosphorus-containing compounds that are soluble.

Another key element, one that enables plants to resist disease and insect damage, is potassium. Absorbed as the K^+ ion by plant roots, potassium fertilizer is made from potash. Canada is the world's largest producer of potash.

A farmer may use a variety of pesticides, as well. *Pesticides* are chemicals that control weeds, plant diseases, or insects. A pesticide that controls weeds is called a *herbicide*, while a pesticide that controls insects is called an *insecticide*. When applied properly, pesticides improve the quality and quantity of crops.

Even after a crop has been harvested, certain chemicals may be used to make sure it arrives fresh at the supermarket. The fresh bananas in your local store may have been picked weeks ago in Central America. Before they are distributed to stores, green bananas are exposed to ethylene, C_2H_4, to stimulate the ripening process. Since ethylene is the same gas that is used to make the polymer polyethylene, it may have been used both to ripen your bananas and to make the plastic bag in which you carry them home!

You can eat fresh Canadian apples year-round because after they are picked in September or October, they can be placed in controlled-atmosphere storage.

Figure 8.18 Ethylene, a chemical compound, will help these bananas to ripen.

Here they are sealed in an atmosphere of carbon dioxide, CO_2, where the lack of oxygen slows down their decay.

Chemicals in Your Cabinet

Chemistry has had a major role to play in the medicine cabinet. The active ingredients of medicines are *drugs*: chemical substances that have an effect on the body. The first drugs were actually plants — various leaves and seeds that seemed to relieve people's symptoms. If you had an ache, for example, you might have chewed on the bark of a willow tree. Eventually the active ingredient was isolated from the bark of willow trees, and by 1899 a way had been found to manufacture this compound, acetylsalicylic acid ($C_9H_8O_4$), which is now known as Aspirin™.

One of the first synthetic drugs to be developed was ether, $(C_2H_5)_2O$. Ether is a molecular compound that is a liquid at room temperature but easily vaporizes. It was first used as an anesthetic in 1846, and it had an obvious impact on surgical procedures, especially for the patient. As chemical knowledge and techniques progressed, attention focussed on isolating the active ingredients of traditional medicines. The search for new drugs and cures continues to be a very important area of research.

The Right Mix

Years ago, pharmacists ground up and mixed together the ingredients of many prescriptions themselves. Even though prescriptions these days come ready-mixed from pharmaceutical companies, pharmacists like Ginette Goulet still need to know their chemistry.

Ginette has to know which combinations of prescription drugs and other factors can cause an unwanted chemical reaction and problems for the patient. She lets her customers know, for example, if the prescription they receive should not be taken with milk, or if it should be taken on an empty stomach to be most effective. She also lets them know if certain "over-the-counter" drugs, such as antihistamines, should not be taken until they have finished the course of their prescription. Since some customers may be on more than one prescription at the same time, she needs to know which drugs can be taken safely together, so that there are no conflicts between the prescribed drugs.

As early as high school, Ginette decided that a career in pharmacy would be right for her.

- Assume that you are a high-school student who wants to become a pharmacist. Develop a plan to help you reach your goal.

- If another career is of more interest to you, develop a plan for achieving this career goal instead.

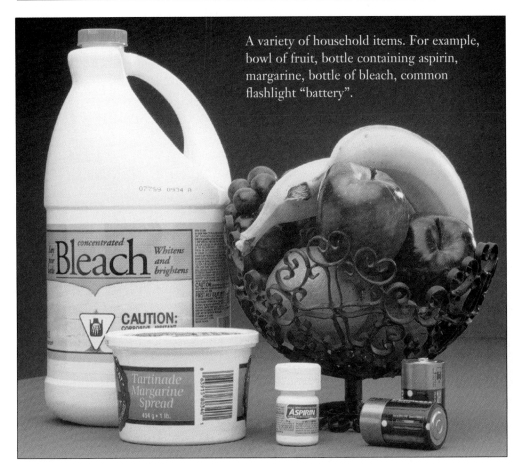

A variety of household items. For example, bowl of fruit, bottle containing aspirin, margarine, bottle of bleach, common flashlight "battery".

Figure 8.19 All of these items have a chemical connection.

Chemicals in Our Food

In 1869, Napoleon III offered a prize for "a clean fat, cheap and with good keeping qualities, suitable to replace butter." The winner was a chemist, Hippolyte Mège-Mouriés. He mixed edible fats, oil, and water, thereby inventing margarine. Only a few foods are, like margarine, the result of chemical invention, but most prepared foods have chemicals added to them. These chemicals include synthetic vitamins, colouring agents, and preservatives. The simple act of cooking food is another way of causing chemical change, making food easier to digest.

Figure 8.20 How many ingredients in this "sport" drink have names that end in "ide" or "ate"? These salts form ions in your body.

Check Your Understanding

1. Give two reasons why fewer workers are needed to operate a modern farm. How does this benefit the consumer?

2. Name three types of chemical products that might be used by farmers, as well as by the home gardener.

3. Which three elements are essential for the healthy growth of plants?

4. **Thinking Critically** How are chemistry and chemical change related to food? Give one specific example to illustrate each.

Now that you have completed this chapter, try to do the following. If you cannot, go back to the sections indicated.

Identify the following families in the periodic table, and compare their electron arrangements: alkali metals, alkaline earth metals, halogens, and noble gases. (8.1)

Explain why the noble gases are unreactive, in terms of their electron arrangement. (8.1)

Explain the reactivity of the alkali metals and the halogens in terms of the electrons present in their outer shells. (8.1)

Give a specific example of two elements that would combine to form an ionic compound. Describe how atoms of each element would form ions. (8.2)

Describe the formation of ionic bonds as the transfer of electrons, and covalent bonds as the sharing of electrons between specific atoms. (8.2, 8.3)

Describe tests that could distinguish between typical ionic and molecular compounds. (8.3)

List the typical physical properties of molecular compounds. Explain these properties in terms of relatively weak attractions between molecules. (8.3)

List examples of substances that have large structures. (8.2, 8.3)

Describe different physical properties of diamond and graphite. (8.3)

Briefly describe the stages in the manufacture of plastics. (8.3)

Describe the importance of chemical compounds to farmers or home gardeners. (8.4)

Briefly describe the use of chemical compounds in your home. (8.4)

Prepare Your Own Summary

Summarize this chapter by doing one of the following. Use a graphic organizer (such as a concept map), produce a poster, or write the summary to include the key chapter concepts. Here are a few ideas to use as a guide:

- Explain the reactivity of an alkali metal with a halogen in terms of rearranging the electrons in their outer shells.
- Explain the formation of ions when a metal reacts with a non-metal.
- Explain the formation of a covalent bond between the atoms of two non-metallic elements.

- Compare the properties of ionic and molecular compounds. Explain these properties in terms of the attractions between ions or molecules.
- Give examples of giant structures, and describe important properties they have as a result of their structure.
- Identify various polymers used in packaging. Relate the properties of a specific polymer to its use.
- Describe specific uses of chemical compounds in modern society.

Reviewing Key Terms

If you need review, the section numbers show you where these terms were introduced.

1. Which groups have special names? Complete the following table: (7.4)

Group	Name	Number of Valence Electrons
1		
	alkaline earth metals	
		7
18		

2. How does the formation of an ionic bond differ from the formation of a covalent bond? (8.2, 8.3)

3. What is meant by the term "valence electron"? How many valence electrons does sulfur have? (8.2)

4. How do ionic compounds differ from molecular compounds when added to water? (8.3)

5. How is a polymer like a chain-link fence? What would be represented by each link in the chain? (8.3)

6. Distinguish between the following terms: pesticide, herbicide, insecticide. (8.4)

Understanding Key Concepts

Section numbers are provided if you need to review.

7. How are the electrons of atoms involved when a chemical change takes place? (8.1)

8. What is meant by a shell of electrons? How is the number of electrons in the outer shell of an atom of a particular element related to the position of the element on the periodic table? (8.1)

9. How does the electron structure of the noble gases help to explain their chemical properties? (8.1)

10. Explain why an alkali metal would react very vigorously with a halogen. (8.2)

11. How does the total positive charge in the formula of an ionic compound relate to the total negative charge? (8.2)

12. How many calcium ions are represented in the formula of each of the following ionic compounds? (8.2)

   (a) CaO

   (b) $CaBr_2$

   (c) Ca_3N_2

13. Describe two ways that a chemical bond can be formed. Give an example of each type of chemical bond. (8.2, 8.3)

14. If ionic bonds are about as strong as covalent bonds, why do ionic solids tend to have much higher melting points than molecular solids? (8.3)

15. Sand is impure quartz, SiO_2, which forms a giant structure held together by covalent bonds.

   (a) What properties do you expect quartz to have?

   (b) Do you think quartz is a good electrical conductor? Explain. (8.3)

16. How are salt, diamond, and polyethylene similar? How are they different? (8.2, 8.3)

17. What is a polymer? Give an example of a natural polymer and a synthetic polymer. (8.3)

18. Explain why a fertilizer should be neither insoluble nor too soluble. (8.4)

Developing Skills

19. Predict some of the properties of lithium bromide. Use a chemistry reference book to check your predictions.

20. Make a web diagram with the term "compounds" in the centre of the diagram.

21. Develop a concept map for chemical bonding.

Problem Solving

22. Using the periodic table, identify how many protons and how many electrons are present in each of the following ions.

(a) K^+

(b) Ca^{2+}

(c) N^{3-}

(d) Al^{3+}

23. When the following pairs of elements combine, they form ionic compounds. Use the periodic table to work out the formulas of the ionic compounds formed. (Note that each pair is given alphabetically.)

(a) barium and fluorine

(b) bromine and potassium

(c) nitrogen and sodium

(d) magnesium and phosphorus

(e) calcium and sulfur

24. Oxygen has six valence electrons. How many valence electrons does the other element have in each of the following oxides?

(a) Na_2O

(b) MnO

(c) PbO_2

Critical Thinking

25. Why do you think hydrogen is usually placed in Group 1 of the periodic table, even though it is not a metal like the other Group 1 elements?

26. Which of the following formulas are impossible? Give reasons for your answers.

(a) $LiCl_2$

(b) KS

(c) MgF_2

(d) AlO_3

27. Carbon dioxide contains covalent bonds, and so does diamond. Yet carbon dioxide is a gas at room temperature, while diamond is a solid with a very high melting point. Explain why these two substances are different.

28. You may have some moth balls at home, or perhaps a solid room air freshener. Are these made of ionic or molecular compounds?

29. There are risks and benefits in the use of all forms of technology. Make a table to list the risks and the benefits in the use of insecticides for agriculture.

Pause& Reflect

1. How is the bonding in a substance related to its properties?

2. How can you use the periodic table to predict the type of bonding that will probably take place between two atoms?

In 1981 archaeologist André Lépine decided to bring up from the sea floor a large cannon and other artifacts he had found on a shipwreck under the Baie de Gaspé. These artifacts had been underwater for more than 200 years and were encased in a lumpy coating of rust. Lépine called on specialist Judy Logan of the Canadian Conservation Institute to see if her team of conservators could clean up and preserve the artifacts.

Q **This thing doesn't look much like a cannon. What made it so crusty and misshapen?**

A The cast iron that the cannon is made of was changed by an electrochemical reaction. The iron reacted with the water, oxygen, and chloride ions from the salt water. This caused corrosion of the metal and produced damaging rust. Then the rust mixed with the silt from the ocean floor and became a great place for coral to grow. The crust of stuff you see covering the cannon is what we call concretion.

Q **Can't you just scrape off the concretion on an artifact like this and then clean up what's underneath?**

A That's not really a good idea. The iron of a cannon in this condition is corroded, so it's weaker. The rust is like strong cement, holding the weak iron and concretion together. If you scraped off the concretion, some of the corroded iron could come off, too. That would damage the cannon, and you'd lose all of the surface detail. Plus, there would still be chloride ions in

the metal, corroding it further even after you'd cleaned the concretion off.

Q **So how can you clean up the cannon if the iron is ready to fall apart?**

A An electrochemical reaction caused the corrosion, and another electrochemical reaction can help to correct it. If an iron artifact still contains a fair amount of uncorroded metal, electrolysis is one of our best tools for removing chloride ions and corrosion from it.

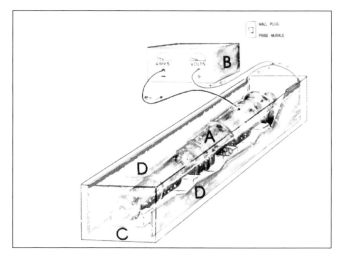

Q **How does the electrolysis work?**

A We wrap a wire around the cannon and place it into an electrolyte. The wire is connected to the negative terminal of a source of electric current (B). The cannon itself becomes the cathode (A). Two high-quality stainless steel plates (D) are suspended in the tank (C), one on either side of the cannon, as the anodes. The conservator introduces a very low current into the tank.

The object gets a negative charge from the current. The chloride ions, which caused most of the corrosion, have a negative charge and so will move away from the negatively charged cathode (the cannon) toward the positive anodes. After a long enough period of time, the chloride ions are gone, and the cannon is safe from further corrosion.

Q But what about the corrosion that is already there?

A The other reason electrolysis is so useful for these artifacts is that it causes a chemical reaction that changes the rust, which is iron oxyhydroxide ($FeOOH$), to magnetite (Fe_3O_4). Magnetite is powdery, so after electrolysis we can chip off sections of the concretion and leave the surface of the cannon behind. The concretion is no longer glued to the cannon by the rust.

Q How long does it take to clean up a cannon like this one?

A This cannon was in electrolysis for more than four years. It was periodically disconnected from the wire and removed so that the outer layer of concretion could be gradually cleaned off. After the concretion and any remaining chloride ions had been removed, the cannon was washed for 21 months to remove the electrolyte and any other materials. Then it was dried and treated with tannic acid to prevent it from rusting.

Q Are there other artifacts that you clean using electrolysis?

A Electrolysis is good for any cast iron objects, such as cannon balls, cooking pots, and stoves that have been underwater or under the ground. We sometimes use it to clean wrought iron axes, hammers, and other tools if they are not too badly corroded. Electrolysis can also conserve lead artifacts, such as water pipes, and silver artifacts, such as coins, medallions, and jewellery. We use other conservation techniques as well to preserve many different types of artifacts.

Q How did you learn this skill of conserving artifacts?

A I studied archaeology at the University of Calgary, and in 1972 I was hired by Parks Canada. They were just beginning a program in conservation because Canada had no facilities for it at that time. After four years of working with them, I spent two years at Queen's University to get my master's degree in conservation. Since then, I've conserved countless objects from shipwrecks, trading posts, and many other fascinating sites.

EXPLORING Further

Underwater Archaeology

The sea is a rich resource for archaeologists because artifacts, even whole ships, can lie relatively undisturbed for centuries. Examining or recovering them can be tricky, however, and electrolysis is just one of many scientific techniques marine archaeologists must use. You can find out more about the science of investigating deep-sea wrecks on the Internet. Begin by going to **www.school.mcgrawhill.ca/resources/**. Go to the **Science Resources**, then to **SCIENCEPOWER 9** to know where to go next.

The Diagnosis and Treatment of a Bone Cancer

Think About It

For those who love athletics, aches and pains are common, but in 1977 a young athlete, Terry Fox, noticed a persistent and unusual pain in his right knee. When the tests were completed, his doctors had devastating news: Terry had osteogenic sarcoma, a type of bone cancer, in his right knee. To save his life, his right leg would have to be amputated immediately. Terry was only 18 years old.

Terry resolved to raise money for cancer research by running across Canada. He began

on April 12, 1980, at St. John's, Newfoundland, with a goal of $1 million. He averaged 42 km a day, an astonishing achievement for any athlete, and donations began to pour in. As Terry ran across Ontario, however, he developed a persistent cough. In September, near Thunder Bay, his "Marathon of Hope" came to an end. Terry's cancer had spread to his lungs, and he died near the end of June 1981, a month before his 23rd birthday. In September each year, communities across Canada and in many other countries hold a Terry Fox Memorial Run. To date, about $200 million has been raised for cancer research.

Prepare and Present

1 Your class will be divided into four groups to represent each of the following: a patient recently diagnosed with osteogenic sarcoma, a surgeon, an oncologist (a doctor who specializes in helping patients with cancer), and a radiologist (a doctor who uses radiation treatments to help cancer patients).

2 Each group should research and prepare a presentation, based on the following information:

- The group representing the patient should research the symptoms of osteogenic sarcoma. You should also form questions to ask the groups representing the specialists involved in the diagnosis and treatment of the disease. What are your options? What is the likely course of your treatment?

- The group representing the surgeon should research how a tumour is graded in terms of its seriousness. A low grade tumour may be treated without amputating the limb, while a tumour that has spread widely may be beyond surgical treatment. If the limb is not amputated, are there increased risks for the patient's survival?

- The group representing the oncologist should research the treatment options involving chemotherapy (chemical treatments that attack cancerous cells). There are usually a number of options, depending on how serious the bone cancer

is and whether it has spread to other organs. Try to find out common side effects of chemotherapy, both short and long term.

- The radiologist group should research the role of a radioactive compound, technetium phosphate, in the diagnosis of bone cancer. Treatment of a tumour may involve the use of X-rays, radioactive sources such as cobalt-60, or beams of particles such as protons or neutrons. The effectiveness of different radiation treatments varies. What are the advantages and disadvantages of each type of treatment?

3 The case will be presented to the class. The patient group should start by describing the symptoms. The surgeon group should then describe the diagnosis and recommended surgical treatment. Either the oncologist group or the radiologist group could present next. The patient group may ask questions at any time during the presentations.

Analyze

1. In what ways was the "patient" involved in decisions about the treatment of the disease?

2. How clearly did the specialist groups present information regarding the risks and benefits of the treatments proposed?

Chemistry Play-Off

Use your knowledge of chemistry to create a game based on the different kinds of substances you have encountered in this unit. Your game should focus on one, or a combination, of the following:

- the development of theories about matter
- the structure of the periodic table
- practical uses of elements, compounds, alloys, and isotopes
- industrial and economic aspects of chemistry

Challenge

Work in a group to design a game about chemical substances.

Possible Materials

art supplies, such as card, pens, stickers, glue, scissors
dice
your collection of element and compound cards from Chapter 5 (see page 176)
periodic table of the elements (page 562)

Design Criteria

A. The format of your game is up to you to decide. For example, you could use a quiz format, or you could create a card or board game. Your game should be challenging to play, but designed so that it can be learned easily. You may find your "elements and compounds" collection useful as a starting point, although you should not base your game entirely on this. For example, your game may involve alloys, or isotopes.

B. Your game will need to allow varying numbers of players.

C. Your game must be accompanied by written rules, which must be clear and easy to follow for someone who is playing your game for the first time.

D. Your game will bring out some of the chemical principles you have learned in this unit, such as chemical combinations of metallic and non-metallic elements, and also some of the practical uses or technologies associated with chemical substances.

Plan and Construct

1. Your teacher will divide you into groups. In your group, decide on a format for your game and the aspects of chemistry you intend to include in its design. Give your game a title.

2. Either draw or write a plan for your game. Review this plan, to see if you need to add anything to it.

3. Make a list of the materials you will need to use, and a list of the scientific information you will need to collect.

4. Within your group, assign teams to collect and organize information, and to build different parts of your game.

5. Carefully write down a set of rules for your game.

6. Try out your game, and make revisions if necessary.

7. Switch games with one other group, and play the game designed by the other group.

Evaluate

1. (a) How clear did you find the rules for the game that you played?
   (b) How clear did the group playing your game find your rules?

2. In playing your own and others' games, which concepts did you need to recall and which facts did you need to have access to?

3. How did the design process help you think about what you have learned in this unit?

4. Compare all the games created by your class.
   (a) Which game was the most fun to play? Why?
   (b) Which game used chemical concepts and issues most effectively? Explain.
   (c) Which game was the most attractively designed?

Now that you have completed Chapters 5, 6, 7, and 8, you can assess how much you have learned about chemistry by answering the following questions. Before you begin, you may find it useful to return to each Chapter at a Glance and to each Chapter Review.

True/False

In your notebook, indicate whether each statement is true or false. Correct each false statement.

1. All samples of matter must be pure substances or compounds.

2. Solutions are homogeneous mixtures with constant composition.

3. Alkali metals react vigorously with water, oxygen, and noble gases.

4. A chlorine atom has one more electron than a chloride ion.

5. Tempering causes copper to become stronger and more malleable.

6. All compounds with giant structures are ionic compounds.

Completion

In your notebook, complete each statement with the correct term or phrase.

7. A compound consists of substances combined in _____ proportions.

8. Two types of pure substances are _____ and _____ .

9. The rusting of iron is an example of a _____ change.

10. Isotopes of an element have different numbers of _____ .

11. The alkali metals have one less electron in the outer electron shell than the _____ .

12. In the periodic table, elements in the same _____ have similar properties.

Matching

13. In your notebook, copy the descriptions in column A. Beside each number, write the term from column B that best fits the description. A term may be used once, more than once, or not at all.

A	B
• process involving the formation of a new compound	• solution
• the rearrangement of atoms into new substances	• isotopes
• a homogeneous mixture	• mass number
• atoms of the same element with different numbers of neutrons	• chemical change
• the type of ion most commonly formed when a non-metallic element becomes an ion	• negatively charged ion
	• ionic bonding
• the total number of protons and neutrons in the nucleus	• alloy
	• atomic number
• the basis for arranging the elements in the periodic table	• ions
	• chemical bonding
	• physical change

Multiple Choice

In your notebook, write the letter of the best answer for each of the following questions.

14. Look at the diagram of a lithium atom below. Which of the parts labelled (a) to (e) has more than 99% of the mass of the atom?

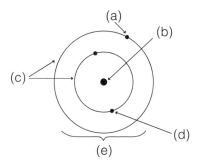

15. Sulfuric acid is used in many industrial processes. If concentrated sulfuric acid has a density of 1.84 g/mL, what is the mass of a 26.2 mL sample?

(a) 0.0702 g

(b) 14.2 g

(c) 26.2 g

(d) 28.0 g

(e) 48.2 g

16. While working in the laboratory, you burn your hand on a hot test tube. Which of the following best describes what you should do?

(a) do nothing unless it is a serious burn

(b) put a plaster on the wound

(c) get help from your lab partner and avoid using the hand

(d) report the incident to your teacher

(e) run cold water on the burn and then report the incident to your teacher

17. A mixture that is homogeneous is classified as

(a) a pure substance

(b) an element

(c) a solution

(d) a mechanical mixture

(e) a compound

18. Which of (1) to (4) are physical properties of gold?

(1) It is yellow.

(2) Its density is 19.3 g/cm^3.

(3) It does not react with oxygen at room temperature.

(4) It is the best electrical conductor of all metals.

(a) (1) only

(b) (2) only

(c) (3) only

(d) (1) and (2) only

(e) (1), (2), and (3) only

19. Which of these ideas about atomic structure was developed by Rutherford?

(a) electrons orbit in fixed shells

(b) atomic number should be the basis for the periodic table

(c) the atom has a nucleus and an electron cloud

(d) the muffin model of the atom

(e) all atoms of an element are identical

20. Which atom or ion has the same number of electrons as the Cl^- ion?

(a) Ne

(b) Cl

(c) K^+

(d) Li^+

(e) N^{5+}

21. In which of processes (1) to (3) is ethylene used?

(1) ripening fruit

(2) manufacturing anesthetics

(3) manufacturing polythene bags

(a) (1) only

(b) (2) only

(c) (1) and (3) only

(d) (1) and (2) only

(e) all three

Short Answer

In your notebook, write a sentence or a short paragraph to answer each of the following questions.

22. State three quantitative physical properties that could be used to help identify an unknown metal.

23. Explain the difference between
    (a) a physical property and a physical change
    (b) a chemical property and a chemical change
    (c) a physical change and a chemical change
    (d) a solute and a solvent

24. What is the difference between a mineral and an ore? Why are ores usually concentrated where they are mined?

25. What is electrolysis? Briefly describe either of the two electrolysis experiments in this unit.

26. Distinguish between the terms "mass number" and "atomic number."

27. How is the spectrum produced by sunlight different from the spectrum produced by energized hydrogen gas?

28. Why is an atom's outermost shell of electrons important?

29. How did Bohr modify Rutherford's model of the atom?

30. Relate the electron structure of aluminum to its position in Period 3 and Group 13 of the periodic table.

31. Draw electron shell diagrams for calcium and argon. How would these electron diagrams compare with electron diagrams for strontium and krypton?

32. Name two metals with very different reactivities, which are nevertheless used for the same practical purpose. Explain your answer.

33. As you go down a group of non-metals, does the chemical reactivity generally increase or decrease? Explain, in terms of electron structure.

34. How did Boyle change the way scientists had thought about elements?

35. What inference did Dalton make about hydrogen and oxygen atoms, based on the electrolysis of water? Compare Dalton's reasoning with a modern model for the structure of water molecules.

36. How does the modern periodic table differ from the one that Mendeleev developed?

37. Copy the diagram below of Thomson's experimental apparatus, and add labels to each part, explaining what Thomson observed.

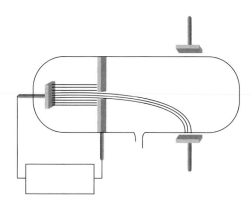

38. (a) Draw and label the apparatus used by Rutherford to deduce the existence of the nucleus in gold atoms.
    (b) Briefly summarize Rutherford's main inferences about the structure of atoms.
    (c) In Rutherford's experiment, most of the alpha particles were not deflected. What inference did Rutherford make about matter based on this observation?

39. Carbon dioxide and a polymer such as polyethylene both contain covalent bonds. Why are the properties of these two substances so different?

40. State two physical properties and one chemical property of oxygen.

41. Why do molecular compounds have low melting and boiling points?

Problem Solving

Show complete solutions for all problems that involve equations and numbers. Use the GRASP problem-solving model or a model suggested by your teacher.

42. State the number of protons, neutrons, and electrons in each of the following ions, and name the element.

    (a) $^{56}_{26}Fe^{3+}$ (b) $^{66}_{30}Zn^{2+}$ (c) $^{14}_{7}N^{3-}$ (d) $^{120}_{50}Sn^{4+}$

43. How many oxygen ions are represented in the formula of each of the following ionic substances?

    (a) MgO

    (b) Fe_2O_3

    (c) P_2O_5

44. Each of the following pairs of elements is given alphabetically. When these elements combine, they form an ionic compound. Using the periodic table, write the formulas of the ionic compounds formed by:

    (a) oxygen and potassium

    (b) sodium and sulfur

    (c) bromine and magnesium

    (d) aluminum and iodine

    (e) beryllium and oxygen

45. Which of the following formulas are impossible?

    (a) FO_3

    (b) Na_2O_3

    (c) HCl

    (d) Ca_2Cl

Critical Thinking

46. Find the element cesium (Cs) in the periodic table. From its position in the periodic table, predict

    (a) whether it is a metal or a non-metal

    (b) whether it is more or less reactive than sodium

    (c) whether it is malleable or brittle

    (d) what its state is at room temperature

47. A reaction between two chemical substances in solution may produce a new compound that appears as a precipitate. What can you say about the solubility of a precipitate in water? Why is this evidence that a chemical change has taken place?

48. Bronze, which is an alloy of tin and copper, was used to make tools before they were made from iron. Explain why the Bronze Age came before the Iron Age. (Hint: Look at Appendix D on page 564.)

49. One goal of the alchemists was to make gold from other metals, often starting with copper or lead. What properties do copper and lead have that are similar to the properties of gold? Why was the alchemists' goal impossible to achieve?

50. Suppose you were given a lump of plasticzne containing a hidden key and a long thin needle. How could you find out the location and size of the key? How would this be like Rutherford's gold foil experiment?

Applications

51. Conduct some research at your local library or on the Internet into the alloys from which aeroplanes are made. Is aluminum widely used? What about steel? Do different types of aeroplanes (for example, the supersonic passenger jet Concorde) use different alloys? Why?

52. Even the rarest of elements found in Earth's crust are used in specialized industrial or technological applications. Research applications for some of the following rare elements: lanthanum, selenium, tantalum, thallium, yttrium.

53. Find out more about the design and development of the electron microscope. In which sciences and industries has it played an important role? How similar are the design principles of electron microscopes to those of a gas discharge tube? What differences are there?

Characteristics of Electricity

Crumpled pylons, fallen poles, and lifeless wires littered the countryside after one of the longest lasting ice storms of the century. Over a period of six days, as much as 80 mm of ice accumulated on exposed surfaces. The ice glazed everything, coating buildings, bending trees to the breaking point, and destroying power lines. Over 1.5 million people were left in the cold and the dark in Eastern Canada. Health Canada delivered thousands of blankets, batteries and flashlights to people in need. As many as 1300 transmission towers and 35 000 poles toppled to the ground, unable to withstand the tremendous weight of the ice. High voltage transmission lines lay in tatters. Convoys of power company, military, and telephone crews became heroes as they came to the rescue of thousands of people. The sound of gasoline powered electrical generators, donated from various parts of Canada, reverberated across the starkly beautiful landscape. In some regions, generator sharing was required by farmers who needed electrical power to run water pumps and milking machines. Even with sharing, there were not enough generators to go around. In darkened cities, the only lighted buildings were those that had their own emergency generators.

Disasters such as ice storms make us realize how much modern societies depend on electricity. Everyone uses it, but how many people know how electricity is generated, how the energy is transmitted through those kilometres of power lines, and how it operates your toaster or your television set? In this unit, you will find the answers to these questions. You will also consider some of the environmental problems caused by the generation and transmission of electrical power. Understanding electricity is the first step toward proper use and conservation of this very important modern convenience.

Unit Contents

Static Electricity

Opening Ideas...

- What causes lightning and why does it strike tall buildings and trees?

- Why do you sometimes, but not always, get an electric shock from a doorknob?

- Why do clothes taken from a clothes dryer sometimes cling together?

Science Log

Think about the questions in Opening Ideas. Discuss your ideas with your classmates. Collect some possible answers and write them in your Science Log. Because lightning provides such a dramatic display, many myths about it have arisen throughout history. Are any of your answers based on myths? As you study this chapter, return to your Log to see if you want to change any of your answers.

It is a hot, muggy evening and ominous, anvil shaped clouds appear overhead. Without warning, the sky explodes with fireworks far more spectacular than any artificial display. Booming thunder reverberates through the night sky. A tree in the path of the lightning is split from top to bottom as if by a mighty axe. Streetlights flicker and one section of the city goes black. Lightning bolts dance across the sky as the electrical storm continues.

Lightning looks like a giant spark. Is it? What causes a spark or a bolt of lightning? Electricity out of control can cause serious damage. Can we control it? If so, how? What are some other noticeable effects of electrical activity? Just what is electricity, anyway?

In this chapter, you will learn about electric charges. You will find out how these charges are capable of creating dramatic effects, such as those you see in these photos. You will also discover ways to control and use electric charges.

Key Concepts

In this chapter, you will discover

- how objects become charged
- how positive and negative charges interact
- the difference between insulators and conductors
- what causes lightning

Key Skills

In this chapter, you will

- learn how to charge an object
- learn how to use an electroscope
- learn how to ground a conductor

Key Terms

- charged
- electric charge
- static electricity
- neutral
- insulator
- conductor
- law of attraction and repulsion
- positive charge
- negative charge
- electroscope
- induction
- spark
- ground
- lightning
- lightning rod
- electrostatic precipitator

Stick to the Wall

Have you ever rubbed a balloon on your clothing, then touched it to a wall and it stuck? Why did it stick to the wall? What is the scientific explanation?

How does a balloon's surface change when you rub it on cloth or wool?

Safety Precaution

Do not eat or drink anything in the laboratory.

What You Need

rubber balloon
variety of materials such as: salt, shredded tissue paper, aluminum foil, plastic food wrap, crushed wheat, rice puffs

What to Do

1. Blow up a rubber balloon and tie off the open end.

2. Vigorously rub the surface of the balloon with a piece of wool or across your clothing.

3. Bring the balloon close to a sample of each material you collected.

4. Touch the balloon all over with your hands and repeat step 3.

What Did You Discover?

1. What did each material do when you brought the balloon near it the first time? Record the response of each type of material.

2. Record any differences you observed in the responses of the materials.

3. Write a sentence explaining why you think the materials responded to the balloon after you rubbed it with a cloth. Write a sentence explaining why you think they responded differently after the balloon was touched with your hands.

4. Share your explanation with the class.

5. After you study this chapter, review your explanation and decide whether it is accurate. You may decide to change it.

9.1 Static Electricity All Around Us

It is a cold, dry winter night and you have just returned home after playing your favourite winter sport. As you try to get warm under the covers, you admire the new carpet in your room. Maybe a snack would help warm you up. You step into your slippers, walk across the carpet, and reach for the doorknob. Ouch! The shock is so strong you can see the spark in your dimly lit room.

Figure 9.1 Have you ever reached for a doorknob and received a shock? You can also get shocks from petting a dog or cat, or sometimes just from reaching toward another person. You will find out why as you read this chapter.

Figure 9.2 Thales lived in Greece about 600 B.C.E. He was the first to record observations about a change in the properties of amber when rubbed with fur.

Carpet Shocks and Lightning

The shocks you get from walking across a carpet and touching a metal doorknob look like exceedingly small lightning bolts. In fact, that is exactly what they are. What could possibly be similar about an electrical storm and walking across a carpet? In a thunderstorm, water droplets and ice crystals in the clouds are buffeted by the strong winds, colliding and rubbing against each other. When you walk across a room, your shoes or socks rub against the carpet. Why would rubbing create the condition that results in sparks?

In your Starting Point Activity, you rubbed a balloon against cloth and made it interact with many different materials. You probably saw no sparks, but, under the right conditions, you might have. Rubbing different materials together changes their characteristics. The Greek philosopher Thales noticed that when he rubbed amber with fur, the amber attracted small pieces of straw and wood shavings. The fur also attracted these materials. Hundreds of years later, scientists studied these effects in more detail. They discovered that many combinations of materials, when rubbed against each other, attract straw, small pieces of paper, and various other objects. The scientists used the word **charged** to describe materials that attracted other materials after rubbing. They said that the materials carried an **electric charge**. Since the charges remained stationary on the surface of the charged object, they called it **static electricity.** Materials that do not carry a charge are said to be **neutral.**

Conductors and Insulators

For many materials such as the balloon, the charge stays on the spot where you rub the object. Such materials fit into a class called **insulators.** Insulators are materials that do not allow charges to move freely on or through the object. Materials that do allow charges to move freely are classified as **conductors.** Most metals are conductors and most non-metals are insulators.

Figure 9.3 When you rub a rubber balloon, the charges (×) remain in place. When you rub a metallic balloon, the metal conductor allows the charges to move freely. The charges distribute themselves over the entire surface.

Try wearing latex rubber gloves and charging a metallic balloon with a cloth. Do the same without wearing the rubber gloves. What does the result tell you about latex rubber and about the metallic balloon? You can learn more about charging materials by rubbing them together when you carry out the next investigation.

Pause& Reflect

Now that you know the difference between conductors and insulators, go back and review your Starting Point Activity. Read your explanation for the change in the response of materials to the rubbed balloon after you touched it with your hands. What happened when you touched the rubbed balloon? (Hint: The human body is a conductor.) If your answer was not correct and you want to change your explanation, write down your new ideas. State why the original ideas were not correct.

Charge It

Many combinations of materials, such as shoes on carpet and amber on wool, will become charged when you rub them together. In this Investigation, you will examine the responses of several different combinations of materials after rubbing them together. You will draw some conclusions about the way charged and neutral materials interact. You will then examine how two charged objects interact with each other.

Part 1

How Charged and Neutral Objects Interact

Problem

How do neutral objects respond to charged objects?

Safety Precaution

Handle the glass rod carefully.

Apparatus

plastic comb
acetate strips
glass rods
ebonite rods
polyethylene
fur
wool

Materials

small pieces of paper

Procedure

1. Make a table such as the one shown here to record your data.

Interaction of Charged Objects and Neutral Objects

Charged Object	Response of Neutral Pieces of Paper
plastic comb	
glass	
ebonite	

2. Place several bits of paper on your desk or table.

3. Rub the comb with wool (or if it is your own comb, you may run it through your hair).

4. Slowly move the comb close to the bits of paper. Write a phrase in your table to describe the way the paper responded to the comb.

5. Repeat steps 3 and 4 using the glass rod rubbed with polyethylene.

6. Repeat steps 3 and 4 using the ebonite rod rubbed with fur.

7. Wash your hands before leaving.

Analyze

1. Write a statement summarizing the response of neutral pieces of paper to charged objects.

Conclude and Apply

2. Write a hypothesis that would predict the response of any neutral objects to charged objects.

Part 2

How Two Charged Objects Interact

Problem

How do charged objects interact with each other?

Safety Precautions

Handle the glass rod carefully.

Apparatus

support stand	2 plastic combs	polyethylene
clamp	2 acetate strips	fur
stirrup	2 glass rods	wool
	2 ebonite rods	
	latex rubber glove	

Procedure

1. Make a table such as the one shown here.

Interaction of Two Charged Objects

Charged Object in Hand	Charged Object in Stirrup			
	Plastic Comb	Acetate	Glass	Ebonite
plastic comb				
acetate				
glass				
ebonite				

2. Rub a plastic comb with wool and place the comb in the stirrup, as shown in the photo.

3. Rub the second plastic comb with wool and slowly bring it near one end of the comb in the stirrup. In your table, record the interaction between the two combs.

4. In separate steps, rub the ebonite with fur, rub the glass with polyethylene, and rub the acetate with rubber. One at a time, bring the charged objects near the comb in the stirrup. In your table record the response of the comb in the stirrup to each of the other charged objects.

5. Repeat steps 3 and 4, first with a charged acetate strip in the stirrup, then with a charged glass rod, and finally with a charged ebonite rod in the stirrup.

Analyze

1. How did identical charged objects interact with each other? For example, how did one charged comb interact with the second charged comb?

2. List all pairs of objects that interacted in the same way as the identical objects interacted.

3. List all pairs of objects that interacted in a manner opposite to the interaction between identical objects.

Conclude and Apply

4. Write a sentence explaining why you think that some charged objects attract each other, while some charged objects repel each other.

Bending Water

What You Need

large plastic comb
wool, flannel, or felt cloth

What To Do

1. Turn on the water from a tap so that the water forms a small, steady stream.

2. Rub the plastic comb briskly with the wool, flannel, or felt.

3. Slowly bring the solid back of the comb closer to the stream of water, until you observe a change in the movement of the water.

What Did You Discover?

1. What happened when the comb approached the water? Explain your answer.

2. How was the response of the water similar to the response of any of the materials that you tested in Investigation 9-A, Part 1 or 9-A, Part 2? Which materials?

3. Do you think that the water is charged or neutral? Explain your answer.

4. Think of a way to test your answer to question 3. Write a procedure. If you have the opportunity, carry out your test.

Pause& Reflect

In your Science Log, summarize your ideas about static electricity and the interactions of charged and uncharged materials. If you have any questions about static electricity, write them down. As you continue your study, search for information that will answer your questions. Also, look for information that will tell you whether your current ideas are correct.

Check Your Understanding

1. What is similar about a spark and a lightning bolt?

2. How do some charged objects interact with each other differently from the way a charged object interacts with neutral objects?

3. How do charged conductors and insulators differ from each other?

4. Explain why a person can get a shock after walking across a carpet.

5. In the investigations, what was the reason for touching the charged balloon with your hands?

6. **Thinking Critically** What do you think would happen if you rubbed two identical objects together? Would they attract each other, repel each other, or neither attract nor repel each other? Why?

9.2 Making Sense of Static Electricity

You have been collecting a lot of information about charged objects and static electricity. For example, you have discovered that charged objects attract neutral objects. As well, you have determined that identical charged objects repel each other. In fact, some pairs of non-identical charged objects repel each other. However, some pairs of charged objects attract each other. Maybe you discovered that any two objects that attract the same third object, repel each other. Now it is time to make sense of this information.

As you probably recall, scientists devise models to help organize their ideas. The model may be in words, a mathematical equation, or an illustration or diagram. Whatever form it takes, the model provides an explanation for the observations. A model also helps scientists design more experiments to test their explanations.

Types of Charge

As scientists studied more and more types of charged materials, they discovered that all charged objects fit into two categories. Every charged object in category *A* repels every other charged object in *A*, but attracts all charged objects in category *B*. Likewise, all charged category *B* objects repel each other and attract all charged *A* objects. From this information, scientists devised a model. The model states that there are two types of charges. Category *A* objects carry one type of charge and *B* objects carry the other. From this model and the data, they concluded that "Like charges repel and unlike charges attract." You will see this conclusion written as the **law of attraction and repulsion**.

The famous American inventor and politician Benjamin Franklin (1706-1790) named the charges "positive" and "negative." He named the type of charge on amber that had been rubbed with fur a **negative charge**. The fur itself carried a **positive charge**.

Figure 9.4 These charges are following the law of attraction and repulsion.

Do Neutral Objects Lack Charge?

The law of attraction and repulsion explains why charged objects attract or repel each other. However, it does not explain why charged objects attract neutral objects. To understand why this happens, think about what makes an object neutral. You know that when you rub two neutral objects together, they both become charged. So the charges must come from the neutral objects. This means that neutral objects already have some charges. Since they are neutral, they must have the same number of both positive and negative charges.

How can either positively or negatively charged objects attract neutral objects, if the neutral objects are insulators and have equal numbers of both charges? Charges in the molecules that make up insulators cannot move on or through the material, but the molecules can rotate or stretch. Study the illustrations in Figure 9.5 to see how this rotation or stretching can result in an attraction.

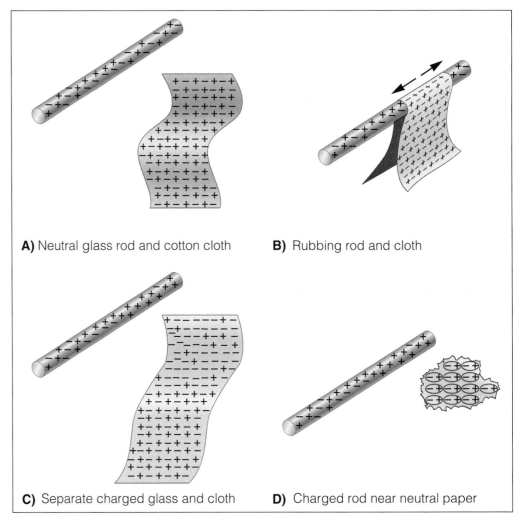

A) Neutral glass rod and cotton cloth **B)** Rubbing rod and cloth

C) Separate charged glass and cloth **D)** Charged rod near neutral paper

Figure 9.5 (A) Glass rod and cotton cloth have equal amounts and equal distribution of positive and negative charges. (B) Negative charges are rubbed from the glass rod onto the cotton cloth. (C) The glass has an excess of positive charges and the cotton cloth has an excess of negative charges. (D) When the positively charged glass rod comes near the neutral scrap of paper, it distorts the distribution of charges in the paper.

Positive charges in a charged object (glass rod) attract the negative charges in the neutral object (paper). Negative charges in an insulator cannot move through the object, but pull to the ends of their molecules and distort all the molecules in the object. Now one edge of the object (paper) has an excess of negative charges and the opposite edge is slightly positive. The positive charges in the glass rod attract the negative charges on the edge of the paper. Although the paper still has an equal number of positive and negative charges, they are rearranged.

Testing for Charge

A metal leaf **electroscope** can detect the presence of charge. These electroscopes come in many sizes and shapes, but they all have one thing in common. They have one or two lightweight strips of metal that bend easily. These metal leaves are attached to a central metal rod with a metal sphere at the top. Sometimes the leaves and rod are enclosed in glass or plastic, so that small air currents cannot blow them around.

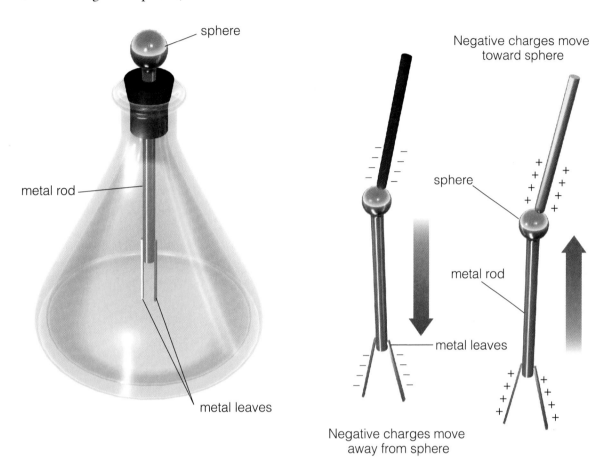

Figure 9.6 When a negatively charged rod touches the sphere of the electroscope, negative charge spreads throughout the metal. Since the leaves are both negatively charged, the free ends repel and move away from each other. When a positively charged rod touches the sphere, negative charges move toward the sphere, causing the leaves to be positively charged.

Figure 9.6 shows how an electroscope displays the presence of charge. Since the sphere, rod, and leaves are metal, charges can move freely within them. When the metal leaves become charged for any reason, the excess charges move as far from each other as they can. The leaves then become charged and repel each other. When the leaves move away from each other, you know they are charged.

You do not even have to touch the sphere of an electroscope to make the leaves separate. If you bring a negatively charged rod near, but not touching, the sphere, it will repel the negative charges in the sphere. The negative charges will move down to the leaves. The sphere will be left with a temporary positive charge. Take away the negative rod and the negative charges on the leaves will go back to the sphere and the leaves will go back to their original position. This is called charging by **induction**. Remember this for the next investigation.

Charge Detective

If you know the nature of the charge on one object, you can use it, along with an electroscope, to detect charge on another object and to determine whether that charge is positive or negative. In this investigation, you will determine the type of charge on some of the same materials you examined in Investigation 9-A.

Problem

An ebonite rod rubbed with fur is negatively charged. How can you use this information to determine the type of charge on a glass rod rubbed with silk or polyethylene and on a plastic comb rubbed with wool?

Safety Precautions

- Be careful not to give the electroscope too large a charge. The leaves may be forced off the metal rod. This will happen when the leaves are deflected too far away from the electroscope.
- Handle glass rod carefully.

Apparatus

metal leaf electroscope
glass rod
silk or polyethylene
ebonite rod
fur
comb
wool

Procedure

1 Examine the metal leaf electroscope. Find the parts shown in Figure 9.6.

2 Touch the metal sphere with your fingers. This will neutralize the electroscope, if it has any charge on it.

3 Rub the ebonite rod with fur to make the rod negative.

4 Slowly move the rod toward the sphere of the electroscope, but do not touch it. Note the position of the electroscope leaves. Withdraw the rod some distance from the electroscope and again note the position of the leaves.

5 Draw sketches of the appearance of the electroscope leaves for each of the two positions of the rod, in step 4. As shown in the sample sketches, include the location of the rod. Label your sketches.

6 Rub the ebonite rod with fur again. Touch the rod to the sphere of the electroscope and then withdraw the rod. Draw a sketch of the electroscope, showing the position of the leaves.

7 Rub the glass rod with silk or polyethylene.

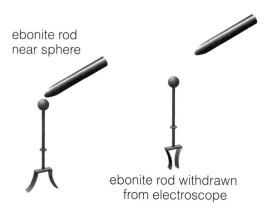

ebonite rod
near sphere

ebonite rod withdrawn
from electroscope

8 With the electroscope still in the condition that you left it after step 6, slowly bring the glass rod near the sphere, but do not touch it. Draw sketches of the electroscope and rod before you brought the rod near the sphere and when the rod was near the sphere.

9 Rub the plastic comb with wool and repeat step 8.

10 Wash your hands after this investigation.

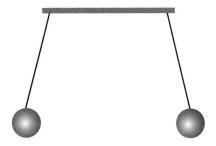

Analyze

1. Do not write on your original sketches. For your analysis, draw a duplicate set of sketches identical to those you made during your observations.

2. Write negative signs on the ebonite rod in your duplicate sketches.

3. Analyze each sketch and decide where the positive and negative charges would have to be to cause the electroscope to respond as it did. Add positive and negative signs to your sketches and write explanations for their locations.

Conclude and Apply

4. Write a procedure for determining the charge on any object by using a rod with a known type of charge and an electroscope.

Extend Your Knowledge

The balls in the illustration represent pith balls (extremely light-weight) coated with a conductor. No charges are shown in the figures because it is your job to add them.

5. Make sketches similar to, but larger than, the figures.

6. Draw eight, equally distributed positive charges on every pith ball. These charges will remain on each pith ball.

7. Assume that you have a total of 12 negative charges to add to each figure.

8. In the first figure, add negative charges to make the ball on the right neutral and leave the ball on the left positively charged.

9. In the second figure, the balls touch. Think about what would happen. Add the twelve negative charges to show what you think would happen.

10. In the third figure, the balls are repelling each other. Add negative signs to show the number of negative charges on each ball.

11. Write a paragraph that explains why the balls in the third figure repel each other.

Tools of Science

Pocket dosimeters are very specialized electroscopes that are designed to detect nuclear radiation (gamma rays) or X-rays. When workers are in high risk areas near nuclear reactors, they wear radiation dosimeters in their pockets to check radiation levels. Astronauts also carry them on board every space flight.

The dosimeters must be charged in order to detect radiation. Dosimeters are charged by inserting them into a special instrument or, for some dosimeters, by simply twisting the ends several times. You can read the scale by looking through a window in the end of the pen-shaped device. When radiation passes through the device, it causes atoms or molecules to break apart into positive and negative charges. These new charges combine with the charge on the dosimeter and neutralize some of the charge. The extent to which the dosimeter is discharged indicates the amount of radiation that has passed through the device and, of course, through the person wearing the dosimeter. You can read the radiation dose by holding the pen-shaped dosimeter to a light and reading the scale. Workers in high risk areas read their dosimeters frequently. If the reading approaches an unacceptable level, the workers leave the area.

Pause & Reflect

Look at the photo of the girl on the first page of this chapter. The instrument she is touching is called a Van de Graaff generator. The sphere is very highly charged. From what you have learned about charges and electroscopes, explain why her hair is standing on end.

Check Your Understanding

1. Describe the evidence that led the way for scientists to discover the law of attraction and repulsion.

2. What makes objects neutral?

3. How can you tell the difference between a positively charged object and a negatively charged object by using an electroscope?

4. Why must the sphere, rod, and leaves of an electroscope be conductors?

5. Explain the difference between a negatively charged object and a positively charged object.

9.3 Explaining Static Electricity

All of the concepts you have learned about static electricity so far were known to scientists before the end of the eighteenth century. Yet scientists had no idea what electric charges were and how they were related to the matter that made up materials such as amber, wool, fur, or rubber. In 1600, William Gilbert (1544-1603) proposed that electricity was a fluid, separate from the matter that made up the objects. This "fluid theory" was accepted by scientists for over a hundred years.

Word CONNECT

J.J. Thomson's newly discovered particle was named "electron" after the Greek word "*elektron*". Research the original meaning of the Greek word "elektron."

Gaining and Losing Electrons

New evidence compels scientists to modify established theories. In 1897, when J.J. Thomson (1856-1940) discovered the electron, the fluid theory of electricity had to be discarded. Now, 2600 years after Thales discovered that rubbing amber with fur changed its characteristics, we know that the negative charge that remains on the amber consists of electrons.

What is the electron theory of charge? How does it explain the observations that some materials become negatively charged by rubbing, while others become positively charged? In Chapter 7, you learned about the Bohr-Rutherford model of the atom. All matter consists of atoms with positively charged nuclei, containing protons and neutrons, and negatively charged electrons surrounding the nucleus. Different elements have distinct characteristics. Atoms of some elements hold their electrons more loosely than others. Rubbing removes the more loosely held electrons from one material and deposits them on the other. Positively charged protons remain in place. They do not move from one object to another. Materials that gain electrons become negatively charged and those that lose electrons become positively charged.

Figure 9.7 Back to the drawing board to work out this new electron theory of charge.

Pause& **Reflect**

Now that you have gained more information about electrons, and conductors, go back and review your answers to the questions in Investigation 9-B. Do your answers fit your current ideas about conductors and insulators? If not, correct your answers.

Conductors, Insulators, and In-Between

Now that you know about electrons, you can better understand conductors, insulators, sparks, and many other events and observations. You learned that a conductor is a material that allows charges to move freely. Since electrons are the charges that move through solids, a conductor must be a material that holds its electrons loosely. This is in fact the case. Electrons can jump from one metal atom to the next. However, some metals allow much more free movement of electrons than others. For example, silver is a much better conductor than aluminum, because electrons move much more freely within silver than within aluminum.

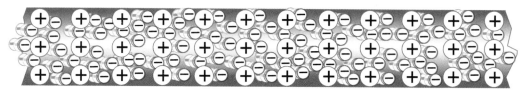

Figure 9.8 Electrons travel through conductors by moving from one atom to the next.

You have probably already figured out that insulators are materials that hold their electrons very tightly. As well, some insulators hold electrons much more tightly than others. Just as some conductors are better than others, some insulators are better. In fact, some materials are in between insulators and conductors. They will allow electrons to move, but not at all freely. These fair conductors provide a lot of resistance to the movement of electrons. Nevertheless, the electrons can move a little.

Table 9.1 Some Common Conductors and Insulators

Good Conductors	Fair Conductors	Insulators
aluminum	silicon	amber
copper	carbon	cotton
gold	Earth	ebonite
iron	human body	fur
magnesium	humid air	glass
mercury	nichrome	paper
nickel	water (salty)	plastic
platinum		porcelain
silver		rubber
tungsten		silk
		sulfur
		water (pure)
		wood
		wool

Pepper Copier

Rubbing an insulator causes it to become charged only on those places where you rub. Charged material attracts uncharged material. Therefore, you should be able to charge a precise area of an insulator and attract some neutral objects to it. How can you make a copy of an image using these principles of electric charge?

Safety Precaution

What You Need

plastic Petri dish with lid
ground pepper
paper
scissors
wool cloth

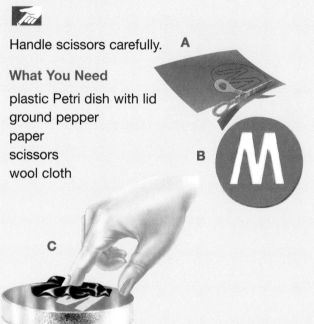

What to Do

1. Cut out a circle of paper the size of the Petri dish.

2. Make a stencil by cutting a letter or shape out of the paper.

3. Put a very small amount of pepper in the Petri dish. Place the lid on the dish and gently shake it to scatter the pepper over the bottom.

4. Hold the paper on the top of the lid and briskly rub the stencil area with the wool cloth.

5. Remove the stencil. Turn the dish up side down, while holding the lid on. Turn the dish right side up again. (Hold the dish and lid only at the edges.)

What Did You Observe?

1. Describe the appearance of the Petri dish.

2. What caused the pepper to take the shape of the stencil?

3. How does this resemble the way a photocopier works?

Air: Conductor or Insulator?

What happens when two oppositely charged objects approach each other, but do not touch? If the charge is great enough, you will see a **spark** or an electrical discharge. After the spark, the objects are no longer charged. The excess electrons on the negatively charged object "jumped through the air" to the positive one.

At first, it seems as though this should not happen because air, especially dry air, is a very poor conductor. It should not allow electrons to move through it. However, when two objects carry very large, opposite charges, the strength of the interactions can actually pull apart some gas molecules in the air. These molecules split into positive and negative ions. When one molecule splits, it prompts nearby molecules to split as well. Then, when a

Figure 9.9 A spark is caused by electrons jumping from one conductor, through the air, to another conductor.

path of ionized molecules forms in the air, it becomes a conductor. The excess electrons on the negatively charged object move through this new "conductor" onto the positively charged object. The electrons move exceedingly fast and collide with more molecules in the air, exciting these molecules so much that they emit light. All of these events happen so fast that all you see is a spark.

Putting Electrostatics to Work

The design of photocopiers is based on a unique electrical property of a material called selenium. In the dark, selenium is an insulator. When bright light hits it, the selenium becomes a conductor. Follow the steps in Figure 9.10 to see how this property of selenium is used in photocopiers.

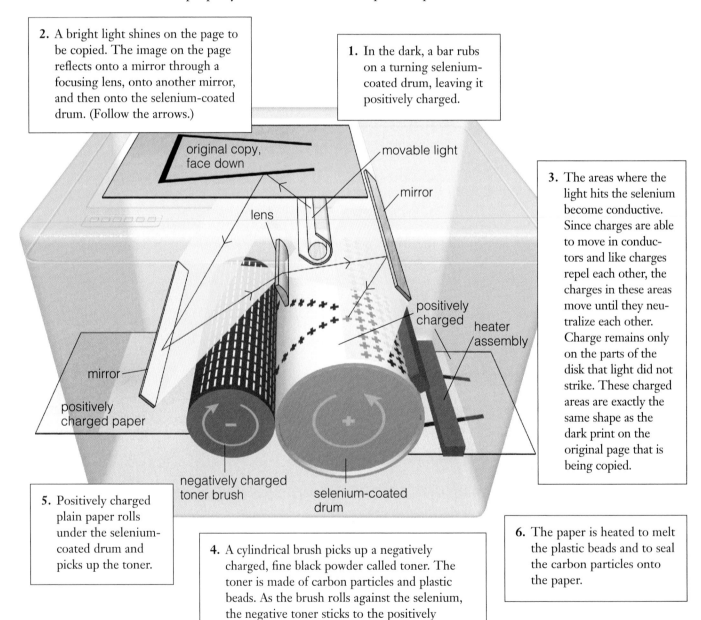

2. A bright light shines on the page to be copied. The image on the page reflects onto a mirror through a focusing lens, onto another mirror, and then onto the selenium-coated drum. (Follow the arrows.)

1. In the dark, a bar rubs on a turning selenium-coated drum, leaving it positively charged.

3. The areas where the light hits the selenium become conductive. Since charges are able to move in conductors and like charges repel each other, the charges in these areas move until they neutralize each other. Charge remains only on the parts of the disk that light did not strike. These charged areas are exactly the same shape as the dark print on the original page that is being copied.

5. Positively charged plain paper rolls under the selenium-coated drum and picks up the toner.

4. A cylindrical brush picks up a negatively charged, fine black powder called toner. The toner is made of carbon particles and plastic beads. As the brush rolls against the selenium, the negative toner sticks to the positively charged part of the drum. Now the shape of the toner on the drum is exactly the same as the original image on the page.

6. The paper is heated to melt the plastic beads and to seal the carbon particles onto the paper.

original copy, face down

movable light

mirror

lens

positively charged

heater assembly

mirror

positively charged paper

negatively charged toner brush

selenium-coated drum

Figure 9.10 Photocopiers rely on the law of attraction and repulsion.

Grounding

If a parent says to you, "You're grounded!" you know exactly what they mean. But, when your teacher tells you to **ground** a conductor, what does that mean? Believe it or not, grounding means exactly what it says. Grounding a conductor means to connect it, through some conducting material, directly to the ground, or Earth. Although Earth is not an excellent conductor, it is so huge that it can accept or give up many electrons without any significant change in its charge. You could compare the situation to pouring a cup of water into the ocean. One extra cup will have no noticeable effect on the sea level. So, when you want to remove excess electrons from your apparatus or gain electrons, you can attach a wire to a metal object, such as a water pipe, that goes deep into the ground. The next activity will show you how grounding can be useful.

Pause& Reflect

You learned about ions, excited atoms, and molecules in Chapters 7 and 8. Go back and review this information. Then write a paragraph in your Science Log that uses the information from these chapters to help explain sparks.

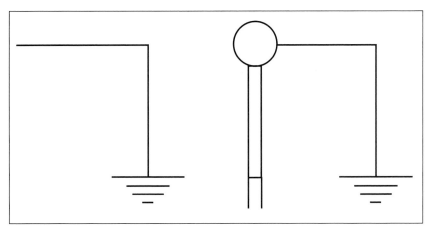

Figure 9.11 The symbol for "ground" is on the left. The figure on the right shows a grounded electroscope.

Science Inquiry ACTIVITY

Do Not Touch!

How can you permanently charge an electroscope without touching it with a charged object?

What You Need

electroscope
ebonite rod
fur

What To Do

1. Rub the ebonite rod with the fur.

2. Bring the ebonite rod near the sphere of the electroscope, but do not touch it.

3. While holding the ebonite rod near the sphere, ground the sphere by touching it with your finger. Withdraw your finger, while the ebonite rod remains near the sphere. (You can ground the sphere with your finger, because your body is a conductor.)

4. Withdraw the ebonite rod and record your observations.

What Did You Observe?

Was the electroscope charged or neutral after you withdrew the ebonite rod? How do you know? Make sketches of the process. Include positive and negative signs to show where charges were located. Write a paragraph that explains why the electroscope responded as it did.

Figure 9.12 When a gasoline truck rolls down the highway through blowing wind and dust and over bumpy roads, it often becomes charged. While filling the truck with fuel, a tiny spark near the gasoline fumes could cause a huge explosion. So, before transferring any gasoline, the truck is grounded to prevent sparking.

As you can see in the photograph of the gasoline truck, grounding can prevent serious accidents. The grounding of electrical appliances around the home also prevents serious, even fatal, shocks. Metal casings of appliances, such as stoves, refrigerators, washers, and driers, should always be grounded. To understand what could happen, imagine that a metal refrigerator casing were not grounded. The wiring inside might become loose and touch the casing, giving it a very large charge. If you reached to open the door, you would receive a dangerous shock. However, if the appliance is grounded and wiring becomes loose and touches the casing, the excess charge is carried away to Earth.

Electronic instruments such as computers, must be grounded because they are very sensitive to surges of electrical energy that could be caused by a spark. Electrical wiring in homes, businesses, and industries is always grounded. A common way to ground wiring is to connect a wire to copper water pipes that go deep into Earth below the building. The third prong on plugs that fit into wall sockets connects to this ground wire. This simple technique prevents fires and saves lives.

Pause& Reflect

You just charged an electroscope by induction in the "Do Not Touch" activity. Do you remember what "charging by induction" means? If not, reread the section called "Testing for Charge" on page 303. Now make notes in your Science Log to help you remember what induction means.

Check Your Understanding

1. What is the fluid theory of electricity? Why did scientists reject the theory?

2. What type of charge moves through conductors? Explain how it moves.

3. What does it mean when you say that a conductor is grounded?

4. List two examples of conductors and two examples of insulators.

5. Use the electron theory to explain how one object can be negatively charged and another can be positively charged.

6. What must happen to some of the molecules in the air for a spark to occur?

9.4 Controlling Static Electricity

Now it is time to take your new knowledge out of the laboratory and apply it to the world around you. This is what scientists do. They make observations, such as watching lightning strike. They collect all that is known about the phenomenon and formulate a hypothesis or model. Next, they go to the laboratory or to the field to test their model. If necessary, they modify it. Then, when they believe they have gathered enough information, they apply their knowledge in some practical way. Of course, this process may require many scientists studying and experimenting for many years before they collect enough information. Nevertheless, their results might eventually lead to devices, chemicals, or techniques that affect your everyday life.

What Causes Lightning?

Figure 9.13 Most lightning that strikes Earth comes from these anvil shaped clouds that tower high above the ground.

You started this chapter looking at a picture of **lightning**. Now that you know more about static electricity, you can picture it in a different way. You read that the strong winds and the collisions of water droplets and ice particles in the clouds strip electrons from some particles and deposit them on others. As well, strong updraughts in the centre of the storm cloud carry smaller ice crystals and particles up while larger ones fall down. For reasons that meteorologists do not completely understand, negative charges collect at the bottom of the clouds, where the temperature is above -20°C. The higher, colder parts of clouds are positively charged.

Word CONNECT

A meteorologist is a person who studies atmospheric conditions and weather. The word "meteorologist" comes from the Greek words "*meteoros*" and "*logia*." Research to find the meanings of these two words. How do they describe a meteorologist?

-50°C
-20°C
65°C

Figure 9.14 A thundercloud is mostly negatively charged on the bottom and positively charged on top. The temperature may be as high as 65°C at the bottom and as low as -50°C at the top.

INTERNET CONNECT

www.school.mcgrawhill.ca/resources/
To find out more about thunderstorms or view more dramatic photos of lightning, go to the above website. Go to **Science Resources**, then to **SCIENCEPOWER 9** to find out where to go next. Write a short article about your findings.

DidYouKnow?

About 65 % of all lightning bolts go from one cloud to another, without ever hitting the ground.

The negative charges on the bottom of the clouds repel electrons on the surface of Earth, leaving the ground positively charged just below the cloud. From this point, the process is just like any other spark. The strong attraction between the negative cloud and the positive ground pull electrons off atoms and molecules in the air. This process is most likely to occur over the highest point on the ground. Once a chain of ions forms, a gigantic discharge occurs between the cloud and ground. So many electrons crash through the air so fast, colliding with other molecules, that the air not only lights up, it heats up. The temperature of the air near a lightning bolt can reach as high as 33 000°C, several times hotter than the surface of the Sun. The heat causes the air to expand rapidly. Air molecules colliding with more air molecules as they move around, produce a shock wave that we hear as thunder. The heat can trigger forest fires and building fires. If the lightning hits a person, the electrical activity can stop the heart or respiration, nearly always killing the person.

Lightning Rods

Now that you understand lightning and why it can do so much damage, can you think of a way to control it or at least prevent some of the damage? You probably could not prevent the lightning from striking. However, maybe you could find a way to direct the flow of electrons away from buildings and prevent fires. Where do electrons travel most easily? They travel through conductors. Lightning rods are based on just these principles.

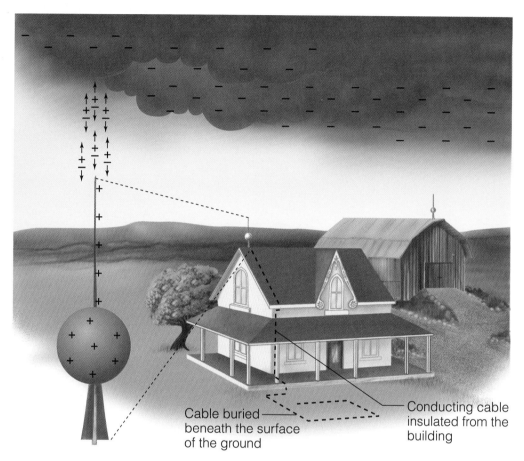

Cable buried beneath the surface of the ground

Conducting cable insulated from the building

Figure 9.15 The sphere and point of a lightning rod become positively charged, because the negative charges on the bottom of the cloud repel electrons. Free to move, negative electrons leave the lightning rod and go into the ground.

A **lightning rod** is charged by induction, just like the sphere on your electroscope when you brought a negatively charged rod near it. The positively charged lightning rod is the highest point in the area. It attracts the negative ions that have formed in the air, while the cloud attracts the positive ions. A chain of ions thus forms between the cloud and the lightning rod. This chain of ions acts as a conductor providing a path for the lightning bolt. When the lightning bolt strikes, it hits the lightning rod. The electrons are carried around the building and into the ground by a heavy conductor, often made of braided wire. Since the electrons do not go through the building, they cannot heat it enough to start a fire.

Math CONNECT

The light from lightning travels so fast that it takes almost no time to reach us. But the sound from the thunder takes about three seconds to travel one kilometre. You can tell how far away a lightning flash is by measuring the time between the lightning flash and the thunder that follows. Try it! Imagine you heard thunder six seconds after you saw a lightning flash. Determine how far you were from the lightning bolt.

DidYou**Know**?

Benjamin Franklin was the first to guess that a lightning discharge was similar to electric sparks caused by electric charges moving through air. To test this idea, he fastened a metal key to one end of a long silk thread and a metal rod to the other. He attached the metal rod to a kite and flew it during a lightning storm. Sure enough, he observed sparks escaping from the key. He lived to tell the tale, but the next two people who tried it were not so fortunate. They were killed by the lightning. Caution! Do not repeat Franklin's experiment. Fortunately, Benjamin Franklin lived long enough to invent the lightning rod.

silk cloth

metal key

Solving Problems with Electrostatics

A knowledge of electrostatic principles can not only help prevent damage from such things as lightning. It can also help us solve problems that are not caused by charges.

One very serious environmental problem in modern societies is the amount of ash and other contaminants released from the smoke stacks of ore smelting plants or coal burning power plants. An **electrostatic precipitator** can help remove these contaminants, as shown in Figure 9.16.

Figure 9.16 The smoke stacks on the left are the same as those on the right. The plant was operating when both photos were taken. The only difference is that on the left the electrostatic precipitator was not in operation and on the right it was.

The electrostatic precipitator is actually quite a simple device. Its components are shown in Figure 9.17. Exhaust gases enter a cylinder that has walls made of a grounded conductor. Another conductor, insulated from the walls, runs down the centre. This central conductor is so highly charged that it causes molecules in the gases to split into ions. These ions initiate electrical discharges, much like lightning.

Each discharge causes more ions to form. Nearly all particles and liquid droplets in the exhaust gas become ionized. The charged, central conductor repels the ions and drives them to the outside wall. Since the outside wall is grounded, it neutralizes the ions when they hit. The neutralized ions form liquid droplets or solid particles. The liquids run down the wall and the solids stick to it. Solids can be removed by vibrating the wall or, if necessary, scraping them off.

Painting With Charges

How can you give an object a thin, smooth layer of paint and ensure that the surface is thoroughly covered? Charge it! The process is called electrostatic spray painting. The object being painted, such as the automobile in the figure, is given a positive charge. As the paint leaves the nozzle of the gun, it becomes negatively charged and is then attracted to the positive target. The result is an excellent paint job.

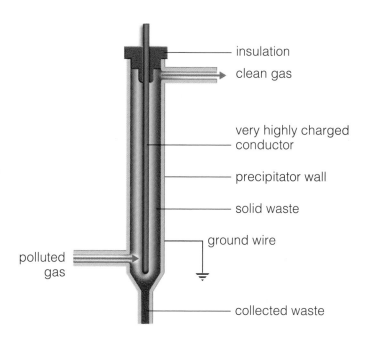

Figure 9.17 Electrostatic precipitators are so efficient that they can remove up to 99.99 % of the solids and liquids from the exhaust gases.

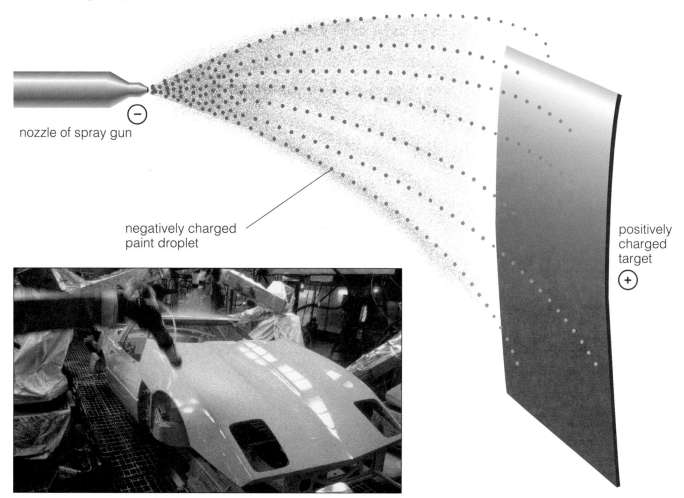

Figure 9.18 Electrostatic spray painting saves paint, speeds drying, and gives a smooth surface.

Everyday Electrostatics

The Pepper Separator

Think About It

How can you separate salt and pepper after they have been mixed together?

What You Need

salt
pepper
plastic ruler
flannel or wool cloth
paper

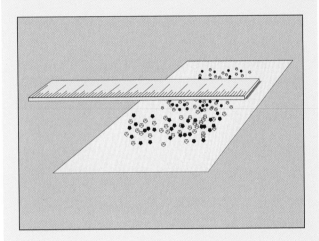

What To Do

1. Place salt and pepper on a smooth sheet of paper and mix them thoroughly.

2. Briskly rub a plastic ruler with the flannel or wool cloth.

3. Slowly move the ruler above the mixture. Record your observations.

What Did You Learn?

Were you able to separate the salt and pepper? Explain why.

Separating salt and pepper may be interesting, but it is not a very important electrostatic process. The principles of electrostatics are more useful, for example, when industries use them to separate minerals from ore. Electrostatic effects happen around you every day. Do you ever find items of clothing stuck together when you take them out of the drier? When two different materials tumble and rub together in the clothes drier, some combinations become oppositely charged and cling together.

You might want to do some further research into the applications of electrostatics. For example, how do fabric softeners reduce static cling? How do electrostatic air filters clean the air in homes and hospitals? Learn about negative ion generators. Electrostatics is even used in studying living cells. Pick a topic that interests you and research it.

INTERNET CONNECT

www.school.mcgrawhill.ca/resources/
To find out more about electrostatics in industry, go to the above website. Go to **Science Resources**, then to **SCIENCEPOWER 9** to find out where to go next. Write a short article about your findings.

Check Your Understanding

1. Explain how a lightning rod can prevent lightning from causing a house or barn to catch on fire.

2. What is thunder?

3. Why is the central conductor of an electrostatic precipitator highly charged?

4. What is "static cling"?

Now that you have completed the chapter, try to do the following. If you cannot, go back to the sections indicated.

Describe the first observations that led to the concept of static electricity. (9.1)

Explain the difference between insulators and conductors. (9.1)

Explain the concept of a "scientific model." (9.2)

Describe the data that led scientists to conclude that there are two types of charges. (9.2)

Explain why a charged object can attract a neutral object. (9.2)

Describe the elements of an electroscope. (9.2)

An electroscope can be charged by contact or by induction. Explain the difference. (9.2)

Describe the fluid theory of electricity and explain why it was discarded. (9.3)

Use the electron theory of charge to describe the properties of conductors and insulators. (9.3)

Describe the step-by-step process that results in an electric spark. (9.3)

Explain how and why you would ground a conductor. (9.3)

Describe the parts of a lightning rod and explain the function of each part. (9.4)

List three ways in which electrostatics can affect your everyday life. (9.4)

Prepare Your Own Summary

Summarize the chapter by doing one of the following. Use a graphic organizer (such as a concept map), produce a poster, or write the summary to include the key chapter concepts. Here are a few ideas to use as a guide.

- Explain how rubbing two different materials together changes their characteristics.
- Describe the origin of the terms "positive" and "negative" to describe charged materials.
- State the law of attraction and repulsion.
- Explain why metals are good conductors.
- Air is usually a good insulator. Explain how air can become a good conductor and what happens when this occurs.
- Explain why thunder accompanies lightning.

- Describe an electrostatic precipitator and explain how it works.
- Describe the unique property of selenium that makes it useful in photocopiers.

CHAPTER

9 Review

Reviewing Key Terms

If you need to review, the section numbers show you where these terms were introduced. Use the list of key terms at the beginning of the chapter to fill in the blanks.

1. A neutral object has an equal number of ▅▅▅▅▅▅ and ▅▅▅▅▅▅. (9.2)

2. The charge spreads throughout the entire surface of a ▅▅▅▅▅, when it becomes charged. (9.2)

3. The nucleus of an atom contains ▅▅▅▅ and ▅▅▅▅. The space surrounding the nucleus contains the ▅▅▅▅. (9.3)

4. Benjamin Franklin named the two types of charges ▅▅▅▅ and ▅▅▅▅. (9.2)

5. You can charge an electroscope by ▅▅▅▅, if you bring a charged rod near to the sphere but do not touch it. (9.2)

6. A lightning rod is connected to a braided coil to ▅▅▅▅ it. (9.4)

7. The study of charges that are not moving is called ▅▅▅▅. (9.1)

8. When molecules in air break down into ions, it forms a ▅▅▅▅ which sets the stage for a ▅▅▅▅. (9.3)

Understanding Key Concepts

Section numbers are provided, if you need to review.

9. Describe one way to charge objects. Explain why this method causes objects to become charged. (9.2)

10. List the types of interactions between charged objects and between charged and uncharged objects that led to the law of attraction and repulsion. (9.2)

11. Since all matter is made of atoms that have positive and negative charges, how can an object be neutral? (9.2)

12. State one practical reason for grounding a conductor. (9.3)

13. Explain how the charges that were named "positive" and "negative" by Benjamin Franklin are related to the parts of an atom. (9.3)

14. Use the electron theory to explain how insulators and conductors work. (9.3)

15. Describe the property of clouds that causes lightning. (9.4)

16. Explain how you can charge an electroscope permanently without touching it with any charged object. (9.3)

17. You can get a shock after walking across a nylon carpet and touching a metal door knob, but not a wooden door knob. Explain why this is true. (9.3)

18. Assume you rub a material with fur and the material becomes charged. Explain how you could use a negative ebonite rod or a positive glass rod to determine the type of charge on the material (9.2)

Developing Skills

19. Complete the following concept map.

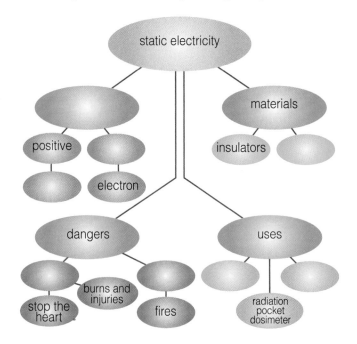

20. Scientists were studying the concepts of electrostatics long before J.J. Thomson discovered the electron. List at least three features of electrostatics that scientists understood before they knew about protons and electrons.

21. Explain the cause of lightning in your own words.

22. Imagine that you walk into a room where someone has been working with an electroscope. There is no one there and nothing is near the sphere of the electroscope but the leaves are spread wide apart. You rub an ebonite rod with fur. As you slowly bring the rod near the sphere of the electroscope, the leaves begin to fall back down and lie near each other.

   (a) Explain why the leaves of the electroscope were in the condition in which you found them.

   (b) Explain what happened as you brought the ebonite rod near to the sphere of the electroscope.

Problem Solving

23. Imagine that you go into a room and someone tells you that a large metal can might be highly charged, because an electric wire had been touching it. You need to know whether it is charged, because it might be too dangerous to touch. Devise a method for testing it without touching it. Use only materials that you would find around the house.

24. Every time you walk across a certain carpet and reach for the doorknob, you get a shock. Devise a plan that will allow you to avoid getting shocked.

25. No matter how hard you rub two objects together, you cannot charge them. Give a plausible explanation.

26. Why are the handles of screw drivers often made of plastic or rubber?

27. Carpet manufacturers use the principle of electrostatics to design carpets. How do you think they might design a carpet that would reduce the chance of getting an electric shock after walking across it?

28. Four pith balls, A, B, C, and D, are suspended on insulating threads. Spheres A, B, and C attract each other. Ball C repels D. If A is positively charged, what type of electric charge is on B, C, and D?

29. If a metal marble, resting on insulating material, is given a negative charge, will the charge be distributed evenly throughout the entire marble or will it all be on the surface? Use the properties of charge and of conductors to explain why you chose your answer.

30. Sometimes, when you are petting a cat or dog on a cold, dry day, you can hear little popping or crackling sounds. Explain what might be causing these sounds.

Critical Thinking

31. You are caught in a thunderstorm. Should you run under a tree or run farther to get into a car? Give reasons for your answer.

32. Platinum and silver are excellent conductors yet they are rarely used in common applications. Why?

Pause&
Reflect

   1. Describe something that you have learned about electrostatics that has an important effect on your life.

   2. Choose a scientific model of some concept related to static electricity. Explain why it helps you to understand that concept.

Opening Ideas...

- What happens when you slide the switch on a flashlight? How does the switch control the light?

- What is the difference between a 60 watt and a 100 watt light bulb? What is a watt?

- Why are some electrical cords so much larger than others?

Science Log

Think about the questions in Opening Ideas. Discuss the answers with your classmates. Write your conclusions in your Science Log. As you study this chapter and learn more about electricity, review your Science Log entries. If your answers to these questions are not complete, write the correct answers in your Log.

As you jump from your seat to cheer for the homerun, you totally forget that it is night and the sky is dark. Electric lights turn night into day, at least on the baseball field. A bolt of lightning only lights the sky for a few seconds but when you harness electrical energy and control it, you can use it to play football or baseball at night. You can see to drive home after the game. You can even use it to study at your desk at home after dark. The technology for controlling and using electrical energy has changed the way we live.

In this chapter, you will study the main concepts of electricity. You will learn about the fundamental components of an electric circuit that are necessary for turning on a light, heating water in a tea kettle, or turning on a computer. You will discover the meaning of electric current, potential difference and power, and how a light bulb or another electrical device receives energy from a source of electricity. You will also determine the efficiency of an electrical appliance.

Move

Key Concepts

In this chapter, you will discover

- the meaning of potential difference, current, resistance, and power
- the components of a simple electric circuit and their functions
- the relationships among potential difference, current, resistance, and power
- how electrical energy is transported and converted into other forms of energy

Key Skills

In this chapter, you will

- use a circuit diagram and assemble a simple circuit
- learn how to use a voltmeter and an ammeter
- solve problems involving current, potential difference, resistance, and power
- determine the efficiency of an electrical appliance

Key Terms

- dry cell
- positive terminal
- negative terminal
- circuit
- switch
- circuit diagram
- battery
- resistor
- load
- current
- coulomb
- ampere
- ammeter
- electrical potential energy
- potential difference
- volt
- voltmeter
- resistance
- ohm
- Ohm's law
- power
- watt

Making Light Bulbs Glow

Have you ever changed the batteries in a flashlight and studied the inside? Did you wonder what parts of the flashlight make contact with the battery and how the batteries make contact with the bulb? How can you connect a wire, a flashlight bulb, and a dry cell together so that the bulb will light up?

What You Need

one D dry cell (1.5 V)
one flashlight bulb (2 V)
two pieces of insulated copper wire with both ends bare

Safety Precaution

Disconnect the copper wire if it gets hot.

What to Do

1. Try to make the flashlight bulb light up, using the bulb, one dry cell, and one piece of wire. Touch the flashlight bulb to different places on the dry cell. Touch the wire to different places on the light bulb and the dry cell until the flashlight bulb lights up. Find more than one way to make the correct connections.

2. Draw a sketch showing the bulb, the wire, and the dry cell for each successful connection.

3. Try to light the bulb using the bulb, one dry cell, and two pieces of wire.

4. Draw a sketch showing the bulb, the two wires, and the dry cell for each successful connection.

What Did You Discover?

Write a paragraph that summarizes all of the components and contacts between these components that are necessary in order to light a light bulb. Include a labelled sketch.

10.1 Pushing Charges Around

It is still dark when the clock radio comes on. You reach over and hit the snooze button. Nine minutes later, when the radio comes back on, you realize that you must get up. Still groggy, you reach for the lamp and turn the switch. You are startled, then frustrated, when the light does not go on. Like everyone around you, you probably take electricity for granted. Possibly, you have never thought about what happens when the light goes on. How does the switch work? Why does the bulb light up? What happens when a light bulb burns out? Now is the time to find out.

Closing the Gap

In your Starting Point Activity, you found all of the components that are necessary to light a light bulb. You used a **dry cell** as a source of energy, conducting wires to carry the energy to the flashlight bulb, and the bulb to convert the energy into light. You discovered two locations on the battery where contact is necessary. These sites are called the **positive terminal** and the **negative terminal**. You also found two locations on the light bulb where contact is necessary. Most importantly, you discovered that you must have a closed path to connect the components. This closed path is called an electric **circuit**. Although the circuit will function without a **switch**, it is more convenient to have one. You can open and close the switch without moving any other component of the circuit.

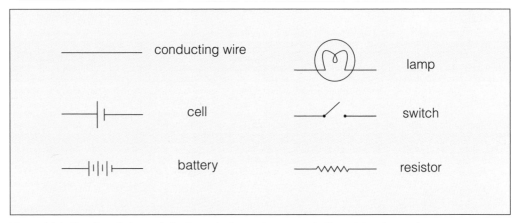

Figure 10.1 Circuit symbols are similar to words; they make communication quick and accurate.

Pause&
Reflect

Make a table in your Science Log to record the symbols and names of circuit elements. Record the symbols in Figure 10.1. Leave room to add to your list as you discover more symbols in your study of current electricity.

You can describe a circuit with words, but it is more practical to use a **circuit diagram**. These diagrams use symbols to represent each of the components, or elements, in the circuit. Figure 10.1 shows some of these symbols. You will notice two terms among the symbols that you have not yet encountered in this discussion. A **battery** is a combination of cells. The symbols for batteries and cells are similar because both represent a source of energy. A **resistor** is used to represent any one of many different components, called **loads**, that convert electrical energy to other forms of energy. For example, motors, toasters, lamps, radios, televisions, microwave ovens, and electric kettles convert electrical energy to motion, heat, sound, and light. There are so many different electrical devices that it would not be practical to use a different symbol for each. The resistor represents something that they all have in common. They all resist the movement of charge through the circuit.

Moving Charges

A cell or battery provides energy to push negative charges through the conductors in a circuit. This movement of charge is called **current**. If you were to describe a current of water, you might state the number of litres of water that flow past a point in a water pipe every minute. Similarly, scientists describe electrical current as the amount of charge that passes a point in a conducting wire every second. The symbol for current is I and the symbol for charge is Q. Using t to represent time, the mathematical model for current is

$$I = \frac{Q}{t} \qquad \text{current} = \frac{\text{charge moving past a point}}{\text{time}}$$

Charge, Q, is measured in **coulombs** (C), current, I, is measured in **amperes** (A) and time is measured in seconds. A current of 1.0 A means that 1.0 C of charge is moving past a point in the circuit every second. The following table summarizes these quantities. If you want to see how to use this formula, study the model problems in "Stretch Your Mind" on page 328.

Table 10.1 Symbols and Units for Current

	Symbol	Unit (quantity)
Charge	Q	C (coulomb)
Current	I	A (ampere)
Time	t	s (second)

An instrument called an **ammeter** measures electric current. The circuit symbol for an ammeter is a circle with an "A" in the centre. You can learn more about current and ammeters by doing the next investigation.

Current at Home

Table 10.2 lists the current through some common electrical devices. Notice that the amount of current needed to operate different appliances and instruments varies.

DidYouKnow?

One coulomb of charge is equal to the amount of charge on 6.25×10^{18} electrons.

DidYouKnow?

The terms "coulomb" and "ampere" were named in honour of two French physicists who studied electricity and magnetism, Charles Augustin de Coulomb (1736-1806) and André Marie Ampère (1775-1836).

Pause&Reflect

Start a table in your Science Log for symbols and units, like the one shown in Table 10.1. Each time you encounter a new unit, add it to your table.

Table 10.2 Current in Household Appliances

Appliance	Current (A)
radio	0.4
100 W lamp	0.8
colour television	1.7
toaster	8.8
microwave oven	11.7
electric kettle	12.5
electric range	40

Figure 10.2 Compare the current required by appliances that convert electrical energy into heat, to the current required by devices that convert electrical energy into light or sound. What pattern do you see?

INVESTIGATION 10-A

Measuring Current

In this activity, you will assemble a simple circuit. You will learn where to place a switch and practice connecting an ammeter. You will measure and compare the electric current at various locations in the circuit. Finally, you will compare the currents in circuits that have different light bulbs.

How do you think the current between the negative terminal of the battery and the light bulb will compare with the current between the light bulb and the positive terminal of the battery? Make a hypothesis and discuss it with a partner. Then do the activity to test your hypothesis.

Problem

Where should the switch be placed in a circuit? How does the current at one point in the circuit compare to the current at other points in the circuit?

Safety Precautions

An ammeter must be connected correctly to prevent damage to the meter. The positive terminal of the ammeter is connected to the positive terminal of the battery or power supply. The negative terminal of the ammeter is connected to the negative terminal of the battery or power supply. Trace the connecting wires from each terminal of the ammeter back to the battery to check that the connections have been made correctly, as shown in Diagram A. There must be a load, such as the light bulb, to limit the flow of electrons in the circuit.

• Have your teacher check the connections of the ammeter in the circuit before closing the switch.

Apparatus

ammeter
battery (6 V)
bulb (6 V)
bulb (9 V)
conducting wires (4)
hand lens
switch

Procedure

1 Make a table such as the one shown here, to record your data.

Properties of a Simple Circuit

Location of Switch and Ammeter	Bulb Type	Filament Diameter (smallest; largest)	Bulb Brightness (dimmest; brightest)	Electric Current (amperes) A
between positive terminal and bulb	9 V			
between negative terminal and bulb	9 V			
between negative terminal and bulb	6 V			

2 Use the hand lens to determine which kind of bulb has the larger diameter filament and record this in the table.

3 Connect the circuit as shown in Diagram A with the ammeter between the positive terminal of the battery and the bulb. Use a 9 V bulb.

4 Close the switch. Record the brightness of the bulb and the current.

Skill
POWER
If your ammeter has more than one scale and you need help learning how to read it correctly, turn to page 600.

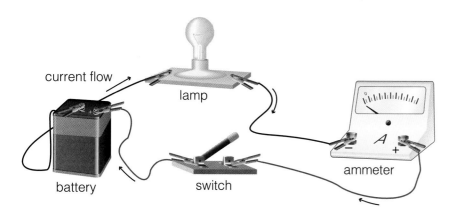

current flow

lamp

battery

switch

ammeter

A

⑥ With the ammeter reading a current, unscrew the 9 V bulb. Repeat step 4.

⑦ Open the switch. Remove the 9 V bulb and replace it with the 6 V bulb. Repeat step 4.

Diagram A Since current moves through every point in the circuit, an ammeter must be inserted directly into the circuit so all the current will run through it. Why is this ammeter showing zero current?

⑤ Connect the circuit as shown in Diagram B with the ammeter between the negative terminal of the source and the bulb. Repeat step 4.

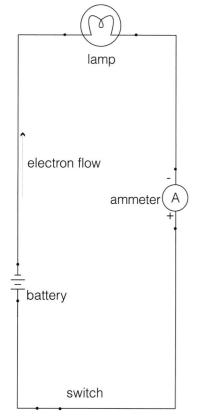

lamp

electron flow

ammeter A

battery

switch

Diagram B

Analyze

1. How does the location of the switch (near the negative terminal or the positive terminal of the battery) affect the current in the circuit?

2. How does the current between the negative terminal of the battery and the light bulb compare to the current between the light bulb and the positive terminal of the battery?

3. **(a)** Which light bulb glows more brightly, the 9 V bulb or the 6 V bulb?

   (b) Which light bulb permits more current to flow?

   (c) Which light bulb has the smaller diameter filament?

Conclude and Apply

4. Write a statement that summarizes whether it matters where the switch is located in a simple circuit.

5. How does the current in any one location of the circuit compare to the current at other places in the circuit? Write a sentence that describes the current throughout the circuit.

6. What happened to the current in the circuit, when you unscrewed the bulb? Write an explanation that accounts for these results.

7. **(a)** Which light bulb decreases the current the most?

   (b) Which light bulb has the smallest diameter filament?

   (c) Which light bulb places the largest load on the circuit?

   (d) Write an explanation for the relationship between current and brightness of the bulb.

If 240 C of charge pass a point in a conductor in 5.0 min, what is the current through that point in the conductor?

Given
Q = 240 C
t = 5.0 min

Required
Current, I, in amperes (A)

Analysis
Use the formula

$$I = \frac{Q}{t}$$

Convert time from minutes to seconds because one ampere is one coulomb per second. (1 A = 1 C/s)

Solution
$$t = 5.0 \, \text{min} \times \frac{60 \, \text{s}}{\text{min}} = 300 \, \text{s}$$

$$I = \frac{Q}{t}$$

$$= \frac{240 \, \text{C}}{300 \, \text{s}}$$

$$= 0.80 \, \text{A}$$

Paraphrase
When 240 C of charge pass a point in a conductor every 5.0 min, the current in the conductor is 0.80 A.

DidYouKnow?
When Benjamin Franklin named charges "positive" and "negative" no one knew what charges were made of or which charges moved. Franklin guessed that it was the positive charge that moved. He showed current leaving the positive terminal of a battery, travelling around the circuit, and arriving at the negative terminal. This is exactly opposite to the direction of electron flow. However, Franklin's system was used for so long that it became the standard for describing current. Many advanced text books still use Franklin's direction.

Charges Pushing Charges

In the circuits that you assembled in your investigation, a battery provided the energy to push electrons around the circuit. Electrons left the negative terminal of the battery, travelled through the conductor, through the light bulb, and then back to the battery. On the average, electrons move less than 3 cm in one minute. So why did the light go on as soon as you closed the switch? The answer is similar to the reason that water starts to run out of the tap as soon as you turn the handle. The pipes were already full of water. The moment you open a valve, the water in the pipes is pushed out by the pressure of the water a long way from the tap. Just as the pipes are filled with water, electrons are always distributed throughout the conductors. Every electron that leaves the negative terminal of the battery pushes the one ahead of it. As you know from your study of electrostatics, electrons do not need to touch in order to repel or push on other electrons. They exert a force from a distance. Electrons move throughout the entire circuit from the moment the switch is closed.

Skill POWER
For tips on solving numerical problems, turn to page 603.

The Best Current Model

How can you make an appropriate model for the motion of electrons in an electric circuit?

What You Need

Obtain a set of wooden blocks, six plastic drinking straws, and three bar magnets.

What to Do

1. Line up a group of wooden blocks in a straight line. Make sure the blocks are touching.

2. Push on an end block several times at different speeds. Observe the block at the other end. How does the speed with which you push affect the length of time between the moment when you start pushing and the moment when the block at the other end starts to move?

3. Using the straws as rollers, line up the magnets as shown here. Carefully push the magnet at one end. Observe the motion of the magnet at the other end.

What Did You Discover?

Write a summary of the way the blocks model the motion of electrons in a circuit. Explain the motion of the magnets. Write another paragraph that explains how the magnets model electrons in a circuit. Which is the better model, the wooden block model or the bar magnet model? Why does one method model the motion of electrons better than the other?

Check Your Understanding

1. Define the following terms: (a) coulomb, (b) current, (c) circuit, (d) switch.

2. Draw a circuit diagram using symbols. Include a battery, a switch, a lamp, an ammeter, and conducting wires. Add arrows to show the direction of the flow of electrons. Describe the function of each part of the circuit.

3. Write the relationship between current, I, charge, Q, and time, t, in words and in symbols. Write the relationship between the units for these quantities.

4. **Thinking Critically** For a circuit, such as the one you sketched in question 2, why does the lamp go off when you open the switch? Base your answer on the necessary conditions for circuits.

5. **Apply** Predict which current will be greater, the current passing through an electric iron or the current passing through an electric razor, when each is plugged into a 120 V outlet. Explain how you made your prediction.

10.2 Energized and De-energized Charges

In your study of electrostatics, you learned how sparks and lightning occur. The energy for pushing electrons through air came from separated positive and negative charges. An excess of electrons accumulates in the lower layers of clouds, making the layer negatively charged. A deficit of electrons causes the ground to be positively charged. The positively charged ground pulls on electrons, while the negative charges in the clouds repel them. For a brief moment, charges race through the air and a bolt of lightning appears. Tremendous amounts of energy are converted into light and heat. Then it is over.

In a circuit, movement of electrons is continuous and controlled. However, the reason that electrons move in a circuit is much the same as the reason they move in a lightning bolt. An excess of electrons accumulates at one terminal of a battery, making it negatively charged. At the same time, electrons withdraw from the other terminal, leaving it positively charged. In a battery, energy from chemical reactions does the work of separating the charges. The energized electrons now have the ability to do work on something else, such as lighting a bulb or heating a burner on a stove. The electrical energy stored in the battery is called **electrical potential energy**. Although the electrons have the potential for doing work, they cannot do it until the battery is connected to a load and the circuit is closed.

Figure 10.3 Energy for lightning or for sending current through a circuit is stored in the form of separated negative and positive charges.

(A) Electrons in the battery are "energized" by chemical reactions.

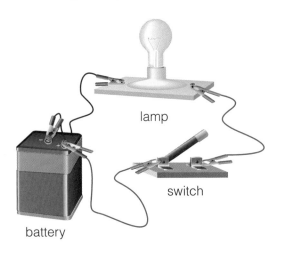

Figure 10.4

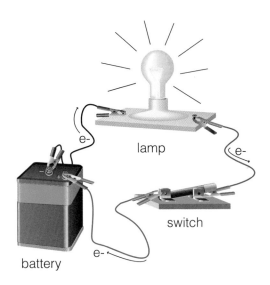

(B) When the switch is closed, the energized electrons flow from the battery to the light bulb, where the electrical energy is converted into light. De-energized electrons return to the battery to become energized again.

All forms of energy are measured in joules (J). However, when describing the energy of electrons in an electrical circuit, we describe the potential energy possessed by each coulomb of charge instead of the total energy of all of the charges. As well, we always compare one point in a circuit to another. The term **potential difference** means the difference in potential energy per coulomb of charge at one point in the circuit compared to the potential energy per coulomb of charge at another point in the circuit. The units for potential energy per unit of charge are joules per coulomb (J/C). This combination of units has a special name, the **volt** (V), named in honour of Count Alessandro Guiseppe Antonio Anastasio Volta (1745-1827). If one coulomb of charge has one more joule of potential energy at one point in a circuit, compared to another point in the circuit, the potential difference between those two points is one volt. You can write this relationship in mathematical form using V for potential difference, E for energy and Q for amount of charge.

$$V = \frac{E}{Q} \qquad \text{potential difference} = \frac{\text{energy}}{\text{charge}}$$

In a battery, 45 J of chemical energy are converted into electrical energy by separating positive and negative charges. This energy places 15 C of negative charge at the negative terminal, leaving a deficit at the positive terminal. What is the potential difference between the negative and positive terminals of the battery?

Given
E = 45 J
Q = 15 C

Required
Potential difference, V, in volts (V)

Analysis
To find potential difference, use

$$V = \frac{E}{Q}$$

Solution

$$V = \frac{E}{Q}$$

$$V = \frac{45 \text{ J}}{15 \text{ C}}$$

$$= 3.0 \text{ J/C}$$
$$= 3.0 \text{ V}$$

Paraphrase
A battery that uses 45 J of chemical energy to separate 15 C of charge has a potential difference of 3.0 V between the terminals of the battery.

Table 10.3 Symbols and Units for Potential Difference

	Symbol	Unit (quantity)
Energy	E	J (joule)
Charge	Q	C (coulomb)
Potential Difference	V	V (volts) V = J/C

To gain a better understanding of potential difference in a circuit, compare the electric circuit with the water circuit in Figure 10.5. In the water circuit, the pump lifts water to a higher level against the pull of gravity. A valve at the top of the pipe controls whether the water runs down. When the water runs down, it turns a waterwheel. In the electric circuit, the battery (similar to the pump) raises electrons to a higher potential energy level at the negative terminal, compared to the positive terminal. The switch, like the valve, determines whether or not the electrons are allowed to flow "down" in electric energy. When the electrons are allowed to flow, the current runs through the motor and causes it to turn. You can measure the potential difference between two points in a circuit with an instrument called a **voltmeter**.

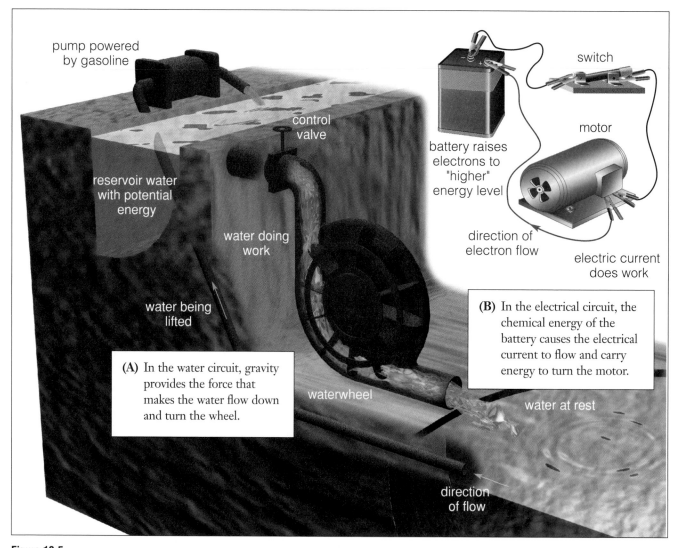

pump powered by gasoline

switch

control valve

motor

battery raises electrons to "higher" energy level

reservoir water with potential energy

water doing work

direction of electron flow

electric current does work

water being lifted

(B) In the electrical circuit, the chemical energy of the battery causes the electrical current to flow and carry energy to turn the motor.

(A) In the water circuit, gravity provides the force that makes the water flow down and turn the wheel.

waterwheel

water at rest

direction of flow

Figure 10.5

Making a Physical Model

In this activity you will build a model that demonstrates the relationship among electric charge, electric energy, and potential difference.

What You Need

modelling clay
paint stir stick
cellophane tape
12 tapioca particles or dried peas
scissors
stiff paper

What to Do

1. Use the modelling clay to support the paint stick vertically on a table.

2. Cut four 2 cm by 8 cm cards from stiff paper.

3. Print the following information on the cards: 3 V = 3 J/C; 6 V = 6 J/C; 9 V = 9 J/C; 12 V = 12 J/C.

4. Tape the cards equal distances apart on the paint stick.

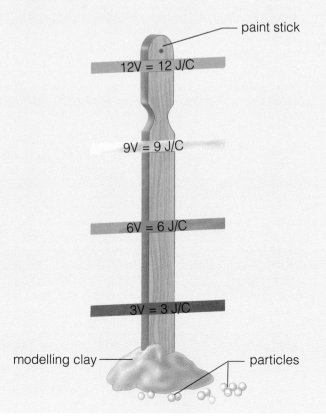

paint stick

12V = 12 J/C

9V = 9 J/C

6V = 6 J/C

3V = 3 J/C

modelling clay — particles

5. Assume that each tapioca particle or dried pea represents one coulomb of charge.

6. Tape four particles to the 3 V card, three particles to the 6 V card, two particles to the 9 V card, and one particle to the 12 V card.

7. Make a table with the headings shown below:

Potential Difference V (volts)	Charge Q (coulombs)	Electric Energy E (joules)

8. Fill in the table for each level of the model. Hint: Remember that the total charge is different at each level.

9. Clean surfaces after completing the activity.

What Did You Discover?

1. Where should you place the two remaining particles to represent zero energy?

2. How much energy is needed to "lift" a coulomb of charge from the table to the 12 V level?

3. What is the total electric potential energy stored in the 9 V level? The 6 V level? The 3 V level?

4. How much energy would be released, if the charges in the 9 V level drop to the 6 V level? Explain your answer.

5. Write a sentence explaining the relationship among electric energy, electric charge, and potential difference.

6. A 9 V transistor radio battery is very small compared to a 12 V car battery. Use your model to help explain why two 9 V batteries, connected in a way that would produce a potential difference of 18 V, would not be able to start a car.

Energy Around a Simple Circuit

In this activity, you will assemble a simple circuit and measure the potential difference across the source. Then you will measure the potential difference across two different light bulbs. Do you think that the potential differences across the two light bulbs will be the same or different? Make a hypothesis and discuss it with a partner. Then do this activity to test your hypothesis.

Problem

How does the potential difference across the source compare to the potential difference across the load? When using the same source, how do the potential differences across two different loads compare?

Safety Precaution

The negative terminal of the voltmeter must be connected to the negative terminal of the battery or power supply. It may be connected directly to the negative terminal of the battery or through connecting wires. You can recognize the negative terminal of the voltmeter, because it has a negative sign (-) and is black. The positive terminal (+) is red.

• Have your teacher check the connections of the voltmeter in the circuit before closing the switch.

Apparatus

voltmeter
battery (6 V)
bulb (6 V)
bulb (9 V)
conducting wires (5)
switch

Skill
POWER

If your voltmeter has several scales and you need help using it, turn to page 600.

Procedure

1 Make a table such as the one shown here to record your data.

Potential Differences in a Simple Circuit

Connection of Voltmeter	Bulb Type	Bulb Brightness (dimmest; brightest)	Potential Difference (volts) V
across the battery	9 V		
across the bulb	9 V		
across the bulb	6 V		
across the unscrewed bulb	6 V		

2 Connect the circuit to measure the potential difference of the source as shown in Diagram A. Use the 9 V bulb.

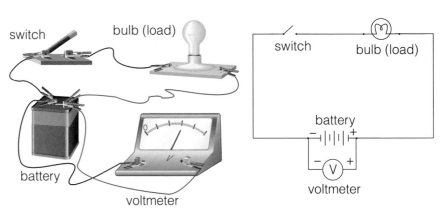

Diagram A

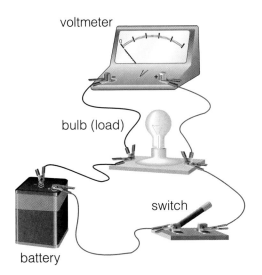

voltmeter

bulb (load)

switch

battery

Diagram B

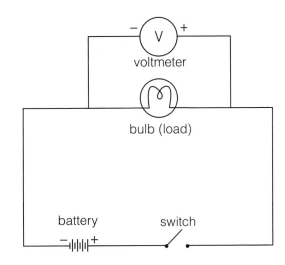

voltmeter

bulb (load)

battery   switch

③ Close the switch. Record the brightness of the bulb and the potential difference across the battery.

④ Open the switch, remove the voltmeter, and reconnect it across the bulb as shown in Diagram B.

⑤ Close the switch and record the potential difference across the bulb.

⑥ Replace the 9 V bulb with a 6 V bulb. Repeat step 5.

⑦ Open the switch and unscrew the 6 V bulb. Then close the switch and record the reading across the unscrewed bulb.

Analyze

1. How does the potential difference across the battery compare to the potential difference across the 9 V bulb?

2. How does the potential difference across the battery compare to the potential difference across the 6 V bulb?

3. How does the potential difference across the 9 V bulb compare to the potential difference across the 6 V bulb?

4. How does the brightness of the 6 V bulb compare to the brightness of the 9 V bulb?

5. What happens to the potential difference across a bulb when you unscrew the bulb?

Conclude and Apply

6. How does the energy that the battery gives to each coulomb of charge compare to the energy that this charge gives to the load? Explain how your observations led you to your answer.

7. Compare your answers to steps 3 and 4 of Analyze. Give a reasonable explanation about why those two observations can both be true.

8. If no current flows through a load, how much energy does the load receive? Explain how your observations support your answer.

Across Canada

Monique Frize began studying chemistry at the University of Ottawa but was not content in this department. When a third-year electrical engineering student showed her his lab, Monique was "absolutely taken by the use of electricity to make things happen and to see results on an oscillo-scope" (an electronic instrument that converts waves in electric current into visible waves on a screen). This experience prompted her to change programs after her third year at university. She enrolled in electrical engineering in 1963. No woman had ever entered any field of engineering at this university. Monique describes the experience of being the only woman in the class as "daunt-ing," but she studied hard and graduated in 1966.

Over the last 30 years, Dr. Frize has worked in many areas. She started as a biomedical engineer in hospitals, ensuring that hospital equipment was safe and effective. She did research on cardiac pacemakers in the 1970s, studying how magnetic fields can cause interference.

Today, Dr. Frize develops software tools that help physicians make more accurate diagnoses. She is an engineering professor at two universities in Ottawa, Ontario; in The Department of Systems and Computer Engineering at Carleton University and the School of Information Technology and Engineering at the University of Ottawa. Dr. Frize teaches engineering courses, supervises graduate students, and writes articles for journals and conferences. Dr. Frize is bilingual. Her francophone background has been an advantage in many of her positions.

Monique Frize

When students seek advice, Monique Frize says, "A univer-sity degree combined with good communication and people skills should lead to a successful job search." She says that writing and verbal skills are very important in any career. Dr. Frize stresses that engineering is not just about "con-structing bridges and buildings." It is a "people field," she states emphatically.

Check Your Understanding

1. Explain the meaning of the term "potential difference."

2. Explain how to connect a voltmeter to a circuit to measure the potential differ-ence across a light bulb. Use a sketch to clarify your explanation.

3. How is a battery in a circuit similar to a pump that raises water up into a reser-voir?

4. **Thinking Critically** If a circuit contains a 12 V battery, a switch, and a light bulb, what is the potential difference across the light bulb?

5. **Thinking Critically** A bulb is connected to a battery having a potential dif-ference of 6 V. A voltmeter is connected across the bulb. What is the reading on the voltmeter, when the bulb burns out?

10.3 Resisting the Movement of Charge

Have you ever crawled through a narrow tunnel in a cave? If you have, you know how difficult it is and how slowly you move. As the tunnel becomes more narrow, the resistance to motion becomes greater. Only a small "current" of people can move through the tunnel. The situation is similar for electrons travelling through the filament of a light bulb. The atoms of the filament resist the flow of electrons. **Resistance** is a property of a substance that hinders motion and converts electrical energy to other forms of energy. For example, the resistance of the tungsten wire filament in a light bulb is over 400 times greater than the resistance of copper connecting wires. When a current flows through the high resistance filament of the light bulb, the filament converts much of the energy carried by current into light and heat. When the same current flows through the copper connecting wire, the amount of energy converted into heat is so small that you hardly notice it.

Describing Resistance

How much energy does it take to push a 50 kg crate across a room? This depends entirely on how much resistance there is to the sliding motion. If you are trying to slide a rough wooden crate across a carpet, it would take a tremendous amount of energy. However, if you were pushing a smooth crate across a tile floor, it would take much less energy.

How much electrical energy does it take to push a coulomb of charge through a filament of a light bulb? It depends on the resistance of the filament. Electrical resistance is defined as the ratio of the potential difference across the load, V, to the current through the load, I. Using R to represent resistance, the mathematical model for resistance is

Figure 10.6 You might describe the resistance of a crate to movement as the energy it takes to move 1 kg of crate across a room. Then you could compare any two crates, not just crates of the same size.

$$R = \frac{V}{I} \qquad \text{resistance} = \frac{\text{potential difference}}{\text{current}}$$

According to this relationship, the units of resistance are volts per ampere (V/A). Once again, this combination of units is given another name, the **ohm**, in honour of Georg Simon Ohm (1789-1854). The symbol for the ohm is the Greek letter omega, Ω. If a potential difference of one volt across a filament causes one ampere of current to flow through a filament, then the electrical resistance of the filament is one ohm.

Ohm was the first person to publish results of experiments on the resistance of wires of various sizes. Ohm constructed wires of many different lengths and thicknesses. Today, we simply call these devices resistors because all they do is resist the flow of current. Ohm applied a potential difference across his wire resistors and measured the current through them. He discovered that, for each resistor, no matter what potential difference he applied, the resistance was the same. The results of

Pause&
Reflect

Add the symbol for resistance, *R*, and the unit ohm, Ω, to your table of symbols and units in your Science Log.

DidYouKnow?

In Ohm's day, it was not possible to go to the hardware store and buy resistance wire. Fortunately, Georg learned how to make resistance wires of different diameters, while helping his father, who was a locksmith.

DidYouKnow?

Henry Cavendish had discovered the relationship between voltage and current about 50 years earlier than Ohm. Unfortunately, he did not publish the results. Imagine the benefits to technology, if the relationship between voltage and current had been known half a century earlier.

Math CONNECT

What is the resistance of a light bulb if 2.4 A runs through it, when a potential difference of 12 V is placed across the bulb?

his observations are now called Ohm's law, in his honour. The mathematical formula for Ohm's law is

$$V = IR$$

Any electrical device that has a constant resistance, regardless of potential difference, is called an **ohmic** resistor, because it follows Ohm's law. However, many electrical appliances are not ohmic because their resistances change when the potential difference across the device is changed.

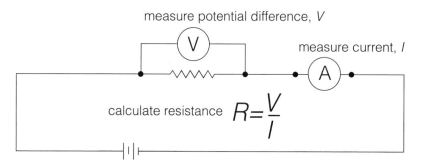

Figure 10.7 To find the resistance of a light bulb or any other electrical device, measure the current *(I)* passing through it and the potential difference *(V)* across it. Then divide potential difference by current *(V/I)*.

Model Problem

What is the resistance of the heating coil of an electric heater, if a current of 12.5 A runs through it, when it is connected to a wall outlet?

Given
$I = 12.5$ A
Heater is connected to a wall outlet.

Required
Resistance, *R*, in ohms (Ω)

Analysis
A wall outlet provides a potential difference of 120 V.

Use the expression $R = \dfrac{V}{I}$ to find resistance.

Solution
$$R = \frac{V}{I}$$
$$= \frac{120 \text{ V}}{12.5 \text{ A}}$$
$$= 9.60 \text{ V/A}$$
$$= 9.60 \text{ }\Omega$$

Paraphrase
The resistance of an electric heater is 9.60 Ω, if the current through it is 12.5 A, when the potential difference between the ends is 120 V.

Wasting Energy?

At first, it might seem that there is no purpose for simple resistors that do not convert energy into light, sound, or any other useful kind of energy. However, resistors are very important in circuits. You can use them to control current or potential difference in a circuit to suit the specific needs of other electrical devices in the circuit.

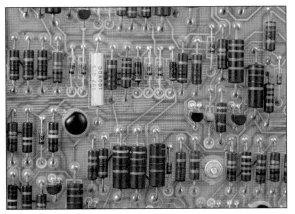

Figure 10.8 Because the resistance of these resistors is the same at any potential difference, an electrical engineer can use them to precisely control current and potential difference in various parts of a circuit.

Math CONNECT

Mathematicians define the slope of a line as the rise over the run. To find the slope, choose two points on the line. Name the coordinates of the points (x_1, y_1) and (x_2, y_2). Then determine the rise by calculating the vertical distance between the points, $(y_2 - y_1)$. The run is the horizontal distance between the points or $(x_2 - x_1)$. Calculate the slope by using the formula

$$\text{slope} = \frac{\text{rise}}{\text{run}} = \frac{(y_2 - y_1)}{(x_2 - x_1)}$$

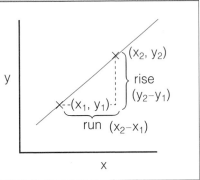

Measuring Resistance

You can study the resistance characteristics of a simple resistor or any other electrical device by connecting it in a circuit such as the one shown on page 340. You would set the potential difference at several different values and observe the current. Plotting the data on a graph is a good way to analyze the information. Plot the potential difference on the vertical axis and the current on the horizontal axis as shown in Figure 10.9.

The data points for the resistor that are plotted on this graph give a straight line. You can find the resistance by calculating the slope because the slope gives potential difference divided by current or V/I. The resistance is

$$R = \frac{(5.0\ \text{V} - 1.0\ \text{V})}{(0.25\ \text{A} - 0.05\ \text{A})} = \frac{4.0\ \text{V}}{0.20\ \text{A}} = 20\ \Omega$$

If the plot of potential difference versus current for an electrical device is not a straight line, you cannot calculate the resistance from a slope. The absence of a straight line means that the resistor is not ohmic.

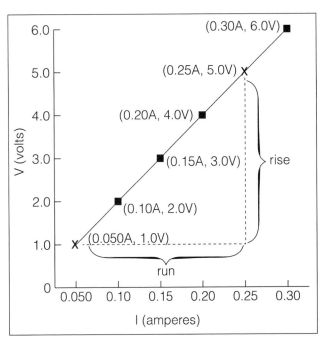

Figure 10.9 The data points for potential difference and current for a resistor are plotted on the graph and a straight line connects the points. Two points, labelled "x" are chosen to calculate the slope.

Potential Difference and Current for a Resistor

The small resistors used inside electrical devices, such as tape recorders and radios, are called radio resistors. In this activity, you will investigate the relationship between the electric current flowing through a resistor and the potential difference between its ends. What do you think the graph of potential difference versus current will look like? Sketch a graph showing your prediction and share your ideas with a partner. Then do the activity to test your predictions.

Problem

What is the relationship between the potential difference across the ends of a radio resistor and the electric current flowing through it?

Safety Precautions

Review the procedure for connecting the voltmeter and the ammeter.

• Have your teacher check the first circuit before you close the switch.

• Be sure to use an appropriate range on each meter.

Apparatus

ammeter
variable power supply
connecting leads (6)
two different radio resistors
switch
voltmeter

Procedure

① Make two tables similar to the one below for recording the data. There should be enough rows to record data for five different potential differences.

Resistor Characteristics

Potential Difference V (V)	Electric Current I (mA)
0	0

② Connect the circuit shown here. (Notice that an arrow through the symbol for a battery indicates that the potential difference is variable. You can adjust it with a dial.)

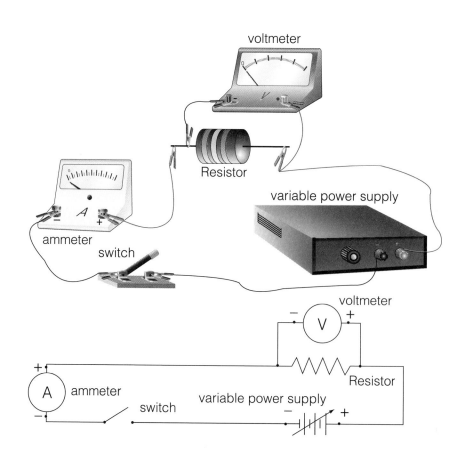

3 Adjust the power supply to give a potential difference close to one volt. Record the potential difference and current in your table.

4 Repeat step 3 four more times for potential differences between one volt and six volts or as instructed by your teacher.

5 Repeat steps 3 and 4 for the second radio resistor.

Analyze

1. On the same sheet of graph paper, plot a potential difference against current graph for each resistor. Plot current on the x-axis and potential difference on the y-axis. Use a different colour or plotting symbol for each set of data.

2. Draw a line of best fit through the data points for each resistor.

3. Calculate the slope for each graph to determine the electrical resistance. Be sure to include units for the rise, the run, and the final slope.

Conclude and Apply

4. Describe the graph of potential difference against current.

5. Describe the relationship between voltage and current for the resistors.

6. What is the resistance of each resistor? Hint: Resistance, R, is equal to the potential difference, V, divided by the current, I. The mathematical model is

$$R = \frac{V}{I}$$

The slopes of your lines are

$$\frac{V}{I}$$

7. Are the resistances of the two resistors the same or different?

8. Write an equation for each resistor using the symbol for potential difference, V, electric current, I, and the value of the resistance, R. How well does Ohm's law apply to the resistors? Explain.

Extend Your Knowledge and Skill

Design an experiment to determine if a light bulb behaves according to Ohm's law. Obtain a bulb from your teacher. Take the necessary readings from when the bulb is very dim to when it is very bright.

Safety Precaution

CAUTION: Use voltages within the range of the light bulb. Your teacher will tell you the maximum potential difference to use.

If you have access to a computer, plot a graph of the data using a spreadsheet program. Write a paragraph describing your procedure, results, and conclusion. How do you know that the filament of a light bulb is not an ohmic resistor?

Computer **CONNECT**

If you have access to a computer, use a spreadsheet program to plot the data.

DidYouKnow?

Every measurement has an error associated with it. When plotting a graph, you can indicate that you know there is an error by drawing a small circle (diameter 2 mm) around each point.

Skill
P O W E R

If you need help in plotting points, drawing a line of best fit or calculating the slope of a line, turn to page 587.

Pause& Reflect

By now, your Science Log table should be complete with symbols and units for charge, energy, time, current, potential difference, and resistance. If any of these quantities are missing, don't forget to add them. Also, add the symbol for a variable power supply to your list of symbols for circuit elements.

Designing Circuit Materials

Understanding the characteristics of conducting materials allows electrical engineers to design efficient resistors and conductors. Four different characteristics affect the resistance of a wire. These factors are listed in the following table.

Table 10.4 Factors Affecting Resistance of Wire

Factor	Effect
Length	Resistance *increases* with length. If the length doubles, the resistance doubles.
Cross Sectional Area	Resistance *decreases* with area. If the cross sectional area doubles, the resistance is half as great.
Temperature	As the temperature of the wire increases, the resistance *increases*.
Material	Due to the structure of their atoms, some metals allow electrons to move more freely than others.

power cable (20th century)

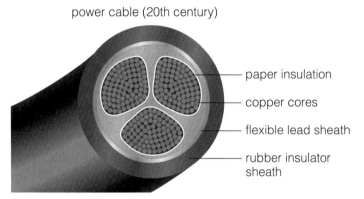

paper insulation

copper cores

flexible lead sheath

rubber insulator sheath

Figure 10.10 One very large copper wire would make a power cable very stiff. To reduce the resistance of the conductor while increasing the flexibility, modern power cables are made of many smaller diameter copper wires.

Some resistors are made of graphite or other poor conductors, while many resistors are made of long thin wires, wound in a spiral to reduce their size.

Conducting wires that carry large currents have large diameters to minimize the resistance. This is why the power cable of an electric stove is larger than the power cord of an electric kettle. Both use wires made of copper, a good conductor. However, a power cable has many more wires enclosed in an insulating sheath.

Check Your Understanding

1. In your own words, explain the meaning of electrical resistance.

2. What combination of units is equivalent to the ohm?

3. List three characteristics of a wire that affect its electrical resistance.

4. **Apply** A light bulb passes a current of 0.83 A when the potential difference across the bulb is 120 V. What is the electrical resistance of the bulb in ohms?

5. **Apply** What is the potential difference across an electric water heater element that has a resistance of 32 Ω when the current through it is 6.8 A?

6. **Think Critically** Matt says that if the resistance of a load becomes larger, the current through it becomes larger as well. Angela says that if the resistance of a load becomes larger, the current will decrease. Do you agree with Matt or with Angela? Explain your answer.

10.4 Powerful Charges

How many ways can you describe an athletic performance? "Look at the force he puts behind that kick!" "She skates with such energy!" "She had to do a lot of work to become that good at shooting a basketball." "He sure is a powerful batter!" The terms "force," "work," "energy," and "power" can be used in similar ways to describe an athlete. However, in physics, each of these terms has its own specific meaning and each must be used correctly. You have learned about charges exerting attractive or repulsive forces on each other. You discovered that batteries do work to separate positive and negative charges and give them energy. What is electrical power?

Figure 10.11 Even if the two lead runners use the same amount of energy getting from the start to the finish line, the front runner has more power. Power is defined as energy used over a certain amount of time. Since the front runner uses the same amount of energy in a shorter time, she has more power.

Time and Energy

In every area of physics, **power** is defined as energy per unit time. Electrical power describes the amount of electrical energy that is converted into heat, light, sound, or motion every second. As well, electrical power can describe the amount of electrical energy that is transmitted from one place to another in a certain amount of time over power transmission lines.

The symbol for power is P. The equation that defines power in mathematical form is

$$P = \frac{E}{t} \qquad \text{power} = \frac{\text{energy}}{\text{time}}$$

Since the unit of energy is the joule and the unit of time is the second, power can be expressed in joules per second. The joule per second has been renamed the **watt** (W) in honour of James Watt (1736-1819). When one joule of electrical energy is converted into light and heat by a light bulb every second, the power of the bulb is one watt.

There are many ways to calculate electrical power. If you would like to see one example, study "Stretch Your Mind" on the next page.

When working with electric circuits, one rarely refers to energy and time. It is much more common to use the quantities of potential difference and current. So it would be more convenient to have a formula for power that included these quantities. To derive the relationship, start with the general definition for power

$$P = \frac{E}{t}$$

Recall that potential difference is energy per unit charge, or

$$V = \frac{E}{Q}$$

When you multiply both sides of the equation by Q, you find that

$$QV = \frac{QE}{Q} \text{ or } E = QV$$

Because E and QV are the same, you can replace E in the formula for power with QV. You then have

$$P = \frac{E}{t}$$

$$= \frac{QV}{t}$$

Where have you seen Q/t? It is the definition of current I. Remember

$$I = \frac{Q}{t}$$

Now you can replace Q/t in the formula for power with I. Finally you have $P = IV$

If you know the potential difference across an electrical device and the current through it, you can calculate the power using $P = IV$. This value tells you how many joules of electrical energy are being converted into another form of energy every second.

Model Problem

A current of 13.6 A passes through an electric baseboard heater when it is connected to a 110 V wall outlet. What is the power of the heater?

Given
I = 13.6 A
V = 110 V

Required
Power, P, in watts (W)

Analysis
Since you know the potential difference and the current, use the equation $P = IV$ to calculate the power.

Solution
$P = IV$
    = 13.6 A × 110 V
    = 1496 W
    = 1.50×10^3 W

Paraphrase
If 13.6 A of current passes through an electric baseboard heater when it is connected to a wall outlet providing a potential difference of 110 V, the power of the heater is 1.50×10^3 W. Can you verify that the resistance of the coil of the heater is about 8.10 Ω?

Pause& Reflect

Review the units and symbols for the new quantities that you have learned. Add the unit and symbol for power to the table in your Science Log. Include the relationships between watts, joules, and seconds.

The Power Rating

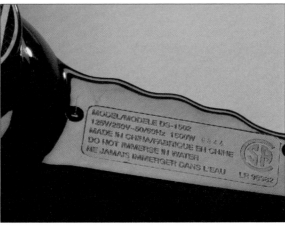

Figure 10.12 How could you find the current that would pass through the hair drier or the light bulb?

Many electrical devices, such as light bulbs, hair driers, and electric kettles, have their power rating marked on the device. This value tells you how much energy they use every second that they are in operation. How can you use this information to determine the amount of energy an electrical device would use in a certain amount of time? Since the formula for power is $P = \frac{E}{t}$, you can multiply both sides by t and solve for E.

$$Pt = \frac{Et}{t} = E$$
$$E = Pt$$

To find out how much electrical energy the device uses, multiply the power rating in watts by the time in seconds that the device is in use.

$$\text{Energy (joules)} = \text{power (watts)} \times \text{time (seconds)}$$

Nothing is Perfect

If an electrical device were perfect, all of the electrical energy that it uses would be converted into the desired form of energy. For example, in an electric mixer, all electrical energy would be converted into motion. All of the electrical energy that goes into a light bulb would be converted into light. However, no device is perfect. Some energy is always converted into heat. Even electrical appliances that are supposed to convert energy into heat are not 100% efficient. Consider an electric tea kettle that is designed to heat water. Some energy escapes to the outside and does not heat up the water. Although no device is 100% efficient, engineers try to design electrical appliances and devices as high in efficiency as possible without making them too expensive.

You can determine the efficiency of an electrical device by using the following relationship.

$$\text{Percent efficiency of electrical device} = \frac{\text{Useful energy output}}{\text{Total electrical energy input}} \times 100\%$$

For example, the "useful energy output" of a lamp is the amount of energy that the lamp converts into light. The "useful energy output" of an electric kettle is the amount of energy that the kettle transfers into the water as heat. In the next investigation, you will determine the efficiency of an electric kettle. First, study the model problem.

Model Problem

An electric kettle has a power rating of 1000 W. It takes the kettle 4.00 min to heat 600 mL (0.600 kg) of water from 22.0°C to 100°C. If it takes 1.96×10^5 J (196 000 J) of energy to heat the water, what is the efficiency of the kettle?

Given

$P = 1000$ W

$t = 4.00$ min

Useful energy output $= 1.96 \times 10^5$ J

Required

Percent efficiency

Analysis

Time must be in seconds because power is in watts and a watt is a joule per second. Convert time to seconds.

The "total electrical energy input" is electrical energy used by the kettle.
To find the energy used by the kettle, use the formula $E = Pt$.
To find the effiency of the kettle use

$$\text{Percent effiency} = \frac{\text{Useful energy output}}{\text{Total electrical energy input}} \times 100\%$$

Math **CONNECT**

Chemists have shown that it takes 4180 J of energy to raise the temperature of 1.0 kg of water by 1.0°C. Using this information, can you verify that it takes about 196 000 J of energy to heat 0.60 kg of water from 22°C to 100°C, an increase of 78°C?

Solution

Convert time into seconds.

$$t = 4.00 \; \text{min} \times \frac{60 \text{ s}}{\text{min}} = 240 \text{ s}$$

Find the electrical energy used by the kettle.

$$E = Pt$$
$$= 1000 \text{ W} \times 240 \text{ s}$$
$$= 240\,000 \text{ J}$$
$$= 2.40 \times 10^5 \text{ J}$$

$$\text{Percent efficiency of electrical device} = \frac{\text{Useful energy output}}{\text{Total electrical energy input}} \times 100 \text{ percent}$$

$$\text{Percent efficiency} = \frac{1.96 \times 10^5 \text{ J}}{2.40 \times 10^5 \text{ J}} \times 100\% = 81.7\%$$

Paraphrase

The kettle is about 81.7% efficient when heating 600 mL of water from 22°C to 100°C.

Efficiency of an Electric Kettle

Think About It

A scientist made the observations shown in the photographs and recorded the data described in the text below each photograph. It is your job to determine the efficiency of the kettle for boiling water. From previous information, you know that 4180 J of energy is required to raise the temperature of 1.00 kg of water 1.00°C. To heat 1.00 kg of water from 26°C to 70°C, (a change of 44°C), 44 × 4180 J or 183 920 J of energy is required. To heat 1.00 kg of water from 26°C to 96°C, (a change of 70°C), 70 times 4180 J or 292 600 J of energy is required.

Measure exactly 1.00 L (1.00 kg) of water in a graduated cylinder and pour it into a 1500 W electric kettle.

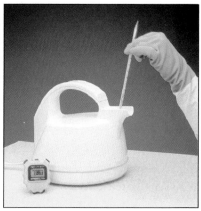

Record the temperature of the water then turn on the kettle and start the timer.

T = 26°; t = 0 s

What to Do

1 Create a table to organize your data. Include all of the data from the information under the photographs and the data for the amount of energy required to raise the temperature of 1.00 kg of water from 26°C to 70°C and from 26°C to 96°C. Include space in your table to record calculations for electrical energy used by the kettle and efficiency of the energy transfer for the two temperature ranges.

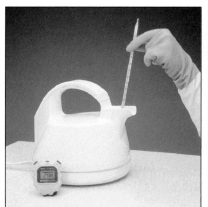

After a few minutes, read and record the temperature and the elapsed time.

T = 70°; t = 163 s

When the water just starts to boil, read and record the temperature and elapsed time. Turn off the kettle.

T = 96°; t = 264 s

2 Use the power rating of the kettle and the elapsed times to calculate the amount of electrical energy used by the kettle, to heat the water: **(a)** from 26°C to 70°C; **(b)** from 26°C to 96°C. Record these values in your table.

3 Use the answers to step 2 and the known amounts of energy required to raise the temperature of the water, to calculate the efficiency of the electric kettle for heating the water:

(a) from 26°C to 70°C; **(b)** from 26°C to 96°C.

Analyze

1. Compare the efficiency of the kettle for heating the water over the two temperature ranges. If there is a difference in the efficiency, propose an explanation for the difference.

2. How might you design an electric kettle to improve the efficiency?

DidYou**Know**?

MJ is the short form for megajoule, a unit for a large amount of energy. One megajoule is equal to one million joules ($1MJ = 1 \times 10^6 J$).

Power of Household Appliances

The power ratings of some common appliances are shown in Table 10.5. The approximate amount of energy used by each appliance in a typical household in one year is also listed. Check an appliance in your home to see if you can find a power rating.

Safety Precaution

Do not check the power rating stamped on the appliance while it is operating.

Table 10.5 Power Ratings and Energy Use for Appliances

Appliance	Power P (W)	Average energy used per year E (MJ)	Appliance	Power P (W)	Average energy used per year E (MJ)
clothes dryer	4356	3600	CD player	85	500
dish washer	1200	1300	TV (colour)	200	1600
range and oven	12 200	4200	washing machine	512	400
refrigerator	615	6600	water heater	2475	5000

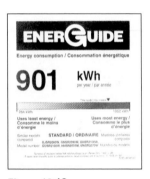

Figure 10.13

"EnerGuide" labels such as the one shown in Figure 10.13, help you make smart choices when purchasing appliances for the home. You can find these labels on nearly all large appliances such as stoves, refrigerators, washers, driers, and air conditioners. The large number in the centre of the label tells you the approximate amount of energy this appliance will use in one year. The two numbers at the end of the bar below the large number tell you how much energy is used per year by the least efficient (left) and the most efficient (right) appliances of the same type that are currently on the market. All appliances are tested according to procedures accepted by the Canadian Standards Association.

Pause&
Reflect

You have learned many formulas in this chapter. Write the list below in your Science Log. Be sure you know which quantity each symbol represents and the units for that quantity.

$R = \dfrac{V}{I}$;

$V = IR$; $P = \dfrac{E}{t}$

Check Your Understanding

1. What is the relationship between energy and power? State your answer in words and in a mathematical model.

2. What does it mean to say that a radio is not 100% efficient?

3. **Apply** A washing machine has a power rating of 512W. If one cycle lasts 30 min, how much energy does the machine use per cycle?

4. **Apply** A CD player that was on for 1.00 h used 360 000 J of electrical energy. What is its power in watts?

5. **Apply** If a light bulb uses 30 000 J of electrical energy and emits 900 J of light energy, what is the percent efficiency of the light bulb?

6. **Thinking Critically** A washing machine has a power rating six times greater than a CD player. However, a washing machine uses less energy in the average household during one year than a CD player. Explain why this is true.

Now that you have completed this chapter, try to do the following. If you cannot, go back to the sections indicated

List and describe the functions of the basic components of an electric circuit. (10.1)

Sketch a circuit diagram that has enough components to turn a light bulb on and off. (10.1.)

Describe the relationship between current and charge in words and as a mathematical model, including units. (10.1)

Explain how to connect an ammeter to measure current in a circuit. (10.1)

Explain the relationship between energy and potential difference in an electric circuit. (10.2)

Explain what happens to the energy of an electric charge as it moves around a simple circuit. (10.2)

Explain the relationship between the potential difference across the battery and the potential difference across a load such as a light bulb, in a simple circuit. (10.2)

Explain how to connect a voltmeter to a circuit, when you want to measure the potential difference across a load. (10.2)

Define electrical resistance and name the unit of resistance. (10.3)

List the four factors that affect the resistance of a wire. (10.3)

Describe the relationship between resistance (R), potential difference across a resistor (V), and current through a resistor (I), in words and as a mathematical model. (10.3)

Explain the meaning of Ohm's law. (10.3)

Explain the relationship between energy and power. (10.4)

Explain how to use the power rating on an electrical appliance to find the energy the appliance uses in a specific amount of time. (10.4)

Explain how to find the efficiency of an electrical device. (10.4)

Prepare Your Own Summary

Summarize the chapter by doing one of the following. Use a graphic organizer (such as a concept map), produce a poster, or write the summary to include the key chapter concepts. Here are a few ideas to use as a guide:
• If electrons travel very slowly through a conductor, explain why a light goes on immediately after you turn on a switch in an electrical circuit.

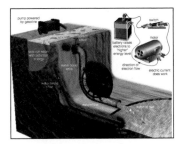

• State which components in an electrical circuit perform a function similar to the gasoline pump, the valve, and the water wheel in this diagram. Explain why the functions are similar.
• Discuss the importance of the word "difference" in the term "potential difference."
• How can you use an ammeter and a voltmeter to determine the resistance of an electrical device?
• Explain why a 100 W light bulb is brighter than a 25 W light bulb.
• Explain why light bulbs are only 5 to 10% efficient.

Reviewing Key Terms

If you need to review, the section numbers show you where these terms were introduced. Use the list of key terms at the beginning of the chapter to fill in the blanks.

1. The rate of flow of electric charge is called ▇▇▇▇▇▇▇. (10.1)

2. The energy per unit charge is called ▇▇▇▇▇▇▇. (10.2)

3. The location on a battery that has an excess of electrons is called the ▇▇▇▇▇▇▇. (10.1)

4. A component of a circuit that restricts the flow of current has ▇▇▇▇▇▇▇. (10.3)

5. The instrument that measures current in a circuit is a ▇▇▇▇▇▇▇. (10.1)

6. In your notebook, match the term in column A with the correct unit in column B. A unit may be used once, more than once, or not at all.

A	B
• power (10.4)	• ohm
• current (10.1)	• second
• resistance (10.3)	• watt
• potential difference (10.2)	• joule
• charge (10.1)	• newton
• time (10.1, 10.4)	• volt
• energy (10.2, 10.4)	• coulomb
	• kilogram
	• ampere

Understanding Key Concepts

Section numbers are provided if you need to review.

7. Define current in words and mathematical symbols. (10.1)

8. Which appliance uses the larger current, a toaster or a desk lamp? (10.1)

9. What is the function of a battery in a circuit? (10.2)

10. What unit is equivalent to a joule per coulomb? (10.2)

11. Use the water circuit (Figure 10.5) to help explain the function of the following in an electric circuit. (10.2)
    (a) battery
    (b) switch
    (c) motor
    (d) wire conductors

12. Explain the difference between an ohmic resistor and a non-ohmic resistor. (10.3)

13. Which has the greater electrical resistance, a filament in a light bulb or a copper conducting wire? (10.3)

14. How does the length of a wire affect its electrical resistance? (10.3)

15. Explain the difference between the quantities power and energy. (10.4)

16. What is the form of the "useful" energy output of a: (a) radio, (b) electric mixer, (c) iron. (10.4)

Developing Skills

17. (a) Plot the data in the table below on a graph. Plot potential difference on the vertical axis and current on the horizontal axis.

    (b) Draw a straight line that fits the data points as well as possible.

    (c) Calculate the slope of the line.

    (d) Explain the meaning of the slope.

Potential Difference and Current

Potential Difference V (V)	0.00	0.60	1.0	2.0	4.0	8.0	16
Current I (A)	0.00	0.03	0.05	0.10	0.20	0.40	0.80

18. Draw a circuit diagram that shows how you would connect a voltmeter to measure the potential difference across a light bulb.

19. Draw a circuit diagram that shows how you would connect an ammeter to measure current through a resistor.

20. **Concept Map** Write the electrical quantities in a circle as shown in Figure 10.14. One mathematical relationship among three of the quantities is given as an example. Find four more mathematical formulas that relate three of the quantities. Using different colours, sketch triangles with points at the related quantities and write the mathematical formula inside the triangle, as shown in the example.

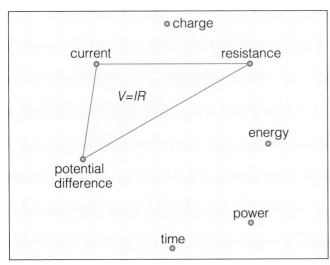

Figure 10.14

Problem Solving

21. If the motor of a 615 W refrigerator runs for 14 h every day, how much energy does the refrigerator use
    (a) every day? **(b)** in a year?

22. A battery uses 810 J of energy to run a portable radio for 30 min. What is the power of the radio?

23. A light bulb has a resistance of 96.8 Ω. What current flows through the bulb when it is connected to a 120 V source of electrical energy?

24. A current of 0.50 A flows through a light bulb, when a potential difference of 120 V is placed across the light bulb. What is the resistance of the light bulb?

25. If a current of 5.00 A passes through the motor of a refrigerator when it is plugged into a wall socket (120 V), what is the resistance of the refrigerator?

26. A flashlight bulb has a resistance of 3.0 Ω. What current passes through the bulb if it is connected to a 1.5 V dry cell?

27. How much energy does a 1200 W dish washer use when it runs for 20 min?

28. A colour television has a resistance of 80 Ω. How much current passes through the television when it is plugged into a wall socket (120 V)?

Critical Thinking

29. You have attached an iron to an extension cord and have been using the iron for nearly half an hour. The extension cord feels hot. Explain why? What should you do if you need to continue ironing?

30. Suppose you wanted to be able to adjust the brightness of a light bulb in a lamp. Describe one way that you might be able to do this.

31. Which of the two following methods of heating water do you think would be the more efficient? Explain your reasoning.
    (a) Heating water in an electric kettle
    (b) Heating water in a pot on the stove

32. Halogen lamps are said to provide as much light as standard (tungsten filament) bulbs that have higher power ratings. How is this possible?

Pause& ──Reflect

1. Look at your answers to the Opening Ideas questions in your Science Log. Have any of your ideas changed? If so, write the correct answers in your Log.

2. What is the most interesting new concept that you have learned from this chapter? Write a paragraph about this concept.

11 Practical Electricity

Opening Ideas...

- When you turn on too many electrical appliances, why do some of the lights and outlets in the house go off but not all of them?

- How does a dimmer switch work?

- How does a fuse or a circuit breaker protect your home from fires?

- What are some ways to conserve electricity?

Science Log

Read the questions in the Opening Ideas. Compare your ideas with those of your classmates. Write your ideas in your Science Log. As you study this chapter, check your answers. If you discover that any of them are not correct, write revised answers in your Science Log.

Ever since Thomas Edison invented the first practical light bulb, people have been fascinated by electric lights. The lights on the community centre in the photograph above welcome people to this new subdivision throughout the year. Strings of lights are used to decorate patios, store displays, and many public places.

Why have such strings of lights become more popular than they were twenty to thirty years ago? If you had tried to use the lights that were available then, you would be able to answer this question quite easily. If one bulb burned out in the old style lights, every bulb would go out. Imagine the frustration of removing and replacing every bulb until you found the one that had burned out! What is the difference between the old style lights and modern strings of lights in which all other bulbs remain lit when one burns out? You will find out when you read this chapter.

Electrical energy can power beautiful spectacles of light. However, if used incorrectly, electricity can cause disastrous fires. How can electrical wiring cause a fire? How do proper wiring and safeguards help prevent catastrophes, such as fires and electric shocks? Even when electricity does not cause a crisis, it still costs money. How do you calculate the cost of electrical energy? What are some ways to conserve electrical energy? In this chapter, you will study electrical circuits in the home. You will also investigate ways of conserving the valuable resources we use to produce electricity.

Dimming the Lights

How does one electrical device affect another? What is the best way to connect more than one light bulb with another electrical device in a circuit?

What You Need

battery (6.0 V)
2 flashlight bulbs (6.0 V)
potentiometer (variable resistor)
switch
7 connecting wires

Key Concepts

In this chapter, you will discover

- the difference between series and parallel circuits
- the potential difference and current characteristics of series and parallel circuits
- the meaning of equivalent resistance of a circuit
- how to determine the cost of operating an electrical device
- how circuit breakers work
- how to conserve electric energy
- the components of circuits in the home

Key Skills

In this chapter, you will

- connect loads in series and in parallel from a circuit diagram
- determine the equivalent resistance of series and parallel circuits
- determine the efficiency of incandescent light bulbs

Key Terms

- series circuit
- parallel circuit
- fuse
- circuit breaker
- equivalent resistance
- kilowatt hour
- short circuit

Starting Point  ACTIVITY

What to Do

1. Connect the two light bulbs, the potentiometer, and the switch to the battery, one after the other, as shown in diagram A. In the figure, the symbol of a resistor with an arrow through it represents the potentiometer.

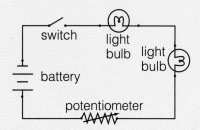

Diagram A

2. Have your teacher check your circuit. Close the switch. Change the resistance by turning the knob on the potentiometer clockwise, then counterclockwise. Observe any effects on the brightness of the light bulbs. Open the switch.

3. Unscrew one light bulb and close the switch. Observe any effects on the other light bulb. Open the switch.

4. Reconnect the bulbs, the potentiometer, and the switch, as shown in diagram B.

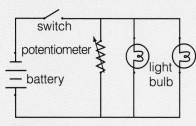

Diagram B

5. Repeat steps 2 and 3.

What Did You Discover?

Which method of connecting a circuit is better for household circuits? Explain how you made your choice.

11.1 Practical Circuits

You have performed several investigations in which you connected a light bulb or resistor to a battery and observed some characteristics of the circuit. In every case, except the last Starting Point Activity, you used one power source and one load. Having a separate source to power every electrical appliance or device is not very practical. In your home, lamps, televisions, stoves, refrigerators, computers, and many other devices operate from the same source of electrical energy. Yet each appliance seems to operate independently of the others. Does turning on one appliance affect the current through, or the potential difference across, any other appliances? How are the circuits connected to allow each device to be turned on, while the others remain off? You found some clues in your Starting Point Activity. You will find more answers as you study this chapter on circuits.

Charges Moving Around a Single Loop

The first circuit that you connected in your Starting Point Activity is called a **series circuit**. A series circuit has only one path for current to flow. You could compare a series circuit to a race track with several sharp curves. All cars are filled with gas during a pit stop and travel around one closed loop, such as the one in Figure 11.1.

Unlike cars, electrons cannot accumulate, or pile up, at any point in a circuit. As you learned in Chapter 10, all electrons push on the electrons ahead, resulting in a smooth, even flow of current. Therefore, the current at any one point in a series circuit is exactly the same as the current at any other point in the circuit. The charges making up the current flow from one load, such as a light bulb, to the next. The charges pass through every load before returning to the power source to be energized again.

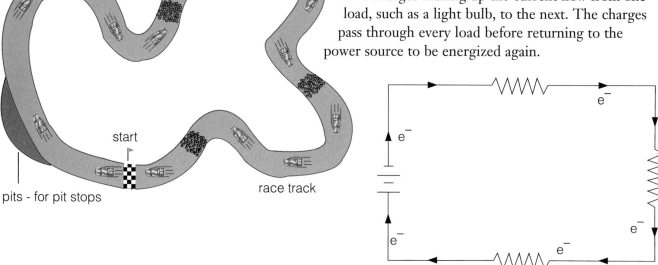

Figure 11.1 Every car on the race track follows the same path. The cars are like electrons flowing around a series circuit.

Charges Moving Around Branching Loops

The second circuit that you connected in your Starting Point Activity is called a **parallel circuit**. A parallel circuit is more like city streets than a race track. Cars have many pathways to travel, each with its own sharp curves or narrow areas. One path might be a six lane freeway, while another is a two lane side street. Eventually, however, all cars must return to a service station for more energy. In a parallel circuit, charges flow around two or more different loops. After leaving the power source, they eventually reach a "fork in the road." Some charges take one path, while other charges take the other. Like cars on a freeway compared to a side street, the current in a parallel circuit is not the same at different points. Nevertheless, all of the charges return to the power source to be re-energized, after travelling around different branches of the circuit.

How do single loops and branching pathways affect the resistance to flow of current? How does the resistance to flow of current in a series circuit differ from the resistance in a parallel circuit? You can get a sense of the resistance in different types of circuits by performing the next investigation.

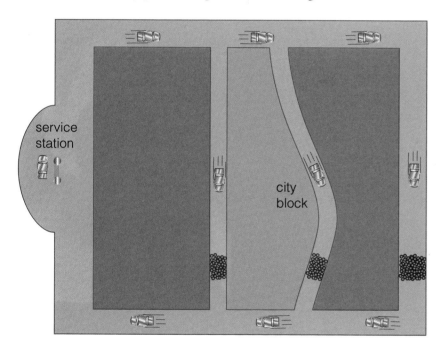

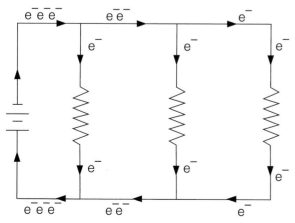

Figure 11.2 Cars travelling on city streets are like electrons in a parallel circuit. They may choose from several different pathways.

"Sensing" Resistance

You can compare the resistance to the flow of air through a tube to the resistance to current in a circuit. In this investigation, you will test the resistance to air flow of several combinations of tubes and straws. You will use your results to make predictions about series and parallel electrical circuits. You may want to review the factors that affect resistance in a wire listed in Table 10.4 on page 342.

Problem

If you connect identical tubes side-by-side (in parallel), would this help or hinder the flow of air? How would connecting a medium diameter and a small diameter tube end-to-end (in series) affect the results? Think about these questions and share your ideas with a classmate. Then do the activity to test your ideas.

Safety Precautions

- Use care when cutting with scissors.
- Use new straws and stirrers only.
- Do not draw water up the straws.

Materials

11 narrow diameter coffee stirrers
3 medium diameter drinking straws
1 wide diameter drinking straw
tape
water

Apparatus

beaker
scissors

Procedure

1 Make a table as shown below to record your data.

2 Cut all the drinking straws to the same length as the coffee stirrers.

3 Start with one single, narrow diameter coffee stirrer. Hold the coffee stirrer, so that 1 cm of the tip is under water. Gently blow bubbles through water, as shown in the photograph.

Resistance to Air Flow

Tube Configuration	Blowing Ease (difficult, medium, easy)	Air Flow Rate (fast, medium, slow)	Resistance to Air Flow (large, medium, small)
one narrow diameter coffee stirrer			
one medium diameter drinking straw			
one wide diameter drinking straw			
four narrow diameter coffee stirrers in series			
four narrow diameter coffee stirrers in parallel			
one narrow diameter coffee stirrer and one medium drinking straw in series			
one narrow coffee stirrer and one medium drinking straw in parallel			

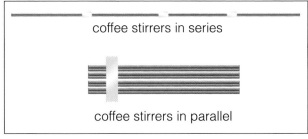

Diagram A

coffee stirrers in series

coffee stirrers in parallel

Diagram B

coffee stirrer in series with
medium diameter drinking straw

coffee stirrer in parallel with
medium diameter drinking straw

④ Next, use a medium diameter drinking straw. With the tip 1 cm below the surface of the water, blow with the same gentle pressure you used in step 3. Repeat the procedure with a wide diameter drinking straw.

⑤ Compare (a) the blowing ease, (b) the air flow rate, and (c) the resistance of the tube to the flow of air for the three tubes of varying diameter. Record the results in your table.

⑥ Use masking tape to assemble four coffee stirrers in series and four coffee stirrers in parallel, as shown in diagram A. Make sure the seal at each connection prevents air from leaking.

⑦ With the tips 1 cm below the surface of the water and using the same gentle pressure as before, blow through the coffee stirrers in series. Repeat the procedure with the coffee stirrers in parallel. Repeat step 5 for the two combinations of stirrers.

⑧ Use masking tape to assemble one coffee stirrer and one medium diameter straw in series and in parallel, as shown in Diagram B. Make sure the seal at each connection prevents air from leaking.

⑨ With the tip 1 cm below the surface of the water and using the same gentle pressure, blow through the tubes in series. Repeat the procedure with the tubes in parallel. Repeat step 5 for the two combinations.

⑩ Place all straws in a waste container and wash your hands.

Analyze

1. Why was it important to cut all of the straws to the same length as the coffee stirrers?

2. Which of the three single tubes has the greatest resistance to air flow?

3. Which arrangement, series (end-to-end) or parallel (side-by-side), has the greatest resistance to air flow for the four narrow coffee stirrers and for the two tubes having different diameters?

Conclude and Apply

4. To use the "air tube" model to make predictions about electrical circuits, it must accurately model the electrical resistance of wires to current. Explain how your answer to question 2 ensures that the tubes are good models. Hint: Refer to the information about factors affecting resistance in wires in Table 10.4 on page 342.

5. Use your answer to question 3 to predict which electrical circuit will have the greatest overall resistance to the flow of current, a set of resistors in series or in parallel.

Some people understand concepts better when they are expressed in words. Others understand concepts better when they are expressed in equations. Many people need a diagram to visualize a concept. A combination of all three usually works best. Examine the diagrams, word equations, and symbol equations and try to put them all together. Does one method help you to understand the concept better than another?

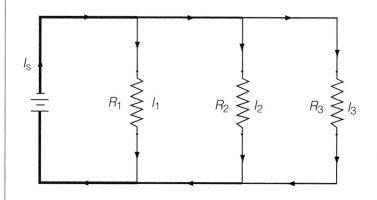

$$I_s = I_1 + I_2 + I_3$$

The sum of the current passing through the three resistors is the same as the current entering and leaving the source.

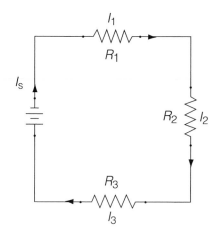

$$I_s = I_1 = I_2 = I_3$$

The current passing through each of the three resistors and the current entering and leaving the source are exactly the same.

Pause&
Reflect

Start a chart in your Science Log that will summarize the character-istics of series and parallel circuits. Make two columns, one with the heading "Series Circuits" and the other with the heading "Parallel Circuits." Under each heading, write a sum-mary of the characteristics of the cur-rent in each type of circuit. Leave room for additional information as you learn more about these circuits.

Have you found an answer to the question in the introduction about the difference between old style strings of lights and modern strings of lights? If you have con-cluded that the old style of lights were connected in series and modern lights are connected in parallel, you are right. You have already learned one very important property of series and parallel circuits.

Check Your Understanding

1. Define the term "series circuit."

2. Make a circuit diagram of a series circuit consisting of three light bulbs, a switch, and a battery.

3. Define the term "parallel circuit."

4. Make a circuit diagram starting with a battery and a switch. Then, add three light bulbs in parallel with each other.

11.2 Comparing Circuits

In your Starting Point Activity, you discovered that the characteristics of series and parallel circuits are quite different. In a series circuit, changes in one component of the circuit have a much greater influence on the performance of other components than in a parallel circuit. To fully explain the reasons for these different responses of circuit components, you need to know what is happening to the potential difference, as well as the current in these two types of circuits.

In the next investigation, you will study the magnitudes of the current through each load, as well as the potential differences across each load in series and parallel circuits. Then you will be able to put these pieces of information together and explain how the two types of circuits function.

Making the Right Connections

What is the best way to connect electrical appliances and devices in the home or office? Imagine that appliances, such as a toaster, microwave, television, and lamp, were connected in a series circuit. If you turned on the toaster, the lamp would become dim. If you started to make microwave popcorn, the television would go dim. If the bulb in the lamp burned out, all electrical devices would go off. Since adding more components to a series circuit changes the potential difference across all of the components already in the circuit, series circuits are not suitable for household circuits. The performance of household appliances relies on a constant potential difference that can be supplied only by a parallel circuit.

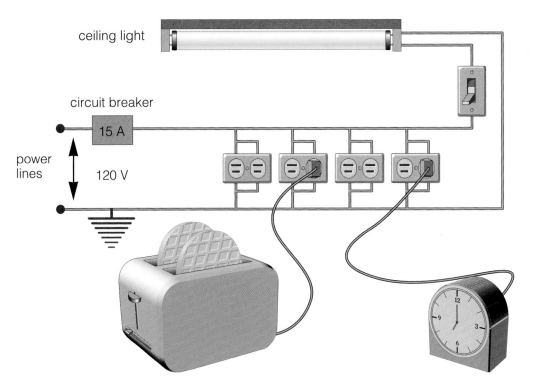

Figure 11.3 Power companies supply your home with a system that can provide either 120 V or 240 V. Most appliances use 120 V. However, electric stoves require 240 V.

Properties of Series and Parallel Circuits

In Chapter 10, you learned that the resistance of a light bulb changes when it heats up or cools down. Light bulbs are not ohmic resistors because the resistance changes with temperature. When making a detailed study of current and potential difference in circuits, you do not want the resistance of a component of the circuit to change as more current passes through it. Therefore, in this investigation, you will use radio resistors, because they are ohmic. If you do not remember the meaning of ohmic resistor, go back and review the discussion on page 338.

What happens to the amount of current through, and the potential difference across, one resistor, when more resistors are connected in series with it? What happens to the amount of current through, and the potential difference across, one resistor, when more resistors are connected in parallel with it? Make some predictions. Then, follow your teacher's instructions. Your teacher will probably choose to do this investigation as a class. He or she will ask each student to make some of the connections. Everyone will record the class data.

Safety Precaution

Carefully follow the directions below.

Apparatus

ammeter
battery (6 V)
8 connecting leads
3 radio resistors
switch
voltmeter

Part 1

Series Circuits

Problem

How are the current and potential difference affected as more and more resistors are connected in series?

Procedure

1 Make a table as shown here to record your data.

2 Connect the circuit shown in diagram A. Be sure the ammeter is in series with the resistor and the voltmeter is in parallel with the resistor. Close the switch.

3 Read and record the current in the circuit, and the potential difference across the resistor. Call it resistor #1. Record this value of potential difference in every row under

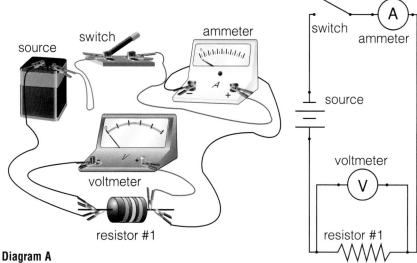

Diagram A

Current and Potential Differences in a Series Circuit

Number of Resistors Connected	Current in the Circuit I (A)	Potential Difference V (V)		
		Across the Source	Across each Resistor		
			#1	#2	#3
1					
2					
3					

"Potential Difference Across the Source."

④ Open the switch. Connect a second resistor in series with the first, as shown in diagram B. Close the switch. Read and record the current in the circuit and the potential difference across resistor #1, with the second resistor in place.

⑤ Open the switch. Disconnect the voltmeter from resistor #1 and connect it across resistor #2. Close the switch. Read and record the potential difference.

⑥ Open the switch. Connect a third resistor in series with the first two, as shown in Diagram C. Close the switch. Read and record the current through the circuit and the potential difference across resistor #2, with all three resistors in place.

⑦ Open the switch. Disconnect the voltmeter from resistor #2 and connect it across resistor #3. Close the switch and read and record the potential difference.

⑧ Open the switch. Disconnect the voltmeter from resistor #3 and connect it across resistor #1. Close the switch. Read and record the potential difference with all three resistors in place.

⑨ Keep the data on this table for use in another activity.

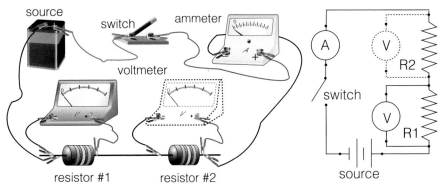

Diagram B

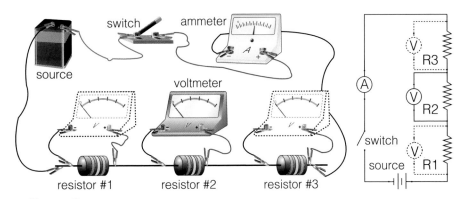

Diagram C

Analyze

1. As more resistors are connected in series with the first, what happens to
   (a) the current in the circuit?
   (b) the potential difference across each resistor?

2. Why was it valid to use the first reading of potential difference across resistor #1 for the potential difference across the source?

3. Examine the potential differences across the three resistors in series and the potential difference of the source. What relationship can you find between these values?

Conclude and Apply

4. Write a word equation showing the relationship between the current leaving the source and the current through each resistor.

5. Write a word equation showing the relationship between the potential difference across the source, and the potential difference across each resistor.

INVESTIGATION 11-B

Part 2

Parallel Circuits

Safety Precaution

Carefully follow the directions below.

Problem

How are the current and potential difference affected as more and more resistors are connected in parallel?

Procedure

① Make a table as shown below to record your data.

Current Through the Source in a Parallel Circuit

Number of Resistors	Current, I, through Source
1	
2	
3	

② Connect the parallel circuit shown in diagram D, leaving all of the switches open.

③ Close switch 1. Read and record the current. Note that current is passing only through resistor #1.

④ Close switch 2, allowing current to pass through resistor #2 as well as through resistor #1. Read and record the current.

⑤ Close switch 3 allowing current to pass through all three resistors. Read and record the current.

⑥ Open switch 1 and disconnect the ammeter.

⑦ Make a table as shown below to record your data.

Current through and Potential Difference across Resistors Connected in Parallel

Resistor Number in Parallel	Current, I, through Resistor	Potential Difference, V, across Resistor
1		
2		
3		

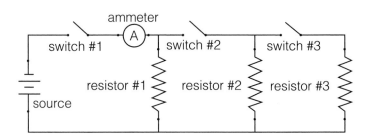

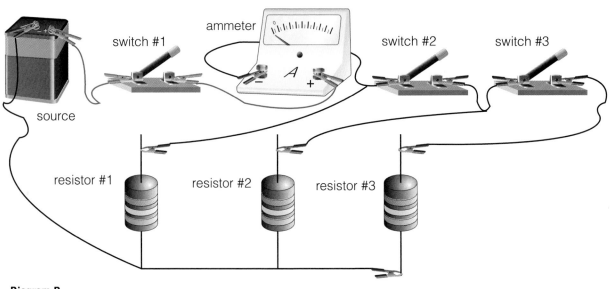

Diagram D

8 Connect the ammeter in series with the first resistor, after the first branch point, as shown in diagram E. The ammeter will read only the current through resistor #1.

9 Connect a voltmeter across resistor #1, as shown in diagram E.

10 Close switch 1. (Switches 2 and 3 should still be closed, as well, allowing current to pass through all three resistors.) Read and record the current through resistor #1, and the potential difference across resistor #1, while current is passing through all three resistors.

11 Open switch 1. Disconnect the ammeter and voltmeter and reconnect the ammeter in series with, and the voltmeter in parallel with, resistor #2.

12 Close switch 1. Read and record the current through and the potential difference across, resistor #2, while current is passing through all three resistors.

13 Repeat steps 11 and 12 for resistor #3.

14 Save these data for use in another investigation.

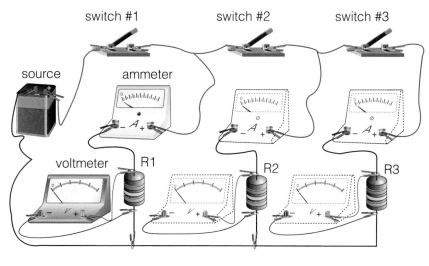

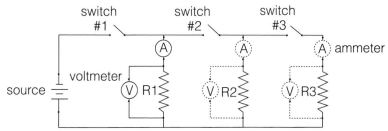

Diagram E

Analyze

1. What happens to the current through the source as current is allowed to pass through one, then two, and finally three resistors that are connected in parallel?

2. Examine the values of the current through the individual resistors in a parallel circuit. Compare these currents with the current that passes through the source when current is passing through all three resistors. What relationship can you find between these values?

3. Compare the potential difference across the individual resistors and across the source in a parallel circuit. What do you notice about these values?

Conclude and Apply

4. Write a word equation showing the relationship between the current through the source and the sum of the currents in the branches.

5. Provide an explanation for the relationship between the potential differences across the individual resistors and across the source in a parallel circuit.

DidYou**Know**?

You have probably seen outlets with reset buttons, such as the one in the photograph. These buttons indicate that the outlet is connected to a ground fault interrupter (GFI). These devices are required in areas such as bathrooms and outdoor locations where water and electricity create a hazard.

Current passes from the source, through the GFI, to the outlet and appliance. Then the current returns through the GFI to the source. Suppose someone is using a hair drier when water is splashing and some water gets on the drier. Some current might pass from the hair drier, through the person's body to ground, without returning to the GFI. The GFI would detect this difference in current and immediately open the circuit, preventing a potentially fatal electric shock.

Practical electrical circuits for the home are parallel circuits, as illustrated in Figure 11.3. In your investigation, you discovered that the potential difference across each load in a parallel circuit is the same. Therefore, each electrical appliance or device in a parallel circuit has the same potential difference across it. Turning on one appliance will not cause the lamps to become dim.

One potentially serious problem does exist with parallel circuits in the home. As you discovered in your investigation, the current through the wire connected to the source increases whenever another branch in the circuit is closed. In just the same way, when you turn on any appliance in your home, the current in the wires closest to the source increases. When current increases, the temperature of the conducting wires rises. If you turn on too many appliances at the same time and the current increases too much, the wires could become hot enough to start a fire. To guard against such an electrical fire, household circuits always include fuses or circuit breakers.

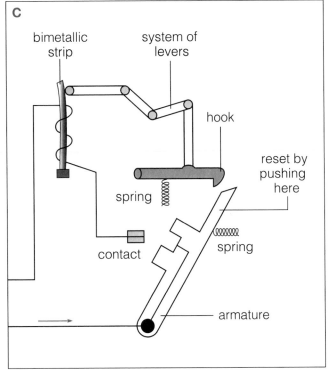

Figure 11.4 The conductor in the fuse in A, will melt if the current rises above 20 A. Behind every switch in the circuit breaker box in B is a mechanism, such as the one illustrated in C. When the current is too high, the switch automatically opens. You can reset the circuit breaker by pushing the switch the distance that it moved and then back to its original position.

A **fuse** has a metallic conductor with a melting point that is much lower than the melting point of the conducting wires. When the current reaches a predetermined level, well below the amount of current that could cause a fire, the metal in the fuse melts. All current stops flowing, thus preventing a potential fire. Fuses are rarely found in modern homes and offices. However, you will find them in electric stoves and automobile electrical systems.

A **circuit breaker** has the same function as a fuse but accomplishes the task in a much different way. One type of circuit breaker is shown in Figure 11.4 C. Current flows through an armature, a contact, and a bi-metallic (two metal) strip. If the current increases, the temperature of the bi-metallic strip rises. As the temperature increases, one of the metals expands more than the other. The different expansion rates cause the strip to bend and release the hook. When the armature swings away, the circuit is opened and current stops flowing. When you reset the breaker switch, it pushes the armature back in place and current flows again. Of course, if you do not correct the problem that caused the excessive current, the breaker switch will open again.

Resistance in Series and Parallel Circuits

When you conducted your investigation on current and potential difference in parallel circuits, you discovered that the current through the source increased every time you added another branch containing a resistor to the parallel circuit. This increase in current is the reason for fuses or circuit breakers in household circuits. While working with these concepts, did you wonder why adding a parallel branch containing a device that "resists the flow of current" results in an increase in the current? A concept called **equivalent resistance** of a circuit will help answer this question.

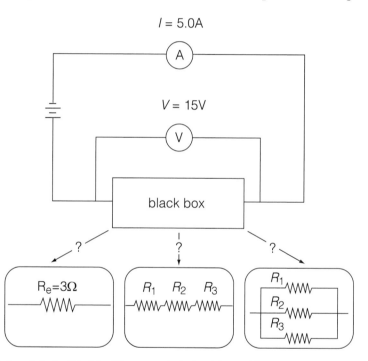

Figure 11.5 Whatever is in the "black box" has an equivalent resistance of 3 Ω.

Pause& Reflect

Before doing a more detailed study of electrical resistance in series and parallel circuits, review your results from Conduct an Investigation 11-A. What predictions did you make about resistance in series and parallel circuits? Why? Your observations from that investigation should help you gain a better understanding of electrical resistance in series and parallel circuits.

To better understand the concept of equivalent resistance, imagine that you are given a circuit, such as the one illustrated in Figure 11.5. You are than asked to determine what is in the "black box." Recalling that resistance is calculated by $R = V/I$, you determine the resistance of the contents of the box to be $R = V/I = 15\ V/5\ A = 3\ \Omega$. Your response would be, "The black box has a three ohm resistor in it." What would you say if you were then told that there were three resistors in series or that there are three resistors in parallel to each other in the box? You might say, "No matter what is in the box, the contents of the box have a resistance that is equivalent to a three ohm resistor." You would be right. The equivalent resistance of a series or parallel circuit is the resistance of one resistor that would yield exactly the same current and potential difference readings as the readings that the circuit produces. In the next investigation, you will learn more about equivalent resistances of series and parallel circuits.

Equivalent Resistance of a Circuit

Think About It

How would the equivalent resistances of three resistors compare if the resistors were first connected in series and then connected in parallel to each other?

What You Need

Use the data that you saved from Investigation 11-B.

Part 1
Equivalent Resistance in Series

What to Do

1 Copy the table below to record your data.

Series Circuit

Resistor	Current I (A)	Potential Difference V (V)	Resistance R (Ω)
1			
2			
3			
entire circuit			

2 Use the data table from Part 1 of Investigation 11-B. Copy the value from the last row of the column with the heading "Current in the Circuit I(A)" into every row in the column labelled "Current I(A)" in your table called *Series Circuit*.

3 Copy the values from the last row of the table from Part 1 of Investigation 11-B under "Potential Difference across each Resistor" into your new Series Circuit table. The numbers in the bottom row under #1, #2, and #3 in that table should go in the "Potential Difference" column in the new table, beside 1, 2, and 3. Copy the value from "Potential Difference Across the Source" into the last row under "Potential Difference" in your new table.

4 Calculate the resistance for each resistor and the equivalent resistance for the circuit by using the formula $R = V/I$. Write these results in the last column.

Analyze

Examine your values for the resistance of the three individual resistors in the series circuit. Compare these values to the equivalent resistance of the entire circuit. What relationship do you see between these values? Write a word equation that expresses this relationship.

Part 2
Equivalent Resistance in Parallel

What to Do

1 Make another table exactly like the table on the left, but give it the title *Parallel Circuit*.

2 Use your data table *Current through and Potential Difference across Resistors Connected in Parallel* from Part 2 of Investigation 11-B. Copy the values from it directly into the columns for current and potential difference, for resistors 1, 2 and 3. The values for potential difference should be the same or almost identical. Write this value in your *Parallel Circuits* table under "Potential Difference V (V)" for the entire circuit.

3 Refer to your table *Current Through the Source in a Parallel Circuit* from Part 2 of Investigation 11-B. Use the value for the current through the source when all three resistors were connected, as your value for "Current I(A)" of the entire circuit in your table called *Parallel Circuit*.

4 Calculate the resistance for each resistor and the equivalent resistance for the circuit by using the formula $R = V/I$. Write these results in the last column.

Analyze

Compare the value of the equivalent resistence of your parallel circuit to the values of resistance for the individual resistors. Is the equivalent resistance greater than, similar to, or smaller than any of the values for the individual resistor? Give a possible explanation for these results.

The observations you made about the equivalent resistance of resistors in series and in parallel are true for all such circuits. The equivalent resistance of resistors in series is always larger than the resistance of any of the individual resistors. In fact, it is always the sum of the resistances of all the resistors in the series circuit.

$$R_{equivalent} = R_1 + R_2 + R_3 + \cdots$$

For example, if you had three 1.0 Ω resistors in series, the equivalent resistance would be

$$R_{equivalent} = R_1 + R_2 + R_3$$

$$R_{equivalent} = 1.0\ \Omega + 1.0\ \Omega + 1.0\ \Omega$$

$$R_{equivalent} = 3.0\ \Omega$$

The equivalent resistance of resistors in a parallel circuit is always smaller than the smallest resistance in the circuit. It is not easy to see how you would calculate the equivalent resistance of resistors in parallel. How do you get a value that is smaller than any individual resistance? If you are curious, read about it in Stretch Your Mind.

The formula for the equivalent resistance of several resistors in parallel is

$$\frac{1}{R_{equivalent}} = \frac{1}{R_1} + \frac{1}{R_2} + \frac{1}{R_3} + \cdots$$

For example, if you had three 9.0 Ω resistors in parallel the equivalent resistance of the circuit would be calculated as follows.

$$\frac{1}{R_{equivalent}} = \frac{1}{9.0\ \Omega} + \frac{1}{9.0\ \Omega} + \frac{1}{9.0\ \Omega}$$

$$\frac{1}{R_{equivalent}} = \frac{3}{9.0\ \Omega}$$

$$\frac{1}{R_{equivalent}} = \frac{1}{3.0\ \Omega}$$

Multiply both sides of the equality by 3.0 Ω x R$_{equivalent}$ to get

$$R_{equivalent} = 3.0\ \Omega$$

The equivalent resistance of three 9.0 Ω resistors in parallel is 3.0 Ω.

Pause & Reflect

Add information about the equivalent resistance of series and parallel circuits to the table in your Science Log that summarized these circuits.

Check Your Understanding

1. How does the potential difference across resistors in a series circuit compare to the potential difference across the source?

2. How do the potential differences across the individual resistors in a parallel circuit compare with each other?

3. How does the potential difference across each individual resistor in a parallel circuit compare to the potential difference across the source?

4. Explain how a circuit breaker works.

5. Define and use an example to explain equivalent resistance for both series and parallel circuits.

11.3 Electrical Energy in the Home

Now that you have learned the fundamentals of electricity, you are ready to look at some very practical aspects of cost and conservation in using electrical energy at home. How does the electric company know how much energy you use? How much does electrical energy cost? How can you conserve energy and reduce the cost? What potential hazards exist in the home, even when the circuit breakers work properly? How can you avoid these hazards?

Paying for Energy

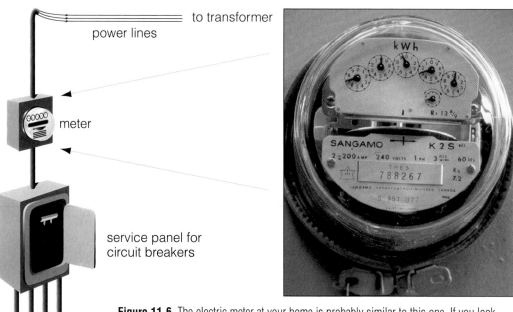

Figure 11.6 The electric meter at your home is probably similar to this one. If you look closely at your meter, you will be able to see the flat disk at the centre turning. The rate of turning indicates the rate at which electrical energy is being used within the house.

Power lines from the nearest transformer usually connect to an electric meter before the lines enter your home. Every time you turn on a load, such as a lamp, a television set, a microwave oven, or an iron, more current passes through the meter, causing the dials to turn. An electric power company employee reads the meter to see how much electrical energy you and your family have used since the

Figure 11.7 Imagine that these dials represent the dials on an electric meter read on the dates shown.

last reading. Many electric companies bill their customers every two months. Each dial on the meter represents one digit in a five digit number. When the needle is pointing between numbers, read the lower number. For example, look at the dials in Figure 11.7. The reading for August 30 is 20 769 units and the reading for October 28 is 23 930 units. To find out how much energy was used over the two month period, subtract the August 30 reading from the October 28 reading.

$$
\begin{array}{r}
23\ 930 \text{ units} \\
-20\ 769 \text{ units} \\
\hline
3\ 161 \text{ units}
\end{array}
$$

The unit of energy for electric meters is the **kilowatt hour** (kW•h). A kilowatt is a unit of power representing a thousand watts. A kilowatt hour is the amount of energy transmitted by one thousand watts of power over a period of one hour. Now study the model problem to see how to use these values to calculate an electric bill.

DidYou**Know**?

The amount of energy that a person uses on a low activity 24 h day is about the same as the energy that a 100 W light bulb uses when it is on for 24 h. People, of course, obtain energy from food.

Model Problem

A family uses 3000 kW•h of electrical energy in a two-month period. If the energy costs 8.0 cents per kW•h, what is the electric bill for the two month period?

Given
E = 3000 kW•h
Unit cost = 8.0 ¢/kW•h

Required
Total cost in dollars

Analysis
Convert unit cost from cents to dollars.

Then find the total cost by using the following formula.

Total cost (dollars) = Total energy used in kW.h × cost in $/kW.h

Solution

$$\frac{8.0\ \cancel{¢}}{\text{kW•h}} \times \frac{\$1.00}{100\ \cancel{¢}} = \frac{\$0.080}{\text{kW•h}}$$

$$\text{Total cost} = 3000\ \cancel{\text{kW•h}} \times \frac{\$0.080}{\cancel{\text{kW•h}}} = \$240$$

Paraphrase
The cost of electrical energy used in this home over a two month period was $240. Thus represents an average of $4 a day.

Typical Household Circuits

Imagine that you are watching television when your sister turned on the iron. While waiting for it to heat up, she started to dry her hair. If all of these appliances were in the same room, all electrical devices in the room, including your television, might go out. If the large current tripped a breaker switch, why didn't lights go out throughout the entire house?

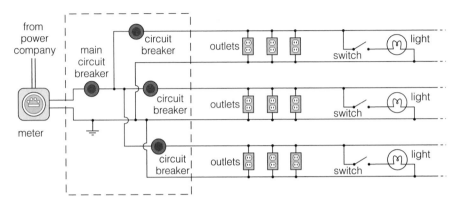

Figure 11.8 The dotted line encloses the wiring that is located inside of a typical circuit breaker panel. Only three circuits are shown here but usually there are many more.

Every house, school, or office building, has several different circuits, each with its own breaker switch. If something trips one breaker, only those appliances or devices plugged into one circuit will go out. Figure 11.8 shows how wiring inside of a circuit breaker panel forms several circuits connected to the main power supply. A very large cable brings power into the house from the power company. This cable has its own circuit breaker that can cut off electrical to the entire house. Smaller cables connected to the main circuit create more circuits. If a large current in one circuit trips a breaker switch, other circuits will not be affected.

Wiring to a kitchen is somewhat different that wiring to a bedroom, for example. It would be very frustrating if you were busily cooking an elegant meal and, when using several appliances at once, a breaker switch trips and causes all appliances to go out. To avoid such a situation in a kitchen, the two outlets in one double plug are sometimes connected to separate circuits. Since stoves require a very large current, they are usually on a circuit of their own. As well, stoves are supplied with 240 V whereas all other outlets supply 120 V.

In older homes, you might see outlets built into the base board, just a few centimetres above the floor. However, in modern buildings, the outlets are at least 45 cm above the floor. In basement rooms, outlets are likely to be nearly 1 m above the floor. These changes are designed to avoid serious electrical problems that would occur if the house were flooded. Water might easily rise a few centimetres above the floor, but it is much less likely to rise to 45 cm or a metre. Many safety factors, in addition to fuses and breaker switches, are built into typical household wiring.

Efficient Energy Use

You have just learned how to read an electric meter and calculate the cost of the energy. However, these numbers do not tell you how efficiently energy is used in your home. One of the most common uses of electrical energy is the incandescent lamp. Do the next Think and Link Investigation to learn about the efficiency of incandescent light bulbs.

Word CONNECT

Look up the definition of the word "incandescent." How appropriate is this term for describing standard light bulbs? Keep the meaning in mind while you are doing Think and Link Investigation 11-D.

Efficiency of an Incandescent Light Bulb

Although many improvements have been made in the incandescent light bulb since Thomas Edison (1847-1931) invented it in 1879, the basic principle remains the same. An electric current runs through a tiny tungsten filament making it so hot that it glows. If the bulb contained air, oxygen in the air would react with the hot tungsten filament and it would burn up. Standard tungsten filament bulbs are filled with nitrogen or argon, because they do not react with the hot filament. How efficient is this method of producing light?

Think About It

A lighted bulb is too hot to touch. How much of the electrical energy goes into heating the bulb and surroundings and how much is converted into light?

DidYou**Know**?

A 12 V, 12 W bulb has a power of 12 W only when it is connected to a 12 V source. Connecting it to a source having any other potential difference will cause the power to differ from the rated value.

Safety Precaution

The bulb, socket, and wiring shown in the following photographs are designed to be water tight and safe. In addition, the power supply will immediately go off, if the current reaches a predetermined value. DO NOT attempt any experiment involving electrical energy and water!

What to Do

① Read the explanations describing the two experiments in the photographs below.

(A) The teacher connects a 12 W incandescent light bulb to a power supply and sets the potential difference at 12 V. She submerges the bulb in exactly 100 mL of cool water. The thermometer reads 14°C. She turns on the power supply and the timer. After 14.1 min, the water reaches a temperature of 30°C. The teacher turns off the power.

(B) The teacher repeats the previous experiment with only one change. The water now contains India ink, making it black. The light is on, but you cannot see it because all of the light energy is absorbed by the ink in the water. This time, it takes only 12.4 min for the temperature of the water to rise from 14°C to 30°C.

② Make a table as shown below to record your data.

Energy and the Incandescent Bulb

Substance	Power Rating of Light Bulb P (W)	Elapsed Time t (s)	Electrical Energy E (J)	Form of Energy Absorbed (light, heat)
clear water				
India ink in water				

③ Study the following points in order to interpret the data accurately.

- It takes the same amount of energy to heat the two 100 mL samples of water from 14°C to 30°C. The total amount of energy absorbed by the water and water-ink solution in the two beakers is the same.

- The clear water absorbs the heat energy emitted by the bulb, while the light energy escapes through the water.

- In the solution of India ink in water, the water absorbs the heat energy. The India ink absorbs the light energy and converts it into heat. Very little energy escapes from the beaker.

④ Refer to the captions describing the demonstration and write the power rating and elapsed time in the first two columns in the table.

⑤ Use the formula $E = Pt$ to calculate the electrical energy that was converted into heat and light in the two cases. Record your answers in the third column.

⑥ Use the information given in step 3 to fill in the last column.

⑦ Analyze the information in the last two columns. Use that information to determine how much of the electrical energy was converted into light energy.

⑧ Calculate the efficiency of the bulb by using the following equation.

Percent efficiency of bulb =

$$\frac{\text{Light energy output} \times 100\%}{\text{Electrical energy input}}$$

Analyze

1. Notice that the low and high temperatures of the water and India ink solution were about 8°C below and 8°C above room temperature. Why was it important to use a temperature range that went from below, to the same amount above, room temperature?

2. Why was it important to use exactly the same amount of water in the two experiments?

3. Summarize your findings about the efficiency of an incandescent light bulb.

Conserving Energy

You have just discovered that standard light bulbs use electrical energy very inefficiently. Most of the energy is converted into heat. What are the alternatives to the standard incandescent bulb?

  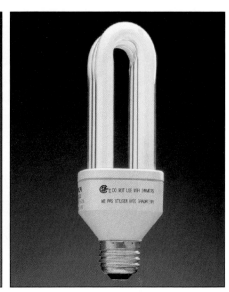

Figure 11.9 The three types of light bulbs that are currently available are (A) the standard tungsten filament bulb, (B) the tungsten-halogen bulb, and (C) the compact fluorescent bulb.

When a tungsten filament is raised to a temperature higher than that of a standard light bulb, it produces a higher ratio of light to heat. However, if the temperature of a standard light bulb filament were raised, the bulb would burn out faster. Light bulbs burn out because the tungsten in the filament evaporates. In halogen bulbs, the halogen gases, usually iodine or bromine, help to preserve the tungsten filament. Since halogen bulbs can be operated at very high temperatures, they are more efficient than standard bulbs that are filled with nitrogen or argon. Halogen bulbs are much more expensive than ordinary bulbs, but they last from two to six times longer. However, halogen bulbs have one serious disadvantage. Due to their very high operating temperatures, they create a fire hazard.

Fluorescent lighting is based on a different principle than incandescent lighting. A stream of electrons bombards a gas, such as mercury vapour, that is sealed inside the tube. The gas molecules become excited and in turn excite a film of material on the inside of the bulb, causing it to glow. Because fluorescent bulbs do not require a high temperature, they use 75% less energy than standard incandescent bulbs to produce the same amount of light. Although they are more expensive than standard light bulbs, they last from ten to thirteen times longer.

One way of conserving electrical energy is to turn out the lights when they are not needed. A long hall or stairway, where there is only one switch at the end, can make this difficult. Two switches, one at each end of the hall, that control the same light can solve this problem. In the next investigation, you can test your electrical design abilities by devising a two-location switch.

DidYouKnow?

The black layer that you see on the inside of a used standard light bulb is the tungsten. When the filament is hot, the tungsten evaporates and deposits on the inner surface of the bulb. Not only does the filament degenerate, but the black layer reduces the amount of light that the bulb emits.

The tungsten filament in halogen lamps also evaporates when the lamp is operating. However, the halogen gas combines with the evaporated tungsten and causes it to redeposit back onto the filament, instead of depositing on the inner surface of the bulb.

Two-Location Switches

A two-location switch is really two switches that work together on the same light or set of lights. When the lights are out, either switch can turn them on. When the lights are on, either switch can turn them off. A key component of a circuit for two-location switches is the three-way switch shown here.

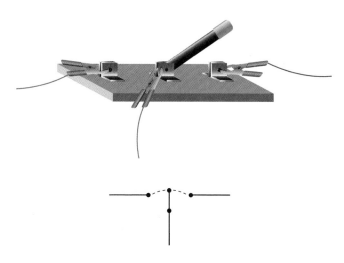

A three-way switch has three wires leading to it. A central pole can make electrical contact with either of two connecting wires.

Challenge

Design a circuit that has a two-location switch. Construct and test your circuit.

Apparatus
battery (6 V)
8 connecting wires
2 light bulbs (6 V) with sockets
2 three-way switches

Design Criteria

A. You must use at least seven of the connecting wires and all of the other materials.

B. Both switches must be able to turn the same two lights on or off.

C. You will have 30 min to design, construct, and test your two-location switch circuit.

Plan and Construct

1. Work in small groups. With your group, draw circuit diagrams and discuss how the circuit will function. Continue to modify your diagrams until the group is satisfied that the plan will work.

2. Connect the circuit that you have designed.

3. Have your teacher check your circuit before you close the switch in either direction.

5. Test your circuit.

6. If your circuit did not work properly, modify the design and try again.

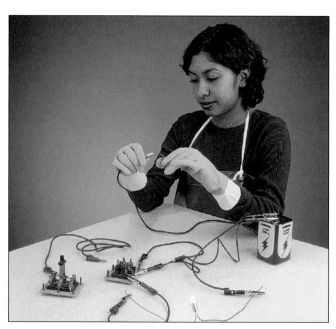

Evaluate

1. Did the first design that you tested work properly? If not, explain why.

2. What modifications are needed to use your design in a circuit in a house?

Electrical Safety at Home

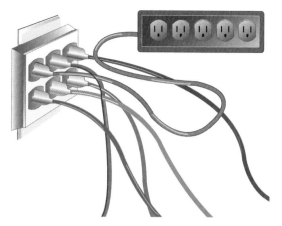

Figure 11.10 What is wrong with this picture?

The electrical outlet in Figure 11.10, is just one of several outlets on one parallel circuit. This circuit will probably soon be overloaded and the circuit breaker will open. However, it will do no good to reset the circuit breaker, unless the device or appliance that is causing the problem is removed. If you need to use several appliances or electrical devices at the same time, plug them in to different circuits. A guide in the circuit breaker panel will indicate which rooms are on which circuits.

Figure 11.11 Always replace or repair worn electrical cords.

When you unplug a device from an electrical outlet, always hold it by the plug itself. Pulling on the cord will soon cause it to break at the point of attachment to the plug, as shown in Figure 11.11. As the cord begins to fray, the two connecting wires may come into contact with each other, causing a short circuit. A **short circuit** means

Outside Link **ACTIVITY**

Conserving Electricity

Turning out the lights is an important way to conserve energy at home, but there are many more ways. Find as many as you can.

What to Do

1. Research ways of conserving electrical energy at home. You can check the Internet, obtain literature from your local power company, or use the library. Find ways to conserve electrical energy that involve each of the following categories.
   (a) cooking
   (b) laundry
   (c) refrigerator and freezer
   (d) water heater
   (e) crafts and recreation

2. Bring your list to class. Combine all the lists. How many means of conservation did your class find to save electrical energy at home?

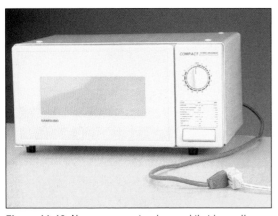

Figure 11.12 Never use an extension cord that is smaller than the cord on the electrical appliance.

that the two connecting wires touch and the current bypasses the device. Since the wires have very little electrical resistance, the current becomes very large very quickly. The wires can heat up enough to start a fire.

When you need to use an extension cord, be sure that it is as thick as, or thicker than, the cord on the appliance that you plan to use. Appliances that produce heat, such as toasters and irons, often have a thick cord, because they require a large current. The large current passing through a thin extension cord will cause excessive heating. The current may never reach the level that will trip the circuit breaker, but it may cause a small extension cord to become hot enough to start a fire.

Check Your Understanding

1. Explain the meaning of the unit "kilowatt hour."

2. Why can halogen lamps operate at a higher temperature than standard nitrogen-filled incandescent light bulbs? Why is this desirable?

3. State two ways to conserve electrical energy at home.

4. What might happen if you iron clothing in the kitchen, while you are cooking dinner in the microwave oven and toasting bread?

5. **Apply** A business office uses 5000 kW•h of energy in a two month period. If electrical energy costs 7.50 cents per kW•h, what would the electric bill be for that two month period?

Now that you have completed this chapter, try to do the following. If you cannot, go back to the sections indicated.

Sketch a series circuit that has a battery and three resistors. (11.1)

Explain the meaning of the term "series circuit." (11.1)

Sketch a parallel circuit that has a battery and three resistors. (11.1)

Explain how a parallel circuit differs from a series circuit. (11.1)

Explain why parallel circuits are used in the home. (11.2)

Explain why the potential for a fire exists when you turn on additional electrical devices connected to the same parallel circuit. (11.2)

Explain how a fuse can prevent fires. (11.2)

Explain how a circuit breaker works. (11.2)

Define the term "equivalent resistance." (11.2)

Compare the equivalent resistance of a series circuit to the resistance of the individual resistors in the circuit. (11.2)

Compare the equivalent resistance of a parallel circuit to the resistance of the individual resistors in the circuit. (11.2)

Compare the efficiencies of incandescent light bulbs and fluorescent bulbs. (11.3)

List three ways to avoid an electrical fire or a serious electric shock in the home. (11.3)

Prepare Your Own Summary

Summarize the chapter by doing one of the following. Use a graphic organizer (such as a concept map), produce a poster, or write the summary to include the key chapter concepts. Here are a few ideas to use as a guide:

- Explain the benefits of buying decorative lights that have the bulbs connected in parallel rather than in series.
- Compare the current passing through different points in a series circuit.
- Compare the potential difference across resistors that are connected in parallel.
- Explain how to calculate the cost of electrical energy.
- Compare cars on a racetrack to electrons in a circuit. State the type of circuit that fits the comparison.

- Explain how a power company determines the amount of electrical energy that a certain household has used.

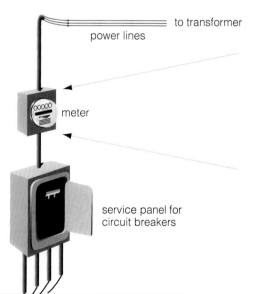

to transformer
power lines
meter
service panel for circuit breakers

Reviewing Key Terms

If you need to review, the section numbers show you where these terms were introduced.

Indicate whether each of the following statements is true or false. If a statement is false, write the correct statement.

1. A parallel circuit has several different pathways for electrons to travel. (11.1)

2. The equivalent resistance of a series circuit is smaller than the resistance of any of the resistors in the circuit. (11.2)

3. A fuse will open the circuit when the current becomes too high. (11.2)

4. When you reset a circuit breaker, you close the circuit. (11.2)

5. The potential difference across each resistor in a series circuit is always the same. (11.2)

6. A kilowatt hour is a unit of power. (11.3)

7. The current stops flowing when there is a short circuit. (11.3)

Understanding Key Concepts

Section numbers are provided if you need to review.

8. Draw two circuit diagrams, one to illustrate a series circuit and the other to illustrate a parallel circuit. (11.1)

9. What is the smallest number of pathways a parallel circuit can have? Explain. (11.1)

10. Two identical light bulbs are connected to a battery in a series circuit. What will happen to the brightness of one bulb, if the other bulb is unscrewed? (11.1)

11. Which type of circuit do the following statements describe? (11.2)
    (a) The potential difference across each resistor is the same.
    (b) The current through each resistor may be different.

12. Assume that a microwave oven, a toaster, an electric mixer, and a radio are all plugged into the same household circuit. Explain what happens to the current in the wires connected directly to the source, when, one by one, you turn on the radio, the toaster, the microwave, and finally the electric mixer, without turning off any of the appliances. (11.2)

13. Where, in a circuit, should a circuit breaker be located? Why? (11.2)

14. List three ways to conserve electrical energy at home. (11.3)

Developing Skills

15. Complete the following concept map by using the following terms:

    series circuit   parallel circuit
    single path   main circuit
    branching paths   current the same
    currents add   voltages add
    home circuits

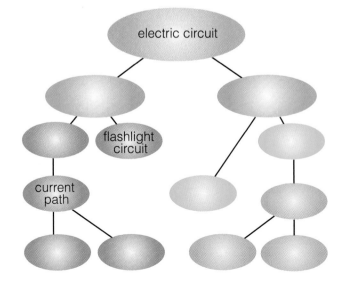

16. The figure below shows a circuit containing a dry cell, conducting wires, a switch, and two light bulbs. If the switch is closed, will the bulbs light up? Explain.

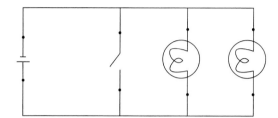

17. Draw a circuit diagram showing a series connection of a dry cell, a switch, and a bulb. Show a voltmeter connected to measure the electrical potential difference across the source and an ammeter connected to measure the current in the circuit. Label the positive and negative terminals of the cell, the voltmeter, and the ammeter.

18. A student wants to use a voltmeter, an ammeter, and a battery to measure the equivalent resistance for two resistors connected in series and in parallel. Draw schematic diagrams to show each set-up. Label the positive and negative terminals of the battery and the meters.

Problem Solving

19. Suppose that you want to build a circuit with a source, a switch, a motor, and a lamp. You want the lamp to indicate when the motor stops working. Draw the circuit.

20. A circuit has a source, two light bulbs, and two switches. The two light bulbs do not have any effect on each other and each is controlled by its own switch. Draw the circuit.

21. A family used 4250 kW•h of electrical energy during one billing period. If the power company charges 7.50 cents per kW•h, how much must the family pay for electrical energy for that billing period?

April 30

June 29

22. The figure above shows the dials on an electric meter at the beginning and the end of a two month period. How much electrical energy did the household use during the two month period?

Critical Thinking

23. Imagine that a friend lives in an older, renovated house that still has a fuse box. When a fuse blows out, they must replace it with a new one. Your friend tells you that it is not a problem, if there are no new fuses. You can simply put a penny in the fuse slot. The copper conducts current and closes the circuit. What advice would you give to your friend about the practice of replacing a fuse with a penny? Explain.

24. Assume that, in your home, you have a chandelier with a dimmer switch. The dimmer switch works like the potentiometer (variable resistor) that you used in the Starting Point Activity in this chapter. Your older brother insists that when the light must be on, it should always be kept very dim to save on electrical energy. Is your brother correct? If not, explain why he is wrong.

Pause & Reflect

1. In your Science Log, review the answers to the questions in Opening Ideas. If any of your answers need to be corrected or improved, make those changes. If you were unable to answer any of the questions, answer them now.

2. In what ways will your use of electrical energy change as a result of the knowledge you have gained by studying this chapter?

3. What advice would you give to others about electrical safety?

Opening Ideas...

- How do batteries work?
- What are fossil fuels and how are they used to generate electrical energy?
- Why are electrical transmission lines operated at very high voltages?
- What happens inside a nuclear reactor?
- How does producing electrical energy affect the environment?

Science Log

Discuss the questions in the Opening Ideas with the class or with a classmate. Write as many answers as you can in your Science Log. Explain what evidence you have for each answer and what activities you might use to check your answers. Write other questions you might have about the production of electrical energy. Look for answers as you explore this chapter.

Many times a day, you walk into a room and flip on a light switch. Do you ever think about the source of the electrical energy that you use so often? Do you know what kind of power plant supplies your electrical energy? Is it a hydro-electric plant? Could it be a nuclear reactor? If not, it is probably a thermo-electric power plant that burns a fossil fuel. How many kilo-metres of transmission lines are necessary to bring the electric power from the power plant to your home or school? If you are like most people, you have probably not given these questions much thought.

Electrical power has been avail-able for several generations, so no wonder we take it for granted. We also become accustomed to new developments very rapidly. For example, nearly everywhere you go, you see someone talking on a cell phone. Improvements in batteries allow us to take our power with us. In this chapter, you will learn more about the production of electrical power, both in large, stationary power plants and in tiny portable batteries.

Environment

Key Concepts

In this chapter, you will discover

- how chemical reactions produce electricity
- the difference between primary and secondary cells
- the most common forms of energy used to generate electricity
- the environmental challenges caused by electrical energy generation
- the difference between renewable and non-renewable energy sources

Key Skills

In this chapter, you will

- connect cells in series and in parallel
- construct a voltaic cell and investigate the factors that affect its operation
- operate a solar cell and study its characteristics

Key Terms

- voltaic cell
- electrode
- electrolyte
- dry cell
- wet cell
- primary cell
- secondary cell
- fuel cell
- solar cell
- hydro-electric
- fossil fuels
- thermo-electric
- nuclear fission
- thermonuclear
- fuel rod
- direct current
- transformer
- alternating current
- open pit mining
- acid rain
- scrubber
- greenhouse gas
- global warming
- fission products
- thermal pollution
- non-renewable
- renewable
- tidal range
- fusion

Starting Point ACTIVITY

What Makes an Electric Cell?

In previous investigations, when you used an electrical cell as a source of energy, did you wonder what components are needed to make the cell work? This activity will give you some clues.

What You Need

Obtain a 10 cm piece of aluminum wire (or a strip cut from a pie plate), a 10 cm length of copper wire, two connecting wires, a voltmeter and a lemon. In addition, collect a variety of other fruits and vegetables, such as a potato, a cucumber, and a tomato.

What To Do

1. Insert the aluminum wire (or strip) and the copper wire into the lemon, about 1 cm apart. Push them deep into the lemon without going all the way through.

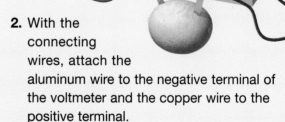

2. With the connecting wires, attach the aluminum wire to the negative terminal of the voltmeter and the copper wire to the positive terminal.

3. Observe and record the reading on the voltmeter.

4. Repeat the procedure with the other fruits and vegetables that you collected.

What Did You Discover?

1. Which fruits and vegetables made good electric cells?

2. What were the roles of the copper wire, the aluminum wire, and the fruit?

Portable Power

Figure 12.1 How many battery powered devices can you find in this picture? How many of these devices do you use in an average day?

How many times a day do you use battery powered devices? How long has it been since you last looked at your watch or used your calculator? Batteries are just one source of electrical energy that makes our everyday tasks easier. Remember, batteries are merely several cells that are connected together. Whom should we thank for these ingenious little inventions?

The Source of Cells

Like many other important scientific discoveries, the original observations that led to the development of electrical cells were made by accident. Luigi Galvani (1737-1798), an Italian physician and researcher, was studying frog nerves and muscles. He and his assistants observed that a frog muscle twitched when they touched a nerve with a metal scalpel. One assistant thought he saw a spark at the same time.

Galvani began to study the effects of electric sparks on frog nerves and muscles. Soon he observed that a frog's muscle would twitch when touched by two different metals, in the absence of any electric sparks. He believed that the frog tissues generated the electricity. Galvani called it "animal electricity." His interpretation of his own observations was soon proven incorrect by his friend Allesandro Volta. Volta showed that a potential difference could be generated between two different metals by placing them in a solution containing a salt or acid. The presence of two different metals in a solution was creating the potential difference, not the living tissue of the frog. In 1800, Volta invented the "voltaic pile" shown in Figure 12.2. This "battery," or series of cells connected together, was the first, dependable source of continuous electric current.

DidYouKnow?

Although the details of Galvani's original concepts of "animal electricity" were incorrect, his work provided important foundations for the field of neurophysiology, the study of the nervous system. We now know that nerves conduct electrical impulses and that these impulses can stimulate muscles to contract.

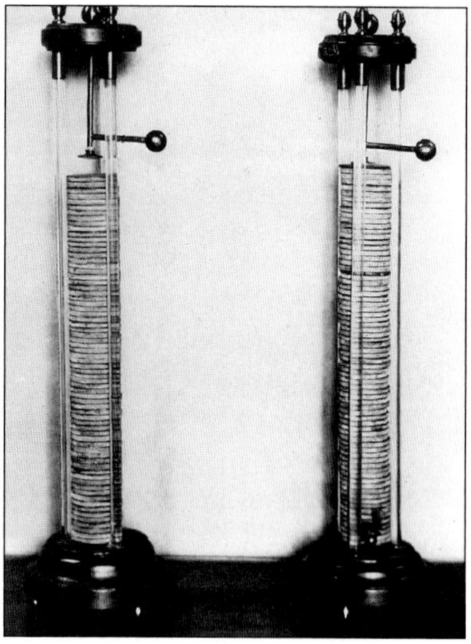

Word CONNECT

Allesandro Volta coined the term "galvanism" in honour of Luigi Galvani. Research the meaning of the terms "galvanism," "galvanic," "galvanize," and "galvanometer." How do they relate to Galvani's work?

Figure 12.2 These voltaic piles are made of a stack of alternating zinc and copper disks separated by pieces of fabric soaked in salt water.

Reactions in Electrochemical Cells

How do **voltaic cells,** such as the cell you built in your Starting Point Activity, create a potential difference? The exact chemical reactions that occur in various types of cells are different. However, they all based on one principle. Any two different types of metals or metal compounds have different attractions for electrons. If a pathway is available, one metal will donate electrons to another different type of metal. For example, in your "lemon cell" the aluminum wire was donating electrons to the copper wire. The acid in the lemon took part in the reaction.

In a voltaic cell or in any electrical cell, the two metals are called the **electrodes.** These metal electrodes must be immersed in a solution that can conduct an electric current. Such a solution is called an **electrolyte.** Examine Figure 12.3 while you follow the steps in a typical reaction.

Aluminum atoms release electrons that go through the conducting wire to the copper. When an aluminum atom loses electrons, it becomes positively charged. In Chapter 8, you learned that electrically charged atoms are called ions. These aluminum ions cannot stick to the metal strip, because they go into solution in the acid. Notice that the aluminum strip disintegrates as the aluminum ions go into solution. Acid solutions have hydrogen ions. When the electrons arrive at the copper strip, hydrogen ions pick up the electrons and become neutral. The uncharged hydrogen turns into a gas and forms bubbles on the copper strip.

Figure 12.3 Copper and aluminum metal strips are submerged in an acid solution. As electrons move from the aluminum strip to the copper strip through the conducting wire, they light up the light bulb.

Tools of Science

A thermocouple is another device that relies on two different metals to produce a potential difference. However, in a thermocouple, the two metals are in direct contact with each other in two different places called junctions. When the two junctions are at different temperatures, a potential difference exists between them and a small current flows.

The potential difference between the junctions of a thermocouple depends on the temperature difference. This feature makes it possible to use thermocouples to detect temperature. As shown in the illustration, one junction is held at a reference temperature such as an ice bath. The other junction is placed at the location where the temperature is to be measured. Thermocouples can be used for very high temperatures where thermometers are not practical. They can also be used to activate temperature sensitive switches. Thermocouples can even be made tiny enough to implant in the tissues of living organisms.

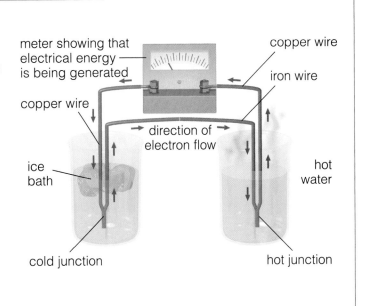

Electricity and the Environment **383**

Building a Better Battery

In this activity, you will study several variations of voltaic cells. You will discover factors that enhance or reduce the usefulness of the cells.

Problem

What factors affect the potential difference and current from a voltaic cell?

Safety Precautions

- Wear a lab apron and safety goggles.
- When handling the metal strips that have been in acid, wear protective gloves and use absorbent paper.
- Sulfuric acid is corrosive. Use only dilute sulfuric acid. If you get acid on either your skin or clothing, rinse the area(s) immediately with water. Call your teacher at once.
- Check with your teacher to see that the ammeter and voltmeter are connected correctly before making the final connection.

Materials

latex gloves	paper towel
dilute sulfuric acid	salt solution
distilled water	tap water

Apparatus

ammeter (0-1A)	copper strips (2)
aluminum strip	voltmeter (0-5V)
beaker or battery jar	steel wool
conducting wires (4)	zinc strip

Procedure

1 Make a table as shown below.

2 Polish both sides of the metal strips with steel wool.

3 Fill the beaker $\frac{2}{3}$ full with dilute sulfuric acid.

4 Place a zinc strip and a copper strip in the solution. Do not let them touch.

5 With separate conducting wires, connect the zinc strip to the negative terminal of the voltmeter and the ammeter. Connect the copper strip to the positive terminals of the voltmeter and the ammeter.

Factors Affecting a Voltaic Cell

Factor Changed	Metal Strips	Solution	Current (A)	Potential difference (V)	Action at Strips
Initial reading	copper and zinc	sulfuric acid			
After running for 5 min	copper and zinc	sulfuric acid			
Wipe bubbles off	copper and zinc	sulfuric acid			
Change surface area of metals in solution	copper and zinc	sulfuric acid			
Use one new metal strip	aluminum and zinc	sulfuric acid			
Use identical strips	copper and copper	sulfuric acid			
Change solution to water	copper and zinc	distilled water			

6 Read and record the values for current and potential difference. Note and record whether bubbles form on either metal strip.

7 Allow the cell to operate for about 5 min. Watch for the formation of bubbles on the surface of the metal strips. Record your observations. State whether there are more bubbles on the zinc or on the copper strip.

8 Read the meters after the cell has been running for 5 min and record the results.

9 Wipe away any bubbles from the metal strips with absorbent paper. Wear protective gloves when you wipe the strips. Repeat step 6.

10 Once again, wipe away any bubbles from the metal strips. Raise the metal strips so that only half of the length is still in the dilute sulfuric acid. Repeat step 6.

11 Remove the copper strip and replace it with an aluminum strip. Repeat step 6.

12 Replace the zinc strip with a copper strip so there are two copper strips in the solution. Repeat step 6.

13 Rinse the metal strips with tap water and replace the solution in the voltaic cell with the distilled water. Replace one copper strip with a zinc strip. Repeat step 6.

14 Dispose of acid and clean acid spills according to your teacher's direction.

15 Clean all surfaces and wash your hands thoroughly before you leave.

Conclude and Apply

1. What evidence did you observe on the surface of the copper strip to indicate that a chemical reaction was taking place?

2. What happened to the electric current and electric potential difference as time passed?

3. What effect did each of the following actions have on the **(a)** potential difference; **(b)** the current?
   - Removing the bubbles from the surface of the metal
   - Changing the surface area of the metal strips in the solution
   - Using aluminum and zinc instead of copper and zinc
   - Using identical metals

4. Which factors appear to determine the potential difference?

5. Which factors seem to increase the current?

6. Using the copper and zinc strips, which combination of factors produced the largest current?

7. Which pair of metals produced the largest potential difference: copper and zinc or aluminum and zinc?

8. If you were designing a voltaic cell, which combination of metals and conditions would you use? Why?

......

Do you think the voltaic cell will still work if the sulfuric acid is replaced with a concentrated salt water solution? Do an experiment to test your prediction.

Pause&
Reflect

In your Science Log, review your answers to the question about cells and batteries in the Opening Ideas. Also review your answers to the questions in the Starting Point Activity. Do your answers agree with the information you just learned about cells? If not, revise your answers.

DidYou**Know**?

In 1836, English chemist John Daniell (1790–1845) developed the Daniell cell with electrodes made of copper and zinc, using sulfuric acid and copper sulfate solutions as electrolytes. It was the first reliable source of electric current.

Flaws of the Voltaic Cell

The development of the voltaic cell was an exciting breakthrough in the field of electricity. However, the original design had several flaws that limited its usefulness. First, the zinc electrode reacted with the sulfuric acid and the electrode was used up. In addition, bubbles of hydrogen gas formed on the copper electrode. These bubbles prevent the solution from touching large portions of the surface of the copper electrode and therefore slow the action of the cell. Consequently less electric current flows. As well, hydrogen gas is very explosive. A spark could ignite the hydrogen causing an explosion. The corrosive sulfuric acid would be spattered in all directions. Even an accidental spill of sulfuric acid could cause serious harm. Significant changes had to be made before cells could be a practical source of electrical energy.

Check Your Understanding

1. Make a sketch of a simple voltaic cell connected to a light bulb. Label the three essential components of the cell.

2. What is the function of the electrodes in an electrical cell?

3. What is an electrolyte and what is its function in an electrical cell?

4. What is the main difference between a cell and a battery?

5. List three problems that reduce the usefulness of a voltaic cell.

Across Canada

Reginald Fessenden

Radio waves are electromagnetic waves that travel through the air without wires. Around the world, from Africa to Asia, to your kitchen or car in Canada, radio is an important communication medium. Many people think radio broadcasting was invented by Italian-born Guglielmo Marconi. Marconi did send the first Morse code signal across the Atlantic, from England to St. John's, Newfoundland in 1901. However, Marconi did not believe that the same principle — turning electricity into electromagnetic waves — could be used to transmit the human voice. Canadian Reginald Fessenden did.

Fessenden was born in East Bolton, Québec. As a boy he studied French, Latin, and Greek. Later he turned to science, attending university in Lennoxville, Québec. In the 1880s he worked with American inventor Thomas Edison. Edison did not believe, either, that it was possible to broadcast the human voice. But Reginald Fessenden never gave up his dream.

On Christmas Eve, 1906 sailors at sea were astounded to hear a voice coming from the apparatus they used to receive Morse code. Some probably thought it was a ghost, but it was Reginald Fessenden. He made a short speech, played his violin, and sang Christmas carols with his wife and a friend. Radio broadcasting had been invented. To this day it still uses principles discovered by "the forgotten Canadian," Reginald Fessenden.

12.2 Practical Cells and Batteries

In the 200 years since Volta developed his voltaic cell, a wide variety of cells and batteries have been developed for numerous applications. Many different combinations of metals and metal compounds now act as electrodes. Chemicals which react with hydrogen and convert it into water are included in the batteries, preventing the build up of the explosive hydrogen gas. One of the most important changes in the technology is the development of the **dry cell.** As the name implies, the electrolyte is not in liquid form, but instead it is mixed into a paste or gel. Problems caused by spilling and leaking are avoided. Nevertheless, some **wet cells,** with a liquid electrolyte are still used. For example, automobile batteries still contain a solution of sulfuric acid.

The development of rechargeable cells and batteries is another significant step in the advancement of the technology. To recharge a dead cell, a potential difference from another source is applied to the cell, forcing the chemical reactions to go in reverse. The recharged cell returns to its original condition. Non-rechargeable cells that can only be used once and then discarded are called **primary cells.** Rechargeable cells are called **secondary cells.** Table 12.1 presents information about several modern cells of both types.

Tools of Science

Electrical energy from a battery can make robotic muscles flex and grasp like the fingers of a hand. Joseph Bar-Cohen, a physicist at Caltech's Jet Propulsion Laboratory has adapted a flexible polymer for this purpose. The polymer is made from chains of carbon, fluorine, and oxygen atoms. When an electric charge is applied to one side of the polymer, charged particles get pushed to the opposite side. Because like charges repel each other, the far side lengthens and the near side shortens. If four strips of the polymer are attached together like fingers, the robotic hand can pick up small rocks. The device is not very strong; it can only lift 10 g (the mass of a ball point pen). However, it is inexpensive, durable, light, and operates on $\frac{1}{20}$ of a watt of power. Plans are being made to incorporate these polymer "muscles" into robots designed to explore asteroids.

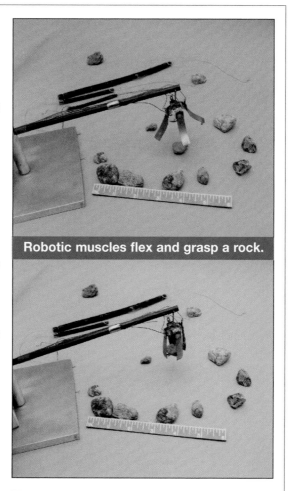

Robotic muscles flex and grasp a rock.

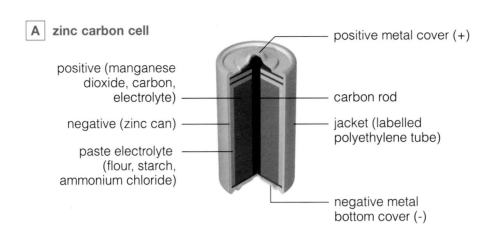

A | zinc carbon cell

positive metal cover (+)

positive (manganese dioxide, carbon, electrolyte)

carbon rod

negative (zinc can)

jacket (labelled polyethylene tube)

paste electrolyte (flour, starch, ammonium chloride)

negative metal bottom cover (-)

Table 12.1 Modern Cells and Batteries

Name	Primary/ Secondary	Dry/Wet	Positive Electrode	Negative Electrode	Electrolyte	Typical Uses	Pros and Cons
zinc carbon	primary	dry	manganese dioxide and carbon rod	zinc	ammonium chloride	flashlights, portable radios, CD players	not efficient at low temperatures
alkaline	primary	dry	silver oxide	zinc	potassium hydroxide or sodium hydroxide	flashlights, portable radios, CD players	last longer than zinc carbon, expensive
silver oxide	primary	dry	silver oxide	zinc	potassium hydroxide or sodium hydroxide	calculators, hearing aids, watches	small, long lasting, reliable
zinc air	primary	dry	oxygen gas from the air	zinc	potassium hydroxide	calculators, hearing aids, watches	highest energy per unit mass, discharges rapidly
lead acid	secondary	wet	lead oxide	lead	sulfuric acid	cars, motorbikes, snowmobiles, golf carts	dependable, heavy, corrosive liquid
nickel cadmium	secondary	dry	nickel hydroxide, graphite	cadmium oxide and iron oxide	potassium hydroxide	electric shavers, laptop computers, power tools, portable TVs	rechargeable hundreds of times

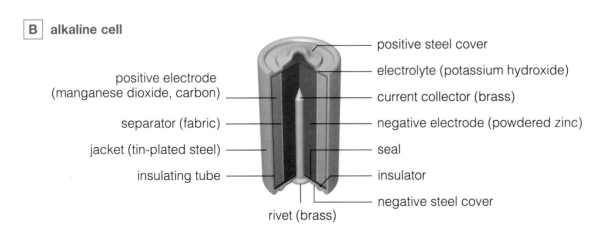

B | alkaline cell

positive steel cover

electrolyte (potassium hydroxide)

positive electrode (manganese dioxide, carbon)

current collector (brass)

separator (fabric)

negative electrode (powdered zinc)

jacket (tin-plated steel)

seal

insulating tube

insulator

negative steel cover

rivet (brass)

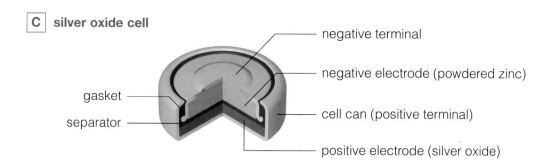

C silver oxide cell

negative terminal

negative electrode (powdered zinc)

gasket

cell can (positive terminal)

separator

positive electrode (silver oxide)

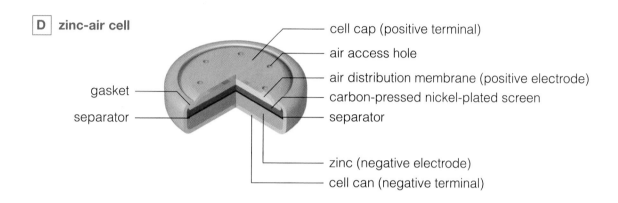

D zinc-air cell

cell cap (positive terminal)

air access hole

air distribution membrane (positive electrode)

gasket

carbon-pressed nickel-plated screen

separator

separator

zinc (negative electrode)

cell can (negative terminal)

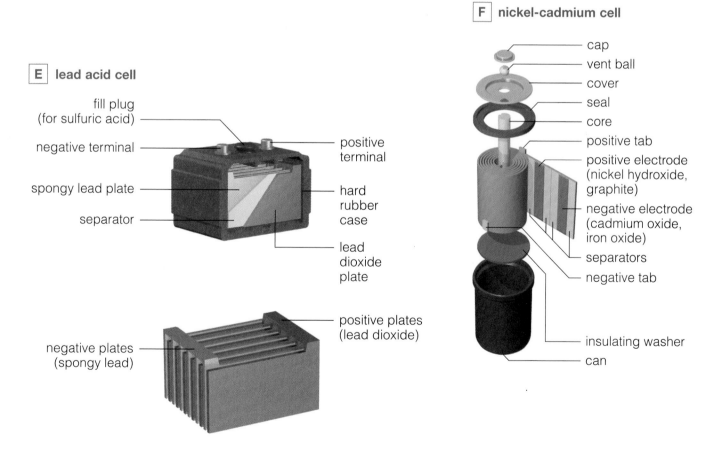

F nickel-cadmium cell

E lead acid cell

fill plug (for sulfuric acid)

negative terminal

spongy lead plate

separator

positive terminal

hard rubber case

lead dioxide plate

positive plates (lead dioxide)

negative plates (spongy lead)

cap

vent ball

cover

seal

core

positive tab

positive electrode (nickel hydroxide, graphite)

negative electrode (cadmium oxide, iron oxide)

separators

negative tab

insulating washer

can

Figure 12.4 Modern cells and batteries: (A) zinc carbon cell, (B) alkaline cell, (C) silver oxide cell, (D) zinc-air cell, (E) lead acid battery, (F) nickel-cadmium cell

INVESTIGATION 12-B

Building Batteries

You have learned that a battery is two or more electrical cells attached together. Have you ever wondered why cells are combined and how they are connected? In this activity, you will connect three dry cells in several different ways. You will measure the potential difference across the "batteries" for each arrangement. You will also observe the brightness of a bulb powered by the "battery."

Safety Precautions

Be sure to connect the voltmeter correctly.

Apparatus

3 D dry cells
flashlight bulb (6V)
6 connecting leads
voltmeter

Procedure

1 Make a data table with the headings shown here.

2 Connect one dry cell to the flashlight bulb as shown in diagram A.

3 Connect the voltmeter across the dry cell as shown.

4 Observe and remember the brightness of the bulb. You will compare the brightness of the bulb in the following steps to the brightness you have observed here.

5 Measure and record the potential difference across the dry cell.

6 Connect two dry cells in series with each other and with a light bulb, as shown in diagram B. Be sure that the positive terminal of one cell is connected to the negative terminal of the next.

Cells in Series and in Parallel	Potential Difference (V)	Brightness of Bulb (same, brighter, dimmer)
One cell		standard for comparison
Two cells in series		
Three cells in series		
Two cells in parallel		
Three cells in parallel		

Diagram A

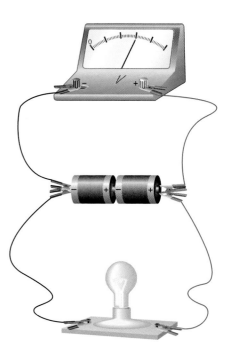

Diagram B

7 Connect the voltmeter across the cells, as shown.

8 Observe the brightness of the bulb and compare it to the brightness you observed in step 4. Record your observation in your data table.

9 Measure and record the potential difference across the dry cells.

10 Connect three dry cells in series with each other and with a light bulb, as shown in diagram C. Be sure that the positive terminal of one cell is connected to the negative terminal of the next.

11 Connect the voltmeter across all of the cells, as shown.

12 Repeat steps 8 and 9.

13 Reverse the third dry cell so that the positive terminals of the second and third cells are in contact and the negative terminal of the third cell is in contact with the connecting wire, as shown in diagram D.

14 Repeat steps 8 and 9.

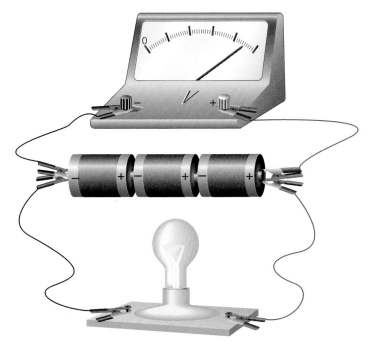

Diagram C

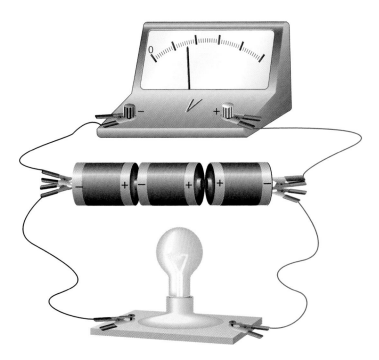

Diagram D

15 Connect two dry cells in parallel with each other and connect them to a light bulb, as shown in diagram E. Be sure that a connecting wire is in contact with the negative terminal of both cells and another connecting wire is in contact with both positive terminals.

16 Connect the voltmeter across all the cells, as shown.

17 Repeat steps 8 and 9.

18 Connect three dry cells in parallel with each other and connect them to a light bulb, as shown in diagram F. Be sure that one wire connects all of the negative terminals and another wire connects all of the positive terminals.

19 Connect the voltmeter across all the cells, as shown.

20 Repeat steps 8 and 9.

Diagram E

Diagram F

Analyze

1. Compare the brightness of the bulb and the values for potential difference for a single cell with those of two and three cells connected in series.

2. Compare the brightness of the bulb and the values for potential difference for a single cell with those where there are three cells, but the third is in the opposite direction from the first two.

3. Compare the brightness of the bulb and the values for potential difference for a single cell with those of two and three cells connected in parallel.

Conclude and Apply

4. Write a statement that summarizes the effect of putting two or more cells in series with each other. Include information about potential difference and current.

5. Explain how you arrived at conclusions about current, when you did not use an ammeter.

6. Write a statement that explains what happened when three cells were connected in series with each other, but the third cell was in the opposite direction from the first two.

7. Write a statement that summarizes the effect of putting two or more cells in parallel with each other. Include information about potential difference and current.

Is Bigger Better?

As you discovered in your investigation, the potential difference across a group of cells connected in series is the sum of the potential differences across each individual cell. For example, a 9 V battery, such as the one in Figure 12.5, is made of six 1.5 V cells connected in series. After examining Figure 12.5, you might wonder why 1.5 V cells come in such different sizes. If both cells were generating the same current, the large D cell would last much longer than the small cells from the (9 V) battery. The type of chemical reaction that takes place determines the potential difference a cell can generate. The total amount of chemicals determines how many reactions can occur and, therefore, how long the cell or battery will last.

Figure 12.5 Each of the six tiny cells that make up a 9 V battery generates 1.5 V, just as the large D cell does. Why is there such a big difference in the size of 1.5 V cells?

Special Cells

Fuel cells are similar to other electrical cells because they use energy from chemical reactions to separate positive and negative charges. The most important difference is that the fuels, hydrogen gas and oxygen gas, are contained in tanks outside of the cell. The gases are fed into the cell where the chemical reaction occurs. The by-product, pure water, is then released from the cell.

In the past, fuel cells have been too expensive for common applications. Their use was limited to unique situations, such as providing electrical power for submarines and spacecraft. However, due to recent successes in their development, fuels cells may soon be economical for more common applications. Ballard Generation Systems, with headquarters in Burnaby, British Columbia, is a world leader in the development of fuel cells. For more than ten years, Ballard and Daimler-Benz have been cooperatively developing the "New Electric Car" they call the NECAR. They have demonstrated that fuel cell powered electric vehicles are feasible. Many other automobile companies throughout the world have

DidYouKnow?

Fuel cells not only provide electrical energy for the space shuttle. The water produced as a by-product from the chemical reactions in the fuel cells supplies much of the water for the crew.

Figure 12.6 This passenger vehicle is powered by a Ballard fuel cell.

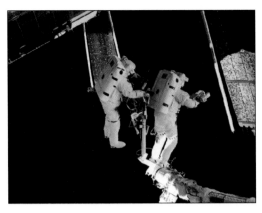

purchased Ballard fuel cells to test their usefulness in automobiles and buses. Ballard also produces fuel cells for stationary power.

Solar cells use solar or light energy to separate positive and negative charges. Solar cells are often used to provide electrical energy for small calculators and large satellites. As well, the new space station will have large panels covered with solar cells to provide electrical energy.

Figure 12.7 Can you find the panels of solar cells on this communications satellite?

DidYou**Know**?

Many fish have electric organs that can produce a large potential difference. They use this electrical energy to detect enemies, navigate, and possibly to communicate. The South American fresh water eel, *Electrophorous electricus,* can generate the largest potential difference of any fish. The electric organ consists of thousands of flat, specialized muscle cells, called electroplaques, that make up about 40% of the eel's mass. Each cell generates a potential difference of about 0.15 V. Because the cells are connected in series, the electric organ can generate a total potential difference of about 600 V. The eel releases a burst of electrical energy, lasting about $\frac{3}{1000}$ of a second, to stun prey. This "electric shock" causes the prey to stop breathing and drown. Then the eel consumes its meal.

muscles used for swimming

spinal cord

muscles

The electric organs make up most of the fish's body.

cross-section of an electric eel

Check Your Understanding

1. Explain the difference between dry cells and wet cells. Discuss the advantages of dry cells over wet cells.

2. What is the difference between a primary cell and a secondary cell?

3. How would you construct a long lasting 6.0 V battery from eight 1.5 V cells? Explain and make a sketch of the way you would connect the cells.

4. How do fuel cells differ from typical electrical cells?

5. What is the source of energy for solar cells?

12.3 Stationary Power

Canadians use about 2 000 000 000 000 000 000 J (2×10^{18} J) of electrical energy every year. From where does it all come? Most of Canada's electrical energy comes from harnessing rapidly flowing rivers, burning fossil fuels, and splitting atoms to release nuclear energy.

Energy From Flowing Rivers

Hydro-electric plants, such as the one pictured on page 380, produce most of the electrical energy used in Canada. Hydro-electric plants use water (hydro) pressure to generate electrical energy. Large dams cause the water level to rise high above the power plant. In previous science courses, you learned that as the water level becomes higher, the pressure at the bottom becomes greater. The water pressure at the bottom of a dam is enormous. Figure 12.8 shows how this pressure is used to produce electricity.

A channel, called a penstock, directs the water from the bottom of the reservoir to a turbine. The high pressure of the rapidly flowing water turns enormous turbines, which then turn the generators. The generators convert the kinetic energy, or energy of the turning motion, into electrical energy. High voltage power lines carry the electrical energy over many kilometres from the hydro-electric plant to cities, towns, and farms.

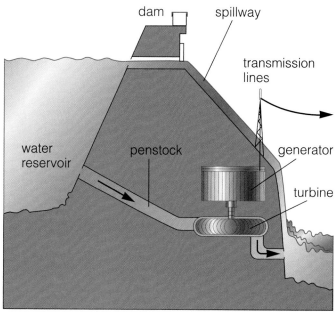

Figure 12.8 Energy is stored in the reservoir due to the tremendous mass of water and its height above the base of the dam. The turbine and generator convert this stored energy, called gravitational potential energy, into electrical energy.

DidYou**Know**?

Electrical energy from hydro-electric plants originates from the Sun. In order for water to run downhill and fill reservoirs behind dams, it must be lifted high up in the hills and mountains. The Sun provides the energy to evaporate water from oceans, lakes, and rivers, and this water vapour rises high in the air above the land. When the water vapour condenses and forms clouds that release rain and snow, water flows back down into reservoirs and eventually drives the turbines.

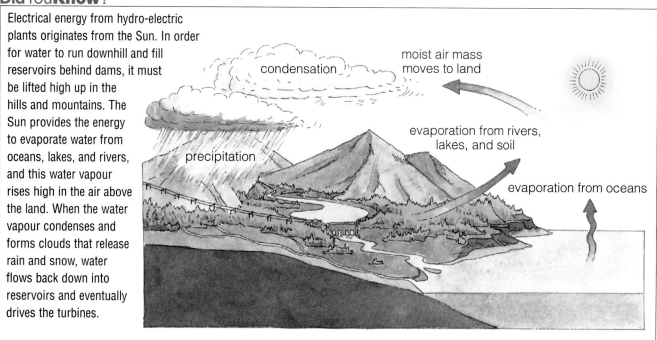

Energy from Fossil Fuels

When you hear the word "fossil," you probably think of the skeleton of a fish imbedded in a rock or outlines of leaves or shelled sea creatures, as shown in Figure 12.9. Do you know what **fossil fuels** are and how they are related to the fossil you see in the photographs? Coal, crude oil, and natural gas are products of once living tissues, just like the fossils you see in rocks. However, instead of being pressed into rocks, the decaying tissues piled up, possibly on the bottom of a lake or ocean. Later, they were covered by sand and soil, sometimes several kilometres deep. The tremendous pressure and heat converted these decaying tissues into coal, oil, or natural gas, the materials we call fossil fuels. Now, millions of years later, we dig or pump fossil fuels from the ground and burn them for energy.

Figure 12.10 illustrates the operation of a **thermo-electric** generating plant.

Figure 12.9 The scientific name of this fossilized fish is *Priscacara Peali.*

The term "thermo-electric" means using heat (thermo) to generate electrical energy. Follow the steps in the figure to understand how energy stored in coal is converted into electrical energy. First, the coal is pulverized and blown into the furnace to make it burn rapidly and efficiently. Heat from the burning coal converts water into steam. The high pressure steam flows through pipes into a turbine. From this point, the process is very similar to the system in a hydro-electric plant. The spinning turbine turns a generator that produces electrical energy. When the steam leaves the turbine, it enters a chamber that has water pipes carrying cool water to help convert the

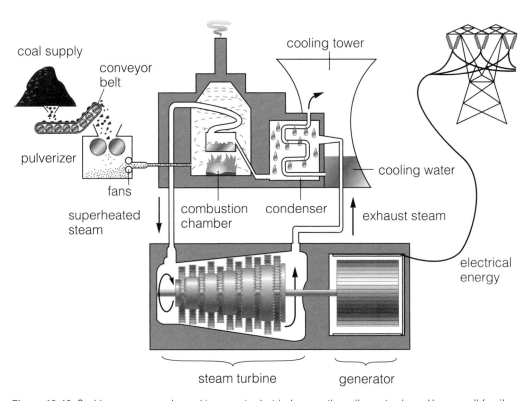

Figure 12.10 Coal is more commonly used to generate electrical energy than oil or natural gas. However, all fossil fuel burning plants function much the same as the coal burning plant illustrated here.

steam back into liquid water. The condensed water flows back to the furnace, where it is once again converted into steam and the process is repeated.

Energy from Splitting Atoms

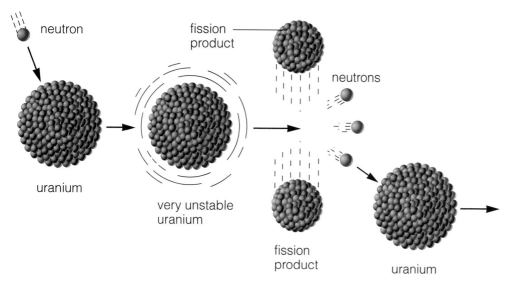

Figure 12.11 When a uranium atom absorbs a neutron and splits, or fissions, it emits neutrons as well as two smaller atoms called fission products. If one of the new neutrons collides with another uranium atom and causes it to fission, a chain reaction can take place.

Uranium atoms are the largest atoms of any naturally occurring element on Earth. In the 1930s, physicist Enrico Fermi (1901-1954) discovered that bombarding uranium with tiny particles called neutrons caused uranium atoms to split into two smaller atoms called **fission products**. In this process, called **nuclear fission,** a tremendous amount of energy is released as well as two or three more neutrons. If these neutrons penetrate other uranium atoms and cause them to split, the process continues. Figure 12.12 shows how this energy is converted into electrical energy. This process is called **thermonuclear** electrical generation, because the heat comes from nuclear reactions.

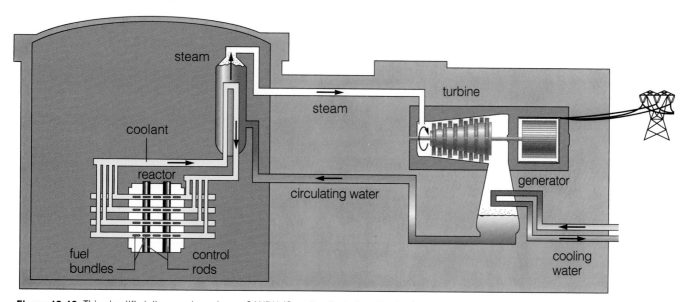

Figure 12.12 This simplified diagram shows how a CANDU (Canadian Deuterium Uranium) reactor produces electricity from nuclear energy. CANDU reactors are designed and built in Canada and are used around the world.

The uranium fuel is formed into small pellets and placed in **fuel rods.** The fuel rods are inserted into the reactor core and the fission reactions are initiated. The reactions are regulated by lifting and lowering control rods. Control rods absorb some of the neutrons, so the reactions do not go out of control. The fission reactions produce tremendous amounts of heat, which is carried away from the reactor core by a fluid coolant that flows around the fuel rods. Pipes carry the coolant from the reactor through a tank of water, where the heat converts the liquid water into steam. From this point, the process is very similar to a thermo-electric generating station. The steam turns a turbine that turns a generator that converts the energy of motion into electrical energy. The steam leaving the turbine is cooled and condensed by another set of pipes, carrying coolant water.

Canada's Energy Resources

Over 98% of Canada's electrical energy is produced by hydro-electric, thermo-electric, or thermonuclear plants. In some remote areas, gasoline powered generators produce electrical energy. In even fewer cases, gas turbines are used to produce electrical energy. Gas turbines differ from steam turbines, because the high speed exhaust gases from burning fuel turns the turbines, instead of heating water to steam. Figure 12.13 shows the amount of electrical energy produced by the different methods in each of the provinces.

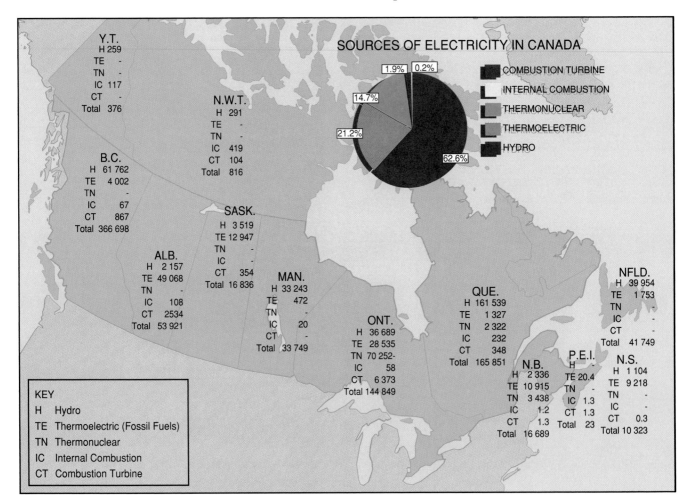

Figure 12.13 The values for the amount of electrical energy generated in each province are given in GW•h (gigawatt hours). A gigawatt is a billion watts or 10^9 W. A GW•h is the amount of energy transmitted by a gigawatt of power over a period of one hour (1.0 GW•h = 3.6 x 10^{12}J).

Delivering Energy to the Consumer

Hydro-electric, thermonuclear, and thermo-electric generating plants are usually located great distances from the cities and communities they serve. Consequently, electrical energy must be transmitted over many kilometres of power lines.

Perhaps you have seen electrical substations such as the one shown in Figure 12.14. Did you wonder why electrical energy was transmitted at such high voltages, if these voltages are so dangerous? Find out by doing the following activity.

Figure 12.14 Exposure to high voltages can stop your heart. Large currents can also heat your body tissues very fast, causing serious burns.

Risk and Benefit of High Voltage Transmission

Suppose a power company wanted to transmit 1.0 MW (megawatts or million watts) of power over 100 km of power lines. What would be the advantage of transmitting the power at 500 000 V instead of 20 000 V?

A power company would look for ways to minimize the loss of power between the generating plant and the customer. You have learned that current passing through a wire can cause heating. So, the most significant losses would occur due to heating of the transmission lines.

To find the amount of power lost to heat, you can use the formula $P = I^2R$.

If you want to know why this formula is correct, read about it in Stretch Your Mind (page 400). Now what you need to know is the resistance of the power lines. For typical copper conductors used in high voltage lines, the resistance of 100 km of wire is about 100 Ω.

What To Do

1. Use the formula $P = IV$ to find the current in the transmission lines, when 1.0 MW of power is transmitted at 500 000 V. Note that 1.0 MW is 1 000 000 W or 1.0×10^6 W.

Science Inquiry **ACTIVITY**

The value 500 000 V can also be written as 5.0×10^5 V.

2. Use your answer for step 1 and the formula $P = I^2R$ to find the amount of power lost to heat in 100 km of transmission lines, when 1.0 MW of power is transmitted at 500 000 V.

3. Find the percent of power lost to heat, when 1.0 MW of power is transmitted at 500 000 V. Hint: Use the formula

$$\text{percent power lost} = \frac{\text{power lost to heat} \times 100\%}{\text{total power transmitted}}$$

4. Find the current in the transmission lines, when 1.0 MW of power is transmitted at 20 000 V.

5. Use your answer for step 4 and the formula $P = I^2R$ to find the amount of power lost to heat in 100 km of transmission lines, when 1.0 MW of power is transmitted at 20 000 V.

6. Find the percent of power lost to heat, when 1.0 MW of power is transmitted at 20 000 V.

What Did You Discover?

Write a paragraph that explains why power companies transmit power at very high voltages when transmitting power over long distances.

Changing the Voltage

In the Science Inquiry Activity, you discovered that transmitting power at a very high potential difference and low current dramatically reduces power losses due to heating of the transmission lines. However, you also know that the potential difference provided by an outlet in your home or school is 120 V. How and where are the potential differences changed?

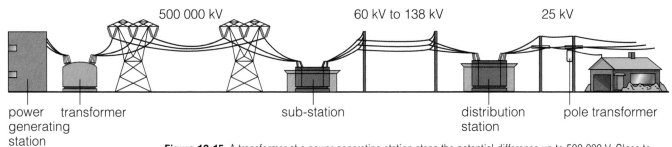

500 000 kV   60 kV to 138 kV   25 kV

power generating station   transformer   sub-station   distribution station   pole transformer

Figure 12.15 A transformer at a power generating station steps the potential difference up to 500 000 V. Close to the customer, transformers at sub-stations and distribution stations step the potential difference down. In local neighbourhoods, small transformers perched high on power poles step the potential difference down again to 240 V.

The large metal boxes in Figure 12.14 contain **transformers.** Electrical transformers are instruments that can increase (step up) or decrease (step down) the potential difference of power lines. Figure 12.15 shows you how transformers change the voltage between the generating station and your home or school.

The need for transformers limits the choice of current that power companies can use. There are two types of current that transmit power equally well, **direct current** (d.c.) and **alternating current** (a.c.). In direct current, electrons travel continuously in one direction. Cells and batteries produce direct current. However, transformers cannot operate on it. When using direct current, there is no practical way to step up or step down voltage. Therefore, power companies supply alternating current that transformers can use. In alternating current, the electrons change direction and go back and forth very rapidly. In North America and many other parts of the world, the power companies supply alternating current that goes through 60 complete back-and-forth cycles every second.

12.5 Alternative Sources of Energy

Canadians enjoy a high standard of living. To achieve this, we use huge amounts of energy. Although Canada has a wealth of natural resources such as coal, oil, natural gas, and uranium, these are all **non-renewable** resources. Non-renewable means that they cannot be replaced or that we are using them much faster than they are forming. It took millions of years to form the fossil fuel deposits and we are using them very rapidly. As well, uranium can never be replaced. Before these non-renewable resources begin to run out, we must learn to use **renewable** energy sources. Renewable resources can be replaced as fast or faster than they are used. For example, energy from the Sun, wind, and tides are renewable sources of energy.

Using Solar Energy

Earlier in this chapter, you read about solar cells that convert energy from the Sun directly into electrical energy. Silicon is the main component of these solar cells. Very small amounts of other elements are added to the silicon by a process called doping. Two types of silicon, p-doped and n-doped silicon, are joined to make a solar cell, as shown in Figure 12.21. Normally, electrons cannot move across the junction from the p-doped silicon to the n-doped silicon. However, light energy from the Sun can give the electrons enough energy to "jump" across the junction. These electrons can only return to the p-doped silicon by flowing around the external circuit. As the electrons flow around the external circuit, they can transfer their energy to a load.

Currently, solar cells are not used on a large scale because they are very expensive to produce. As well, the surface must be cleaned frequently to ensure that light reaches the entire surface. Even the cleanest solar cells convert only about 15% of the light energy into electrical energy. If researchers can improve the efficiency and reduce the cost, solar cells may replace some non-renewable energy sources.

Figure 12.21 Electrons in the p-doped silicon absorb energy from light and "jump" into the n-doped silicon layer. As they travel around the circuit to get back to the p-doped layer, the electrons transfer the energy to a load.

The Operation of a Solar Cell

In this activity, you will investigate some factors that affect the operation of a solar cell. What do you think will affect the amount of electrical energy a solar cell will produce? Make a hypothesis and discuss it with a classmate. Then do this activity to check your ideas.

Problem

What factors affect the efficiency of a solar cell?

Apparatus

		Materials
socket	small electric motor with fan blades	tissue paper
60 W bulb	converging lens	
100 W bulb	voltmeter	
solar cell		
connecting leads		
opaque screen		

Procedure

1 Make a table identical to the one below.

Factors Affecting the Operation of a Solar Cell

Power rating of light bulb (W)	Conditions			Speed of electric motor (fast, medium, slow) or Potential Difference
	Area of solar cell exposed	Angle of light to solar cell surface	Concentration of light	
60	all	90°	diffuse	reference for comparison
100	all	90°	diffuse	
100	half	90°	diffuse	
100	shaded	90°	diffuse	
100	all	90°	concentrated	
100	all	45°	diffuse	

② Connect the solar cell to the motor (or voltmeter, if you do not have a motor with a fan).

③ Screw the 60 W bulb into the socket. Position the bulb 20 cm directly above the solar cell, as shown in the figure.

④ Turn on the bulb and record the speed of the fan blade: fast, medium, or slow. Remember the speed (or potential difference), because you will compare the data that you observe in later steps to your observations is this step.

⑤ Make the following changes, one step at a time. Then, compare the speed of the fan (or the potential difference) with the speed (or potential difference) you noted in step 4. Record your observations in the table.

(a) Replace the 60 W bulb with a 100 W bulb.

(b) Cover half of the solar cell with the opaque screen.

(c) Cover the solar cell with a single layer of tissue paper to diffuse the light.

(d) Concentrate the light onto the solar cell using a converging lens.

(e) Shine the light on the solar cell at an angle of 45° but keep the same average distance from the bulb.

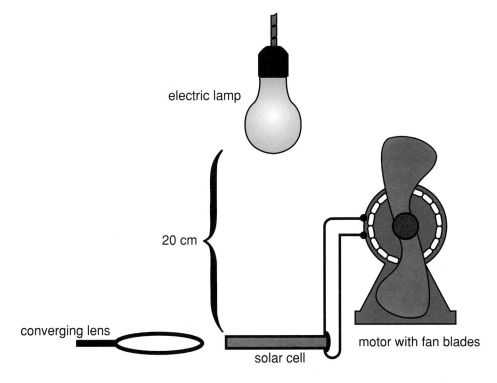

electric lamp

20 cm

converging lens

solar cell

motor with fan blades

Conclude and Apply

1. How do the following conditions affect the operation of the solar cell?

   (a) brightness of the light

   (b) area of the solar cell exposed

   (c) shading of the solar cell

   (d) concentration of the light

   (e) angle of the solar cell to the direction of the light

2. Write a paragraph that describes the conditions that cause a solar cell to produce the maximum amount of electrical energy.

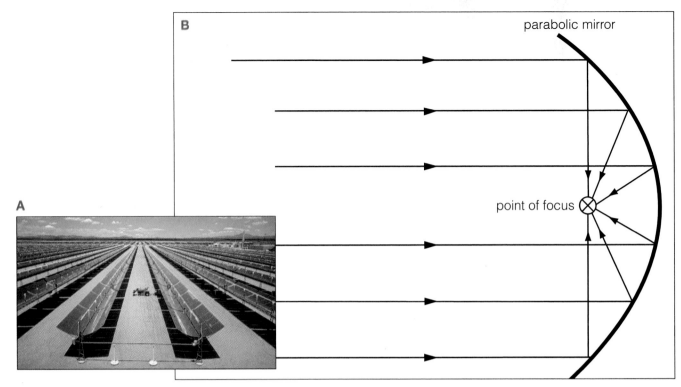

Figure 12.22 The reflecting surfaces in photograph A have a shape called a parabola. Diagram B is a cross section of the parabolic reflector showing how this shape focusses the light on one point.

Silicon solar cells are not the only devices that can harvest solar energy and convert it into electrical energy. Figure 12.22 A is a photograph of a solar "farm" in the Mojave Desert. The reflectors are curved in a very precise way, so that the light striking the surface is reflected toward pipes carrying oil. The hot oil flows back to the generating station where it boils water into steam and drives a steam turbine and electrical energy generator.

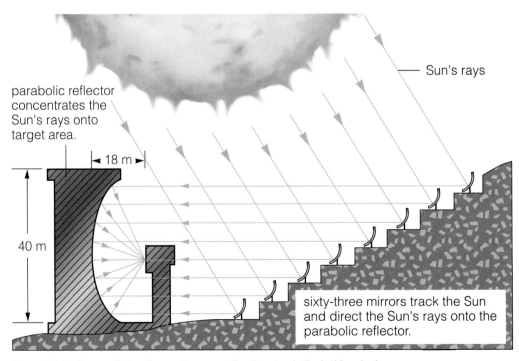

Figure 12.23 These reflectors focus solar energy directly onto a boiler in this solar furnace.

Figure 12.23 shows another approach to using mirrors to focus solar energy. The 63 mirrors are mechanically adjusted to move with the Sun so that, throughout the day, they are directing the solar energy to a giant parabolic reflector. This reflector focuses the solar energy onto a boiler and converts water into steam. The steam turns a turbine and an electrical generator.

All forms of solar energy conversion to electrical energy work only when sunlight is reaching the collectors. Therefore solar energy devices are often used along with other forms of electrical energy generation. For example, at night or when clouds shade the solar collectors ordinary fossil fuel burning thermo-electric generators may provide backup energy.

Harnessing Wind Energy

Figure 12.24 The Darrieus Rotor in the photograph on the left looks like a giant eggbeater. Yet it is very effective in harnessing wind power. The turbine in the photograph on the right is located at the Cowley Ridge Wind Electric Project near Lundbreck, Alberta.

Windmills have dotted the landscape for many years. However, until recently, they only pumped water from wells. Now windmills are beginning to harness the wind to generate electrical energy. Researchers are testing two types of windmills, shown in Figure 12.24, to determine which is the more effective for different wind conditions.

Any region with an average annual wind speed above 11 km/h has the potential for effectively converting wind energy into electrical energy. Some Atlantic provinces and prairie provinces are testing wind-electrical energy generation. By 2010, wind energy may supply a significant amount of Canada's electrical energy.

Figure 12.25 The windmills at this wind farm each generate 65 kW of electrical power. Imagine how much electrical energy a much larger wind farm could generate in the prairies. Imagine the sound of thousands of windmills spinning away in the countryside.

Like solar energy, wind is intermittent. As a result, wind-electrical energy generation must be used in combination with other electrical energy sources or the energy must be stored. For example, the wind energy might be used to charge storage batteries. As well, wind energy could pump water into an elevated reservoir which could, at any later time, generate hydro-electric energy. Wind energy or solar energy could be used to split water molecules into hydrogen and oxygen gas, to be used later as fuel for fuel cells. Wind is a promising source of electrical energy for many parts of Canada.

Tidal Energy

The photograph in Figure 12.26 looks a little like a hydro-electric generating station. Although its function is much the same, it is not in a dam on a river. The station in the photograph generates electrical energy from tidal waters in the Bay of Fundy.

On nearly every ocean shoreline on Earth, tides rise and fall about twice a day. The **tidal range,** or difference in the water level between high tide and low tide, can vary from less than 1.0 m

Figure 12.26 Nova Scotia's Annapolis Tidal Generating Station, located in the Bay of Fundy, was the first of its kind in North America.

to nearly 17 m. Although a great deal of energy exists in these moving waters, it is very difficult to capture that energy. Only a few shorelines around the world have a large enough tidal range, as well as a proper shape, for trapping tidal waters. Figure 12.27 B shows that the Bay of Fundy offers several ideal locations. Figure 12.27 A illustrates a tidal basin that provides a place where water can be trapped behind a barrier, similar to a dam. Figure 12.27 C shows how a tidal generating station works. The design of the generating station at the Bay of Fundy traps tidal waters that have come in at high tide and uses the energy of the water as it

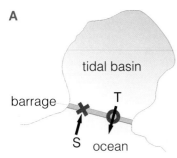

Figure 12.27 A A tidal basin with a narrow opening provides the opportunity to build a barricade, called a barrage, that traps the tidal waters behind it.

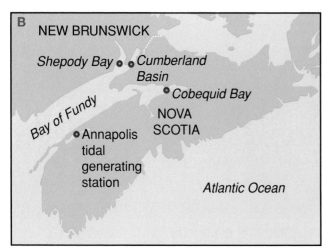

Figure 12.27 B The dots show the locations of the existing Annapolis Tidal Station and three other basins that have the potential for building stations.

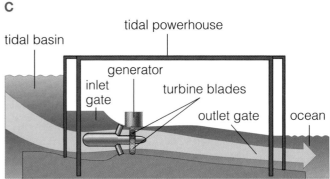

Figure 12.27 C The tidal powerhouse is quite similar to a hydro-electric generating station in a dam. As the water that has been trapped in the basin flows out, the water pressure turns turbine blades that turn an electric generator.

flows out of the bay. Several other designs for tidal energy generating stations have also been tested. For example, one design allows the station to use the energy of the water as it flows into the basin and then again when it flows out of the basin. This design increases the number of hours a day that the station can generate electrical energy.

Fusion, a Form of Nuclear Energy

You have learned about technologies that harness the energy of the Sun to generate electrical energy. You have also discovered that the energy for hydro-electric power, fossil fuels, and wind power comes from the Sun. Have you wondered how the Sun gets its energy? Could we mimic the way the Sun generates energy and use it to generate electricity? For over 40 years, researchers have been trying to harness this process.

The Sun generates energy from nuclear **fusion** reactions. Fusion means combining or merging. In fusion reactions, two very small atoms fuse to form one larger atom and usually one small particle. When the small nuclei combine, or fuse, enormous amounts of energy are released.

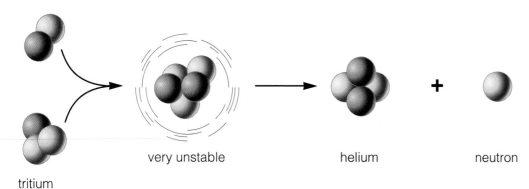

deuterium

very unstable   helium   neutron

tritium

Figure 12.28 This reaction, in which deuterium (heavy hydrogen) and tritium (radioactive hydrogen) fuse, occurs at slightly lower temperatures than other fusion reactions. Therefore, it is the reaction of choice for future fusion reactors.

The fusion reaction most likely to be used to generate energy is shown in Figure 12.28. Deuterium and tritium are relatively rare, different forms of hydrogen. Normal hydrogen has only a proton in its nucleus. Deuterium has one proton and one neutron, while tritium has one proton and two neutrons. When deuterium and tritium fuse, they form a very unstable nucleus that immediately splits into a helium nucleus and a free neutron. For the reaction to occur, the deuterium and tritium must collide with tremendous force. The only way to generate a large enough force is to raise the temperature of the gases to nearly 100 million degrees Celsius ($1 \times 10^8 °C$). Of course, you cannot contain materials at these temperatures in normal tanks or vessels of any sort. The

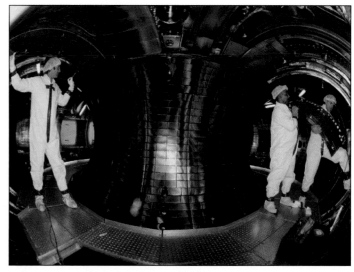

Figure 12.29 These workers are inspecting the inside of the experimental Tokamak fusion reactor at Princeton University.

most promising method of containment is to magnetically suspend the materials. A photograph of the inside of an experimental Tokamak fusion reactor is shown in Figure 12.29. Coils carrying current wrap around the chamber. This electric current acts like a big magnet suspending the fuel in the centre of the chamber. Fusion reactions take place in this chamber.

Fusion reactions have been achieved in experimental reactors. However, they can only be sustained for about half a second. To become a practical instrument for the generation of electrical energy, controlled reactions must be continuous. Although researchers know that much research must be done before practical and economical fusion reactors are available, they are hopeful that this will happen within fifty years.

Fusion research is extremely expensive but many people believe that it is necessary. Fossil fuels and uranium will eventually run out. An alternative source of large amounts of energy will be required. The fusion reactions use deuterium, which is difficult to replace. However, 1 g of deuterium yields as much energy as 8 t of coal or enough to fill a small gravel truck. One in about 7000 water molecules has an atom of deuterium. So, the ocean could provide enough deuterium to last hundreds of years or more. In addition, fusion power is environmentally friendly. It releases no greenhouse gases nor gases that cause acid rain. Large amounts of highly radioactive materials do not accumulate. It provides a clean, relatively safe form of electrical energy generation. Nuclear fusion may be our most important source of energy in the future.

Check Your Understanding

1. Explain the difference between renewable and non-renewable energy resources.

2. Describe two different ways to convert solar energy into electrical energy.

3. What problem exists when you use either solar or wind energy to generate electrical energy?

4. Describe the necessary conditions for the use of tidal energy to generate electrical energy.

5. What is nuclear fusion? How does it differ from nuclear fission?

6. Nuclear fission reactions take place is a large, sturdy tank. Why is it impossible to use the same type of vessel for nuclear fusion reactions?

Now that you have completed this chapter, try to do the following. If you cannot, go back to the sections indicated.

List the three essential elements of a voltaic cell and explain their function. (12.1)

Describe two features of voltaic cells that limit their usefulness. (12.1)

Explain the difference between a dry cell and a wet cell. (12.1)

Explain the difference between a primary cell and a secondary cell (12.1)

Describe the difference between a cell and a battery. (12.2)

Explain why some cells are much larger than other cells that produce the same potential difference. (12.2)

Explain how a fuel cell differs from other types of cells. (12.2)

Describe the form of the energy stored in a reservoir behind a dam, before it is converted into electrical energy. (12.3)

Explain the function of turbines and generators. (12.3)

Describe the formation of fossil fuels. (12.3)

Describe the source of energy for nuclear reactors. (12.3)

Describe the function of control rods in a nuclear reactor. (12.3)

Explain why electrical energy is sent over power transmission lines at very high potential differences. (12.3)

Describe the function of a transformer. (12.3)

List at least six different environmental challenges created by the major forms of electrical energy generation in Canada. (12.4)

Explain the difference between renewable and non-renewable resources. (12.5)

Describe the limitations of using solar energy for electrical energy generation. (12.5)

State the conditions that are necessary to make wind energy a feasible way to generate electrical energy. (12.5)

Describe the way that tidal energy is converted into electrical energy. (12.5)

Explain the difference between nuclear fission and nuclear fusion. (12.5)

State the difficulties encountered when trying to harness fusion energy to generate electrical energy. (12.5)

Prepare Your Own Summary

Summarize the chapter by doing one of the following. Use a graphic organizer (such as a concept map), produce a poster, or write the summary to include the key chapter concepts. Here are a few ideas to use as a guide:
- What observations led to the development of the voltaic cell?
- How were voltaic cells improved to make practical cells for everyday use?
- How is the energy stored in fossil fuels converted into electrical energy?

- How is steam used in the generation of electrical energy?
- What causes thermal pollution and how does it affect the environment?
- Why is it necessary to search for alternative sources of energy?
- What are the limitations or negative effects of using wind energy and tidal energy for the production of electrical energy?

Reviewing Key Terms

If you need to review, the section numbers show you where these terms were introduced.

1. Explain how the terms in italics are used incorrectly in the following statements.

   (a) This *secondary* cell is dead, so I have to throw it away and buy a new one. (12.2)

   (b) Look, I think I've found the entrance to an old *open pit* coal mine. (12.4)

   (c) We are going on a tour of a dam to see the *thermo-electric* generating station. (12.3)

2. Write statements that correctly use the following terms:

   (a) electrolyte (12.2)

   (b) transformer (12.3)

   (c) thermal pollution (12.4).

3. Explain the relationship between greenhouse gases and global warming. (12.4)

4. Explain the relationship between acid rain and scrubbers. (12.4)

Understanding Key Concepts

Section numbers are provided if you need to review.

5. Why is it necessary to use two different metals or metal compounds to make a cell or battery? (12.1)

6. Make a sketch of three dry cells connected in series. If each cell has a potential difference of 1.5 V, what is the potential difference across all three cells? (12.2)

7. Make a sketch of three dry cells connected in parallel. If each cell has a potential difference of 1.5 V, what is the potential difference across all three cells? (12.2)

8. List five steps, in order, that describe the burning of coal to generate electrical energy. (12.3)

9. What steps in thermonuclear production of electrical energy are very similar to the steps in thermo-electric energy production? (12.3)

10. Why must reservoirs behind dams with hydro-electric generating plants be very deep and very large? (12.3)

11. What form of electrical energy generation leads to the formation of acid rain? Explain. (12.4)

12. What is the most serious environmental problem associated with thermonuclear energy generation? (12.4)

13. List three non-renewable resources and three renewable resources that are being used or could be used to generate electrical energy. (12.5)

14. What are deuterium and tritium and how might they be used in the production of electrical energy? (12.5)

Developing Skills

15. You have the following materials: a fresh orange, a rotting orange, a copper strip, a zinc strip, conducting wires, and a voltmeter. Describe an experiment to determine whether the fresh or the rotting orange contains the better electrolyte.

16. Alkaline batteries are more expensive than zinc-carbon cells. A classmate claims that they are the best buy because they last longer.

   (a) Design an experiment using a flashlight to test the claim. Make sure you control all the variables.

   (b) If you have time, do the experiment and report your findings to your family.

17. Use the data in Figure 12.13. Use a spreadsheet program to calculate the average electrical energy generated per person per year for each province or territory. Plot a bar graph of the results. Discuss the results with your classmates. Try to identify reasons for the variability across Canada.

18. Make a concept map such as the one below. Insert as many renewable and non-renewable resources as you can. State their effect on the environment.

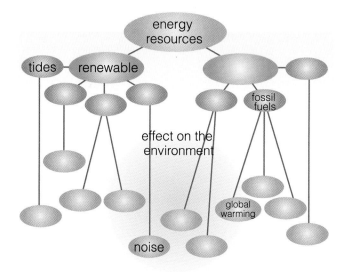

19. Review your results for Investigation 12-C. Create a diagram, bar graph, or some other type of visual to illustrate the percent of energy remaining after each step in the process of burning coal to produce electrical energy that eventually lights an incandescent light bulb.

Problem Solving

20. Assume that every kilometre of electrical transmission line has a resistance of 1.0 Ω. If a distribution station 25 km from your home transmitted 10 kW (10 000 W) of power at 25 kV (25 000 V) of potential difference, how much power would be lost to heat in the transmission lines?

21. Imagine that you want to leave a tape recorder at a certain location to record bird calls for several hours. The tape recorder is powered by a 1.5 V dry cell. The cell you have been using lasts only about half of the time that you want to record the bird calls. However, you don't want to go back to the location and replace the dry cell. How might you connect dry cells to keep the recorder running long enough?

22. Suppose that your family owned a small farm. You wanted to provide as much of your own electrical power as possible. Describe at least three different systems that you might use on your property to generate electricity.

Critical Thinking

23. Review the environmental challenges created by thermo-electric generating plants that burn coal and thermonuclear generating plants. Which do you think creates the more serious problems? Explain your reasoning.

24. Imagine that the electrical power for your home was provided by a fossil fuel burning thermo-electric generating plant. The power company sends out letters to all customers, explaining that they would like to upgrade the scrubbers that remove sulfur dioxide (SO_2) from the smoke that escapes out of the stacks. The current scrubbers are removing 90% of the SO_2, but they want to remove 99%. However, it will increase the cost of electrical power to all customers by 10%. Decide whether or not you would be in favour of the upgrade. Gives reasons for your decision.

25. Research in the harnessing of fusion power is extremely expensive. Based on what you learned about fusion power, write a paragraph supporting or opposing government spending on fusion power research.

Pause& Reflect

1. Review the answers to all of the questions in Opening Ideas that you wrote in your Science Log. If any of your answers were not entirely correct, explain what you have learned to help you answer the questions more correctly.

2. Make a list of the concepts that you learned in this chapter that are important enough to study more thoroughly. Explain why you need to learn more about these concepts.

Ask an Expert

Silvia Wessel, chemical physicist

How do you get a round battery into a narrow space? That's just one of the problems Silvia Wessel and her team at Bluestar Advanced Technologies Corporation are working to solve. Silvia is the vice president of the company and project leader for primary (non-rechargable) lithium battery development.

Q What kind of batteries do you work on at Bluestar?

A The batteries in our project are primary lithium manganese dioxide batteries. They are quite heavy and are used to power specialized equipment. We supply many batteries to the military for soldiers to use in things such as night-vision goggles.

Q Do all batteries contain lithium?

A No. Lithium batteries are very powerful. They generate a lot of current and can last up to ten years. However, lithium is not the safest chemical to have around. It reacts violently with water, so lithium is not used to make household batteries. There are some camera batteries that contain lithium, however.

We have also developed lithium carbon monoxide cells, although they are not in production just now. These cells have a high capacity compared to the regular batteries people buy for household items such as flashlights. "High capacity" means they have a long life. A lithium carbon monoxide cell the same size as a typical D-cell has a capacity of about 15 amp hours compared to the three or four amp hours for a household battery of the same size. One amp hour means that the battery can produce a current of one ampere for a period of one hour.

Q Do the lithium carbon monoxide batteries look like regular batteries?

A Oh, yes. The lithium manganese dioxide ones do as well. It's just the chemicals inside that are different. Actually, having said that, I should add that the lithium manganese dioxide batteries that we supply to the military, will soon look very different than the others. We are working on a new way to package them. Batteries usually come in a metal casing, but we are experimenting with packaging our batteries in a soft plastic pouch. This would make the battery less expensive to produce and more versatile.

Q In what way?

A A cylindrical, metal-case battery takes up a lot of space which means the equipment it goes into has to be that much bigger. A soft battery can be designed to fit into whatever nook or cranny is available inside the piece of equipment.

In addition, if the battery is lighter, the equipment is lighter. That makes it easier for the soldier to carry.

Q Do you spend all of your time developing new types of batteries?

A That depends on our stage of development. All of us in the lab spend a great deal of time making cells. When we want to develop a new type, we keep making cells from scratch. We analyze the materials, the "ingredients" we receive, to see what quality they are and how well they will work. Then, we combine them with the technology in many different ways, trying to get as many amp hours as possible. It involves a lot of trial and error.

My other responsibilities involve figuring out how much it will cost to make large quantities of the batteries we have just designed. Once I know that, we can give clients a price per battery and they can decide whether they want to buy them from us. When an order is placed, I help get the process of making the batteries underway in a separate Bluestar production facility.

Q Does Bluestar develop other types of batteries as well?

A Yes, there are other departments, including one that develops specialized rechargeable batteries. One type of cell they are working with now is lithium ion. These batteries have a very good chance of being chosen for use on NASA's Mars Lander and Rover mission.

Q Do you enjoy your job?

A I do enjoy my work. I take pride in making good batteries and find it very satisfying when a customer tells us that they are very happy with our batteries' performance.

EXPLORING Further

Figure It Out

Why do we need so many different types of batteries? Different circumstances require different features. Think about Silvia's lithium carbon monoxide cells. Bluestar hopes one day to sell these high capacity cells to power companies for use in meters on people's houses. The batteries would provide the power required to send a signal from your house to the power company telling them your meter reading, that is, how much electricity you have used.

Review Silvia's description and explain why these lithium carbon monoxide batteries would be better for the job than a regular household battery of the same size. If one of Silvia's batteries lasted ten years, how many regular batteries would be required to last as long?

A SIMULATION

High-Voltage Power Lines: A Threat to Health?

Think About It

You live in a rural community. One of your neighbours, a dairy farmer, has become convinced that high-voltage power transmission lines on his land are posing a health risk to the herd. He claims that the power lines are emitting dangerous levels of radiation. According to the farmer, the number of calves being born with birth deformities is on the increase. The farmer's claims, aired in the media, have begun to alarm local residents. In particular, parents with young children living in the vicinity of the power lines are worried about talk of a possible link between power lines and childhood leukemia.

In response to the controversy, a scientist was interviewed on a local radio phone-in show. The scientist explained that most of the studies carried out on the effects of exposure to electro-magnetic fields (EMFs) have been inconclusive. However, one new study *has* shown that high levels of electromagnetic radiation might indeed activate a particular chemical in living cells. The study was published in the *Journal of Biological Chemistry*. It revealed that this chemical could act like a kind of switch, triggering a series of events affecting cell division. Since cancer is uncontrolled cell growth, the study suggests a link between the triggering of the chemical activity and malignancy in cells. The scientist was careful to point out that another researcher has attempted to replicate the study, but to date "has gotten no [EMF] effect."

Listener response to the phone-in show was overwhelming. To allay residents' fears and to promote a formal review of the controversy, a public forum has been organized. Start preparing for the meeting by gathering some background information (the Internet is a good starting point).

Plan and Act

1. At the public forum that you will be attending, the following people will make formal presentations:
   The dairy farmer who claims that his cattle are at risk from exposure to EMFs.
   A father of three children who lives near the power lines.
   A power company representative.
   A scientist.

2. What do you think each person's point of view might be before the forum? What are some concerns and considerations they might want to discuss? If any facts or arguments might change their point of view, what do you think those facts or arguments might be?

3. Your teacher will give your group the role of one of these people, along with additional information to help you plan your presentation. As a group, research your role, and then present a strong case at the public forum.

4. Your task, as a class, will be to assess all the evidence presented at the forum, both anecdotal and scientific. You will weigh all the evidence to try to determine the degree of risk that you think might be posed by the high-voltage power lines. You will then devise a plan of action in response to your conclusions.

Analyze

1. Were all points of view well researched and well articulated? If not, how do you think they could be improved?

2. Were all participants given an equal opportunity to express their views and their concerns? If not, how might this be improved?

3. What plan of action did you decide upon as a class? How did your understanding of science and technology influence your plan of action?

Electrical Self-Sufficiency

Imagine that you and your partners have formed a company that can help farmers reduce their electrical energy costs. Your services will include a thorough study of the sources of renewable energy on the farm. You will then draw up plans to describe practical ways to use the resources on the farm to provide electrical energy, as well as ways to conserve energy. If the farmer chooses to proceed with your plans, your company will hire workers and supervise the construction of the electrical generating systems.

To market your services, you need to develop a presentation. You have secured permission from the owner of a local farm to use the farm as a model. The south-sloping, 100 ha dairy farm is located in a region where the average annual wind speed is 12 km/h and approximately 65 percent of the days are sunny. In addition, a fast-flowing stream runs through the property. A family of four owns the farm, which includes a house, a large dairy barn with a milking parlour, and two vertical silos.

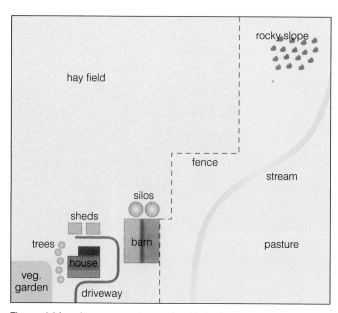

The model farm has some pasture and arable land.

Challenge

Prepare an energy plan for the farm that harnesses renewable energy sources to generate as much electricity as possible. As well, develop plans to conserve energy. Design and construct a comprehensive, attractive display and a creative and stimulating marketing presentation.

Materials

art and construction materials of your choice, for example, jinx wood, modeling clay, Bristol board, poster paints

Design Criteria

A. Design systems for generating electricity from all three of the energy sources available on the farm.

B. Plan and build a model to represent one of the three systems. Make a technical drawing of your model.

C. Create a display using your model, illustrations, and explanations of the three generating systems.

D. Develop an oral presentation based on your display. Include methods for conserving energy on the farm.

Plan and Construct

1. Brainstorm appropriate ways for a farm to convert renewable energy sources into electricity. Your teacher will provide you with a typical energy bill for the farm. Identify topics that you need to research. Divide the research tasks equally among group members.

2. Choose the form of energy conversion for which you will build a model. Decide how to present all three forms of energy conversion on a poster. Determine the materials you will need and find out where to obtain them.

3. Develop an overall plan for your presentation and include a materials list. Present your plan to your teacher for approval.

4. Carry out your plan. Be sure that everyone in the group has responsibilities and understands what they are to do.

5. Prepare an oral presentation to go with your display and your model. Make your presentation to your class. (If you wish, you can make a videotape of your presentation.)

Evaluate

Assess your plan after your presentation. What might you change if you were to start over? Write some notes about any changes you might make. Give reasons for your decisions.

Now that you have completed Chapters 9, 10, 11, and 12 you can assess how much you have learned about electricity by answering the following questions. Before you begin, you may find it useful to return to each Chapter at a Glance and to each Chapter Review.

True/False

In your notebook, indicate whether each statement is true or false. Correct false statements.

1. Like charges attract and unlike charges repel.

2. Grounding a conductor means connecting it through an insulator to the ground.

3. The load in a circuit converts electrical energy to other forms of energy.

4. The battery in a circuit is the source of the electric current.

5. The percent efficiency of an electrical device is the total electrical energy input divided by the useful energy output multiplied by 100 percent.

6. In a series circuit, the potential difference of the source is equal to the potential difference across each load.

7. In a parallel circuit, the current from the source divides among the branches.

8. A short circuit results when the current in a circuit can bypass all the loads.

9. A thermocouple has two junctions, each of which is made of two different metals.

10. When two dry cells are connected in parallel, the potential difference is the sum of the potential differences of each cell.

11. Hydro-electric power plants convert the kinetic energy of moving water into electrical energy.

12. At the present time, most of Canada's electrical energy comes from nuclear energy.

13. Hydro-electric power plants cause the least damage to the environment of any of the top three electrical energy producers.

14. The biggest problem with nuclear energy is the long-term storage of the radioactive waste.

15. Wind energy can be used to produce electricity economically in all parts of Canada.

Completion

In your notebook, complete each statement with the correct term or phrase.

16. Electrostatics is the study of charges _____, whereas current electricity is the study of charges _____.

17. In order to give an electroscope a negative charge by induction, you must bring a _____ charged rod near the sphere before it is _____.

18. In a parallel circuit, the _____ is the same across the branches and the _____.

19. In a parallel circuit, the equivalent resistance is _____ than any of the individual resistances.

20. If a current flowing in a circuit does not pass through a load, it is called a _____ circuit.

21. In any electrical cell, the two metals are called _____ and the conducting solution between them is called the _____.

22. Non-rechargeable cells are called _____ cells, while rechargeable cells are called _____ cells.

23. Energy sources that are used up faster than they are replaced naturally are called _____.

24. The process of joining together two atoms to produce a larger _____ and release nuclear energy is called _____.

Matching

25. In your notebook, copy the descriptions in column A.
Beside each description, write the term from column B that best fits the description. A term may be used once, more than once, or not at all.

A	B
• allows electrons to move freely	• atom
• restricts the movement of charge	• conductor
• has a negative charge	• copper
• has a positive charge	• electron
• has no charge	• insulator
• remains fixed in atoms	• neutron
• moves readily during charging	• nucleus
• consists of two electrodes and a liquid electrolyte	• dry cell
• consists of two electrodes and a paste electrolyte	• voltaic cell
• a cell which cannot be recharged	• secondary cell
• a cell which can be recharged	• primary cell
• a lead acid storage cell	• ni-cad cell
	• wet cell

Multiple Choice

In your notebook, write the letter of the best answer for each of the following questions.

26. The Law of Attraction and Repulsion states:
   (a) Both unlike charges and like charges attract.
   (b) Both unlike charges and like charges repel.
   (c) Like charges attract and unlike charges repel.
   (d) Unlike charges attract and like charges repel.

27. The diagram below shows the connections to the terminals of an ammeter. What is the reading on the meter?
   (a) 0.70 A   (b) 1.70 A   (c) 1.75 A   (d) 3.50 A

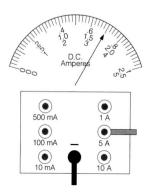

28. Electrical resistance is determined by calculating:
   (a) the potential difference across a load divided by the current flowing through it.
   (b) the current flowing through a load divided by the potential difference across it.
   (c) the current across a load divided by the potential difference flowing though it.
   (d) the potential difference across a load multiplied by the current flowing through it.

29. Which of the following statements describes the current in a series circuit? The current is
   (a) the same at every point
   (b) largest through the load
   (c) largest at the positive terminal of the source
   (d) largest at the negative terminal of the source

30. Two bulbs x and y are connected in parallel to a new dry cell. The switch is closed. If bulb x is unscrewed, the brightness of bulb y will
   (a) double
   (b) halve
   (c) remain the same
   (d) become zero

31. Three dry cells x, y, and z are connected in series to a light bulb. The switch is closed. If one dry cell is then reversed, the current will
(a) increase
(b) decrease
(c) remain the same
(d) become zero

32. The source of energy in the Sun is:
(a) nuclear fission
(b) nuclear fusion
(c) combustion of carbon
(d) burning of hydrogen

Short Answer

In your notebook, write a sentence or a short paragraph to answer each of the following questions.

33. A cork sphere and an aluminum sphere are suspended by insulating threads. A positively charged rod attracts the cork sphere and repels the metal sphere. What can we say about the charges on the spheres?

34. (a) Write the equation for determining the energy consumed E in terms of power P, and elapsed time t.
(b) What are two possible units for energy from this equation?

35. What is efficiency and how can it be measured for an electric kettle?

36. Two identical bulbs are connected in series in an electric circuit. Describe what will happen to the brightness of the bulbs if one of the bulbs is unscrewed.

37. Use symbols to draw a circuit diagram showing two dry cells connected in parallel with each other and in parallel with two light bulbs. Show a voltmeter connected to measure the electrical potential of the two dry cells and an ammeter to measure the electric current through one of the bulbs. Label the positive and negative terminals of the meters and the cell.

Problem Solving

Use the GRASP problem-solving model or a model suggested by your teacher. Show complete solutions for all problems that involve equations and numbers.

38. Suppose your teacher gives you three unknown materials A, B, and C, and a negatively charged electroscope. A, B, and C can be rubbed together in any combination. Explain how you could establish a series showing which material holds on to electrons most strongly and which most weakly.

39. Calculate the resistance of a conductor if the potential difference between its ends is 12 V and the current through it is 0.54 A.

40. A light bulb has a resistance of 96.8 Ω. What current flows through the bulb when it is connected to a 120 V source?

41. What potential difference is necessary to produce a current of 0.50 A in a conductor of resistance 30 Ω?

Critical Thinking

42. Wheat puffs or rice puffs are very light and are electrically neutral. If a negative ebonite rod is placed in the puffs, particles cling to the rod. However, a short time later they fly off in all directions. Explain why this happens.

43. A 12 V battery is used to start a lawn tractor. This battery is about half the mass of a car battery. Do you think the lawn tractor battery will start a car? Explain.

44. A student wants to use a voltmeter, an ammeter, and a battery to measure the equivalent resistance of two resistors connected in series. Draw a schematic diagram to show the setup. Show the positive and negative terminals of the meters and the source.

45. What energy conversions take place in:
(a) a hydro-electric power plant?
(b) a fossil fuel plant?
(c) a nuclear power plant?

46. The diagram shows a connection of a voltmeter, ammeter, variable power supply, switch, and three resistors.

   (a) Draw a schematic diagram of the circuit.

   (b) If the switch is closed, explain how the data collected using the meters could be used to determine the equivalent resistance of the three resistors.

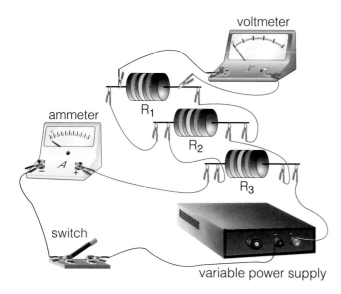

47. Explain why more energy is lost in transmission lines if the electrical energy is sent at an extra-high voltage (EHV) of 765 kV compared to an ultra-high voltage (UHV) of 2000 kV.

48. A new dry cell lights a bulb for five hours. A battery is formed by connecting three identical new dry cells in parallel. The battery is now connected to the light bulb.

   (a) Will the bulb brightness change? Explain

   (b) What will happen to the amount of time during which the battery can light the bulb?

49. Research is taking place into using more wind generators to generate electricity. What are two benefits and two drawbacks in using this source of energy to generate electricity?

Applications

50. Explain why, when testing an unknown charge, the only sure way to identify the kind of charge is to observe its repulsion with a known charge.

51. A hair dryer fan starts as soon as the switch is closed. The cord to the hair dryer is 100 cm long. Your friend tells you that electrons take about 1 min to travel 3 cm. Identify and explain the apparent contradiction.

52. A student performed an experiment to determine if an incandescent light bulb obeys Ohm's law. The potential difference versus current data is summarized in the following table.

Potential Difference vs Current

Potential Difference V (V)	Electric Current I (mA) ($1\ mA = 1 \times 10^{-3}$ A)
0.0	0.00
0.50	0.720
1.0	1.25
1.5	1.67
3.0	2.50
4.5	3.00
6.0	3.33

   (a) Plot a graph of voltage versus current, with current plotted on the x-axis.

   (b) Describe the shape of the graph.

   (c) Is the filament of a light bulb an example of an ohmic or a non-ohmic resistor? Explain.

53. Use symbols to draw a circuit with the following components: a series connection of two dry cells, a parallel connection of two light bulbs, and a switch to turn off both bulbs. Show a voltmeter connected to measure the electric potential of one of the cells and an ammeter connected to measure the total electric current in the circuit.

54. Student A claims that rechargeable batteries are less expensive than non-rechargeable batteries. Student B claims the opposite. Who is correct and why?

Exploration of the Universe

Scientists are explorers. Some travel to previously unknown regions, as did Charles Darwin to the Galapagos Islands, Robert Ballard to the floor of the Atlantic Ocean, and Jane Goodall into the rainforests of Africa. Other scientists stay home and use instruments as a means of discovery. Think of the microscope, for example, which reveals the world of tiny creatures in a drop of pond water.

To study the universe, scientists pursue both methods of exploration. For centuries, of course, "staying home" was the only option. Journeys into space and walks on the surface of another planet were the stuff of fantasy and science fiction. Still, using telescopes and their own powers of thought and imagination, Earthbound astronomers observed and learned an amazing amount about our solar system and beyond.

Today, technology has opened the boundaries. Humans have walked on the Moon, and space probes have toured most of the planets in our solar system. Some of these craft are heading toward the Sun's nearest star relative, a journey that will take about 50 000 years. Instead of postcards, these remote-controlled adventurers send us radio images of where they have been. We can follow their discovery of new moons, volcanoes, oceans of liquid ammonia, and thunderstorms on other worlds.

In this unit, you will learn how ideas about the solar system and universe have changed through time. You will also examine evidence that has led to our current understanding.

Unit Contents

13 The Changing View

Opening Ideas...

- How did early people use what they knew about the movement of the Sun, Moon, and stars in their everyday lives?

- Why can you see some stars and not others at certain times of the year?

- Try to list the nine planets of the solar system in the order of their distance from the Sun.

- Could we live on any other planets? Why, or why not?

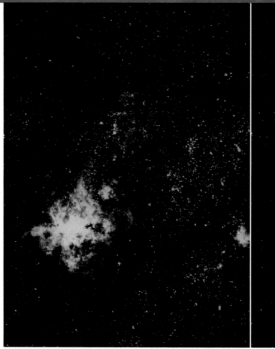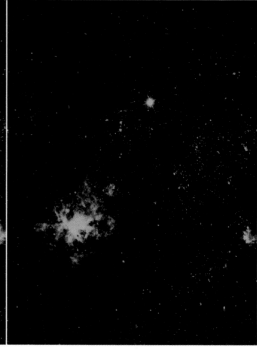

Science Log

Think about the questions above and answer them as best you can in your Science Log. Explain what evidence you have for each answer. What investigations or research might you need to conduct in order to find or check your answers? Look for answers to these questions as you explore this chapter.

Look carefully at these two images of the night sky. What do you see that is the same in both images? What do you notice that is different? These questions may seem simple, but for astronomers like Ian Shelton such questions can lead to discovery. On February 24, 1987, in an observatory in Chile operated by the University of Toronto, Shelton made a dramatic discovery. While examining images of the night sky, he noticed something unusual in one of the pictures. Deciding to check it out for himself, Shelton stepped outside and looked up. Among thousands of stars, he spotted a bright one that had not been easily visible before. What Shelton had discovered was a supernova, an exploding star, the first one so close to Earth since 1604.

Immediately, Shelton notified major observatories of his sighting, and other large telescopes in the southern hemisphere swung around to peer at the brilliant "new star." Confirmations of the sighting flooded into the University of Toronto, and by morning newspapers around the world reported the discovery of what is now called Supernova 1987A.

In this chapter, you will explore our solar system: the Sun and its family of planets and moons. You will start with the view from Earth as seen in earlier times and by other cultures. You will study the view of our solar system as we know it today and compare what we see with the unaided eye to what we can discover using technologies such as telescopes and spacecraft.

from Earth

Key Concepts

In this chapter, you will discover

- how our view of the solar system has changed throughout history
- the characteristics of the main components of the solar system
- the motions of the Sun, Moon, planets, and stars as seen from Earth
- different models that have been used to describe the solar system
- how technology has helped us increase our understanding of the solar system

Key Skills

In this chapter, you will

- compile a database and analyze the information it contains
- calculate and compare distances in the solar system using astronomical units
- learn how to create a scale model of the solar system
- prepare and communicate the results of scientific research

Key Terms

- celestial bodies
- asterism
- constellation
- planets
- retrograde motion
- geocentric
- heliocentric
- celestial sphere
- epicycles
- solar plane
- solar system
- solar prominences
- sun spots
- solar flares
- solar wind
- photosphere
- corona
- inner planets
- outer planets
- astronomical unit (AU)
- asteroids
- comets
- meteors
- meteorites

Starting Point ACTIVITY

What Can You See with the Unaided Eye?

Think About It

The positions of the Sun, Moon, and stars change every day. Long before telescopes were invented, careful observers noted patterns in these movements. Patterns became well enough known to be useful in predicting where and when each body in the sky would move during the day, the month, and the year. Observing with the unaided eye is still something we can do today to gather information about planets, stars, and other bodies in the sky.

What to Do

1. Organize into groups of three or four. Appoint a recorder for each group.

2. Your teacher will hand out a short multiple choice quiz (a copy of this is shown on page 458). Read each question and together select the answer you think is correct. Provide reasons for your choice, such as observations you have made in the past. If your group is not sure of the answer, briefly describe an approach you could use to make the necessary observations and to reach agreement on an answer.

3. When all the groups have finished, your teacher will lead a class discussion about each question.

Skill POWER

For some tips on working in groups, turn to page 573.

13.1 What Our Ancestors Saw

Pause & Reflect

Have you ever witnessed an "eclipse"? Eclipses are very noticeable celestial events. There are two kinds: solar eclipses (in which the Moon passes between Earth and the Sun, briefly blocking our view of the Sun) and lunar eclipses (in which Earth passes between the Moon and the Sun, briefly plunging the Moon into darkness as Earth's shadow moves across it). In your Science Log, describe how each kind of eclipse occurs. Draw a diagram to go along with your explanation. If you need to refresh your memory, use the resources of your library or the Internet.

Word CONNECT

Much of early astronomy was influenced by astrology. Research and record the definitions for "astronomy" and "astrology." How are they different in meaning?

For thousands of years, the sky has been a source of constant, predictable information. Long ago, people watched the sky to tell the time of day, the date, the weather, their position on Earth, and when the tides would be higher or lower than usual.

Farmers took their cues from the changes in **celestial bodies** (the collective term for the Sun, Moon, and stars). They planted and harvested crops according to the well-known celestial patterns. Sailors navigated by the stars and some, like the Polynesians, even guided their boats across vast oceans using the stars. Political and religious leaders often made decisions based on the information they received from those who studied the sky.

Figure 13.1 Stonehenge, a monument made of huge stones placed in a circle, is a reminder of how important celestial observation was to ancient civilizations. It can still be used to calculate and predict celestial motions.

Figure 13.2 Chinese astronomical observatory, built in A.D. 1090. A water-powered clock rotated the instruments in time with the daily motion of the stars.

During the time of the Roman Empire, the services of astrologers were especially in demand. People believed their destinies could be foretold by the stars. Navigation by stars was a valued skill for commerce and trade. Around the world, cultures and civilizations built observatories, created astronomical calendars, and developed the mathematics to predict planetary motion, eclipses, tides, and seasons. As early as 2000 B.C.E., for example, astronomical observations were being made in China. By about 1000 B.C.E., the Babylonians could predict when lunar eclipses would happen.

Many different cultures had their own accounts about how the celestial bodies were formed. For example, in Hindu mythology, one story tells of seven wise men who were married to seven sisters. All lived together in the northern sky. Then six of the women divorced their husbands and moved to another location in the sky. They became Pleiades, an example of an **asterism** (a distinctive star pattern). The seven husbands became the seven stars of the Big Dipper (another asterism). The woman who stayed with her husband became the star we now call Alcor. She remains by the side of Mizar, in the crook of the Big Dipper's handle.

The Algonquin, Iroquois, and Narragansett, saw the **constellation** Ursa Major as a bear running from hunters (a constellation is an officially recognized grouping of stars). According to some stories, because the bear is low enough to brush the maple trees in early autumn evenings, blood from its wounds turns the leaves red. Another group, the Snohomish, have a legend that tells how three hunters chasing four elk became the seven stars of the Big Dipper. One of the hunters is accompanied by a "dog," which you can see if you look carefully at the middle star in the handle.

Outside Link **ACTIVITY**

Astronomical Structures

Knowledge of astronomy was often combined with religion, since both were important aspects of ancient life. Religious structures built by ancient people often used aspects of astronomy in their design.

What to Do

Research the ancient astronomical knowledge in one or more of the following countries, and explain how that knowledge became a design feature in certain important structures: Mexico/Guatemala, China, Egypt, Turkey, Persia (now Iran), England, Greece.

What Did You Discover?

Write a brief summary of your findings and include a sketch or photograph of each structure you study. Present your findings to the class.

Word CONNECT

The entire sky is divided into 88 regions, each associated with a constellation. Therefore, there are 88 official constellations, as recognized by the International Astronomical Union. The less familiar term "asterism" refers to the many unofficially recognized groupings of stars. The best-known asterism in the northern hemisphere is the Big Dipper, located in the constellation Ursa Major. Look up the origins of the words "constellation" and "asterism."

Ursa Major

Check Your Understanding

1. How did knowledge of astronomy help early people plan the activities in their daily lives?

2. What does the term "celestial bodies" mean?

3. **Thinking Critically** What effect do you think seeing a total eclipse would have had on early people?

4. **Thinking Critically** Describe two accounts that different cultures have used to explain what they observed in the sky.

13.2 The Celestial Movie

Figure 13.3 Whether it is the regular parade of Sun, Moon, planets, and stars, or the more dramatic dance of the aurora borealis, there is always something to watch on the "big screen" of the night sky.

Imagine that a special camera pointed at the sky was set up where you live. For a whole year, it recorded the movements of the objects in the sky on one continuous videotape. This videotape would then be played back on your TV screen in very fast motion. What would you see?

One common sight would be clouds. You would see them in various shapes and shades, moving eastward in most regions of Canada, the same direction as the daily wind. Probably you would infer that they are pushed by the wind and do not travel under their own power. You would see clouds form and break up rapidly, and realize that they are not very far away. You might classify clouds as earthly rather than celestial bodies.

The Moon is much farther away and its motion much more regular, a westward path across the sky. Each night it rises in the east an hour later than the previous night. To our eyes, its shape appears to change in phases, waxing from thin crescent, through half circle, to full Moon, then waning to a sliver again. You might also notice that a full Moon rises exactly at sunset, and that the pattern of light and dark regions on its face always looks the same. We never see the back side of the Moon.

This video would show that the Sun is more "dependable" than the Moon. The Sun's face has no phases, and it seems to rise at nearly the same time and place as the previous day. But again, if you were to keep careful track of the Sun's motion, you would see that it rises earlier and farther north every successive morning from near the end of December until near the end of June, setting

Figure 13.4 In which part of the sky would you see the Moon in this phase? Why is only part of the Moon visible?

later each day. Through the summer and fall, it rises later and sets earlier a little farther south each day, and the hours of daylight decrease.

Most of the stars, constellations, and asterisms, you might note, follow the pattern of the Sun and Moon, rising in the east and setting in the west. Not all follow this pattern, however. Some remain visible all night long, every day of the year, never rising or setting.

Careful observation would also show that the stars themselves rise four minutes earlier each night. By getting out of step with the Sun by approximately six hours over a three-month period, the stars in the night sky reveal seasonal patterns.

While the stars would be unchanging in their motion, you might notice five other objects that appear to be "wandering" through the constellations. The Greeks considered these to be special stars, which they called **planets**, from the Greek word for "wanderer." These five planets, Mercury, Venus, Mars, Jupiter, and Saturn, slowly change position relative to the background sky from night to night. Two of them, Venus and Mercury, seem to stay near the Sun. When they are visible, they can only be seen in the early evening or morning. On any given night, Mars, Jupiter, and Saturn seem to share the westward movement of the stars. From night to night, however, these three planets "wander" eastward against their starry background. About once a year, they seem to loop back briefly in **retrograde motion** before continuing eastward (see Figure 13.6).

DidYouKnow?

If you were living in the southern hemisphere, this apparent pattern of the Sun's motion would be different. How? Explain the Sun's seasonal motion there.

Figure 13.5 One notable star that never rises or sets is Polaris, often called the North Star, around which all the other stars appear to be revolving. Early people recognized this star, because it appeared to stay fixed and could be used to find direction at night.

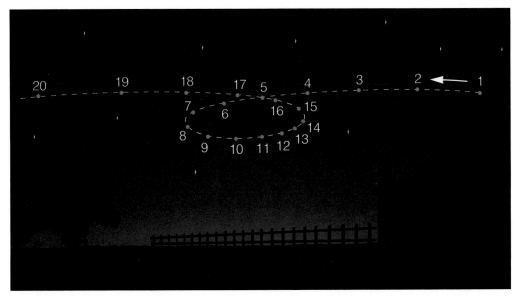

Figure 13.6 Position of Mars compared to the background stars during a period of retrograde motion. Each point represents the planet's new position every 10 days over the retrograde period.

Pause&
Reflect

The importance of the Sun, Moon, and planets to the Romans is shown by the Latin names we still use for the days of the week. In your Science Log, list the days of the week and, in a second column, the corresponding French name (use an English-French dictionary if you need to). With this information, can you now name the celestial body after which each of our seven days is named?

Comparing the Effects of Light Pollution

An advantage of observing or filming the sky in a remote location is the absence of light pollution. Light pollution is the glow in the sky at night caused by high concentrations of artificial lighting, such as that found in and around cities. The effect of this high amount of light is that it makes it difficult for observers of the night sky to see any but the brightest stars.

What to Do

1. Obtain a cardboard tube from an empty roll of paper towels.

2. Select a night when clear skies are predicted. Go outside about two hours after sunset, and look through the cardboard tube at a constellation of your choice.

3. Count the number of stars you are able to see without moving the observing tube. Repeat this exercise on two more clear nights, from the same location and looking at the same constellation.

4. Plan a way to determine the average number of stars that can be observed through the tube from your location.

What Did You Discover?

1. In class, compare the number of stars you were able to see with those that other students saw from their locations.

2. As a class, brainstorm the reasons for the differences in your observations and write these on the chalkboard.

Check Your Understanding

1. Describe the motion of the stars in the night sky as seen by an observer in Canada.

2. Describe how the planets appear to move against the background of the stars.

3. **Apply** Examine Figure 13.6. At which point(s) would an observer see Mars slow down? Stop? Loop backward? Slow down again? Resume its eastward motion?

4. **Thinking Critically**

   (a) What would be the appearance of the Moon if it were in the western sky just after sunset?

   (b) Why would a full Moon always be rising just as the Sun is setting?

5. **Thinking Critically** How high in the sky would Polaris, the North Star, be as seen from:

   (a) the North Pole

   (b) the equator

   (c) an observer on Alberta's Canada-U.S. border?

Quiz:

"What Can You See with the Unaided Eye?"

1. On which of the following dates would the Sun be above the horizon for the most hours?
   (a) March 21; (b) June 22; (c) September 22; (d) December 23

2. In which direction is the Sun at noon in the winter?
   (a) east; (b) southeast; (c) south; (d) southwest; (e) west

3. Suppose the Sun rises due east. When will the Sun next rise due east?
   (a) tomorrow; (b) six months; (c) a year; (d) never

4. If you see the Moon rise tonight at 9:00 P.M., approximately what time will it rise tomorrow night?
   (a) 8:00 P.M.; (b) 9:00 P.M.; (c) 10:00 P.M.; (d) 11:00 P.M.

5. Approximately how many hours of daylight do you get in the summer?
   (a) less than 12; (b) exactly 12; (c) 12 to 16; (d) over 16

6. In which season of the year can you see the Big Dipper?
   (a) winter; (b) spring; (c) summer; (d) fall; (e) all year

7. How much time is there between full Moons?
   (a) a day; (b) a month; (c) three months; (d) a year

8. Suppose you see the Sun south of you. It sets, and rises the next day. How much time will pass until the Sun gets exactly south of you again?
   (a) 12 h; (b) 23 h 56 min; (c) 24 h; (d) a year

(Answers are on page 561 at the back of this book.)

13.3 Modelling Celestial Motion

Early people's search for an explanation for the motion of the stars is part of the ongoing human desire to understand the world we live in. When we pay attention to what is going on around us, we begin to see patterns, such as the general westward motion of the Sun and the stars. The next step, understanding the patterns, requires us first to come up with some basic ideas or theories. We then check these theories by using models. Models are useful scientific tools that have been used throughout the history of science to aid inquiry and to test ideas.

In this section, you will learn about two models that early scientists developed and tested to explain the motions of the Sun, Moon, planets, and stars. The Earth-centred or **geocentric** model was based on ideas of the Greek philosopher Aristotle and dominated thinking about celestial motions for almost 2000 years. The Sun-centred or **heliocentric** model — the one accepted today — emerged much more recently, during the sixteenth century.

Word CONNECT

Find out what the word "concentric" means. Make a sketch to show a series of concentric circles.

The Earth-Centred Model

As you have seen, all the celestial bodies seem to move across the sky from east to west during the day and night, revolving around Earth. It was not hard for early observers to imagine Earth being at the centre of a gigantic sphere on which the Sun, Moon, and planets were attached. Based on the mathematics and geometry of Pythagoras and Euclid, Aristotle used his idea of circles and spheres as perfect forms to create such a model. He placed the stars, whose patterns were unchanging, on the surface of an outer sphere that he termed the "firmament of fixed stars" or **celestial sphere**. Inside this sphere, he arranged more concentric spheres on which were attached the Sun, Moon, and the five known planets.

The Earth-centred model provided a means of predicting the dates and times when celestial bodies rose and set. Ultimately, though, it required up to 55 different inner spheres to account for the observed motions. A particular difficulty was explaining why three of the planets, Mars, Jupiter, and Saturn, sometimes

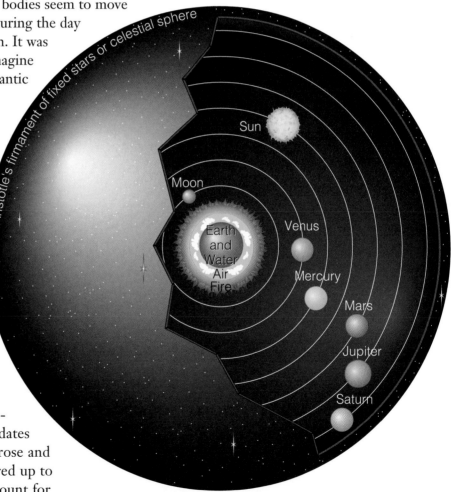

Figure 13.7 Aristotle's Earth-centred model, with its outer celestial sphere and many inner spheres. Since the stars on the celestial sphere were visible from Earth, it was reasoned that the inner spheres had to be "crystalline," or transparent.

Do you know the mean-
ings of the terms "axis,"
"rotate," and "revolve"?
An axis is an imaginary
line around which an
object spins. For Earth,
imagine the axis joining
the North and South
poles. Objects are said to
rotate when they spin on
their axis. Imagine the
motion of a spinning top.
Objects *revolve* when
they orbit around another
object or central point.
Imagine the motion of a
tether ball when it whirls
around the pole to which
it is attached. Each planet
both rotates on its axis
and revolves around the
Sun. In your Science
Log, briefly answer the
following questions.

1. Which motion causes
   day and night on
   Earth: revolving or
   rotating? Explain your
   answer.

2. As Earth revolves
   around the Sun, how
   does its axis of rota-
   tion change relative to
   the Sun? How does
   this affect its seasons?

reversed their direction. To account for this, other scientists such as Ptolemy assigned these planets an additional level of circular motion called **epicycles**. The result was an even more complex arrangement.

As complicated as the system was, it did seem to make sense. To test the theory, you could build a model structure out of wheels, belts, and gears. Then you could place each celestial body in its correct position and start cranking the drive wheel. The individual spheres could rotate and the bodies move. If you built it accurately enough, you could forecast astronomical events, such as the phases of the Moon, when the Sun would be over the equator, when Mars would pass Jupiter, and when eclipses would occur. Although the Earth-centred model did not survive to our time, its influence can still be seen in such terms as "celestial bodies" and "celestial sphere," still in use today.

The Sun-Centred Model

During the time we now call the Renaissance (the period between the fourteenth and seventeenth centuries in Europe), the Western world saw an increase in explo- ration. Confidence in sailing to unexplored regions was largely based on improved navigation and time-keeping, both of which owed their advances to more refined astronomical observations.

In the early 1500s, Polish astronomer Nicholas Copernicus proposed a dif- ferent model to explain the view from Earth. He was troubled by the retrograde motion of planets and the epicycle structure of the Earth-centred model. So he began to develop a model that was simpler than the complex one of Aristotle and Ptolemy. He proposed that, rather than Earth being fixed and the Sun travelling eastward through the stars, the Sun was fixed, and a rotating Earth travelled westward around it. The orbits themselves he arranged on the same **solar plane**. The solar plane is an imaginary, flat disk extending out from the Sun's equator on all sides, along which the planets orbit the Sun (see Figure 13.8).

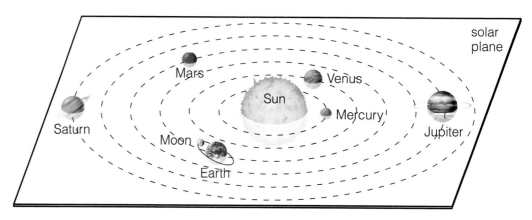

Figure 13.8 The solar plane. Imagine cutting an orange in half and then placing the two halves back together with a large piece of paper between them. All the planets would lie on or near the paper.

DidYou**Know**?

What we know about the Earth-centred view of the ancient Greeks comes largely from the last great philosopher and astronomer of the period, Ptolemy. His life's work was saved by Arabic astronomers when the Greek culture collapsed. Ptolemy compiled all the knowledge of Aristotle's geocentric model in what is known as the *Almagest*, Arabic for "the greatest."

Explaining Retrograde Motion in the Earth-Centred Model

A spirograph drawing tool will help you understand how epicycles in the Earth-centred model were used to explain the retrograde motion of Mars, Jupiter, and Saturn.

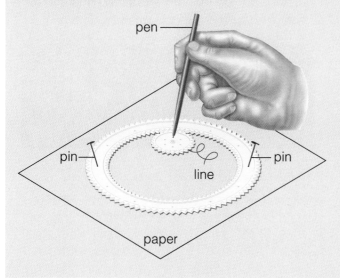

What to Do

1. Your teacher will give each group its own spirograph drawing tool. Pin or tape the large ring with teeth on the inside edge to your drawing paper. This represents the celestial sphere. Earth is in the centre.

2. Inserting a pencil or pen into a small wheel, rotate the wheel around the inside of the ring to produce a looping pattern on the paper.

What Did You Observe?

Compare your picture with Figure 13.6. Briefly describe in your notebook how the diagram in the figure compares to your drawing.

It was Galileo, an Italian astronomer, who found some persuasive evidence that supported the heliocentric model. Again, technology played a big role. Using an early telescope (which in fact was not much better than an inexpensive pair of binoculars today), Galileo made several exciting discoveries. Venus, he noted, exhibited phases just as the Moon did. (He also saw spots on the surface of the Sun, mountains on the Moon's surface, rings around Saturn, and four moons orbiting Jupiter.)

Figure 13.9 Using his telescope, Galileo spotted four moons orbiting Jupiter. Apparently *not* everything revolved around Earth after all. (With modern telescopes, scientists have found that Jupiter actually has 16 moons.)

The Changing View from Earth **437**

Viewing Jupiter's Moons

Simply with the aid of good binoculars, you can see the four moons of Jupiter that Galileo discovered with an early telescope. If you have or can borrow a pair of binoculars, try this outdoor activity.

What To Do

1. First, find out when Jupiter will be crossing the sky. Weekend newspapers often have a night sky column, and the Internet has tables of planetary positions. If Jupiter is visible, it will be one of the two brightest objects in the sky.

2. On the next clear night, head outdoors with your binoculars.

3. Once you have located Jupiter with your unaided eye, prop the binoculars on a steady surface (such as a deck or balcony railing or books piled up on a picnic table) and adjust the focus until Jupiter comes into view. It will just be a sparkle in the binoculars.

4. Look for four tiny pinpricks near the planet. These are the moons. (**Note**: You might see only two or three moons at any one time.)

What Did You Discover?

Draw what you see. Based on what you have learned in this chapter about celestial motion, how might you tell which direction the moons are revolving in?

The Sun-Centred Revolution Continues

Copernicus' model still needed work, however. Predictions based on it were no more accurate, for some events, than those based on the Earth-centred model. Johannes Kepler, a German mathematician employed to study the problem, found the answer. According to his calculations, predictions would be more accurate if planetary orbits were ellipses, rather than circles.

The Copernican Sun-centred revolution was nearly complete. Kepler's laws of planetary motion were strengthened by Sir Isaac Newton's law of gravitation, published in 1687. You may remember from your earlier science studies that, according to this law, there is a gravitational force between all objects, pulling them together. This force becomes stronger as the objects get closer. Edmund Halley used this knowledge to correctly predict the reappearance of the comet that still bears his name.

There was also great excitement in 1781 when a new planet, Uranus, was discovered. Later, using the Sun-centred model and Newton's law, astronomers predicted the position and orbit for another planet. When they trained their telescopes at the spot, they discovered Neptune. Now eight planets were known. The structure of the **solar system** — the family of the Sun, the planets, and their moons — was now well established.

Figure 13.10 The Sun-centred model of Copernicus from his history-changing work, *De Revolutionibus.*

Making a Blink Comparator

Think About It

As was the case with Neptune, the existence of Pluto was suspected before it was actually detected. Its initial discovery, however, was not with the aid of a telescope. Rather, it was through the use of a simple piece of equipment, a "blink comparator." Although computer programs now allow us to examine images more carefully, working with simple blink comparators is a good way to test both the technique and your own powers of observation. Do this activity with a partner. Take turns making one or more blink comparators and then give them to your partner to solve.

What You Need

self-adhesive removable notes
pen or fine-tipped marker

What to Do

To make each blink comparator:

1. Peel off two self-adhesive notes, but leave them stuck one on top of the other.

2. Lift, but do not remove, the top note. On the bottom half of the bottom note, mark 15 to 20 dots in a random pattern. Make them dark enough so that you will be able to see them through the top note. These represent the stars in your "star field."

3. Drop the top note down and mark on it a dot directly over top of each dot on the note beneath. The object is to make two identical pictures, one on top of the other.

4. (a) Add a dot to one of the pictures. This represents a new star that has appeared.
   (b) Mark another star on the bottom note. On the top note, place a dot near it but not in the same place. This represents a star that has moved.

To test the technique:

5. Give your blink comparator to your partner. Have him or her gaze steadily at the patterns, while flipping the top note up and down quickly over the bottom one. Can he or she spot the extra star and the star that moved? Can you spot the extra star in your partner's blink comparator?

Analyze

1. Which method would be better for detecting a difference between two star fields: examining the photos side by side, or arranging them, one on top of the other, and flipping between them? Why?

2. Why are blinking lights placed on top of high radio towers?

Pause & Reflect

People had difficulties in accepting the heliocentric model. Under the old system, Earth was the centre of all things and therefore a "Very Important Place." The new system upset this theory, suggesting that Earth was a moving planet just like the others. It was no longer special. Think of other firmly held ideas or beliefs from the past (not just astronomy related) that people found difficult to accept. List as many as you can in your Science Log, and briefly state why you think people resisted accepting each one.

Explaining Retrograde Motion in the Sun-Centred Model

With the Earth-centred model, the retrograde motion of Mars, Jupiter, and Saturn was explained in terms of epicycles (as you saw with the use of a spirograph). With the Sun-centred model, however, a new theory was needed to account for the motion. In this investigation, you will model, graph, and analyze the motion of a planet as it orbits Earth over a six-month period.

Problem

Why do Mars, Jupiter, and Saturn appear to reverse direction briefly in their westward motion across the sky?

Safety Precautions

When using any electrical equipment, make sure the electrical cords are not frayed.

Apparatus

decorative lights (or star field drawn on front chalkboard)
small flashlight bulb
socket
battery
wires
2 one-metre sticks

Materials

modelling clay or two wooden blocks with a slot to hold metre stick
masking tape

Procedure

1 Make your planet (call it "Mars"). Attach the light bulb ("Mars"), socket, battery, and wires together. Use masking tape to attach the light bulb to the top of a metre stick. Insert the other end into the clay or block so that the metre stick stands upright, as shown in Figure A.

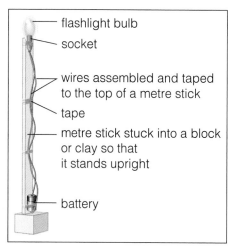

flashlight bulb

socket

wires assembled and taped to the top of a metre stick

tape

metre stick stuck into a block or clay so that it stands upright

battery

Figure A

2 Make "Earth." Stand the second metre stick in its clay or wood foundation. Do not attach a light bulb to the stick.

3 Label positions on the floor that match those in Figure B. The larger circle represents Mars' orbit and the smaller one Earth's orbit. Note that the numbered positions in the larger circle (Mars' orbit) are closer together than those in the smaller circle (Earth's orbit). The numbers show the position of each planet at one-month intervals.

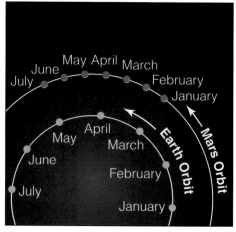

Figure B

④ Make the distant stars. Tape the decorative lights onto a far wall, as shown in Figure C. Draw the star field pattern in your notebook. (If you do not have lights, the "stars" can be drawn on the chalkboard.)

⑤ Organize into pairs. While your partner holds Mars at its January position, place Earth at its January position, as in Figure C. Looking in a straight line from Earth to Mars, note where Mars appears in relation to the pattern of the background stars. Place a dot, labelled "January," at this location on your star field diagram.

⑥ Repeat step 5, moving Mars and Earth to their February positions, then their March positions, and so on. Each time, take a sighting of Mars from Earth. Record the month and the position of Mars for your sighting, on the star field diagram in your notebook.

⑦ When you have moved both planets through all their marked positions and recorded your sightings, connect all the points for Mars in month order. This indicates the motion of Mars through the stars over a six-month period.

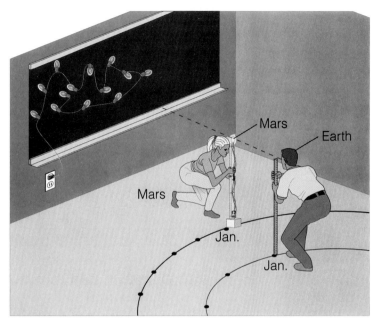

Figure C

Analyze

1. Which planet, Earth or Mars, moves faster in its orbit?

2. Study your diagram. Explain the pattern of Mars' movements over the six-month period.

3. Where are the relative positions of Earth and Mars when Mars appears to be moving backward through the stars?

Conclude and Apply

4. In a paragraph, explain why Mars sometimes appears to be reversing direction in the sky.

Extend Your Knowledge

5. Why would Mars, Jupiter, and Saturn show this type of retrograde motion, but not Venus and Mercury?

6. Would you expect Mars to show retrograde motion at intervals of more than 12 months, 12 months, or less than 12 months?

The View of the Solar System Today

Early scientists constructed a theory for the way the solar system works, the geocentric model, based solely on unaided-eye observations. When parts of that theory were challenged by new observations, scientists revisited the concepts and looked for alternative explanations. The heliocentric model emerged.

This method of scientific inquiry is still at work. As modern exploration of the solar system continues, our view from Earth is sharpened and extended. Today, thanks to advanced technologies such as space probes and radio and optical telescopes, we have information that the solar system is made up of the Sun, its nine planets, and their moons, as well as other smaller objects—asteroids, comets, and meteors—that revolve around the Sun, each in its own orbit. We also know that the solar system is an immense territory, reaching billions of kilometres in all directions from the Sun.

INTERNET CONNECT

www.school.mcgrawhill.ca/resources/

Retrograde motion of planets (the apparent backward looping of planets in the sky) is demonstrated with diagrams and animations at many sites on the Internet. From the above web site, go to **Science Resources**, then to **SCIENCEPOWER 9** to find out more about retrograde motion.

Check Your Understanding

1. According to the Earth-centred model of the solar system, what causes the star trails in Figure 13.5?

2. How does the heliocentric model differ from the geocentric model?

3. How is retrograde motion explained in the Earth-centred model? In the Sun-centred model?

4. Describe how Kepler improved on Copernicus' model.

5. How did the discovery of the planet Neptune support the Sun-centred model of the solar system?

6. **Apply** Imagine that your teacher hands you a package of gold stars and a black umbrella. Your task is to make a model of the celestial sphere. On what part of the umbrella will you place the stars? Explain your reasoning.

7. **Thinking Critically** In earlier studies, you probably made a classroom-sized model of the solar system, perhaps hung from the ceiling.
   (a) What aspects of the solar system did this model portray with reasonable accuracy?
   (b) What aspects of the solar system were missing?
   (c) Why do scientific models always differ from the "real" thing? Explain why models are of value.

13.4 Surveying the Solar System

Now that you have a clear picture of the solar system's heliocentric structure, look at each of the major components in some detail. What are these celestial bodies? How far away are they? What does Earth have in common with them? How is Earth different?

Questions like these have intrigued astronomers ever since the telescope began to reveal more about the night sky. Much information was learned after its invention, but when scientists began applying their knowledge of gravity and Newton's laws to space technology, our understanding of the solar system really expanded. New types of telescopes were developed that could see better and farther. Some, such as the Hubble Space Telescope, were placed in orbit, high above Earth's atmosphere. Space probes such as Venera, Solar Observer, Pioneer, Viking, Voyager, and Pathfinder have been dispatched to visit the Sun and planets. They have sent back photographs and measurements of planet orbits, surfaces, atmospheres, and moons. Humans have actually visited the nearest celestial body, our Moon, and brought back rocks to study.

In this section, you will have the opportunity to learn more about the star of our solar system, the Sun, and to analyze some basic data about the planets.

The Sun

The Sun is a huge globe of mostly hydrogen, the lightest of gases. It is about 1.4 million kilometres in diameter, almost 110 times the diameter of Earth. The Sun is so hot that the gas glows, and it is this light that speeds through space to reach and warm Earth.

The surface of the Sun constantly writhes and churns. Spectacular **solar prominences**, such as the one in Figure 13.11, are streamers of glowing gas that arch into space. Some regions on the Sun are cooler and therefore appear to be darker than their surroundings. These are known as **sun spots**. Near them, violent outbursts called **solar flares** erupt, sending streams of high-energy subatomic particles into space. You will see in Chapter 16 how this outflow of particles, known as the **solar wind**, can affect Earth and some of our activities on it.

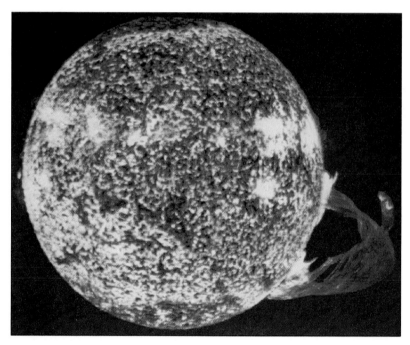

Figure 13.11 The Sun is all "atmosphere," because it is all gas. When people refer to the "surface" of the Sun, they mean the outside of the glowing region called the photosphere.

Word CONNECT

You learned earlier about chemical reactions, which involve the outer electrons of atoms. Nuclear reactions, as the name suggests, involve the protons and neutrons in the nucleus. There are two types: fusion (combining) and fission (separating). Use the library or Internet to find out more about these two nuclear reactions.

The Sun is 330 000 times more massive than Earth, but its main constituents, hydrogen (73%) and helium (25%), occupy an enormous volume. As a result, its average density is much less than that of Earth. In the dense core region, the Sun's own gravity has compressed the hydrogen so much that the 15 000 000°C temperature is high enough for a kind of nuclear reaction (fusion) to take place. About 600 t of hydrogen are converted into helium per second. This is the energy source of the Sun.

The energy released in the fusion process works its way through successive hydrogen layers until it reaches the **photosphere**, the region from where the Sun's light originates. The photosphere's temperature is about 6000°C and the tenuous solar "atmosphere," the **corona**, is about 1 000 000°C. When there is a total eclipse of the Sun, the corona becomes visible, as you can see in Figure 13.12.

Figure 13.12 When there is a total eclipse of the Sun, the Sun's outer atmosphere, the corona, becomes visible.

The Sun is the closest star to Earth. Scientists expect most of the stars in the sky, especially those of the same size and colour, to be similar to our Sun. Because our Sun has planets orbiting it, scientists also expect that many of the other stars have planets.

The Planets

All the planets differ from one another in size, motion, composition, density, and temperature. No two are exactly alike, although some share a few similar features. For example, the **inner planets**, Mercury, Venus, Earth, and Mars are sometimes called the terrestrial planets, because of their terrestrial, or rocky, composition. Jupiter, Saturn, Uranus, and Neptune, the **outer planets**, are similar because of their gaseous composition. Pluto is in a category all by itself. Astronomers still question whether it should be called a planet at all, because of its strange orbit and tiny size.

Scale: A Way to Compare the Planets

Studying the planets in a meaningful way first requires a useful scale with which to make comparisons. A standard approach in astronomy is to compare the planets to the one we know best, Earth, and therefore to use it to establish our scale. For example, because the diameter of Earth is 12 750 km, this length can be denoted as 1 Earth-diameter. On the same scale, then, Venus' diameter (which is 12 100 km) can also be expressed as 0.95 Earth-diameter (12 100 km/12 750 km = 0.95). And Jupiter, with a diameter of 143 200 km, can be expressed as 11.2 Earth-diameters (143 200 km/12 750 km = 11.2).

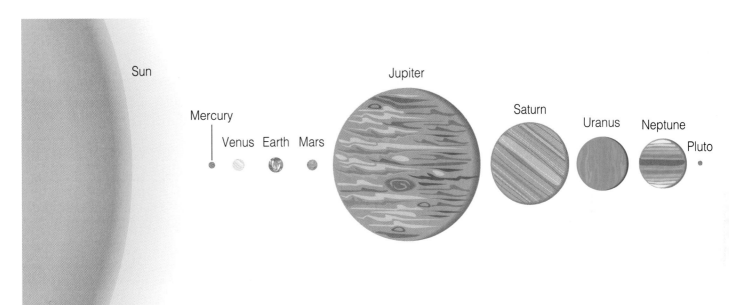

Figure 13.13 This diagram compares the size of the planets with the size of the Sun. Planetary distances are too vast to compare on the same diagram as size. As well the rings of Jupiter, Saturn, Uranus, and Neptune are omitted so that all planets fit in one diagram.

Similarly, a planet's mass (the amount of matter in an object) can be expressed in terms of Earth-mass, and its density (the amount of matter that occupies a particular space, equal to mass/volume) can be expressed in terms of Earth-density. Thus, if a planet's density is greater than 1, its composition is denser than that of Earth.

Useful time scales are days for planet rotation periods and years for their orbital periods (length of time needed to orbit the Sun). For surface temperatures, the Celsius (°C) scale is standard.

There is one more important scale to mention: the one for distance. Distances in astronomy are so immense (so "astronomical") that astronomers had to come up with a new way of measuring such vast expanses. For the study of the solar system, the scale used is the **astronomical unit (AU)**, which is equal to Earth's average distance from the Sun (149 599 000 km). On this scale, Earth is said to be located 1 AU from the Sun. This means that Mars' average distance from the Sun (almost 228 000 000 km) is 1.5 AU (228 000 000 km ÷ 149 599 000 km). Light-years, as you will learn in Chapter 15, are used to express the even greater distances in the universe beyond our solar system. Do you see why the distances are expressed as averages? (Hint: recall that the orbits are elliptical.)

Consulting the Planetary Expert: You

Think About It

You will be provided with a lot of planetary information in this section. One of the best ways to organize any large body of information is to do what scientists do all the time: build a database. A database is a collection of data that is presented in table or spreadsheet form and arranged into useful categories. These can help a researcher detect similarities, differences, and any other patterns in the information. Often the patterns themselves lead to new questions and, in turn, that line of inquiry results in the gathering of new information that gets added to the database.

In this activity, you will have a chance to create your own database of planetary information, which you will then use to interpret your findings. You will also need this information in Chapter 14 to help you analyze a theory for how the solar system formed.

Part 1

Building a Planet Database

What to Do

❶ Your teacher will give you a blank table such as the one shown below, or direct you to make your own spreadsheet on the computer.

❷ Read the planetary "data cards" on pages 472 to 476 in this section. Enter the information you need to complete the columns in your database.

❸ Once you have compiled all the information for your database, answer the following questions. Refer to the information on scale on page 444. These questions will help you understand more about scale and the solar system.

(a) In months, what is Mercury's orbital period?

(b) In kilometres, how far away is each gaseous planet from the Sun?

(c) What is Jupiter's diameter in kilometres?

(d) In hours, how long does it take Saturn to complete a rotation?

(e) Which of the bodies in the chart has the smallest mass?

Skill

POWER

For some tips on doing research in science and communicating your results, turn to pages 560 and 587.

Planet Database	Mercury	Venus	Earth	Mars	Jupiter	Saturn	Uranus	Neptune	Pluto
Size (Earth = 1)									
Distance (AU)									
Mass (Earth = 1)									
Density (Earth = 1)									
Avg. Surface Temperature (°C)									
Rotation Period (days)									
Orbital Period (years)									
Number of Moons									
Other Significant Features									

Part 2

Developing Planet Profiles and Presenting Them to the Class

What to Do 🖼️

1 Organize into nine groups. Your teacher will assign each group a planet. Your group will become "specialists" on that planet. Your job is to develop a profile of your planet that describes its overall characteristics, the features that make it like and unlike other planets. Find as many little-known facts as you can. Include information on how the characteristics of your planet were discovered. For example, has a planetary probe been sent to your planet?

2 Working with your group, brainstorm resources you might use to research the topic. Consider, for example, the library, the Internet, and subject experts at a local university or college.

3 As a group, organize the information you have gathered and prepare a class presentation. Use a variety of media and formats in your presentation, such as audio-visual aids, computer simulations, performance, flip charts, computerized database or spreadsheets, and scale models. As well, prepare a one-page summary of your planet profile to distribute to the rest of the class at the end of your presentation. Do not forget to list your sources of information.

Analyze

Using your planet database and the information you received from the presentations of all the other planet specialists, answer the following questions in your notebook. When you have finished, discuss your answers with the rest of the class.

1. Which planets are most unlike Earth? Why?

2. Which planets are most similar to Earth? How?

3. What pattern do you notice about the surface temperatures on the planets?

4. Venus is considered Earth's twin, yet we would probably not survive on Venus. Why?

5. What is the main difference between the inner and the outer planets? Use the data you have gathered to explain your answer.

6. Why does Venus have a higher surface temperature than Mercury?

7. (a) Describe how the data show a clear pattern in the characteristics of the planets.

   (b) If a planet were discovered beyond Pluto, speculate about what features it might have.

Data Cards for the Inner Planets

Pause&
Reflect

Space probe images of Mercury show that the planet has been hit thousands of times by space debris. Can you think of two reasons why a lack of atmosphere allows the craters to last for millions of years? Write your answers in your Science Log.

Mercury

Mercury has a thin crust and an inner solid layer, both composed of silicate rock. Beneath these is a huge iron-rich core, which makes up 80% of the planet's mass. Its very thin atmosphere consists of trace amounts of sodium and phosphorus that the fierce daytime surface temperatures (as high as 430 °C) "boil off" the planet's crust. Night temperatures drop to −180 °C. About 60% of Mercury's surface is covered by craters. The remaining area is relatively smooth, suggesting evidence of past lava flows from volcanic activity.

Mercury

Size (Earth-diameters): 0.38
Distance from Sun (AU): 0.39
Mass (Earth-masses): 0.06
Density (Earth-density): 1.0
Average Surface Temperature (°C): 350
Rotation Period (days): 58.7
Orbital Period (years): 0.24
Number of Moons: 0

Venus

Venus is enveloped by a thick atmosphere, 96% of which is carbon dioxide gas, 3.5% nitrogen, and the rest small amounts of other chemicals, including sulfuric acid rain. It is this atmosphere that accounts for Venus having the highest average surface temperature of any of the planets. The carbon dioxide is very efficient at trapping the solar radiation that falls on the planet's surface. A thin crust and rocky mantle surround Venus' semi-solid iron-nickel core. Radar mapping from Earth and space probes have revealed

large meteorite craters and extinct volcanoes. A particularly distinctive feature of Venus is that it rotates from east to west, rather than from west to east, as do most of the other planets and the Sun.

Venus

Size (Earth-diameters): 0.95
Distance from Sun (AU): 0.72
Mass (Earth-masses): 0.86
Density (Earth-density): 0.96
Average Surface Temperature (°C): 480
Rotation Period (days): 243
Orbital Period (years): 0.62
Number of Moons: 0

The main characteristic that sets Earth apart from the other planets is the presence of diverse life forms and large quantities of liquid water. Its distance from the Sun, in combination with its particular atmospheric make-up, produces a range of suitable surface temperatures for this to happen. Nitrogen dominates the atmosphere (78%). Life-sustaining oxygen (21%) has been present only for the past 2 billion years, originating from bacterial processes during life's early development. Water vapour (clouds), carbon dioxide, and other trace gases account for the remaining 1%. The thin crust is composed of rocks, some of which are 3.9 billion years old.

A rocky mantle surrounds a molten outer layer and solid inner iron-nickel core.

Earth's Moon orbits the planet in about a one-month period. At the same time, it also completes one rotation on its axis. The Moon's surface is significantly cratered. It also has large smooth areas that indicate past lava flows. Recent evidence shows water ice in the polar regions. Moon rocks brought back to Earth by Apollo astronauts are 4.5 billion years old. Compared with Earth, the Moon is much less dense, and its atmosphere is negligible.

Earth

Size (Earth-diameters): 1
Distance from Sun (AU): 1
Mass (Earth-masses): 1
Density (Earth-density): 1
Average Surface Temperature (°C): 22
Rotation Period (days): 1
Orbital Period (years): 1
Number of Moons: 1

Reddish-orange in colour because of iron oxides in the surface material, Mars is under intense scrutiny from Earth. It has polar ice caps and surface features such as valleys, canyons, volcanoes, and craters. As on Venus, the atmosphere is thin and composed mainly of carbon dioxide (95%). However, Mars' distance from the Sun reduces the amount of solar energy falling on its surface, so temperatures can be chilly, especially during the Martian night. The atmosphere's other parts are nitrogen (2.7%) and trace amounts of argon, oxygen, and water vapour. Robot probes like Pathfinder have explored the surface of the planet and recorded detailed images of the dust storms that are sometimes visible from Earth. An icy permafrost is present on the thin crust. Underneath, a rocky mantle surrounds a solid core.

Mars

Size (Earth-diameters): 0.53
Distance from Sun (AU): 1.52
Mass (Earth-masses): 0.11
Density (Earth-density): 0.71
Average Surface Temperature (°C): –23
Rotation Period (days): 1.02
Orbital Period (years): 1.88
Number of Moons: 2

Data Cards for the Outer Planets

Our knowledge of the outer planets comes mainly from four American spacecraft, Pioneers 10 and 11, and Voyagers 1 and 2. The Voyagers, in particular, made many exciting discoveries, as they went from planet to planet. On August 20, 1977, Voyager 2 was launched at high speed. Within 12 h, it had passed the Moon, a distance that the Apollo Moon mission took several days to cover. Within months, it had crossed the orbit of Mars. The trip to Jupiter, however, would take two years. This gives an idea of the immense distance between Earth and Jupiter. In July 1979, Voyager 2 arrived at Jupiter.

Jupiter

Giant Jupiter is 2.5 times the mass of all the other planets combined. At its centre is a rocky core about twice the size of Earth. The rest of the planet consists mainly of hydrogen in various states. Solid hydrogen forms an inner mantle, surrounded by a liquid hydrogen and helium outer mantle. No solid crust is present. Instead, the surface features visible from Earth are shapes in the atmosphere, like the Great Red Spot. Hydrogen is the main constituent of the atmosphere (90%), followed by helium (almost 10%). Trace amounts of methane, ammonia, and water vapour produce colourful effects in the distinctive cloud bands, formed as a result of Jupiter's rapid rotation. A narrow dust ring encircles the planet. It is composed of particles emitted from an active volcano on Io, one of Jupiter's 16 moons. Scientists believe that the moon Europa may have oceans of liquid water beneath frozen surface ice.

Jupiter

Size (Earth-diameters): 11.25
Distance from Sun (AU): 5.27
Mass (Earth-masses): 318
Density (Earth-density): 0.24
Average Surface Temperature (°C): −150
Rotation Period (days): 0.41
Orbital Period (years): 11.86
Number of Moons: 16

Saturn

The distinctive ring system of Saturn, a large yellowish planet, is composed of ice-covered rock fragments and dust. Although colder than Jupiter, Saturn has a structure that is similar to its large neighbour: a rock and ice core, solid hydrogen inner mantle, liquid hydrogen outer mantle, and atmosphere of 94% hydrogen, 6% helium, and traces of methane, ammonia, and water vapour. Saturn's rapid rotation produces cloud bands visible from Earth. Titan, the largest of Saturn's 18 moons, has an atmosphere.

Saturn

Size (Earth-diameters): 9.45
Distance from Sun (AU): 9.54
Mass (Earth-masses): 95
Density (Earth-density): 0.13
Average Surface Temperature (°C): −18
Rotation Period (days): 0.44
Orbital Period (years): 29.46
Number of Moons: 18

Uranus' rocky core and mantle of ice, ammonia, and methane are surrounded by a generally featureless atmosphere. That atmosphere is made up of 85% hydrogen and 12% helium. It is the 3% methane that absorbs red light and makes the planet seem predominantly blue. Uranus has a ring system similar to Saturn's. Most interesting, however, is the fact that Uranus rotates on an axis tilted 90° to the plane of the solar system. Additional moons, impossible to observe from Earth, continue to be discovered by space probes.

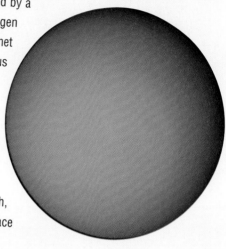

Uranus

Size (Earth-diameters): 4.01
Distance from Sun (AU): 19.19
Mass (Earth-masses): 15
Density (Earth-density): 0.24
Average Surface Temperature (°C): −214
Rotation Period (days): 0.72
Orbital Period (years): 84.01
Number of Moons: 17

Neptune

Almost a twin of Uranus, Neptune has the same internal structure as its slightly larger neighbour and a very similar atmosphere: 85% hydrogen, 13% helium, and 2% methane. A ring structure and a Giant Dark Spot were discovered by the space probe Voyager. One of Neptune's eight moons, Triton, has the coldest measured temperature in the solar system, −235 °C.

Neptune

Size (Earth-diameters): 3.96
Distance from Sun (AU): 30.06
Mass (Earth-masses): 17
Density (Earth-density): 0.27
Average Surface Temperature (°C): −220
Rotation Period (days): 0.67
Orbital Period (years): 164.8
Number of Moons: 8

Pluto

Because Pluto is so far away, very little information is known about it. Its orbit is tilted to the plane of the solar system by 17° and it is elongated enough to put Pluto, at times, closer to the Sun than Neptune. Like Venus, Pluto has retrograde rotation. It spins in the opposite direction to its direction of revolution. A "best guess" for Pluto's structure is that it has a large rocky core, an ice mantle, and a water and methane ice crust. Pluto's moon, Charon, is nearly as large as Pluto itself. Some scientists speculate that Pluto and Charon are examples of large debris left from the formation of the solar system.

Pluto

Size (Earth-diameters): 0.19
Distance from Sun (AU): 39.5
Mass (earth-masses): 0.002
Density (Earth-density): 0.36
Average Surface Temperature (°C): −230
Rotation Period (days): 6.4
Orbital Period (years): 247.7
Number of Moons: 1

In the summer of 1997, an astonishing press conference was held. Scientists from NASA announced that they had found tiny bacteria-like structures inside an ancient rock retrieved from Antarctica. What made this discovery so exciting was their claim that the rock came from Mars, part of the debris thrown into space from the planet's surface when a large object crashed into it long ago.

If the rock truly did come from Mars, and if the shapes seen under an electron microscope really were ancient bacteria, then this would be the first demonstration that Earth is not the only source of life in the universe. Despite the attention this announcement received, the validity of the discovery remains very controversial. Can you find out any more about this story from the Internet or other sources?

The Changing View of the Moon

The Moon is such a familiar sight to us in the night sky, but how has our view of it changed? An effective way to illustrate this is to develop a timeline. A timeline is a representation of key historical events in the order in which they occurred. These events are often plotted to scale on a line.

What to Do

1. Choose a scale for your timeline. For example, it could be in years, decades, or centuries.

2. Using this textbook and other available resources, determine the key events and discoveries that have contributed to our

Science Inquiry ACTIVITY

increased knowledge of the Moon. Plot them on your timeline. Begin as far back in history as you can and continue to recent times.

3. Compare your timeline with another student's. Add any additional information to your timeline you think is important.

What Did You Discover?

1. In your opinion, what has been the most significant discovery about the Moon? Why?

2. What part has technology played in broadening our understanding of the Moon? What has it allowed us to "see" that early people could not?

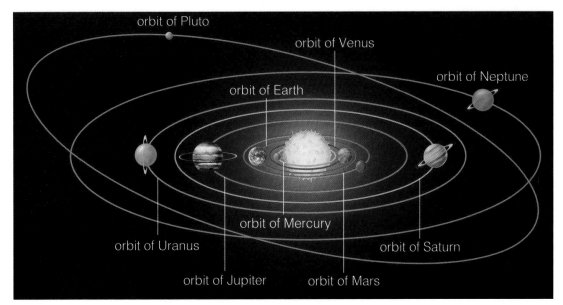

Figure 13.14 Pluto's orbit compared to the orbits of other planets. (Planet sizes are exaggerated.)

Modelling the Solar System

The solar system is so vast and empty that it is impossible to draw the sizes of the Sun and planets and the distances between them to the same scale on a regular piece of paper. For example, if the Sun were the size of a basketball, the planets and next nearest star (Proxima Centauri) would be at the following sizes and distances away:

Celestial Body	Size	Scale Distance from Sun
Sun	basketball	
Mercury	1 mm	10.9 m
Venus	2.4 mm	18.8 m
Earth	2.4 mm	28.1 m
Mars	1.3 mm	43.1 m
Jupiter	27 mm	146 m
Saturn	23 mm	262 m
Neptune	10 mm	544 m
Uranus	9.1 mm	844 m
Pluto	0.5 mm	1106 m
Nearest star	basketball	2700 km

The challenge for you and your class in this activity is to create your own scale model of the solar system, using the above data to guide you.

Science Inquiry

What to Do

1. Each student should represent a planet, holding a scale model or picture of the object at the correct distance from the "Sun."

2. Decide on a size or distance for your base scale. You will need to be practical here. If you decide Pluto is to be represented by a baseball, then the object you choose to represent Neptune would have to be ten times larger. For Jupiter, it would have to be almost 30 times larger. Achieving proportional distances can be tricky. Therefore, consider dividing or multiplying the above figures by a factor that will make modelling and positioning your "planets" manageable.

3. You may have to go outdoors to set up your model. A map of the local area can also be useful to show the locations of outer planets and beyond.

What Did You Discover?

Note that, even at the Sun-as-basketball scale, the distance to the nearest star is in kilometres. According to the scale you adopted for your model, where in Canada, relative to your school, would the nearest star be located?

Other Solar System Bodies

Asteroids

Voyager 2 journeyed to the outer planets making tremendous observations and measurements that have changed our view of the solar system dramatically. The trip was not without risk, since the craft had to pass through a region of millions of **asteroids** located between Mars and Jupiter. These objects, also known as "minor planets," range in size from a metre to hundreds of kilometres. Ceres, with a diameter of 1000 km, is the largest known asteroid. These irregularly shaped bodies are composed mostly of carbonaceous or silicate rock. Some are made of metal-rich materials. Of the millions of asteroids that exist, only about 5000 have been identified and their orbits calculated. Some asteroids have orbits that cross the path of Earth and pose a potential collision hazard.

Comets

Periodically, **comets** are visible to the unaided eye, but most must be detected by telescopes. These objects are made up mainly of dust and ice, leading scientists to develop a "dirty snowball" model for comets. It is speculated that billions of comets orbit the Sun at large distances (hundreds of astronomical units) away from it. Occasionally, a comet will get bumped from its orbit by the gravitational pull of several objects and fall toward the Sun in a very elongated orbit. As the comet approaches the Sun, material begins to evaporate from its surface, forming tails that can be thousands of kilometres long. The tail always points away from the Sun because it is pushed by the solar wind.

When it passed into the inner solar system in 1986, the well-known Comet Halley was observed by five space probes. The European Giotto spacecraft sent the first-ever close-up images of a comet, showing Comet Halley to have an irregularly shaped 16 km by 8 km nucleus.

Meteors and Meteorites

Every day, Earth is bombarded by thousands of dust and rock fragments from space. When they enter the atmosphere, friction causes these particles to heat up and vaporize. If the fragment is large enough, however, it sometimes burns up, generating enough light to make it visible. These are called **meteors**. (They are commonly called "shooting stars," although of course they are not stars at all.) Some fragments are either large enough or tough enough that a remnant survives to strike Earth's surface. These are **meteorites**. These fragments that reach Earth provide scientists with extraterrestrial materials to study.

Figure 13.15 In 1994, the world watched as Comet Shoemaker-Levy collided with Jupiter. Chunks of the comet hit Jupiter several hours apart. Each impact left marks the size of Earth in Jupiter's atmosphere.

Why Do the Seasons Go Round and Round?

In the past, people had well-reasoned ideas about space and astronomy. As you know, many of those ideas have been replaced. In the 1400s, for instance, some people thought Earth was flat. Do you know of any strange ideas or misconceptions about our solar system or another place in the universe? There are some common misconceptions about what causes the seasons. During this investigation, you can find out what these are.

Challenge

Design a questionnaire and conduct interviews to find out how people outside your classroom explain the changing seasons.

Materials

paper and pen, or computer (for questionnaire)
paper and pencil (for use by interview subjects)
ball (to represent Earth)
flashlight (to represent the Sun)

Design Criteria

A. Your questionnaire should be no longer than one page, including the space you leave to write down people's responses.
B. Your questionnaire should include a mix of question types: multiple choice, closed, and open-ended. "Closed" questions are those to which only a one-word response is likely. For example, to the question "Do you think the Moon has an influence on Earth's seasons?" most people would answer yes or no. "Open-ended" questions are those that invite people to answer with a full explanation. An example of such a question: "Describe what is happening to Earth when we move from winter through to summer."
C. Your subject group should be adults outside of school or younger children. You should plan to interview between five and ten individuals in total.

Plan and Construct

1 Design your questionnaire. Include as many questions as you think will be necessary to have people provide you with the information you require. You may also want to have interview subjects draw a diagram, or use the ball and flashlight, to explain what they mean.

2 Decide how many people you want to interview, and arrange when and where you will ask them the questions.

3 Many people are embarrassed by being asked questions they cannot answer. Your questions and approach should take this into account. Each of us has "gaps" in our knowledge, so being sensitive to the fact that your interview subjects may be embarrassed about what they might not know is very important to your interview process. (For example, you might wish to share your results with all subjects interviewed so they see that many people have misconceptions.)

4 During interviews, record each interview subject's answers as you pose each question, so that you accurately capture his or her responses.

5 When you have completed all your interviews, analyze the information and look for patterns. Design a graph to show how many answers you received in each category.

Evaluate

1. How would you categorize the explanations you received about what causes the seasons? How many explanations did you receive in each category?

2. What were the most common misconceptions you heard about the cause of seasons?

3. What do you think would be the best way to teach people about the changing of the seasons?

Out of the Solar System

Like Voyager 1 and the two Pioneer space probes, Voyager 2 has left the solar system and is now travelling through space. It is still working, though, and will continue to send back images and other measurements until about 2030. The fastest-moving object humans have ever constructed, Voyager spent a total of 20 years sailing to the edge of our solar system. It will be at the distance of the nearest star in about 50 000 years.

Pioneers 10 and 11, the first crafts to leave our solar system, have plaques affixed to them. These plaques show a sketch of a human male and female, with the spacecraft in the background for scale. Other markings are meant to show that we are carbon-based life that came from the third planet from a star. In addition to plaques, Voyagers 1 and 2 carry laser disk recordings of Earth noises. It is possible that, in the distant future, some other space-faring intelligence might discover these artifacts of our civilization.

INTERNET CONNECT

www.school.mcgrawhill.ca/resources/
To find out more about the Voyager mission, and those of other spacecraft, go to the above web site. Go to **Science Resources**, then to **SCIENCEPOWER 9** to find sites that contain diagrams of the spacecraft, maps of the journeys, day-to-day accountings, and images. Write a short report on some of the latest findings from these space probes.

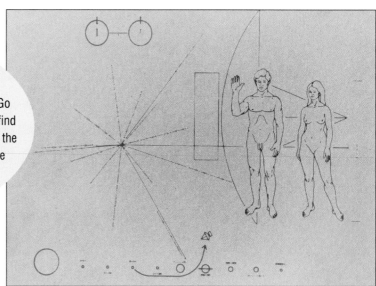

Figure 13.16 This is one of the plaques affixed to the Pioneer spacecraft that left Earth in 1973. If you were to design a plaque for a new space probe, what information do you think would be important to include?

Check Your Understanding

1. What is an astronomical unit and what is it used to measure?

2. Approximately how much larger than Earth's diameter is the Sun's diameter?

3. Which planets are closer to the Sun than Earth? Which are farther away?

4. How does Uranus differ from the other eight planets?

5. What are comets, and how do they differ from asteroids and meteors?

6. **Thinking Critically** Explain why Neptune is sometimes farther from the Sun than Pluto.

7. **Thinking Critically** What evidence is there that water is or was present on Mars?

Now that you have completed this chapter, try to do the following. If you cannot, go back to the sections indicated.

List five reasons why knowledge of celestial motion was important to our early ancestors. (13.1)

Describe the apparent pattern of motion of the Sun, Moon, and stars as seen by an observer on Earth. (13.2)

Name the five planets that the ancient Greeks believed to be "wanderers" through the night sky. (13.2)

Describe the main differences between the Earth-centred model of the universe and the Sun-centred model. (13.3)

Explain the meaning of "retrograde motion." (13.3)

Describe how technology helped Galileo provide evidence in support of the Copernican heliocentric model. (13.3)

Make a labelled diagram showing all nine planets in the solar system, presented in order according to their distance from the Sun. (13.4)

Describe the key features of the Sun. (13.4)

Calculate the distance between the Sun and each of the planets in kilometres. (13.4)

Name the inner (or terrestrial) planets and identify two distinguishing features of each one. (13.4)

Explain why Neptune appears to be blue and Mars appears to be reddish-orange. (13.4)

Describe the reasons that Earth is able to sustain such a wide variety of life forms. (13.4)

Distinguish among the following: asteroids, comets, and meteors. (13.4)

Prepare Your Own Summary

Summarize this chapter by doing one of the following. Use a graphic organizer (such as a concept map), produce a poster, or write a summary to include the key chapter concepts. Here are a few ideas to use as a guide:

• What celestial movements were recorded by early people and how was this information used?

• How did the Earth-centred model explain celestial motion?

• Who were some of the key scientists in developing the Sun-centred model of the solar system, and what was their contribution?

• Why do Mars, Jupiter, and Saturn sometimes appear to reverse direction for brief periods relative to the westward motion of the stars?

• What are the two main groupings of planets in the solar system, and why are they characterized in this way?

• Draw a sketch that shows the nine planets in the solar system, in the order of their distance from the Sun.

Reviewing Key Terms

If you need to review, the section numbers show you where these terms were introduced.

1. In your notebook, match each expression from column A with the correct word in column B.

A
• star of our solar system
• streamers of gas arching from the Sun
• area across which the planets' orbits lie
• everything revolves around Earth
• "dirty snowballs"
• bodies of rock or gas orbiting the Sun
• planets revolve around the Sun
• vaporizing dust or rock fragments
• rocks orbiting the Sun between the orbits of Mars and Jupiter

B
• solar plane (13.3)
• meteors (13.4)
• photosphere (13.4)
• geocentric model (13.3)
• asteroids (13.4)
• Sun (13.4)
• solar prominences (13.4)
• comets (13.4)
• heliocentric model (13.3)
• planets (13.2)
• corona (13.4)

2. Why did Ptolemy introduce epicycles to the heliocentric model? (13.3)

3. Is Uranus an inner planet or an outer planet? Explain your answer. (13.4)

Understanding Key Concepts

4. The diagram below shows the planets and Sun at approximately the same scale for size. The distances between them are not to scale, and are vastly greater than represented here. Copy the diagram into your notebook and, without looking at your planet database, label the planets in order. (13.4)

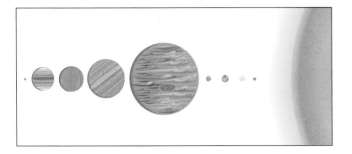

5. Name the planet:
   (a) Which planet was discovered through the knowledge of Newton's law of gravitation? (13.4)

   (b) Which planet has a moon with an atmosphere? (13.4)

   (c) From the surface of which planet did a space probe send back to Earth images of dust storms? (13.4)

   (d) One planet's orbit crosses inside that of another planet. Name the two planets. (13.4)

   (e) This rocky planet is baking hot during the day and freezing cold at night. Which one? (13.4)

   (f) The Sun is almost directly over the equator of all planets except one. Which one? (13.4)

   (g) Which planet has a moon with a possible ocean of water under a crust of ice? (13.4)

   (h) Which planet has a large percentage of oxygen in its atmosphere? (13.4)

6. Why is the Sun's gravitational force so much stronger than that of any of the planets? (13.4)

7. If a large meteorite reached Earth's surface, what feature might it create? (13.4)

8. Comet Halley has an orbital period of 76 years. It was last observed from Earth in 1986. In what year will it be visible again? (13.4)

Developing Skills

9. From the library or the Internet, research the following:

   (a) Galileo discovered the four largest moons of Jupiter. What other astronomical discoveries did he make?

   (b) Who discovered that comets are not just one-time visitors to Earth?

   (c) When will the next total solar and lunar eclipses be visible to us in Canada?

10. Jupiter's Great Red Spot is about 40 000 km long and 12 000 wide. How large is this area in square kilometres?

11. How do the distances between the inner planets compare? How do distances between the outer planets compare? Explain how the distances within each group compare to the group's distance from the Sun.

Problem Solving

12. If you were travelling in a spacecraft at 10 000 km/h, how long would it take to travel from Earth to Mars when the two planets are closest to each other on the same side of the Sun? Hint: Use the information in your planet database to help you calculate the answer.

13. The figure below shows six images of Jupiter and its moons taken one hour apart.

(Astronomers often use negative images, because black objects on a white sky can be easier to see.) The images are out of sequence.

(a) What is the correct order?

(b) Which moons move the fastest: those nearest the planet or those farthest away?

14. Why is the length of Earth's day (24 h) 4 minutes longer than the actual time it takes Earth to rotate (23 h 56 min)? A diagram of Earth and the Sun will be useful in solving this puzzle.

15. We can see phases of the Moon: crescent, half, full. For which two planets can we also see phases? Why? Illustrate with a diagram.

Critical Thinking

16. Why would landing a spacecraft on Jupiter or Saturn be an unlikely event?

17. Why do we see the Sun only during the day and the other stars only at night?

18. Uranus' rings were first spotted from Earth during an eclipse of a star by Uranus. Why would this be?

Pause & Reflect

1. Given your answer to question 12 above, think about which factors might limit the feasibility of making a journey between Earth and Mars (for example, in terms of fuel, costs, time, and human requirements). What planning would you have to do before trying to undertake such a voyage?

2. If Earth is moving through space and spinning, why do we not feel dizzy or sense that we are moving? Do you have *any* evidence that Earth is moving?

14 The Lives of Stars

Opening Ideas...

- How do we know what is in stars?
- Why do star maps show constellations, but not distances between stars?
- Do other stars have planets?
- How could you find out if some stars are younger than others?

Science Log

Using your knowledge of the Sun and our solar system, write your answers to the questions in your Science Log as well as you can for now. Watch for answers to all of these questions as you explore this chapter.

It is easy to believe that stars are mere pinpricks of light, fixed forever in the sky. The approximately 6000 stars visible to the unaided eye seem unchanging in pattern, motion, and shape — like a twinkling ceiling to our universe. When new tools, such as the telescope and Newton's law of gravitation, first gave astronomers the ability to "see" farther, they began to develop new explanations for what they observed.

The discovery of the remote planets in our solar system was just the beginning of this expanding view of the universe. By combining telescopes and photography, astronomers were able to collect and record light from objects too faint to be seen with the unaided eye. These technological improvements revealed not a few thousand stars, but billions of them. Now we can observe fantastic spectacles, such as the Cone Nebula (above), recorded by the Hubble Space Telescope. We can also witness the birth of new stars.

In this chapter, you will look to the stars, those hot, glowing spheres of gas, such as our Sun. Are all stars similar to the Sun? Do they have planets too? How do stars form and from what are they made? Do they last forever? How did our solar system form? By the end of this chapter, you will be able to answer these questions and others related to how stars evolve.

Key Concepts

In this chapter, you will discover

- how astronomers analyze starlight to determine a star's temperature, composition, and size
- what the Hertzsprung-Russell diagram revealed about the properties of stars
- what determines the life cycle of stars
- how new stars and planets are born and evolve
- the currently accepted theory for the foundation of the solar system

Key Skills

In this chapter, you will

- investigate the factors that affect the observable brightness of stars
- analyze the relationship between star colour and surface temperature
- analyze spectral patterns to identify star composition
- interpret data of the seven main star types
- develop and evaluate a theory for the formation of stars and planets

Key Terms

- electromagnetic spectrum
- luminosity
- binary stars
- solar mass
- red dwarfs
- main sequence
- white dwarfs
- red giants
- supergiants
- nebulae
- fusion
- planetary nebula
- black dwarfs
- supernova
- neutron star
- black holes
- inter-stellar medium
- solar nebula theory
- extra-solar planets

Starting Point ACTIVITY

Why Do Some Stars Seem Brighter Than Others?

Think About It

Are all stars equally bright? In this activity, find out what factors might affect apparent brightness. Your group will need three flashlights: a small one (such as a penlight) and two larger ones (such as utility flashlights).

What to Do

1. One group member stands at the back of the classroom holding one small and one large flashlight in each hand. Stand at the front. Darken the room and ask the student at the back to turn on both flashlights. How does the brightness of the two lights compare? Record your observation.

2. Two group members stand side by side at the back of the classroom, each holding one of the large flashlights. Again, stand at the front. Darken the room and ask the students to turn on the flashlights. Again, record your observation.

3. Ask one of the students holding the lighted flashlights to walk toward you, while the other student stays in place. Compare the brightness of the two lights. Now have the student who has approached you hold the small flashlight instead of the large one. How does the brightness of the two lights compare this time? Record your observations.

What Did You Discover?

1. What two factors affect the brightness of light? What does this tell us about the observable brightness of stars?

2. Imagine that two stars, X and Y, emit the same amount of light. From Earth, however, star X appears to be 50 times brighter than star Y. What might you conclude about how far each star is from Earth?

14.1 The Properties of Stars

Look at the sky on a clear night when the Moon is not visible, and you will notice how stars differ in their brightness. Some, even to the unaided eye, are dazzling points of light, while others are very faint. Train a pair of binoculars or a telescope on a small region of the sky and suddenly many, many stars become visible. Until improved technology was available for "collecting" that faint light, it was not known that so many stars existed.

A telescope is a light collector. Its huge lens or mirror is like a giant eye. It collects all the starlight that falls on it and concentrates it in the eyepiece. To store even more light and detect fainter stars, a camera can be placed over the eyepiece and a long time exposure photograph taken. (Computer-controlled digital imaging cameras are frequently used today.) Astronomers have inferred a great deal from starlight about important properties of stars: brightness, colour, temperature, composition, mass, and size.

"Seeing" Light

You may remember from your previous science studies that visible light — the light that the human eye can detect — is a form of radiation, or energy, that is transmitted from one place to another by electromagnetic waves. Other types of electromagnetic radiation also exist, such as radio waves, microwaves, infrared rays, ultraviolet rays, and X rays. As Figure 14.2 shows, each form of electromagnetic radiation has a different range of wavelengths. This arrangement of electomagnetic radiation is called the **electromagnetic spectrum**.

Figure 14.1 Perched high on mountain tops, observatories around the world collect and classify information about stars and other objects in the universe. The one pictured here is operated by the University of Toronto in Las Campanas, Chile, the site from which Ian Shelton discovered supernova 1987a.

Tools of Science

Modern technology, such as the radio telescope, can record wavelengths of electromagnetic radiation not visible to our eyes. Thus we can detect objects that were previously undetectable.

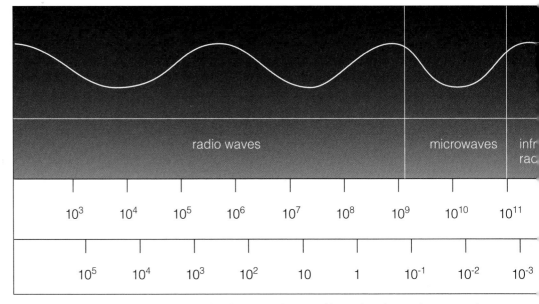

Figure 14.2 The electromagnetic spectrum. What happens to frequency (the number of waves that pass a point per second) as wavelength shortens?

The Brightness of Stars

In the Starting Point Activity, you saw how size and distance can affect how bright a light-emitting object appears. This is also the case with stars. One star can seem brighter than another either because it is larger or because it is closer to Earth. The closest stars to Earth are not necessarily the brightest.

Once astronomers understood the distances to stars, they realized that **luminosity** is a property of the stars themselves. Luminosity is a measure of the total amount of energy a star radiates per second. Just as it is useful to compare information about the planets in our solar system to Earth (the planet we know the best), it is useful to compare other stars to the Sun (the star we know best). In these terms, astronomers have found that some stars are at least 30 000 times more luminous than the Sun, while others are 10 000 times less luminous.

The Temperature and Composition of Stars

Although the stars in the night sky generally look like small points of white light, in fact they range widely in colour. If you studied them with a powerful telescope, you would see that some are bluish white or pale green, and some are yellow or orangey-red.

Astronomers use the colour of a star to infer its surface temperature. (Think of a glowing light bulb or a hot toaster element.) The colour of starlight is identified in terms of wavelengths in the electromagnetic spectrum, to give a measuring tool for star temperature. A yellow star, such as the Sun, is relatively hot, with a surface temperature of about 6000°C. A red star is relatively cool, about 3000°C. A blue star is extremely hot, typically measuring between 20 000 and 35 000°C.

Figure 14.3 To our eyes, stars vary greatly in brightness because of their luminosity and relative distance from Earth.

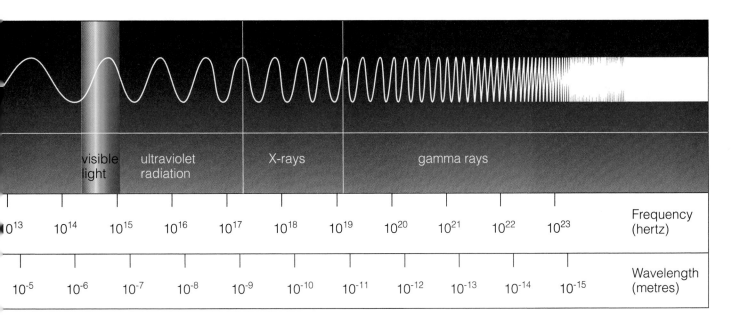

What Can Star Colour Tell You About Star Temperature?

Think About It

Have you ever noticed what happens to the heating elements in a toaster while it is toasting your bread? The change in colour that takes place indicates the change in temperature as the elements heat up and then cool down again. In this activity, an electric light with a dimmer switch (for example, a floor lamp or a ceiling light) will help you analyze the relationship between temperature and colour more closely. It may help you draw conclusions about how star temperature and colour are related.

Safety Precaution

- When using any electrical equipment, make sure that electrical cords are not frayed and light switches are working properly.

- Do not touch hot light bulbs.

What to Do

1. Turn on the light. (The light bulb represents a star emitting light.)

2. Turn the light up to its full brightness, but do not stare directly at the bulb. What colour is the light being emitted?

3. Now slowly start turning the dimmer switch down. Record the colour changes you see. Especially, note the colour when the bulb is turned down very low.

What Did You Discover?

1. When the dimmer switch was turned down, why was the light a different colour than when the dimmer switch was turned up?

2. Formulate a statement about the relationship between the temperature of a light source and the colour of the light emitted.

Colour tells us more about a star than its temperature. Analysis of starlight also indicates a star's composition. To analyze the light in this way, astronomers use a spectroscope, an instrument you used in your study of chemistry. Recall that a spectroscope separates light into a spectrum (bands of different colours), much like a prism separates white light into its rainbow colours. A star's spectrum also shows dark bands across the colours. These bands reveal that some wavelengths of light have "disappeared," absorbed by gases in the star's atmosphere. Each element (hydrogen, helium, mercury, calcium, and so on) leaves its unique pattern of dark bands — like a bar code — on a spectrum. From these spectral patterns, what can you infer about the elements making up a star's atmosphere? Astronomers have used this information, as well as basic star colour or temperature, to classify stars.

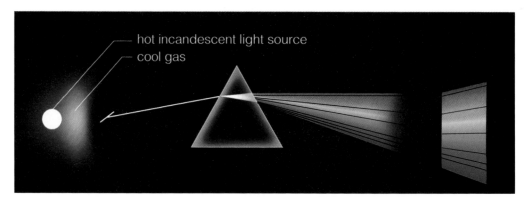

Figure 14.4 Simplified view of how a spectroscope produces the trademark spectral pattern that is characteristic of hydrogen gas.

Long-Distance Chemistry: Analyzing Spectral Patterns to Identify Star Composition

Think About It

In this activity, you get an opportunity to apply the method that astronomers use to detect the chemical make-up of a star. You will examine the simplified spectra of five known chemical elements and use that information to interpret the composition of the Sun and three "mystery stars."

What to Do

1 The figure below displays the spectral patterns for five elements. Study these spectra to familiarize yourself with their patterns.

2 Examine the spectra for the Sun and the three "mystery stars". Using a ruler to help you line up the spectral lines, compare the spectral patterns of the known elements to those of the Sun and the three unknown stars. Then, answer the following questions.

Analyze

1. Which elements are present in the Sun's spectrum?

2. In which two mystery stars is calcium present?

3. Which mystery star contains Na?

4. Only one mystery star contains Hg. Which one is it?

5. Which mystery star's composition is least like that of the Sun?

6. In a paragraph, briefly describe how a star's composition can be inferred by analyzing its spectral pattern.

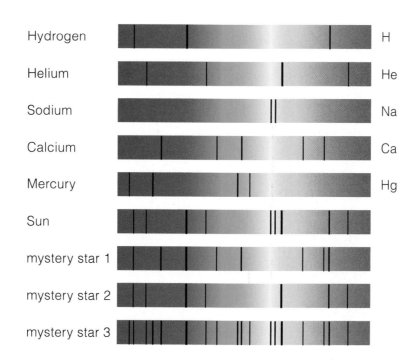

Hydrogen — H

Helium — He

Sodium — Na

Calcium — Ca

Mercury — Hg

Sun

mystery star 1

mystery star 2

mystery star 3

Figure 14.5 Binary stars provide astronomers with the information they need to determine star mass. This imaginary planet has two suns.

The Size and Mass of Stars

Astronomers found they could calculate the size or radius of a star once they knew its luminosity and temperature. (Luminosity can be measured with an instrument much like a photometer, or "distance meter," used by photographers.) Stars, it turns out, come in many sizes, ranging from "dwarf" stars, 0.10 the radius of the Sun, to enormous stars, more than 1000 times the Sun's radius.

Determining the mass of stars was not possible until it was discovered that more than half the stars we can see from Earth are **binary stars**, two single stars orbiting one another. By knowing the size of the orbit of a binary pair, and the time the two stars take to complete one orbit, astronomers were able to calculate the mass of each star.

Star mass is expressed in terms of **solar mass**. The Sun is a 1 solar mass star; other stars range from 0.08 solar mass to over 100 solar masses.

The Hertzsprung-Russell Diagram

As astronomers learned more about the properties of stars, they began to search for patterns in the data. As you know, graphing data can be a useful way to identify patterns. In the 1920s, Ejnar Hertzsprung and Henry Norris Russell plotted the luminosity and colour of several thousand stars. Their graph had star colour on the *x*-axis (ranging from blue to red) and star luminosity on the *y*-axis. From the graph, called a Hertzsprung-Russell (H-R) diagram, astronomers discovered that there are several different types of stars.

Figure 14.7 shows the H-R diagram. You learned earlier that a star's colour indicates its temperature, so you can see why the *x*-axis ranges from high temperature to low temperature. Although the original graph consisted only of dots, this version of the diagram allows you to visualize the different types of stars. Stretching from upper left to lower right is the main sequence, containing 90% of all known stars. Sample stars have been drawn to illustrate that this group ranges from large, bright, hot, blue stars to small, faint, dim, red stars. The Sun is shown near the middle. To begin to understand the original H-R diagram, astronomers had to discover more about stars. The next piece of evidence was the discovery that the luminosity and temperature of main sequence stars are related to their mass.

What of the 10% of known stars not in the main sequence? Hertzsprung and Russell found that some stars were cooler but very bright. Their dots fell far above the main sequence. Find these red giants and supergiants in the diagram and note their sizes. Also, there were some stars that were very hot, yet not very bright. Where are they located in the diagram? What are they called? The fact that some stars are not in the main sequence led astronomers

Figure 14.6 This 20 min exposure shows Orion rising. Notice the different colours of the stars. On the left is the cool, giant star, Betelgeuse. On the bottom right is Rigel, a bright, very hot, blue-white star. While the brightest stars form the constellation, Orion contains a great many dimmer stars as well.

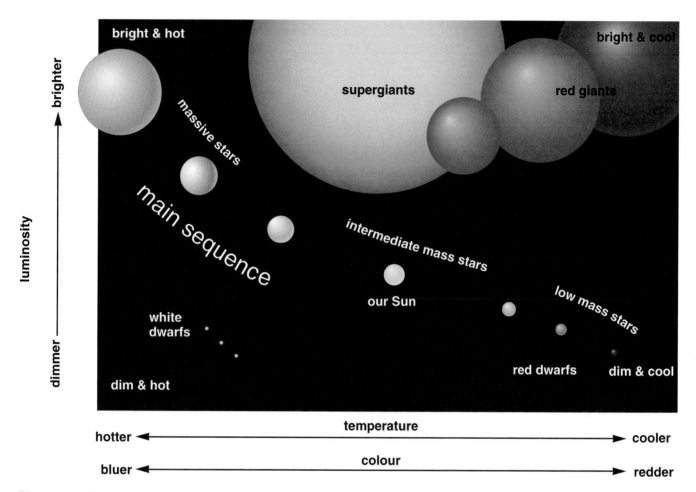

Figure 14.7 This simplified version of the Hertzsprung-Russell diagram is based on data from thousands of stars. It shows that there is a relationship among star colour, temperature, luminosity, and mass. Once astronomers recognized this pattern, they realized that stars were not unchanging and eternal after all. As you will discover in section 14.2, they have a definite, predictable life cycle.

to wonder how these stars came to be. Were they special, rare types of stars that formed in a different way? Or could they be examples of some stages in the life of main sequence stars that went through a drastic change? You will discover astronomers' theories for the formation and evolution of stars in Section 14.2.

Check Your Understanding

1. Write a definition for luminosity. Why is this concept so important for understanding the brightness of stars?

2. Which two factors explain why one star may appear to be brighter than another?

3. A colour photograph of the sky will show that stars actually differ in colour. How can the colour of starlight reveal the temperature of a star?

4. Which instrument does an astronomer use to analyze the spectrum of a star? What does the spectrum of a star tell you?

5. What is the Hertzsprung-Russell diagram and why is it so important to astronomy research?

6. **Thinking Critically** Why might a cooler star appear to be brighter than a hotter star?

14.2 The Evolution of Stars

Figure 14.8 The Eagle Nebula

Newton's law of gravitation states that an attractive gravitational force exists between all masses, and that this force gets stronger the closer the objects become. For example, two apples far apart in space would attract each other and eventually come together. Two atoms of hydrogen would behave the same way, because they also have mass (although it is very tiny compared to that in an apple with its billions and billions of atoms).

Gravity is constantly at work. It is the force that not only helps create and build stars, but that ultimately causes them to die. Figure 14.9 illustrates the evolution of various types of stars. Refer to this figure as you read through this section.

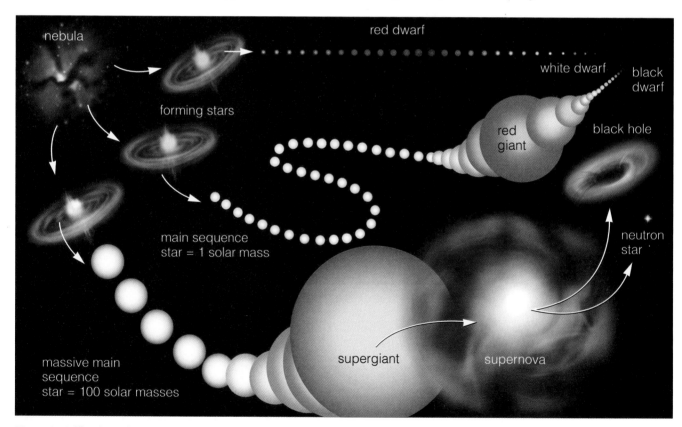

Figure 14.9 The phases in the life of stars

Nebulae

Astronomers speculate that vast clouds of gas and dust called **nebulae** (the plural of nebula) are the birth place of stars. It is in those clouds that gravity works to pull "inter-stellar" material together. The accumulating gas causes the temperature in the centre to rise. When it reaches about 10 000 000°C, the nuclear reaction, **fusion** (the transformation of hydrogen into helium), begins and the star "turns on."

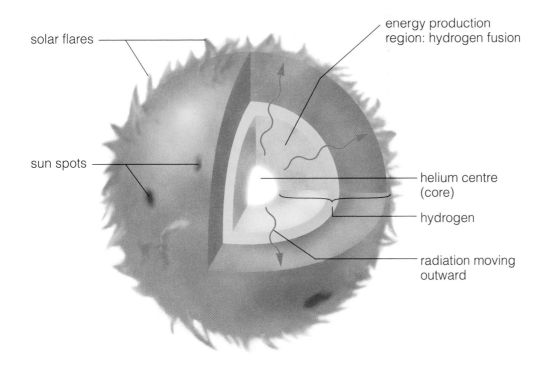

solar flares

energy production
region: hydrogen fusion

sun spots

helium centre
(core)

hydrogen

radiation moving
outward

Figure 14.10 Fusion occurs in the core of stars. In the core, the temperature and pressure are high enough to cause hydrogen atoms to fuse and create helium. The high heat makes the hydrogen atoms so energetic that they collide. When they fuse, energy is released and the star shines.

Main Sequence Stars

Once the fusion process begins, it starts to consume the hydrogen fuel. Helium begins to accumulate in the core of the star. The interior of the star continues to heat up, increasing the pressure and temperature. These forces are balanced by the force of the gravitational pull toward the centre. The result is a stable state. All main sequence stars, including our Sun, are in this condition. The time that a star remains in the stable main sequence phase, before advancing to a later phase, depends on its mass.

Low Mass Stars (Red Dwarfs)

Low mass stars (red dwarfs) consume their hydrogen slowly over a period that may be as long as 100 billion years. During that time, they lose significant mass, essentially evaporating. In the end, all that remains of them is a very faint **white dwarf**.

Intermediate Mass Stars

Intermediate mass stars (such as the Sun) consume their hydrogen a little faster than their low mass neighbours, over a period of about 10 billion years. When the hydrogen has been used up in the core of one these stars, energy production stops and the core resumes its gravity-driven collapse. As the core contracts, the temperature increases and the outer layers of the star begin to expand. By the end of this phase, the star can be 10 to 100 times its original diameter. When the temperature in the core reaches 100 000 000°C, the helium starts fusing into carbon.

Because the star has expanded to such an enormous size, the outer layers are much cooler than when the star was a main sequence star. It therefore appears red, earning the name of red giant. Our Sun will evolve to this phase in about 5 billion years, its diameter expanding beyond what is now the size of the orbit of Mars.

Stellar winds peel away gases, eventually revealing the hot inner region of the star. The result is a **planetary nebula**, a fuzzy "nebulous" object similar in appearance (through a telescope) to a planet such as Neptune, though these bodies have nothing to do with planets. Over time, a planetary nebula disperses into space, its remnant cooling slowly and losing brightness. It then becomes a white dwarf. White dwarfs cannot shrink any further in size, but their super-dense core gradually cools over billions of years. In their final phase, they are nothing more than a dark cinder called a **black dwarf**.

The first white dwarf discovered was a companion star of Sirius, the brightest star in the night sky. Sirius B, as it is known, is 10 000 times fainter than Sirius, has a surface temperature of 32 500°C, and is three-quarters the size of Earth. A teaspoonful of material from this white dwarf would weigh more than 15 t.

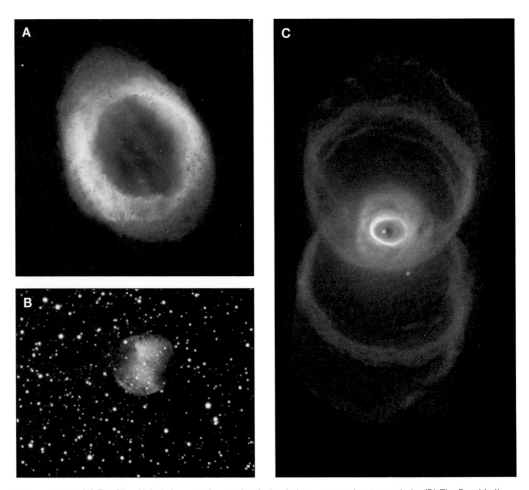

Figure 14.11 (A) The Ring Nebula is a good example of what is known as a planetary nebula. (B) The Dumbbell Nebula and (C) the Hour Glass Nebula are also examples. Over 1500 planetary nebulae have been discovered and each one is huge, many times the size of the solar system.

Massive Stars

High mass stars consume their hydrogen very rapidly. Their core gets so hot that the helium can fuse into heavier elements. So much energy is released in this process that the star swells into a supergiant.

In stellar terms, the evolution of massive stars is extremely fast. For example, a 25-solar mass star on the main sequence will burn hydrogen in its core for only 7 million years (compared to the 10 billion years it will take the Sun). The helium burning phase in that same star will last only 500 000 years. The most dramatic stage of evolution in the core, however, is when silicon is being transformed into iron. That process takes one day.

Supernovas

Massive stars live short, bright, energetic lives, but their final exit is even more spectacular. Once an iron core is achieved, no further fusion processes are available to counteract the force of gravity, and the core collapses. As a massive shock wave bursts from the star's surface a few hours later, it causes a huge explosion, or **supernova**, such as the one Canadian astronomer Ian Shelton saw in 1987.

Word CONNECT

"Nebula" derives from which Latin word? What does the Latin word mean? Based on this definition, why is "nebula" an appropriate word to describe a particular type of astronomical phenomena? How is the word "nebulous" used in the English language? Use it in a sentence.

Pause&Reflect

Initially, the remnant stars from which planetary nebulae form are very bright and have high surface temperatures. In which region of the H-R diagram do you think these stars would lie? Draw a sketch of the diagram in your Science Log and show approximately where you would plot the remnant stars.

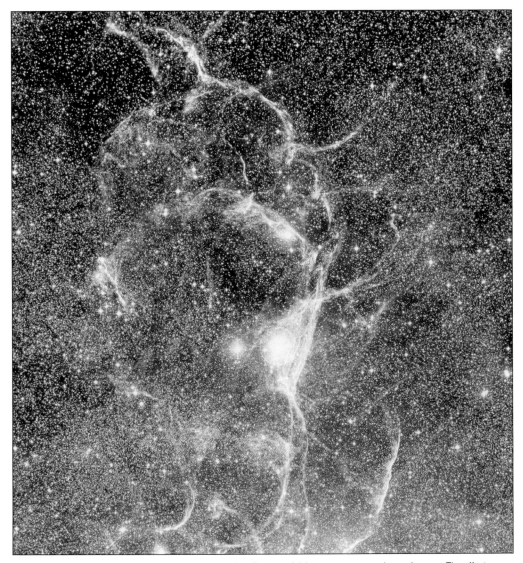

Figure 14.12 A supernova blasts vast quantities of stellar material into enormous regions of space. The effect, as shown in this image of the Vela Nebula, is dazzling.

Interpreting Main Sequence Star Data

Think About It

The classification of stars by surface temperature and spectral pattern is a painstaking process requiring the efforts of many scientists from hundreds of observatories around the world. To make it easier to refer to the different types of main sequence stars, a series of broad categories of star types was developed. These were named O, B, A, F, G, K, and M.

What to Do

Seven main sequence star types are listed in the data table below. Use this information, as well as what you have already learned about the evolution of stars, to answer the questions.

Analyze

1. Which star type in the table is a red dwarf? Explain your answer.

2. Which star type is most similar to the Sun? Explain your answer.

3. Which star types are likely to become supernovas? Why? How long do we have to wait for this to occur?

4. If any planets existed in orbit around the A-type star, could life as we know it develop on them?

5. Our Sun is halfway through its life on the main sequence. If all seven stars formed at the same time as the Sun, which ones could we observe today?

Star Type	Colour	Surface Temperature (°C)	Mass (Sun=1)	Luminosity (Sun=1)	Lifetime on Main Sequence (Years)
O	blue	35 000	40	405 000	1 million
B	blue-white	21 000	15	13 000	11 million
A	white	10 000	3.5	80	440 million
F	yellow-white	7 500	1.7	6.4	3 billion
G	yellow	6 000	1.1	1.4	8 billion
K	orange	4 700	0.8	0.46	17 billion
M	red	3 300	0.5	0.08	56 billion

Neutron Stars

After the supernova phase, a star has one of two fates, depending on its mass. If the remaining core of the supernova is about 1.4 to 3 solar masses, the gravity within it is still capable of crushing the remnant into a small 10 to 20 km diameter, super-dense object called a **neutron star**. This extreme state of matter was speculation for a long time. But in 1967, astronomers, using radio telescopes, detected radio pulses from rapidly rotating objects called pulsars. These turned out to be the neutron stars whose existence had been predicted.

Black Holes

Supernova cores of 3 solar masses or greater have a more astonishing end. It is believed they form **black holes**, objects so compact and dense that not even light can escape. Black holes are the most extreme conclusion of gravity's work in stellar evolution.

DidYouKnow?

With few exceptions, all the chemical elements you know from the periodic table are produced by massive stars. These "element factories" use hydrogen as their raw material, transforming it into helium, carbon, neon, oxygen, silicon, iron, and so on. Stellar winds and supernovas are the distributors of these products, dispersing the material out into space.

Check Your Understanding

1. At what temperature does fusion begin to occur? In what part of a star does it occur? Why?

2. Out of which material do stars begin to form?

3. Which force is active all the time, from creating a star to causing its ultimate end?

4. What causes a star to become a red giant?

5. What property of a star has the greatest effect on what the state of that star will be late in life? Why?

6. What is a white dwarf and how is it formed?

7. **Thinking Critically** Electrical repulsion between electrons keeps atoms apart, even though the atoms' forces of gravity attempt to pull them together. This is what gives matter (rocks, water, a desk) its size and density. But if enough mass accumulates, the combined force of gravity can overwhelm the electric and nuclear forces. The object can shrink into something vastly smaller. Which two final states of massive stars can result from this process? Which of these states requires the most mass?

Across Canada

Werner Israel researches black holes, gigantic areas of mass with incredible amounts of gravity, which suck in everything nearby. Whatever objects go into black holes never emerge again — not even light! This makes black holes very intriguing.

Dr. Israel is a physicist and cosmologist. He studies the orbits and mysterious interiors of black holes to learn what happens inside them and what the nucleus (centre of the black hole) is made of. He is a retired professor, but still conducts his research at the University of Victoria in British Columbia. In 1994 he won the prestigious Killam prize given to distinguished professors.

Dr. Israel has a solid background in mathematics. Using math, he has revealed that black holes are the simplest big objects in the universe. They have a uniform composition throughout. He showed that black holes were similar to electrons (which are also simple) and not complex like stars. With a mathematical formula, it is possible to calculate the mass of a black hole.

When Dr. Israel was a child, his father recognized that he was fascinated by astronomy, and he encouraged his son to learn more about the field. One day he brought his son a set of encyclopedias that he had traded for an old suit. In these volumes, young Werner was able to find the answers to many of his questions. Today, Dr. Israel also attributes his scientific career path to a former math teacher — Samuel Skewes —whose keen insight was an inspiration to his students.

Werner Israel

14.3 The Formation of Stars

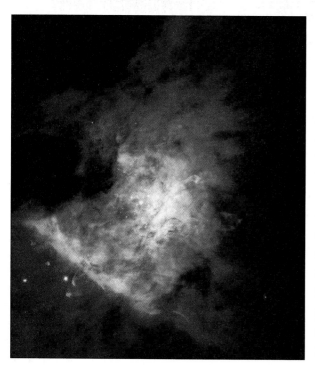

Figure 14.13 In the Orion Nebula, the inter-stellar medium contains a region of gas that is energized by bright blue stars. This causes the nebula to radiate its distinct spectral colours.

For a long time, people thought that the space between the stars, the **inter-stellar medium**, was empty. In fact, as you learned in the previous section, stellar winds, planetary nebulae, and supernovas fill space with huge quantities of gas and dust. This material enriches the inter-stellar medium and is an essential ingredient for making new stars. But what exactly happens to transform this material into a new star? You will explore this question in this section.

In Chapter 13, you learned that it took astronomers centuries of observing and theorizing to arrive at the current model of the solar system. Theories and models about the formation of stars are much more recent developments, relying on new technologies to make the necessary observations. In only about half a century, great strides have been made in decoding the mystery of star formation. Still, the important process of theory-making, testing predictions, and adjusting the model continues. In this section, you will follow the same process by conducting investigations to develop and test a theory for star formation.

Figure 14.14 In the Horsehead Nebula, the inter-stellar medium appears as dark clouds that obscure our view.

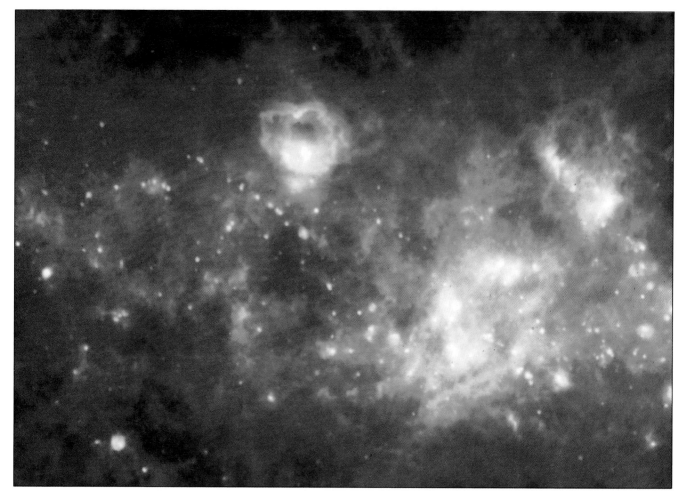

Figure 14.15 The inter-stellar medium is composed mostly of hydrogen (75%) and helium (24%), with traces of other elements such as carbon, nitrogen, oxygen, and carbon-silicate dust. New technologies, such as the Infrared Astronomical Satellite (IRAS), allow astronomers to see through this cloudy medium, right into star-forming regions such as the one pictured here.

SOFIA: The Stratospheric Observatory for Infrared Astronomy

NASA and the German space agency, DLR, are working together to create SOFIA, a Boeing 747-SP aircraft modified to carry a 2.5 m reflecting telescope. SOFIA will be the largest airborne telescope in the world and will make observations that even the largest and highest of telescopes on Earth cannot make. The aircraft will be based near Mountain View, California.

What to Do

1. Using the resources of your library and the Internet, find out more about infrared technology and the SOFIA program.

Outside Link ACTIVITY

2. Write a one-page report of your findings.

What Did You Discover?

1. What is infrared technology?

2. Explain how infrared technology enables us to see something that is not visible to our eyes, even with the aid of a telescope. Include sketches or photographs to support your explanation.

Be a Scientist: Develop a Theory of Star Formation

Scientists develop theories to explain how events happen or why things are as they are. Often a theory will raise many new questions.

Problem

You know that the space between the stars is not empty, but full of clouds of gases and dust. You know that gravity is always at work. And you know about the important role of fusion in a star's evolution. Using all this information, solve the puzzle of how stars form.

There are two parts to solving this puzzle. In Part 1, you will develop a model for a theory of star formation. In Part 2, you will extend your theory to explore a possible link between star formation and the formation of other celestial objects.

Materials

notebook
pencil

Procedure

Divide a blank page of your notebook into six squares. Number each square as shown in the figure here. Then make a quick, rough sketch in each numbered square by following the instructions given in steps 1 to 6. Be sure to answer all the questions. Together the six sketches will form your model of star formation. Under each sketch, write a sentence that describes each stage in the development of the model.

Part 1
Making a Model of Star Formation

1 Begin by drawing a huge cloud of gas and dust (a nebula) of the type that exists in the inter-stellar medium.

Sketch 1: Use the side of your pencil to shade the form of the cloud. Each speck of the lead from your pencil represents atoms of gas or dust particles. Add the labels: nebula, gas particles, dust particles.

2 Which force exists between all atoms? Therefore, what should eventually happen to the cloud?

Sketch 2: Repeat sketch 1, but add arrows to show in which direction the outer regions of the cloud should move. Add the labels: nebula, gas particles, dust particles, gravitational force.

3 All atoms have some random motion, so the cloud would have a little rotation.

Sketch 3: Repeat sketch 2, but add arrows to show the cloud rotating around an axis. Add the labels: nebula, gravitational force, axis, rotation.

4 The image of a shrinking, rotating cloud of gas and dust should be emerging in you mind. Now think of what happens to the spin of a figure skater who pulls her arms in tight. What do you think will happen to the contracting cloud at this stage?

Sketch 4: Draw a smaller cloud than you did in sketch 3. Add arrows to indicate that it is spinning very fast around its axis. Add other arrows to show more mass falling toward the centre of the cloud. What will happen to the temperature in the core as more mass accumulates there? Add the labels: shrinking nebula, axis, rotation, gravitational force.

5 Most of the material along the axis of the cloud collapses into the centre of the object, creating a well-defined central sphere. This leaves outer rings of material orbiting in a plane that looks like a large disk. If enough mass has accumulated in the central sphere to raise its core to 10 000 000°C, what process will start to take place? Can you predict the outcome?

Sketch 5: Draw a small sphere and around it shade a wide, disk-shaped region of dust and gas. Congratulations! You have just created a star.

Part 2
Taking the Model a Step Further

Now develop your model further to extend your theory. The gas and dust in the orbiting disk of material are not likely to be distributed evenly. Some will be in clumps. With gravity always at work, many of these clumps of gas and dust will begin to acquire more material from the disk. This will increase their mass. Some of these clumps will survive to orbit around the new star permanently. Can you predict what these clumps might be?

Sketch 6: Shade in a large spherical region in the centre of the diagram. This represents the new star. Add six much smaller spheres orbiting around it at various distances. Congratulations, again! You have just created planets.

Conclude and Apply

1. Using your sketches 1 to 5, describe in one paragraph a theory for how stars form.

2. Using your sketch 6, describe how the theory of star formation can also be used to explain planet formation.

Off the Wall

Remember that Jupiter, like the Sun, is a huge ball of mostly hydrogen gas. As happened in the Sun, the temperature of Jupiter's core increased as the gas compressed. As massive as it is, Jupiter would have had to accumulate at least 70 times as much gas for its core to have achieved fusion temperature. Had that happened, we would have two suns in the sky today! Can you imagine what sunsets might look like on a planet with two suns? How would the calendar we use today have to be changed?

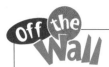

Formation of the Solar System

The theory you developed for how stars and planets form is called the **solar nebula theory**. It explains the basic idea that astronomers currently have about how our solar system formed. Scientific calculations suggest that the Sun is 5 billion years old and its orbiting nine planets are 4.6 billion years old. This is consistent with geological evidence that puts the age of some rocks on Earth at over 3.5 billion years.

Over the years, other theories have been formed and tested. One "catastrophic theory," for example, proposed that another star collided with the Sun, and debris from the collision formed the planets. The theory with the most support today, however, is based on the model you developed, the solar nebula model.

During the formation of our solar system, the smallest of the planets and the ones closest to the new star (the Sun) were blasted with radiation. Because they did not have enough gravity to hold much of their hot atmospheres, they became the rocky, inner planets (Mercury, Venus, Earth, and Mars). Farther out, away from the Sun's intense heat, the outer planets kept their gas. They became the gas giants (Jupiter, Saturn, Uranus, Neptune, and Pluto).

Throughout much of the early history of the solar system, stray rocks and dust that had not fallen into the Sun pounded the planets and their moons. We see evidence of this in the cratered surfaces of Mercury and the Moon. Today, about 4.5 billion years after the formation of the solar system, the space surrounding the Sun has been almost completely cleared of dust and gas. All that remains are the small accumulations that are the planets and their moons, the asteroids, the comets, and some space debris. Earth still encounters some of those pieces of debris. Do you remember what they are called?

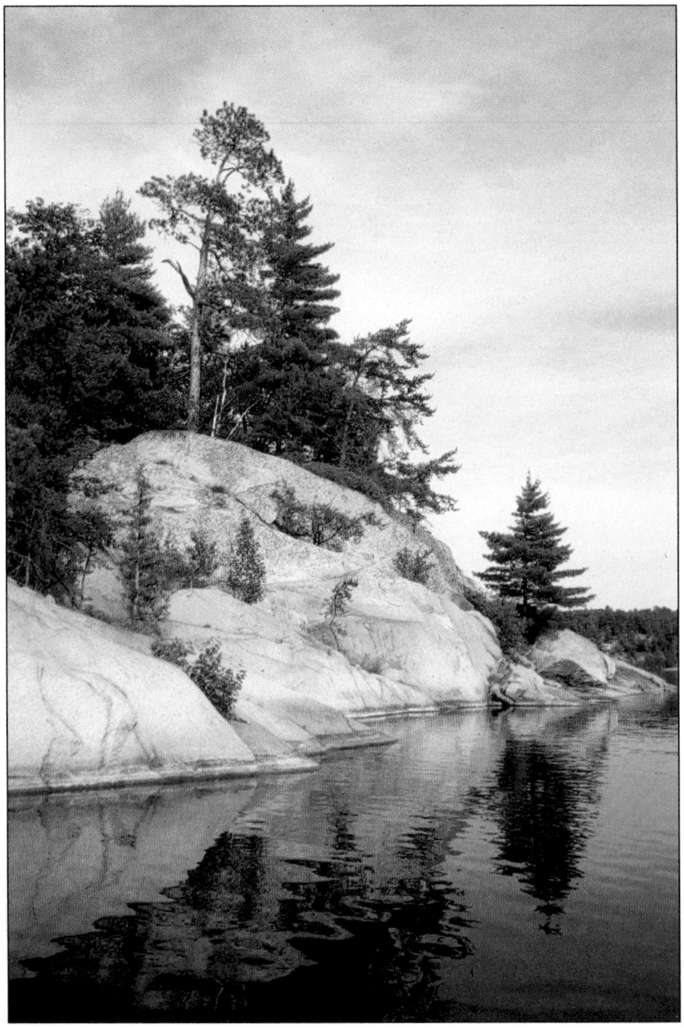

Figure 14.16 The Canadian Shield has some of the oldest rock in the world. In the Red Lake area of Ontario, rocks have been dated at 3.5 billion years old.

The Hunt for Extra-Solar Planets

The solar nebula theory predicts that planets should be fairly common, because they are by-products of the star formation process. Two types of observations have made astronomers increasingly confident that this idea is correct.

First, infrared, radio, and optical telescopes have recorded more than 100 examples of young stars embedded in disks of dust and gas (as your sketch 5 in Investigation 14-C showed). This supports the solar nebula theory of star formation. Figure 14.17 shows an example of such a young star, Beta Pictoris.

Second, new instruments in recent years have detected about a dozen **extra-solar planets,** planets that orbit stars other than the Sun. For example, a planet about 2.5 times Jupiter's mass has been found orbiting a star near the Big Dipper. The list of extra-solar planets is expected to continue growing.

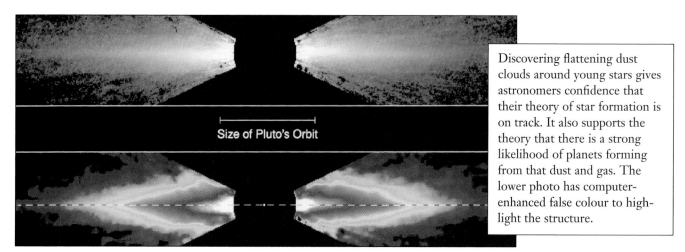

Discovering flattening dust clouds around young stars gives astronomers confidence that their theory of star formation is on track. It also supports the theory that there is a strong likelihood of planets forming from that dust and gas. The lower photo has computer-enhanced false colour to highlight the structure.

Figure 14.17 A Hubble photograph of the disk of dust and gas surrounding the star Beta Pictoris. The star itself, in the centre, was blocked out to reduce its glare.

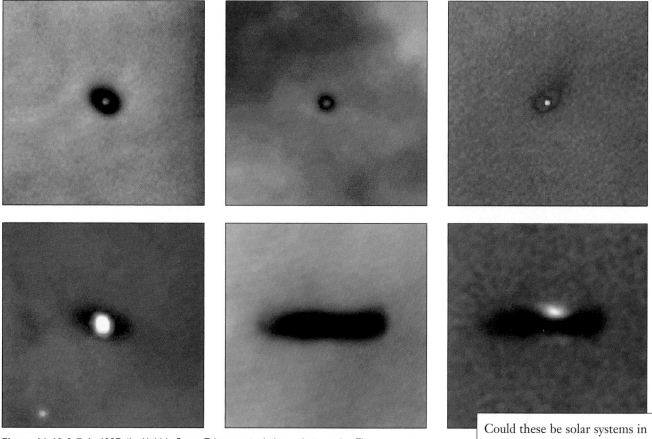

Figure 14.18 A-E In 1997, the Hubble Space Telescope took these photographs. They appear to show flattening gas clouds around a central star. Although the pictures make the stars seem bigger than they really are, a disk of debris shows clearly around the stars.

Could these be solar systems in the making? Scientists will have to watch for the next 100 000 years to know for sure.

Evaluating the Theory of Solar System Formation

Think About It

For a theory to be accepted as a reasonable explanation, the events, actions, and things observed must be predictable. In this investigation, you will play the role of scientist again, only this time with a small group of fellow "scientists." Together you will evaluate and debate the solar nebula theory to see if it supports nine predictions and is therefore a reasonable explanation for how our solar system was formed.

What to Do

❶ Organize into groups of three or four. Your teacher will give you a table such as the one shown below. Find the planet database you developed in Chapter 13. You will need it as a reference to conduct your analysis.

What Is Predicted	What We Know	Does the Solar Nebula Theory Support the Prediction?
1. Since all planets began from the same rotating gas cloud, all planets should rotate in the same direction.		
2. All the planets should orbit in the same direction (the direction of rotation of the original nebula).		
3. All planets should orbit in the same plane.		
4. Inner planets should have thin atmospheric shells.		
5. Outer planets should have thick atmospheric shells.		
6. Larger planets should rotate faster.		
7. In the early phase of the formation of the solar system, much space debris (rocks and dust) should have been present.		
8. The interior of the central star should be hot.		
9. Other stars should have planetary systems.		

2 Working as a group, use your combined knowledge of the solar system to guide you through the investigation. Read each prediction, one at a time. Then, in the second column (What You Know), report what you know happens. Use your notes and planet database from Chapter 13 for reference. If you need more observations to check out a prediction, make a note of what questions you might ask your teacher or what research you might have to do.

Example: Eiko's group discusses the first prediction: "Since all planets began from the same rotating gas cloud, all planets should rotate in the same direction." They consult their planetary databases and agree that all planets rotate in the same direction except Venus and Pluto which spin very slowly in the other direction. In the second column of their table, they write: "Not true. Venus and Pluto spin in the opposite direction to the other planets."

3 Still working as a group, decide whether you believe the solar nebula theory supports the prediction. Be prepared to discuss and debate the evidence among yourselves in reaching your decision. Record the main points of your evaluation in the third column.

Example: Eiko's group discusses how well the solar nebula theory supports prediction one. One group member feels the theory fails because of Venus's opposite rotation. The others think the theory is still valid because it can explain the rotation of most of the other planets. The group writes the following in the third column of their table: "The rotation of two planets, Venus and Pluto, cannot be explained by the theory. But the theory can explain the rotation of the other seven planets, which is pretty good."

4 As a group, draw a conclusion about the soundness of the solar nebula theory based on the third column of your table. Write down the main points that support your conclusion.

Analyze

1. What are the strengths of the solar nebula theory in explaining the formation of our solar system? Which predictions are best supported by what is known?

2. What are the weaknesses of the theory? Which predictions are not supported, or not very well supported, by what is known?

3. Based on your answers above, how would you evaluate the solar nebula theory? Is it a good theory? Why or why not?

4. Which questions remain unanswered about the formation of our solar system?

Tools of Science

In the planning stages at NASA (the National Aeronautics and Space Administration) is Planet Finder, one of the greatest telescopes ever conceived. This is to be a space-borne telescope, as large as a football field. Possessing four huge mirrors, its sensitive instruments should be able to spot an Earth-sized planet. Planet Finder's ability to determine the chemical make-up of the atmosphere of an extra-solar planet might enable it to be the first to detect life in a distant solar system. The target date for Planet Finder's launch is 2010.

INTERNET CONNECT

www.school.mcgrawhill.ca/resources/

With new telescopes coming into use and improvements being made in image processing, discovery of extra-solar planets continues. To stay up to date, go to the above web site. Go to **Science Resources**, then to **SCIENCEPOWER 9**, and follow the links to **Extra-Solar Planets**. Research some of the techniques that astronomers are using today to detect extra-solar planets. Once you have found some information, pool your findings with a small group.

Looking Beyond Our Solar System

Early people thought the Earth was the centre of the universe. Then they realized that it was just one of nine planets that orbited a star, the Sun. Now we have learned that our solar system is only one of many solar systems. How many solar systems could there be? This depends on the number of stars that exist. In the next chapter, you will see that there are many more stars in the sky than you have ever imagined.

Check Your Understanding

1. What is the inter-stellar medium and what role does it play in star formation?

2. (a) What causes the dust and gas in a nebula to fall together into ever bigger accumulations?

   (b) What begins to happen to the nebula in this process?

3. What causes a shrinking, rotating nebula to flatten?

4. At what point does a star "turn on"?

5. Describe why some small accumulations of gas and dust orbiting a new star are able to keep from falling into the star.

6. What evidence do we have that the space surrounding the Sun was once filled with dust, gas, and rock debris?

7. **Thinking Critically** How does the discovery of extra-solar planets support the solar nebula theory of star formation?

8. **Thinking Critically** Explain why it is important to test a theory with predictions.

Now that you have completed this chapter, try to do the following. If you cannot, go back to the section indicated.

Explain why one star seems brighter than another. (14.1)

Describe the difference in temperature between a star that is bluish white and a star that is red. (14.1)

Explain what a spectroscope does, and describe which star property it is used to analyze. (14.1)

Name the two properties of stars that are the basis on which thousands of stars have been plotted on the Hertzsprung-Russell diagram. (14.1)

Describe the evolution of a main sequence star from its birth to its death. (14.2)

Describe how radio telescopes discovered neutron stars, years after their existence was predicted. (14.2)

Outline the solar nebula theory of star formation. (14.3)

Prepare Your Own Summary

Summarize this chapter by doing one of the following. Use a graphic organizer (such as a concept map), produce a poster, or write a summary to include the key chapter concepts. Here are a few ideas to use as a guide:
• What are some of the main properties of stars that astronomers study?

• What is meant by solar mass?
• What is considered to be the birth place of stars? Why?
• Why is gravity such an important force throughout a star's life cycle?
• What is the approximate age of the Sun?

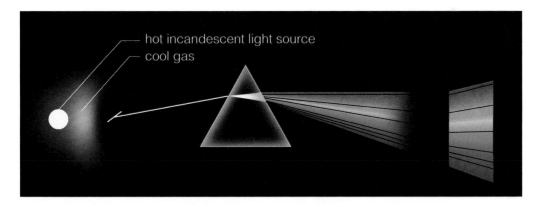
hot incandescent light source
cool gas

Reviewing Key Terms

If you need to review, the section numbers show you where these terms were introduced.

1. In your notebook, state whether each of the following statements about gravity is true or false. If the statement is false, explain why.
   (a) Only Earth has gravity. True or False? (14.2)
   (b) Only planets have gravity. True or False? (14.2)
   (c) All objects have gravity. True or False? (14.2)
   (d) Gravity is a very strong force. True or False? (14.2)
   (e) Gravity can only attract, never repel. True or False? (14.2)
   (f) Gravitational forces get weaker with distance. True or False? (14.2)
   (g) A planet's gravity is caused by its spin. True or False? (14.3)

2. In your notebook, match each expression from column A with the correct term in column B.

A	B
• the process that powers the Sun and other stars	• nebula (14.2)
• gas or dust cloud	• red giant (14.1)
• bands of colour that result when white light is separated	• planetary nebula (14.2)
• ending stage of a very massive star	• supergiant (14.1)
• last shining stage of a small star	• fusion (14.2)
• outer surface of a star expanding into space	• electromagnetic spectrum (14.1)
• star after its initial hydrogen fusion stops	• white dwarf (14.1)
	• black hole (14.2)
	• inter-stellar medium (14.3)

Understanding Key Concepts

Section numbers are provided if you need to review.

3. Give brief answers for the following.
   (a) What makes a star contract? (14.2)
   (b) What causes a star's temperature to increase? (14.2)
   (c) What stops a star's contraction? (14.2)

4. Explain how the Sun differs from a white dwarf. (14.2)

5. In what ways can a star's life end? What is the main factor that determines how one star's fate will differ from that of another? (14.2)

6. The following stages of the formation of the solar system are out of order. In your notebook, write them in order, from 1 to 7. (Some stages occur at the same time, so there could be more than one valid answer.)
   ■ The rotation rate of the cloud increases. (14.3)
   ■ In orbit around the centre of the gas and dust sphere, small accumulations of gas and dust start increasing in mass. (14.3)
   ■ The star "turns on." (14.3)
   ■ The nebula flattens as material along the axis collapses into the centre of the object. (14.3)
   ■ The temperature at the core of the contracting, rotating cloud increases. (14.3)
   ■ A rotating cloud of gas dust begins contracting. (14.3)

- The temperature at the core of the gas and dust sphere reaches 10 000 000°C. (14.3)

Developing Skills

7. Refer to Investigation 14-A on page 465. Draw the spectrum for a mixture of hydrogen and sodium gases.

8. From the library or the Internet, research the following.

   (a) Astronomers tracking Ian Shelton's supernova (1987A) are noticing some unexplainable behaviour. Find the latest image of the supernova and draw the shape of the glowing shell of gas.

   (b) Where are the largest optical telescopes on Earth located? How big are they?

   (c) Find the latest images of stars that may have solar systems in the making. Try to summarize some of the evidence that astronomers are finding.

   (d) Comet hunters often misidentify a nebula as a new comet. Name the common catalogue that lists all the nebula-shaped objects in the sky.

9. Many stars are binary stars. The photograph on this page shows a star field. Some stars appear to be two stars close together — but are they binary stars? In some cases, maybe the two stars are really far apart and just lined up, one behind the other. However, if you noted many examples of where two stars are close together, you might conclude that this was more than just coincidental.

   Study the photograph. Are the stars randomly spaced or do many seem to come in pairs? Try to decide what proportion of the stars shown might be binaries (one out of two? one out of 10?). Which factors would tend to make your determination an underestimate? Which factors would tend to make it an overestimate?

Problem Solving/Applying

10. Earth's gravity holds the Moon in orbit. Otherwise, the Moon would travel in a straight line away from Earth. However, astronauts in Earth orbit float inside their space capsule even though they are much closer to Earth than the Moon is. Why are they "weightless"? (Hint: All objects in a gravitational field fall at the same rate of acceleration toward Earth.)

Critical Thinking

11. Of all the large moons in the solar system, Neptune's moon Triton is the only one to orbit in a direction opposite to its planet's rotational direction. Does this fact support or not support the solar nebula theory for the formation of the solar system? Explain your answer.

12. What led astronomers to believe that extra-solar planets existed around other stars, even before they got the latest observational evidence?

Pause & Reflect

Go back to the beginning of this chapter on page 484 and check your original answers to the Opening Ideas questions. How has your thinking changed?

Vincent van Gogh, The Starry Night, 1889

Opening Ideas...

- Where are you located in the universe? Sketch and label a map that shows your "cosmic address."

- Of what substances is the universe made?

- If stars evolve from young to old, does that mean the universe has a life cycle too?

Science Log

If you know the answers to the above questions, write them in your Science Log. State what evidence you have for each answer. If you don't know the answers, write down the investigations or the information you might need to draw a conclusion.

Billions upon billions of stars exist, and billions of them are much larger than the star in our own solar system. What, then, is the size of the space that contains all these stars? Is the universe infinite or does it end somewhere? How did it begin? Is it still changing?

Artists such as Vincent Van Gogh (1853-1890) did not know the answer to these questions. However, his painting of the night sky, with its suggestion of motion and luminosity, suggests something close to what we understand about the universe today. Cosmology is the branch of astronomy that focuses on the nature, origin, and evolution of the cosmos (a Greek word meaning "universe"). Cosmologists grapple with some of the most challenging and exciting ideas in all of science: Is the universe expanding? When was the first moment in time? Is the universe so big that the light from distant stars has not yet reached Earth?

In Chapters 13 and 14, you learned about our solar system and the stars that exist far beyond our own. In this chapter, you will look outward even farther to explore and map the universe. You will learn how the vast distances between stars and other objects in the universe are measured. You will also find out how we can examine what the universe was like in the distant past. Scientific evidence even tells us when and how the universe may have begun.

Cosmos

Why Is the Night Sky Dark?

Think About It

An early model of the universe described it as infinite, unchanging, and filled with a uniform distribution of stars. In this activity, you have an opportunity to test this model against one common observation: it gets dark at night.

What to Do

1. On a piece of graph paper, mark a dot on one of the grid points near the middle of the paper. Label this dot the Sun.

Key Concepts

In this chapter, you will discover

- how astronomers measure distances in the universe
- what galaxies are and the three main types that exist
- what evidence there is that the universe is expanding
- when and how the universe is believed to have begun

Key Skills

In this chapter, you will

- use triangulation to estimate distance indirectly
- estimate the number of galaxies in the universe
- model the expansion of the universe
- infer from your knowledge and observations why the night sky is dark

Key Terms

- triangulation
- parallax
- light-year
- Cepheid variables
- Milky Way
- galaxy
- open clusters
- globular clusters
- Doppler effect
- red-shifted
- Hubble's law
- Big Bang theory
- quasars
- gamma ray bursts
- neutrinos

Starting Point ACTIVITY

2. On the same piece of paper, begin creating a universe of evenly distributed stars. Do this by marking about 60 to 70 dots on the other grid points around the Sun, making a pattern of evenly spaced dots (stars). (At this scale, and for the purposes of this activity, the Earth and the Sun are assumed to occupy the same dot.)

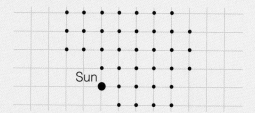

3. Place a ruler across the Sun in any direction and draw a line from the Sun to the edge of the paper. Note the number of stars your line crosses. (If the line does not cross another star, add more dots to your graph paper.) Move the ruler so that it lies in another direction across the Sun and draw another line. Repeat this at least five more times, until you have convinced yourself that every line drawn from the Sun eventually encounters another star.

What Did You Discover?

1. In this model of an infinite and uniform universe, what would you observe wherever you looked in the night sky?

2. In this model, would the night sky be dark or would it be bright with starlight?

3. Now compare what you observe in reality to what the model predicts should happen. Is the model's prediction supported by what your eyes tell you?

4. What assumptions about the model might be incorrect? That is, what explanations might there be for what you really observe about the appearance of the night sky?

15.1 Measuring Distance in the Cosmos

Figure 15.1 For centuries, observers of the night sky could not see more than their Earth-based telescopes revealed. In the last four decades, however, space-based instruments have enabled astronomers to improve their view and understand how large and complex the universe is. Compare the Earth-based view of the Eagle Nebula above with the detailed view obtained by the Hubble Space Telescope showing star-forming regions in Figure 14.8.

Word CONNECT

Find out what the words "cosmos" and "universe" mean. Write the current definitions for each word in your notebook. What are their origins? How are the meanings of the two words connected?

One of the biggest challenges astronomers face in modelling and mapping the universe is measuring distances. How can we determine the distance to a star if we cannot reach it, even with a space probe?

Developing methods to measure the distance of stars from Earth and from each other was a major accomplishment in astronomy. Not only did it provide a way of estimating the size of the universe, it also offered valuable clues about the age of the universe. In this section, you will learn how stellar distances are measured. You will also discover how this knowledge has changed our ideas about the composition, structure, and scale of the universe.

In the 17th century, Newton calculated that Sirius (one of the brightest stars in the sky) is about 1 million times as far from Earth as the Sun is (1 million AU, in modern terminology). He compared the brightness of Sirius to the brightness of Saturn. Therefore, he was able to calculate the distance from Earth to Sirius. The modern estimate of the distance is about 550 000 AU, about one-half of Newton's calculation. This was the first modern effort to measure distance outside our solar system.

Figure 15.2 Sir Isaac Newton was the first scientist who tried to estimate stellar distances.

Measuring with Triangulation and Parallax

Using Triangulation

You and a friend are standing beside a lake, looking out at an island. You are thinking of rowing out to the island, but you do not know how far away it is. Because you do not have a map of the lake and there is no bridge to the island, you have no means of measuring the distance directly. Is there some other way you can estimate it?

The answer is yes. By using a distance you know, you can calculate the unknown distance indirectly. One of the most common ways of doing this is called **triangulation**. Triangulation is a method of measuring distance indirectly by creating an imaginary triangle between an observer and an object whose distance is to be estimated (see Figure 15.3). It is the same method that astronomers use to measure distances to celestial objects.

Figure 15.4 on the next page describes step by step how you could use the technique to estimate the distance across a lake to an island. It is important to remember, when measuring distances with triangulation, that the longer the baseline, the more accurate the results.

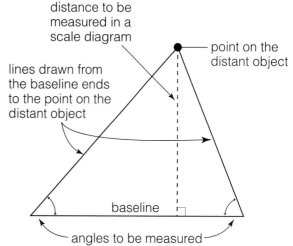

Figure 15.3 To use triangulation, what you need to know is the length of one side of the triangle (the "baseline") and the size of the two angles created when imaginary lines are drawn from either end of the baseline to the same point on the distant object.

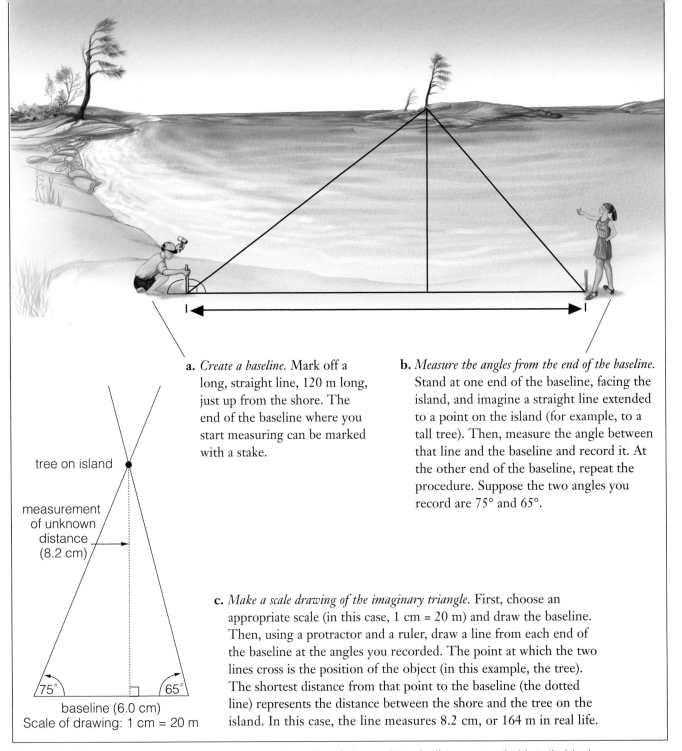

a. *Create a baseline.* Mark off a long, straight line, 120 m long, just up from the shore. The end of the baseline where you start measuring can be marked with a stake.

b. *Measure the angles from the end of the baseline.* Stand at one end of the baseline, facing the island, and imagine a straight line extended to a point on the island (for example, to a tall tree). Then, measure the angle between that line and the baseline and record it. At the other end of the baseline, repeat the procedure. Suppose the two angles you record are 75° and 65°.

tree on island

measurement of unknown distance (8.2 cm)

75°

65°

baseline (6.0 cm)
Scale of drawing: 1 cm = 20 m

c. *Make a scale drawing of the imaginary triangle.* First, choose an appropriate scale (in this case, 1 cm = 20 m) and draw the baseline. Then, using a protractor and a ruler, draw a line from each end of the baseline at the angles you recorded. The point at which the two lines cross is the position of the object (in this example, the tree). The shortest distance from that point to the baseline (the dotted line) represents the distance between the shore and the tree on the island. In this case, the line measures 8.2 cm, or 164 m in real life.

Figure 15.4 This example shows how you and your friend could use triangulation to estimate the distance across the lake to the island.

DidYouKnow?

Almost 2000 years ago, the Greeks used triangulation to calculate the distance between Earth and the Moon. They realized that two people in two different cities pointing at the Moon simultaneously would be holding their arms at different angles from the ground. They used this information to create a triangle. The baseline was 300 km long. Then they used a scale drawing to figure out the distance to the Moon. In making their calculations, the Greeks also understood that they had to take the curvature of Earth's surface into account. Can you explain why this was an important factor and how it would affect the accuracy of results?

Using Parallax

When astronomers use triangulation to determine the distance to a nearby star, they rely on the star's **parallax** to provide them with the angles they need to make the necessary measurements. Parallax is the apparent shift in position of a nearby object when it is viewed from two different points. To experience parallax for yourself, point at a distant object with your finger. Then, keeping your finger in view, blink first one eye and then the other. Your finger tip appears to move compared to the background because you are viewing your finger from two different points. The baseline, in this case, is the distance between your eyes.

To measure distances from Earth to celestial bodies, the longest baseline we can use without leaving Earth is the diameter of Earth's orbit. Sightings have to be taken six months apart — the time it takes Earth to move from one end of the orbital baseline to the other. If a star is close enough, it will appear to move relative to the more distant stars. Figure 15.5 illustrates this point.

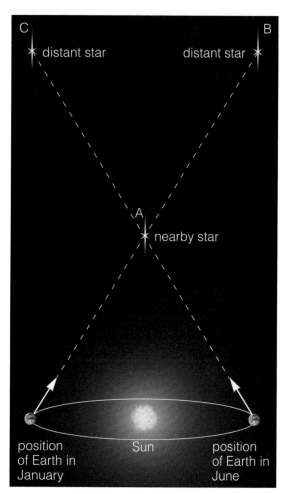

Figure 15.5 Calculating a star's distance from Earth using parallax and triangulation. In January, the nearby star (star A) appears to line up with star B. In June, it seems to line up with star C. The distance star A appears to move in the sky (the apparent distance between stars B and C) is its parallax. This provides the angles needed for using triangulation. (Stars B and C are so far away that they do not appear to shift positions.)

Light-Years

You have probably noticed that Figure 15.5 is very much out of scale. The nearest star to Earth, for example, is Proxima Centauri and it lies more than 272 000 AU from the Sun. Its parallax angle is less than 1/3600 of a degree. Because inter-stellar distances are so much greater than solar system distances, astronomical units quickly become impractical to use (impractical as, for example, using millimetres to measure the distance across Canada). Astronomers therefore created the **light-year**. A light-year represents the distance that light travels in one year, a distance equal to about 63 240 AU. On this scale, Proxima Centauri is 4.28 light-years away.

Tools of Science

Until a few years ago, astronomers using parallax measurements and triangulation could measure the distance to only about 10 000 of the nearest stars. All these stars were no farther than about 126 light-years from Earth. The Hipparcos satellite has recently changed this situation. Because its baseline of observation is longer, the satellite increases the range for triangulation to 1600 light-years. As a result, accurate parallax measurements have been obtained for more than 100 000 stars.

Using Triangulation to Measure an Unknown Distance

How far is it from here to there? In the example described in Figure 15.4, you learned that triangulation can be used to estimate a distance indirectly. Now try the technique yourself.

Problem

How can you estimate the distance to a landmark you can see without measuring that distance directly?

Materials

large chalkboard protractor
long measuring tape
two metre sticks
stake or other marker
ruler
small protractor

Procedure

Outside

1. Organize into pairs. Your teacher will give you and your partner a large protractor, a measuring tape, two metre sticks, and a stake or other marker for the starting end of your baseline.

2. Your teacher will choose a building, radio tower, tree, or other distant object that is clearly visible from the school grounds. You are going to measure the distance to this object from where you are standing.

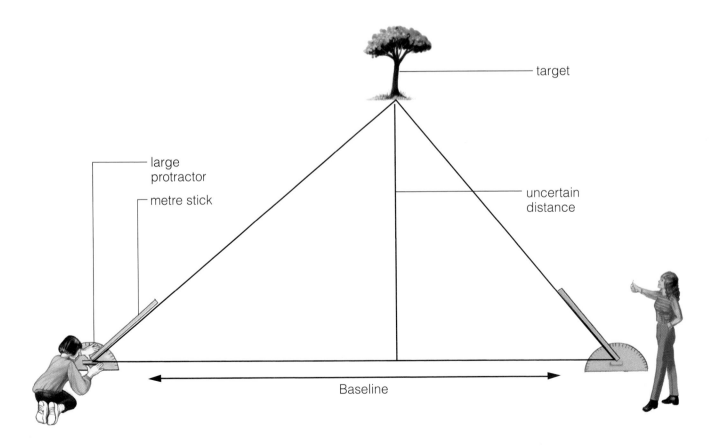

target

large protractor

metre stick

uncertain distance

Baseline

3 With your partner, mark off a baseline, leaving a marker at the end where you start measuring. Record this distance. Remember: The longer your baseline, the more accurate your results will be.

4 At one end of the baseline, place one of the metre sticks on the ground along the baseline. Aim the other toward the object (see the figure on the opposite page). Using the large protractor, measure the inside angle formed by the two metre sticks. Repeat at the other end of the baseline. Record both angles.

In the Classroom

5 Make a scale diagram of the set-up in your notebook.

a. With your partner, select a suitable scale. For example, you might represent 1 m of actual distance by 1 cm.

b. Using the ruler, draw your baseline to scale. Then, with the small protractor, add lines at the angles you measured, extending them just until they cross. This "common point" is the object whose distance away you are measuring. (Refer back to Figure 15.3 if you need guidance.)

c. Inside the triangle you have created, draw a straight line down from the object to the baseline. This should be the shortest distance between the object and the baseline. Measure the length of this line and, applying your scale, determine the true distance to the object.

Pause & Reflect

Why is it important to use a relatively long baseline rather than a short one? Why is triangulation effective for measuring the distance to nearby stars, but not more distant ones? Answer these questions in your Science Log and include sketches to support your explanations.

Analyze

1. Compare your results with those of other students. What length of baseline did other students use? Are the distances you found similar? If not, why do you think that is?

Conclude and Apply

2. Summarize in a paragraph how baseline length seems to affect the accuracy of distances calculated using the triangulation technique. What is the longest possible baseline astronomers have available to them to measure distances to stars from Earth when they use triangulation? Explain your answer.

Extend Your Skills

3. Choose another one or two landmarks. Practise using triangulation to measure how far away they are from your school or home. Once you have made your calculations, check your results against the scale distance on a map.

Cepheid Variables

Measuring parallax from Earth has its limits, since no baseline can be made long enough to measure the enormous distances in the universe. Astronomers therefore needed another tool. They were rewarded with one when, in 1912, astronomer Henrietta Leavitt discovered **Cepheid variables**. These are stars that actually change size and brightness (that is, they pulsate).

What is remarkable — and what made Cepheid variables one of the greatest discoveries in 20th century astronomy — is that these changes occur over very precise and predictable periods of time. Therefore, if you were looking at two Cepheids and noted that they both took one day to go from shining brightly to dimming, and then to shining brightly again, you would also expect them to be the same brightness at their peak. If they were not the same, with one being less bright than the other at the peak of the cycle, you would know that the difference was due to distance. The Cepheid that is not as bright must be farther away than the one that is. (Recall what you learned about the effect of distance on star luminosity in Chapter 14.)

By classifying Cepheid variables according to their maximum brightness and period of change, astronomers have been able to use them as a standard against which to analyze other variable stars and the relative distances between them. Thanks to Cepheid variables, astronomers were able to find the true size of the Milky Way and the distance to other galaxies.

Check Your Understanding

1. Explain what is meant by "cosmos."

2. (a) For what purpose do we use triangulation?

   (b) Which three measurements do you need to apply this technique?

3. (a) Define the term "light-year."

   (b) Is it used to measure interplanetary distances or inter-stellar distances? Explain your answer.

4. How are Cepheid variables used to estimate very great distances in the universe?

5. **Apply**

   (a) A star is found to measure 570 000 AU from the Sun. How would you express that distance in light-years?

   (b) Another star is known to be 8.6 million light-years from Earth. How far is that in kilometres?

15.2 The Discovery of Galaxies

At the beginning of the 20th century, some remarkable discoveries were made that refined our knowledge of where we are in the universe. The discovery of distant galaxies showed us that the universe is much larger and more populated with stars than we had ever expected. Suddenly, we realized that our entire solar system was an exceedingly small part of the universe.

The Milky Way

Figure 15.6 The Milky Way galaxy as seen from Earth on a clear night

If you have viewed the night sky from a cottage, farm, or summer camp, you will have seen the **Milky Way**. Brightest in the summertime, it appears as a hazy white band extending from the southern horizon and across the sky overhead. On very clear nights, the haze looks as though it is caused by high, thin clouds.

In fact, the band is a vast accumulation of about 400 billion stars (including our Sun) that completely encircles the Earth and makes up the Milky Way **galaxy**. A galaxy is a huge group of stars, gas, and dust held together by gravity. Although the stars seem to be so close together that their light blends, they are really far apart. Can you recall, for example, how far away the Sun's nearest stellar neighbour is?

Discovering that our own solar system is part of a much greater structure changed people's concept of the universe once more. Did the vast Milky Way galaxy fill the universe? Or was this galaxy in which we live only one among others, yet farther away and undiscovered?

Imagine it is a warm evening in July and you are observing the sweep of the Milky Way overhead. You want to find some evidence that it really does completely surround Earth. You call someone that evening on the other side of the world to ask whether the Milky Way is visible from there. What would that person see? Why couldn't you wait 12 hours until Earth faces the other direction then take a look for yourself? Hint: It takes more than one night to check if the Milky Way encircles the Earth. Answer the questions in your Science Log.

Star Clusters

Studying the band of stars circling Earth, astronomers observed that some stars occur in clusters. They identified two types. **Open clusters** are collections of 50 to 1000 stars that appear dispersed along the main band of the Milky Way. An example of such a cluster is Pleiades (Figure 15.7). **Globular clusters** are collections of 100 000 to 1 million stars arranged in distinctive spherical shapes. The globular cluster in Hercules is one such example (Figure 15.8). Globular clusters do not lie along the band of the Milky Way, but instead appear in the southern regions of the sky. Astronomers wondered what these different star clusters could tell us about the structure of the galaxy. Where did our own star — the Sun — fit into the picture?

Figure 15.7 Pleiades is an example of an open cluster of stars.

Figure 15.8 The inset photograph shows the constellation of Hercules. You can see this group of stars best in late spring and early summer. The larger photograph shows the globular cluster in Hercules, which lies 23 000 light-years away from the Sun and contains more than 300 000 stars.

Mapping the Size and Shape of the Milky Way

Using Cepheid variables to estimate distances, astronomer Harlow Shapley began trying to map the total size of the Milky Way galaxy. By 1918, these measurements had resulted in a new picture of the galaxy. It appeared as an immense disk-shaped system of stars, with a halo of globular clusters surrounding its centre. The Sun was nowhere near the centre of this disk. Rather, it sat close to the outer edge of the galaxy. Today, we know that the Milky Way is about 75 000 light-years in diameter, with the Sun lying about 25 000 light-years from the central region.

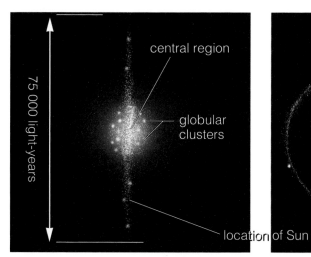

A. Side view of Milky Way galaxy

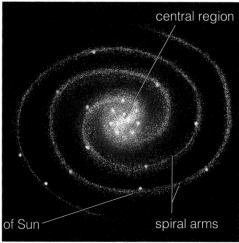

B. Top view of Milky Way galaxy

Figure 15.9 The globular clusters surround the central region of the Milky Way. The Sun and our solar system are near the outside.

Across Canada

At the age of 15, Helen Sawyer saw her first total eclipse of the sun. This event, which she described as "magnificent," inspired her to make astronomy her life.

Less than two decades later, Helen Sawyer Hogg had become well known as a Canadian astronomer and writer. She joined the University of Toronto in 1935, where she taught for 40 years. She frequently visited the David Dunlap Observatory in Richmond Hill, where she used the 185 cm telescope. Her husband, Dr. Frank S. Hogg, was appointed director of the observatory in 1946. Five years later, he died, leaving Helen with three teenaged children.

Dr. Sawyer Hogg charted clusters of stars in the Milky Way. She was an expert on globular clusters. She measured the changing level of brightness in "variable" stars within globular clusters and through these measurements was able to predict the distance of the stars from Earth. Most are between 15 and 70 million light-years away.

This world-renowned astronomer also wrote a column for the *Toronto Star* from 1951 to 1980. In addition, she wrote a book

called, *The Stars Belong to Everyone: How to Enjoy Astronomy* (1976). In this book, she explained the wonders of the night sky in simple terms that the general public could understand. During her lifetime, Dr. Sawyer Hogg witnessed Comet Halley twice. The first time she was only five years old; the second time she was 80—the

Helen Sawyer Hogg

same year (1985) she married her second husband, Frances Priestly. Among her many honours, Dr. Sawyer Hogg has had an asteriod named after her. This asteroid orbits between Jupiter and Mars.

From Earth, we cannot see the centre of the Milky Way galaxy. Our view is blocked by large quantities of inter-stellar material. Using infrared telescopes, however, astronomers have been able to see through the dust and gas. They have learned that the galaxy looks like an enormous pinwheel, with spiral arms of stars radiating from a middle of densely packed stars. In 1990, the Cosmic Background Explorer (COBE) satellite, equipped with an infrared camera, gave us our first close look at the Milky Way's central region. Compare the infrared image of the Milky Way shown here with the diagram in Figure 15.9.

Andromeda and Beyond

The most distant object you can see with your unaided eye is what appears to be a nebula in the constellation of Andromeda. In 1925, astronomer Edwin Hubble was astonished to discover that he could spot individual stars in this nebula. He realized that what he was looking at was not a cloud of gas and dust at all, but another entire galaxy — completely separate from our own! With this one discovery, we learned that the universe is a far, far larger place than ever before imagined. Astronomers were soon discovering hundreds more galaxies—or, as Hubble called them, "island universes." Today, we know that there are as many galaxies in the universe as there are stars in the Milky Way.

Figure 15.10 The Andromeda galaxy is the nearest large galaxy to the Milky Way. It contains some 300 billion stars and is located about 2.5 million light-years from Earth.

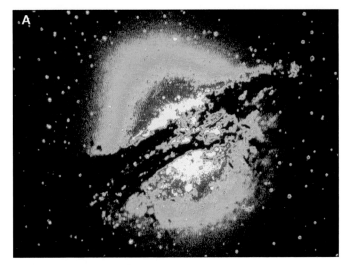

Figure 15.11 A Elliptical galaxy (side view)

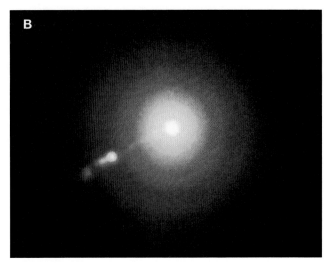

Figure 15.11 B Irregular galaxy (the Large Magellanic Cloud)

Figure 15.11 C Spiral galaxy (side view)

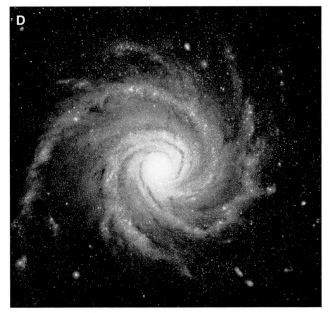

Figure 15.11 D Two spiral galaxies (top view)

Types of Galaxies

As astronomers observed the newly discovered galaxies in more detail, they found they could classify them into three major types: elliptical, spiral, and irregular. Figure 15.11 shows examples of each.

Elliptical galaxies, which seem to be the most common, have a shape similar to a football. They are composed primarily of old stars and have very little inter-stellar gas or dust.

Spiral galaxies, such as the Milky Way and Andromeda, look like flat pinwheels, with arms spiralling out from a central region. These arms are composed of much dust and gas, as well as bright, young, blue stars — evidence that star formation is still going on.

Irregular galaxies are made up of a mixture of young and old stars embedded in gas and dust. Galaxies of this type have no particular shape and tend to be smaller and less common than the other two types. Two examples (visible from the southern hemisphere) are the Large Magellanic Cloud and the Small Magellanic Cloud.

How Many Galaxies Are There?

Think About It

This highly magnified image displays the amount of sky blocked out by the head of a pin held at arm's length. The field of view is so small that there are only one or two stars from our own galaxy in the picture. (They are the objects with the glaring criss-cross markings.) The rest of the objects are galaxies.

What to Do

1 Carefully examine the photograph above, taken by the orbiting Hubble Space Telescope. Count the number of galaxies you see. Can you see any spiral galaxies like our own?

2 Assume that the Hubble picture shows a typical distribution of galaxies in the universe. Your task is to estimate how many galaxies might be in the universe. You can make an educated guess by working with a partner to brainstorm answers to the following questions.

- How many pin heads do you think would cover a postage stamp? Make a sketch of a small postage stamp and use dots made by a fine felt

pen to represent pin heads. Record your estimate in your notebook. Hint: There is a quick way to do this without covering the whole stamp with dots: $A = l \times w$.

- How many postage stamps would cover a piece of $8\frac{1}{2} \times 11$ inch paper? Make another sketch to show your reasoning. Record this estimate. How many pin heads would cover the paper? Record this answer as a power of 10.

- How many sheets of $8\frac{1}{2} \times 11$ inch paper held at arm's length would you need to block out your view of the sky? How many pin heads would cover this area? Record this answer as a power of 10.

3 Based on your estimations in step 2, how many Hubble pictures would be needed to cover the sky? (Remember that the Hubble picture shows the amount of sky blocked out by the head of a pin held at arm's length.) Record your answers as a power of 10.

4 To estimate the number of galaxies in the universe, multiply your total from step 1 by your answer to step 3.

Analyze

1. Assuming the number of stars in the Milky Way galaxy (400 billion) is about average for all types of galaxies, how many stars do you estimate are in the universe? Write your answer as a power of 10.

2. What assumptions are you making when you estimate your answer for question 1? What might make your answer an underestimate? What might make it an overestimate?

Galaxy Clusters

Just as stars occur in clusters within galaxies, so galaxies occur in clusters through-out the universe. For example, the Milky Way and Andromeda galaxies are two of the 30 galaxies that make up a cluster known as the Local Group. As Figure 15.12 shows, even these small clusters appear to be organized into larger "superclusters."

Figure 15.12 There may be more than 100 billion galaxies in the universe, and nearly all of them seem to be organized in clusters.

DidYou**Know**?

With binoculars, you can see Andromeda yourself. In the fall, look in the southeast-ern sky and find a giant diamond. In the winter, the diamond will be in the southern sky, with the top star high in the sky. The figure here will help you locate Andromeda in the fall.

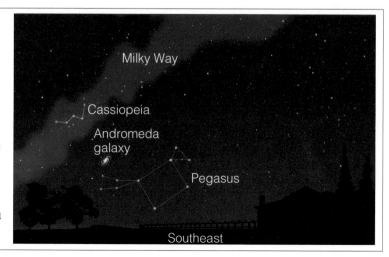

As you have learned in this section, 20th century space exploration revealed a universe more fantastic than people imagined before. The stars you see twinkling at night are not distributed throughout the universe in an even, fixed pattern. Many of them are part of our own neighbourhood galaxy — the Milky Way. Others, revealed only through telescopes, are other galaxies, numbering in the billions and spread vast distances apart. So just how big is the universe? In the next section, you will find out how astronomers have tried to answer this question.

Galaxy A is $\frac{1}{4}$ as bright as Andromeda and is estimated to be two times as far away from us.

Galaxy B is $\frac{1}{9}$ as bright and is estimated to be three times as distant as Andromeda.

1. Mathematically, how would you show the relationship between brightness and distance?
2. Now consider Galaxy C. It is $\frac{1}{100}$ the brightness of Andromeda. Therefore, how much more distant than Andromeda would you estimate it to be? How many light-years away would it be? (Recall that the distance to Andromeda from Earth is about 2.5 million light-years.)

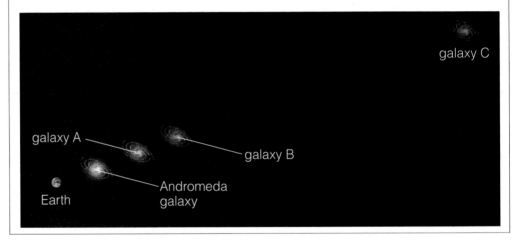

Check Your Understanding

1. **(a)** What is a galaxy?

   (b) What did the existence of galaxies reveal about the size of the universe?

2. Name two types of star clusters and explain how they differ.

3. What evidence is there that Earth is not in the centre of the Milky Way?

4. Explain why we cannot see the stars in the centre of our galaxy.

5. **(a)** What is the name of the nearest spiral galaxy to the Milky Way?

   (b) How many stars does it contain and how far away is it from Earth?

6. Identify the characteristics of the three main types of galaxy.

15.3 The Expanding Universe

The Cosmic Speedometer

In Chapter 14, you learned how spectroscopes are used to identify the chemical make-up of the atmosphere of celestial objects. Spectroscopes also have another important use in astronomy. They can tell us how fast a celestial object is moving toward or away from us. This information is important because it can reveal whether the universe is shrinking or expanding.

You have probably noticed that the siren on an ambulance or fire truck sounds different as the vehicle approaches, passes, and then moves away from you. The siren's change in pitch is called the **Doppler effect** and is caused by the change in the sound's wavelength. As Figures 15.13 A and B show, sound waves are compressed in front of the vehicle as it speeds along. This results in a shorter wavelength and higher pitch. Behind the vehicle, the sound waves stretch out, creating a longer wavelength and lower pitch.

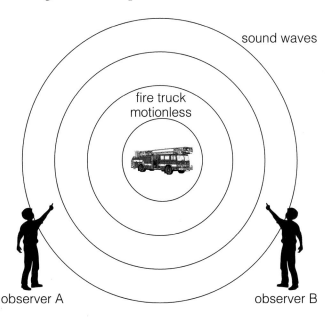

Figure 15.13A When the fire truck is not moving, the siren's sound has the same pitch in all directions because the sound waves are uniform.

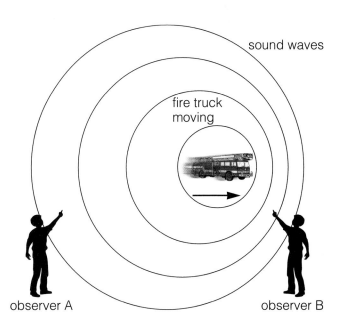

Figure 15.13B When the fire truck is moving quickly, the sound of the siren seems to change in pitch, becoming higher as the truck moves toward the observer and lower as it moves away from the observer.

Light, like sound, travels in waves. Thus, the Doppler effect can be used to measure the speed and direction of light-emitting objects such as stars. While the sound waves from a moving object differ in pitch, the light waves from a moving object differ in colour. If a star is approaching you, its wavelengths of light become compressed. As a result, the dark lines in the star's spectrum shift toward the shorter-wavelength end of the spectrum — the blue end. (See the electromagnetic spectrum in Chapter 14, Figure 14.2.) If the star is going away from you, its spectral lines will be **red-shifted** — moving toward the longer-wavelength part (red end) of the spectrum. Figure 15.14 illustrates how spectral lines in a star can reveal whether the star is moving toward or away from Earth.

spectrum A

spectrum B

spectrum C

Figure 15.14 Dark lines are shown in the spectrum of a stationary star (spectrum A). If the star is moving toward Earth, the lines will shift toward the blue end of the spectrum (spectrum B). If the star is moving away from Earth, the lines will shift toward the red end (spectrum C). The amount of shift that occurs corresponds to the speed with which the star is approaching or receding.

Observing the Doppler Effect

Since we cannot see sound or light waves directly, we can demonstrate the Doppler effect using another type of energy wave we *can* see. Try this simple activity at home.

What to Do

1. Fill a sink half-full of water.

2. Rapidly run the end of a toothbrush or hairbrush back and forth in the water.

3. What do you notice about the waves that are created on the surface of the water around the brush? How do the waves in front of the brush look? How do those behind it look? In

Outside Link ACTIVITY

your notebook, describe the pattern of what you have observed and draw a sketch to illustrate it.

What Did You Discover?

Imagine the brush is a star and Earth is located on a spot at the left side of the sink. Sketch how the waves would look to an observer on Earth when the star is moving away from it. Then sketch how the waves would look when the star is moving toward Earth. Briefly summarize how this information can be used to infer a galaxy's motion relative to the Milky Way.

Modelling the Expanding Universe

It is not easy to visualize a universe expanding in all directions. In this activity, you will have a hands-on opportunity to study the concept of universe expansion.

Problem

If all the galaxies around us are moving away from us, does this mean that our galaxy, the Milky Way, is at the centre?

Materials

paper and pencil
marker
balloon (light colours only)
clothespin
measuring tape

Procedure

1 Make a table like the one below.

	Measurement 1	Measurement 2	Measurement 3
Distance from A to B			
Distance from A to C			
Distance from A to D			
Distance from A to E			
Distance from A to F			

2 Use the marker to draw six dots on an uninflated balloon, placing three marks on each side of the balloon. Make each dot about the size of the eraser at the end of a pencil. Label the dots A to F. These represent individual clusters of galaxies.

3 Partially inflate the balloon and clip the opening shut with a clothespin. (Do not tie the balloon off.) Using the measuring tape (or a piece of string and a ruler), measure the distance between dot A and each of the other five dots. Record these distances in the table under Measurement 1.

4 Unclip the balloon, inflate it some more, and then tightly reclip it. Measure the new distances between dot A and the other dots. Record your results in the table under Measurement 2.

5 Inflate the balloon one last time, until it is almost completely full. Measure your distances and record them in the table under Measurement 3.

Analyze

1. What pattern do you see in the three sets of measurements you took as the balloon was inflated?

2. Is there any one central dot on the surface of the balloon, from which all the others move away?

Conclude and Apply

3. From your observations, what can you conclude about the motion of galaxy clusters relative to one another as the universe expands?

Extend Your Knowledge

4. Explain some of the weaknesses in this model of the universe.

Discovery of the Expanding Universe

By 1929, Edwin Hubble had estimated the distance to 46 galaxies. With the powerful telescope he was using (at the time the world's largest), he was also able to determine faint light spectra coming from these galaxies. He used that information to make one of the most amazing discoveries in recent astronomical history. The spectra of all 46 galaxies were red-shifted, meaning the galaxies were all moving away from Earth. Not only that, but the speed at which they were receding was in proportion to how far away they already were from Earth. The most distant galaxies were moving away fastest, and the closest were moving away more slowly. This relationship is known as **Hubble's law.**

A useful way to understand what is really happening among galaxies in the universe is to consider a rising loaf of raisin bread. Think of the bread dough as the universe and the raisins in it as galaxies. As the dough rises (the universe expanding), the distance between each raisin (galaxy) increases. To observers in any single raisin/galaxy, it would seem that all the other raisin/galaxies are receding from theirs.

The raisin bread model demonstrates another important point. Galaxies do not move freely through space (just as the raisins do not move freely through the bread dough). Rather, space itself is expanding, taking the galaxies with it.

Figure 15.15 Hubble's discovery that most galaxies were red-shifted was the first evidence that the universe is expanding at a constant rate.

Check Your Understanding

1. Briefly describe how a spectroscope is used to measure the speed at which a star is moving away from or toward Earth.

2. The dark lines in the spectrum of a newly discovered star are found to have shifted toward the red end of the spectrum. What does this tell us about the star's motion?

3. What is Hubble's law?

4. If all the galaxies around the Milky Way appear to be moving away from it, why can we not assume that the Milky Way is the centre of the universe?

5. **Thinking Critically** Galaxies outside the Local Group cluster have red-shifted spectra. Within the Local Group, however, some galaxies show a red shift and others show a blue shift. What does this suggest about the nature of the galaxies within the Local Group and those outside?

The Formation of the Universe

Imagine a foot race on a straight track in which all runners reach their maximum speeds quickly and run tirelessly on, never changing their speeds. What would the race look like a few minutes later? The runners would be spread out along the track, with the fastest runner in the lead. Gradually, the distance from one runner to the next would increase. This pattern is exactly what we observe in the universe. Like the runners, the galaxies must have started moving from the same place and at the same time.

Determining the Beginning of Time

You have discovered how astronomers measure the speeds at which galaxies are receding, and how they calculate the distances to far-off galaxies. From these values, it is possible to work backwards to find how long ago all the galaxies were at the same place at the same time. This estimate marks the beginning of the universe.

Math CONNECT

Suppose you are in a race, moving at 5 m/s. Runner A is ahead of you, moving at 9 m/s. Runner B is behind you, moving at 3 m/s. Assume that no one has changed speed since the race began.

1. How fast is Runner A moving away from you?

2. How fast is Runner B dropping behind you?

3. At a point in the race, if Runner A is 60 m ahead of you and Runner B is 30 m back, how many seconds ago did the race start?

The Origin of Matter

The most widely accepted scientific explanation for the origin of the universe is called the **Big Bang theory**. According to this theory, the universe and everything in it began in an instantaneous event that occurred between 15 and 20 billion years ago. This is when the "clock" started. There were no galaxies at time zero. There were not even any atoms.

The seeds of the Big Bang theory originated with the Belgian priest and astrophysicist Georges Lemaître in the early 1930s. Using Hubble's idea that the universe is expanding, Lemaître concluded that the universe must therefore have started out very small and dense. In the late 1940s and 1950s, astrophysicist George Gamow began to formulate the details of this theory. Study Figure 15.16 and make a "cosmic" timeline to help you understand the idea of the Big Bang event.

Echoes of the Big Bang

In the 1960s, astronomers Arno Penzias and Robert Wilson were working at Bell Laboratories in the United States, adapting a microwave antenna for use as a radio astronomy tool. They kept detecting background static in the signals they were receiving, no matter where the telescope was pointed in the sky. All their efforts to silence the static (including removing a bird's nest from the antenna) were unsuccessful. Penzias and Wilson finally concluded that what the telescope was picking up were faint remnants of the radiation given off by the original Big Bang event.

This discovery had tremendous significance. Remember that as a gas expands, it cools. The universe started out compact and very hot, but ever since the Big Bang set off the expansion, the universe has been cooling. Before Penzias and Wilson's discovery, several scientists had predicted that an expanding universe would by now have cooled to between −271°C and −263°C. The temperatures detected by Penzias and Wilson fell within this range, supporting the Big Bang theory's explanation for the formation of the universe.

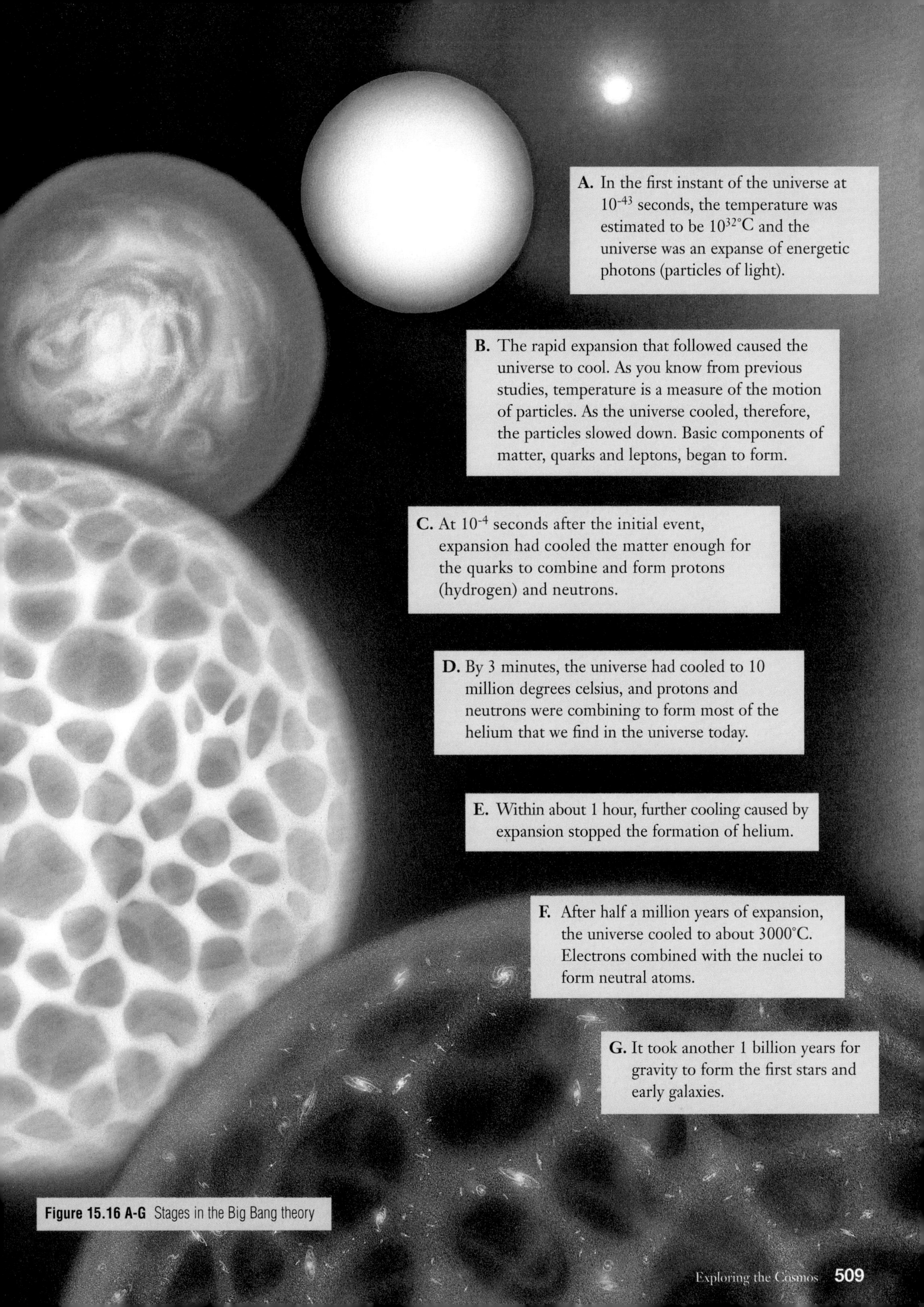

A. In the first instant of the universe at 10^{-43} seconds, the temperature was estimated to be $10^{32}°C$ and the universe was an expanse of energetic photons (particles of light).

B. The rapid expansion that followed caused the universe to cool. As you know from previous studies, temperature is a measure of the motion of particles. As the universe cooled, therefore, the particles slowed down. Basic components of matter, quarks and leptons, began to form.

C. At 10^{-4} seconds after the initial event, expansion had cooled the matter enough for the quarks to combine and form protons (hydrogen) and neutrons.

D. By 3 minutes, the universe had cooled to 10 million degrees celsius, and protons and neutrons were combining to form most of the helium that we find in the universe today.

E. Within about 1 hour, further cooling caused by expansion stopped the formation of helium.

F. After half a million years of expansion, the universe cooled to about 3000°C. Electrons combined with the nuclei to form neutral atoms.

G. It took another 1 billion years for gravity to form the first stars and early galaxies.

Figure 15.16 A-G Stages in the Big Bang theory

Outside Link  **ACTIVITY**

Beliefs About Cosmology Around the World

Think About It

Different cultures and societies all over the world have their own stories and beliefs about how and when the universe formed.

What to Do

1. Using your library, the Internet, and other resources, work with a small group to research how five or six other cultures have explained the origin and formation of the cosmos.

What Did You Discover?

1. How were the beliefs you researched similar? How were they different? What explanations can you offer for these similarities and differences?

2. As an extension, research examples of art that different cultures and societies produce to depict what they imagine about the formation of the universe. Present your findings to the class.

Exploring the Frontiers of the Universe

As much as we have learned about the universe in the last 50 years, there remain many more mysteries and "new frontiers" to explore. Quasars, gamma ray bursts, and missing mass are three of these. Each holds more clues about the size and age of the cosmos, and about its past and future.

Quasars

In the 1960s, astronomers discovered some star-like objects that emitted great amounts of radio waves. They were named **quasars,** for "quasi-stellar radio source." Spectral analysis showed that quasars have extremely large red shifts. Scientists concluded that quasars must therefore be very distant — at the edges of the observable universe. But quasars are also very bright, so the amount of energy they emit must be enormous.

The current thinking about quasars is that they are the result of explosions produced by colliding galaxies. It is thought that most quasars were formed about 12 billion years ago, when newly formed young galaxies were closer together and collisions between them were frequent. These sudden mergers of galaxies forced huge amounts of star material into a central black hole. Some of this material was converted to energy — visible as brilliant light — and some was ejected in jets of high-energy particles. These particles, moving through intense magnetic fields, generated the powerful radio waves that gave us the first sign that quasars exist.

The Hubble Space Telescope will soon peer into the cores of some galaxies that have quasars. The results will tell us how realistic our theories about these mysterious objects are. Research in this area is still so speculative that new evidence may well change all or most of the current ideas about quasars.

Gamma Ray Bursts

Every day, astronomers' instruments detect powerful pulses of gamma rays from somewhere in the sky. These are called **gamma ray bursts**. (Recall that Gamma rays have the shortest wavelengths of all forms of electromagnetic radiation in the spectrum.) The objects that emit these rays give out more energy within seconds or minutes than the Sun in its entire 10 billion year lifetime. Astronomers are not sure of the source of gamma ray bursts. One hypothesis is that when two giant stars collide or a star collapses, a black hole is formed. In the process, a huge amount of gamma radiation is released.

In 1997 and 1998, the combined data from the Hubble Space Telescope, telescopes in Hawaii and the Canary Islands, and detectors aboard an Italian-Dutch satellite enabled astronomers to determine the red shifts of several gamma ray bursts. It was concluded that the source of the bursts was over 10 billion light-years away, almost at the edge of the known universe.

Figure 15.17 It is puzzling how something as small as a quasar could emit such a tremendous quantity of radiation. One explanation is that as two galaxies collide, gas falls into an immense black hole at nearly the speed of light. This generates a beam of energy that we can detect on Earth, billions of light-years away.

Pause& Reflect

A map of gamma ray bursts shows that they come from all over the sky, not just from the band of the Milky Way. Do you think this suggests an origin inside or outside our galaxy? Explain your answer in your Science Log.

DidYou**Know**?

Quasars are believed to be only about the size of solar systems.

DidYou**Know**?

In astronomy, international cooperation is at its highest. When a detector on a satellite, a professional at an observatory, or an amateur in his or her backyard spots something interesting in the sky, notice goes immediately to a reporting observatory. The news flashes around the globe by telephone, fax, and on the Internet. Within minutes, satellites manoeuvre, radio dishes turn, and large telescopes all over the world swing about to observe the phenomenon. Although there is friendly competition to be the first with a discovery or theory, astronomers share their data. For them, there are no national boundaries.

Tools of Science

Deep inside INCO's Creighton Mine near Sudbury, Ontario, sit 1000 t of heavy water in a large tank. This is part of a sophisticated neutrino telescope. The Sudbury Neutrino Observatory has 10 000 light detectors looking into the tank to detect minute flashes of light given off when a neutrino interacts with the heavy water. The point of these observations is to determine what mass, if any, the elusive neutrino has. The answers may provide the solution to the puzzle of the universe's missing mass.

The Mystery of the Missing Mass

Everywhere we look in the universe there are galaxies. Galaxies, as you have learned earlier in this chapter, occur in clusters, held together by gravity. However, when astronomers add up the mass of all matter in the galaxies, the total mass is much too low to explain why galaxies stay clustered. Between 60% and 70% of the amount of mass that astronomers expect to find in the universe is missing.

How could this be? Some astronomers speculate that there may be a countless number of burned-out dark stars, providing mass we cannot see. Another suggestion is that intergalactic space (the space between galaxies) is not as empty as we thought. **Neutrinos**, elementary particles that carry no charge, may fill that space. Neutrinos were produced during the first moments of the formation of the universe and are still produced during fusion in the interior of the Sun. Many scientists today think that neutrinos may hold the secret of the universe's missing mass.

INTERNET CONNECT

www.school.mcgrawhill.ca/resources/

To see the latest Hubble Space Telescope photographs, go to Science Resources, then to **SCIENCEPOWER 9** to know where to go next. An excellent link is the Astronomy Picture of the Day. At this site, you can search through all previous Astronomy Pictures of the Day photographs. Each is accompanied by an informative description. What are the latest findings about quasars and gamma ray bursts? Write a short update on both topics, based on your research.

STRETCH Your Mind

Heavy water — just what is it? Find out how so-called "heavy" water differs from the water you know so well. Use your new knowledge from Unit 2 as a guide, and make a presentation about how an isotope of hydrogen makes heavy water useful for special purposes.

Check Your Understanding

1. Explain why astronomers believe that all the galaxies in the universe must have started their outward motion at the same time.

2. According to the Big Bang theory, how long ago did the universe begin?

3. **(a)** Define the term "quasar".

   (b) Where are quasars believed to be located in the universe?

4. Explain one hypothesis about the creation of gamma ray bursts.

5. **Thinking Critically** What force might halt the expansion of the universe? What do you think might begin to happen then?

Now that you have completed this chapter, try to do the following. If you cannot, go back to the sections indicated.

Use triangulation to measure indirectly the distance to an object. (15.1)

Define "parallax," and explain how astronomers use it to determine the distance to faraway celestial objects. (15.1)

Explain what a light-year is. (15.1)

Name the two properties of Cepheid variables that have made them useful for measuring intergalactic distances. (15.1)

Sketch the Milky Way galaxy as viewed from the side and from above, and label the Sun, central region, globular clusters, and spiral arms. (15.2)

Discuss the importance of Edwin Hubble's discovery of the Andromeda galaxy to our understanding of the universe. (15.2)

Name the three main types of galaxies and describe each one. (15.2)

Explain the Doppler effect and illustrate with an example. (15.3)

Describe astronomers' evidence that the universe is expanding. (15.3)

Explain the significance of the fact that all the galaxies in the universe likely started their outward motion at the same time. (15.4)

Outline the Big Bang theory of how the universe was formed. (15.4)

Define a "neutrino" and explain why astronomers are so interested in studying its properties. (15.4)

Prepare Your Own Summary

Summarize this chapter by doing one of the following. Use a graphic organizer (such as a concept map), produce a poster, or write a summary to include the key chapter concepts. Here are a few ideas to use as a guide:

- What are some of the ways in which astronomers have measured inter-stellar distances?
- Why is it more practical to use light-years than astronomical units (AU) to describe distances in the universe?
- What are galaxies and what three main types exist?
- What evidence do astronomers have that the universe is expanding?

- How could you model the expansion of the universe?
- When and how is the universe thought to have formed?

CHAPTER 15 Review

Reviewing Key Terms

If you need to review, the section numbers show you where these terms were introduced.

1. In your notebook, match the phrase in column A with the correct term in column B.

A
• used to find speeds of object toward or away from us
• "island universe" of stars
• star-like objects with large red shifts
• stars whose brightness changes
• used to find distances to nearby stars

B
• parallax (15.1)
• neutrino (15.4)
• galaxy (15.2)
• Cepheid variables (15.1)
• Doppler effect (15.3)
• quasar (15.4)
• globular cluster (15.2)

2. Place the following terms in order of the size of the object to which they refer. Go from smallest to largest: planet, star, galaxy, nebula, Local Group, solar system, moon.

Understanding Key Concepts

Section numbers are provided if you need to review.

3. What contributions to astronomy did Henrietta Leavitt, Harlow Shapley, Edwin Hubble, Georges Lemaître, and George Gamow make? (15.1 to 15.4)

4. How can the brightness of a celestial object be used to determine its distance? (15.1)

5. Name three types of galaxies. What type is our Milky Way galaxy? (15.2)

6. Why, with the use of optical telescopes, can we see distant galaxies but not see the centre of our own galaxy ? (15.2)

7. Consider three identical stars. One is coming toward us, one is going away from us, and one is not moving relative to us. What will be the difference in the line spectra? (15.3)

8. What evidence do we have that all the matter in the universe was created at one time and place? (15.4)

9. What is the significance of the discovery that there is a background radiation coming from all parts of the sky and corresponding to the radiation that would be emitted by an object between −271°C and −263°C? (15.4)

10. What evidence do we have that a quasar is very distant? (15.4)

Developing Skills

11. A surveyor marks off a 160 m baseline along the edge of a field. She then measures the angle from each end of the baseline to a water tower visible in the distance. She records the two angles: 40° and 70°. Show how the surveyor would apply the technique of triangulation to calculate the distance between the field's edge and the water tower.

12. Draw sketches to illustrate the following. (Add an arrow to point to Earth's location.)

    (a) the appearance of the Milky Way to an observer on Earth

    (b) the Milky Way galaxy to an observer on a nearby galaxy.

Problem Solving/Applying

13. Recall the Science Inquiry Activity on page 453 in Chapter 13, in which you were asked to model the solar system to conceptualize the vastness of space. Consider it again. If you were to add the Andromeda galaxy to the same scale model, how far from "Earth" would you have to position the galaxy? Hint: You may have to change the scale of your model to make the exercise more manageable. For example, the entire solar system could be represented by a peppercorn.

14. Can you propose a method for finding the parallax of more distant stars, using a space probe such as Voyager? Use a diagram to illustrate your ideas.

15. The speed of light is 300 000 km/s.

   (a) What is the speed of light in kilometres per hour?

   (b) The Sun is 1.5×10^8 km away. How long does it take the light from the Sun to get to Earth?

   (c) Suppose we see a gigantic flare erupt from the Sun and conclude that a tremendous number of tiny particles emitted during that explosion have begun racing toward Earth. Quickly we radio the occupants of the space station in Earth orbit, to warn them to get into their protection room. If the particles travel at 20% of the speed of light, how much time do the people have to get under cover?

16. Explain why objects that are farther away look younger to us than if they were closer to us.

Critical Thinking

17. It is thought that there are over 10 billion galaxies. Explain how we can get an idea of this number without photographing the entire sky and counting all the galaxies in all the pictures.

Pause&
Reflect

Recall the Starting Point Activity on page 487 in this chapter. You were asked to test the model of a universe that is unchanging and filled with a uniform distribution of stars. But the question remains: Why is the night sky dark? In 1826, a Viennese astronomer, Heinrich Olbers, argued that every point in the sky should be as bright as a star in an infinite universe of evenly distributed stars. Observation clearly shows that the night sky is dark. This was known as Olber's Paradox. Use your knowledge of cosmology to resolve this paradox.

Hints: Although stars are concentrated in galaxies, the galaxies themselves seem to be everywhere. However, the universe is expanding and had a beginning. If the universe began about 15 billion years ago, will the light from galaxies that are *farther away* than 15 billion light-years from Earth have reached our telescopes yet? Use this information to explain why there should be a limit to the number of galaxies we can see.

Opening Ideas...

- What is the greenhouse effect and how is it related to global warming?

- In what ways do humans use space as a resource?

- Do you think other forms of life might exist elsewhere in the universe? Explain your answer.

- List as many careers as you can think of that might involve the study, use, or exploration of space.

Science Log

Answer the questions above in your Science Log, using the knowledge you have gained from the first three chapters in this unit and from other areas of your studies. If you are unable to answer a question, describe how you would obtain the information you need to draw a conclusion.

The Apollo 8 astronauts circling the moon in 1968 were the first people to view Earth from afar. Since that historic mission, many images of Earth have been taken, showing how small and fragile Earth seems in the vastness of the universe. With the discoveries of space exploration in the late twentieth century, we now understand that Earth's existence is linked to the cosmos — past, present, and future.

In this final chapter of the unit, you will investigate how Earth is affected by its neighbours in space, primarily the Sun and the Moon. In particular, you will learn how Earth's climate — and life as we know it — depends on the thin layer of Earth's atmosphere. You will also discover the importance of satellite technology in our lives and the other benefits space research and travel have contributed to our well-being.

Some controversial issues in space exploration are raised in this chapter, too. Is it likely that intelligent life exists elsewhere in the universe? Should we spend money and effort searching for life elsewhere? Is it worthwhile sending astronauts, when we can send robotic probes into space for much less cost and risk?

Finally, you will explore the wide range of careers related to the study and use of space. The discoveries to be made about the universe are infinite.

Design a Space Station Colony Ship

Many scientists believe that establishing permanently inhabited space stations should be the next major step in advancing space travel and exploration. Supply craft from Earth would visit such stations to deliver food, materials, and new colonists. For flights to more distant space stations, supply ships would need to be self-sufficient for

very long periods of time. In this activity, you will design a supply ship capable of taking a colony of space voyagers to a destination years away.

What to Do

1. Working with a small group, analyze what a supply space ship would need. Assume that the trip your space ship is to make will last at least ten years. The following questions will guide you in setting the design criteria and planning your design.

   (a) How many crew members and passengers will you have?

   (b) What modules or sections will your ship require to accommodate all its operations and the needs of crew and passengers (for example, propulsion, oxygen supply, recreation, and medical aid)?

   (c) What processes that normally occur on Earth will have to take place on the ship? For example, will you have to grow your own food? From where will your supply of fresh water come?

   (d) What shape and layout should your ship have?

   (e) What ages will your crew members and passengers be? Will there be families on board?

2. Make preliminary sketches of the ship and, as a group, discuss what ideas and alternatives work best. Consolidate your plans into one large drawing, designating the ship's layout and labelling its special features.

What Did You Discover?

1. As a class, discuss the technological problems that would have to be solved before a colony ship of any type could be built.

2. **Thinking Critically** How many passengers in total do you think would be the best number to make a journey of this duration in the colony ship you designed? Why?

Key Concepts

In this chapter, you will discover

- what effects the Sun and the Moon have on Earth
- why satellites are so important to many fields of human endeavour
- how the search for extra-terrestrial life and intelligence is being conducted
- what effects microgravity has on organisms and other objects
- how Canada participates in space research and contributes to space exploration

Key Skills

In this chapter, you will

- interpret information from satellite photos
- design a "colony ship" capable of transporting people to a space station at least ten years away
- analyze the effects of everyday activities in a microgravity environment and propose designs to make living in space safe, comfortable, and efficient
- investigate science and technology careers related to the exploration of space

Key Terms

- greenhouse effect
- global warming
- ozone
- magnetosphere
- aurora borealis
- aurora australanis
- geomagnetic storm
- satellite
- geosynchronous satellite
- Global Positioning System (GPS)
- extra-terrestrial life
- SETI
- microgravity

16.1 The Effect of Celestial Bodies on Earth

The Sun's Radiation

The Sun has the greatest influence on Earth of any celestial body. All life on Earth depends on energy produced by the Sun — in the form of both light and heat.

Visible light and much of the Sun's infrared light pass through our atmosphere, and are absorbed by the oceans and land masses. This is how Earth is warmed. Earth's distance from the Sun produces a range of temperatures in which solid water (ice), liquid water, and gaseous water can all exist. Planets closer to the Sun are too warm and planets farther from the Sun are too cold for all three states of water to occur. Thus, Earth is in a narrow zone that supports water-based life such as ours.

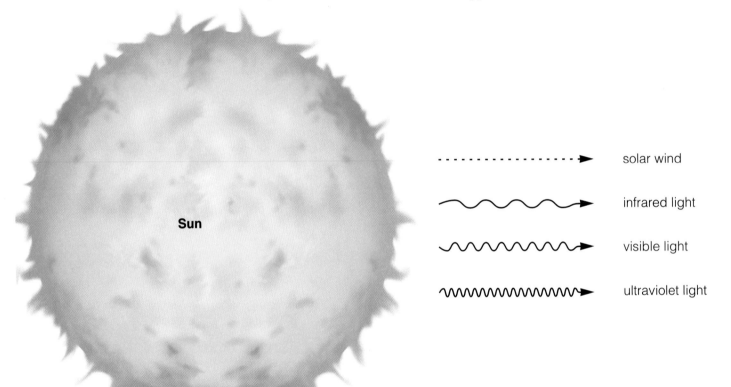

Figure 16.1 In addition to visible light, the Sun emits various kinds of electromagnetic radiation. Flowing out from the Sun are streams of electrons, protons, and other subatomic particles that make up the solar wind.

An important foundation for all life on Earth is the process of photosynthesis, in which green plants use sunlight, together with carbon dioxide and water, to produce glucose. Oxygen is a by-product of the process. This gas is vital for respiration in most organisms. It is thought that photosynthesis altered the balance of atmospheric gases early in the history of the planet, creating an atmosphere suitable for the evolution of modern forms of life.

The Sun is essential for life on Earth, but it is a dangerous neighbour. Earth's atmosphere helps shield us from its harm, as the following examples explain.

The Greenhouse Effect

Heat, as well as light, is vital to life on Earth. Earth's range of temperatures depends partly on our planet's distance from the Sun and partly on Earth's atmosphere. Because Earth is warmed by the Sun, it emits some heat in the form of infrared radiation. However, only some of the heat radiated from Earth's surface escapes back into space. The rest is absorbed by water vapour and gases (mostly carbon dioxide and methane) in the atmosphere (see Figure 16.2). This process is called the **greenhouse effect.** It causes Earth's average temperature to be higher than it would be if these gases (often called greenhouse gases) were not in our atmosphere.

The greenhouse effect has become a concern because human activities have started to alter the levels of greenhouse gases in the atmosphere. Carbon dioxide from car exhaust, forest clearing, coal burning, and other industrial processes traps more outgoing heat. The result is that the average temperature around the world is on the rise. Called **global warming,** this phenomenon is already starting to change some conditions on Earth as we know them. Can you think of what some of these changes might be?

Pause& Reflect

Recall that Venus is warmer than Mercury despite being farther from the Sun. With its high carbon dioxide atmosphere, Venus is an example of a run-away, or extreme, greenhouse effect. In your Science Log, describe what changes might occur on Earth if its temperature were to rise a few degrees.

Figure 16.2 The greenhouse effect has helped life exist on Earth. The Sun's energy travels through the atmosphere and heats Earth's surface. The heat radiated from Earth is prevented from escaping into space by greenhouse gases in the atmosphere.

Simulating the Greenhouse Effect

Have you ever wondered why the interior of a parked car gets so hot on a warm day, if all its windows are left closed? In this investigation, you can model this situation and infer an answer based on your knowledge of the greenhouse effect.

Problem

How can the greenhouse effect be simulated?

Safety Precaution

- Always be careful in handling glass thermometers, especially if they contain mercury.
- If a thermometer breaks, do not touch it. Have your teacher dispose of the glass and mercury safely.

Apparatus

2 empty aquariums, the same size
glass lid to cover one of the aquariums
3 test-tube racks
3 thermometers
3 large index cards or other cardboard

Procedure

1. Arrange the aquariums next to each other on a table in front of a sunny window. Leave about 30 cm space between them.

2. Place a test-tube rack in each aquarium. Gently place a thermometer in the rack. Shade the thermometer by making a small wall with the folded cardboard as shown in the diagram. Place the third test-tube rack between the aquariums. Put the last thermometer in the rack and shade it with the last piece of folded cardboard.

3. Immediately record the temperatures of the three thermometers in your notebook. (The temperature reading on all three should be the same.)

4. Place the glass lid on one aquarium.

5. Record the temperatures of all three thermometers at the end of 5, 10, and 15 min.

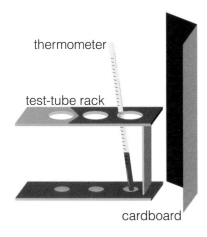

thermometer

test-tube rack

cardboard

Analyze

1. In this experiment, why did you place a thermometer between the two aquariums?

2. Which thermometer indicated the greatest temperature change during your experiment? Explain why, and make a sketch to support your answer.

Conclude and Apply

3. **Analyze** How was the glass lid in this experiment like the greenhouse gases in the atmosphere?

4. **Graph** Make a line graph that shows the temperatures of the three thermometers for the 15 min of the experiment.

5. **Infer** Explain why you should never leave a pet inside a closed car in warm weather.

Earth's Ozone Layer

Ultraviolet radiation from the Sun has an effect on Earth, too. Ultraviolet radiation breaks apart organic molecules, the building blocks of life. How, then, can life survive on this planet, so close to a star that emits large quantities of ultraviolet radiation? An explanation is found in another component of Earth's atmosphere.

Earth's atmosphere contains molecules of **ozone** (O_3). Ozone absorbs much of the Sun's ultraviolet radiation. The bad news, however, is that human activities have started to weaken the effectiveness of the ozone layer. Several industrial chemicals are known to break apart ozone in Earth's upper atmosphere. The result is that more ultraviolet radiation is now reaching Earth's surface. This is leading to an increase in the occurrence of skin cancer. Ultraviolet radiation also damages some plant life. Especially susceptible to greater ultraviolet radiation is the oxygen-supplying plankton (minute plants and animals) living near the ocean surface.

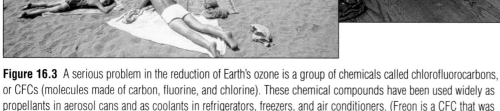

Figure 16.3 A serious problem in the reduction of Earth's ozone is a group of chemicals called chlorofluorocarbons, or CFCs (molecules made of carbon, fluorine, and chlorine). These chemical compounds have been used widely as propellants in aerosol cans and as coolants in refrigerators, freezers, and air conditioners. (Freon is a CFC that was in common use until recently.)

Throughout much of the world, production of ozone-damaging chemicals has been reduced. However, there is still concern that ozone levels will decrease and ultraviolet radiation levels will increase in the early twenty-first century because the chemicals released years ago are still in the atmosphere, breaking down the ozone layer.

INTERNET CONNECT

www.school.mcgrawhill.ca/resources/

Ozone levels in our atmosphere are now being monitored daily by special satellites. The results are accumulated by the Total Ozone Mapping Spectrometer (TOMS) project and displayed on the Internet. You can see up-to-the-minute maps that show the distribution of ozone world wide on your computer screen. Go to **Science Resources**, then to **SCIENCEPOWER 9** to find sites that take you to the TOMS displays. Look at the maps produced by the various satellites. Can you find the value for your region? How does it compare with the values for other places in North America?

Earth's Magnetic Field

As you learned in Chapter 13, streams of high-energy subatomic particles are emitted by the Sun and flow throughout the solar system as the solar wind. These particles could be hazardous to life on Earth, if they were to enter the atmosphere. Earth's magnetic field deflects most of them, however.

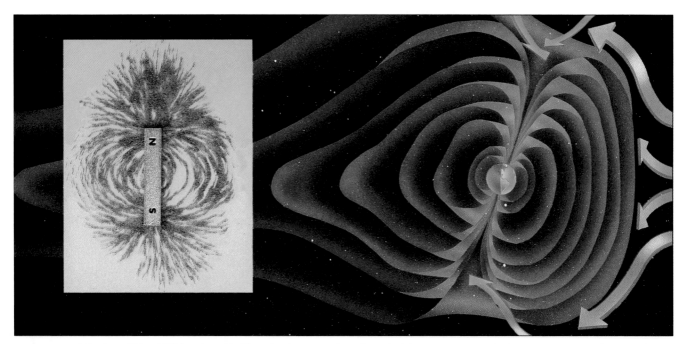

Figure 16.4 Lying from 200 to 5000 km above Earth's surface is a magnetic region called the magnetosphere. High energy particles in the solar wind stream through space, distorting this magnetic field. If there were no solar wind, the magnetic field might look like the field surrounding a bar magnet.

Figure 16.5 (A) The aurora borealis as viewed from Earth
(B) A space shuttle view of the aurora australanis over Australia

The magnetic field around the planet is similar to the magnetic field around a bar magnet (see Figure 16.4). It is produced by the movement of material inside Earth. Unlike the fairly even field that lies around a bar magnet, however, the field around Earth is stretched out by the solar wind. This region is called the **magnetosphere.**

Inside the magnetosphere, some of the high-energy particles from the Sun become trapped. They hurtle along the lines of the magnetic field, becoming concentrated near the north and south poles. When the particles collide with air molecules in the upper atmosphere around the poles, they produce the **aurora borealis** (or "northern lights") at northern latitudes and **aurora australanis** at southern latitudes. The auroras appear as shifting arches or curtains of coloured light in the night sky. Canada is a pioneer in aurora research.

When large flares erupt on the Sun, the solar wind carries increased numbers of high-speed charged particles. About two days later, when they arrive close to Earth, they affect radio transmissions through the atmosphere, disrupting our telecommunications. In the mid-1990s, after one especially energetic eruption called a **geomagnetic storm,** two of Canada's Anik satellites were damaged by the cascade of particles. In 1989, a particularly strong geomagnetic storm caused a blackout of Québec's hydro-electric system.

Off the Wall At present, spacecraft must carry all the fuel they need for propulsion. The fuel is heavy, so even more fuel is required to move the load as well as the spacecraft. Now imagine large spacecraft using the solar wind to "sail" to the outer planets. There are such proposals on the drawing table. A spacecraft with kilometre-long sails made of thin reflecting metal might be able to use the solar wind to move it forward. At first, the effect would be very small. Under the relentless push of the charged particles, however, the craft could eventually reach speeds comparable to those produced by chemical rockets. One day, these designs might become a reality.

The Moon

Although much smaller than the Sun, the Moon also has important effects on Earth. You probably remember from your earlier science studies that one of the best known effects is the pull of the Moon's gravity on the oceans, which produces tides (Figure 16.6). The times for high and low tides can be predicted for each day of the year, and "tide tables" are printed in many newspapers.

Figure 16.6 A High tide.

Figure 16.6 B Low tide.

As Earth turns on its axis, different locations on Earth's surface face the Moon. The ocean bulges on the side of Earth facing the Moon (see A in Figure 16.7) because the water is more affected by the Moon's gravitational pull than is the more distant and massive centre of the Earth (B). At the same time, Earth's centre experiences the force more strongly than does the water and the side of Earth lying directly opposite the Moon (C). As a result of these different forces being exerted, the oceans build up into two bulges, one on side A and the other on side C. These two tidal bulges remain fixed to the Moon's position. Therefore, Earth's daily rotation takes any coastal location in the world through two rising (incoming) tides and two falling (outgoing) tides in a 24 h period.

A complete explanation of the tides must also take into account the gravitational pull of the Sun and other planets in the solar system, as well as the effect of the Earth-Moon system orbiting around a common centre of gravity. Scientists are still trying to understand fully how all these factors play a role in causing and influencing the tides.

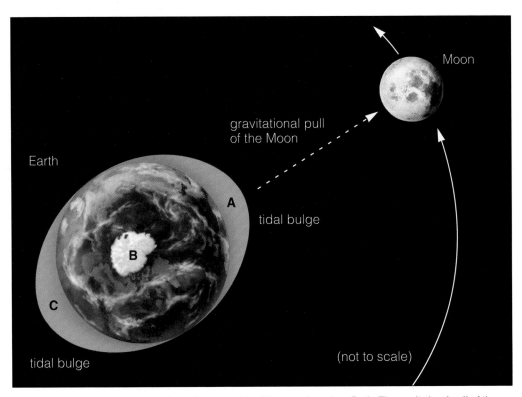

Figure 16.7 The Moon's gravity is the main cause of the tides experienced on Earth. The gravitational pull of the Moon is strongest on the side of Earth facing the Moon (A), less strong at the centre of Earth (B), and weakest at the side farthest from the Moon (C). The result is that ocean waters pile up in two bulges on opposite sides of the planet's surface.

The time between high tides is not exactly 12 h (half a day), because the Moon travels in its orbit as Earth turns. See if you can predict the actual time between high tides. Here are some hints. How long does it take the Moon to orbit Earth? Therefore, around what fraction of its orbit does the Moon go in a day? If the Moon is high in the sky to the south of you, how much more than a complete orbit must your location on Earth's surface have to rotate to bring the Moon south of you again?

If it is high tide at 1:00 P.M. today, when will the next high tide occur?

The Planets and Distant Stars

Many people believe that Earth may be affected by distant stars and planets. However, the distances of these celestial bodies from Earth are so great that their magnetic and gravitational fields are virtually undetectable. Little light or radiation comes from them, so their effect on Earth is negligible.

People in many cultures have thought for centuries about a different kind of effect, however. The planets and distant stars are such an impressive sight that many people believe human affairs must be influenced by the arrangement and movement of these celestial bodies. Astrological horoscopes are said to express these connections. Although astrology and astronomy were linked in ancient times, they are very different now.

Figure 16.8 What's your astrological sign? Many people still believe that a person's character and destiny can be predicted from the movement of celestial bodies, and check their horoscopes daily. Horoscopes are based on the 12 signs of the zodiac, shown here.

Space Debris

As you learned in Chapter 13, the solar system contains billions of asteroids, comets, and meteors that orbit the Sun. On any given night, Earth runs into several thousand small particles and rocks moving through space. Friction with Earth's atmosphere causes most of these to burn up, creating what we call meteors (commonly known as "shooting stars"). Larger rocks can make it all the way through the atmosphere, hitting Earth's surface. These are referred to as meteorites.

Small meteorites do little damage, but large ones can be catastrophic. Figures 16.9A and 16.9B show the results of Earth's encounters with some of these big rocks in the past. Calculations show that if a kilometre-wide rock hit Earth, more energy would be released than if all the world's nuclear arms were detonated simultaneously. The result could be continent-wide forest fires, tremendous tidal waves, and enough dust thrown into Earth's upper atmosphere to block the Sun for a year or more.

It is now thought that the extinction of dinosaurs might have been initiated by a meteorite impact. A year without sunlight would likely have caused the death of most green plants. The huge plant-eating animals would have died, followed by the meat-eaters. Later, sprouting from seeds, the plants would grow in a changed world. With most large reptiles extinct, the small mammals that survived adapted to new environments, and re-populated the planet.

Pause&
Reflect

How big a threat do you think a collision between Earth and an asteroid or comet poses? Is extinction of human life a possibility? What could be done if we detected that a collision was to occur soon? Think about these questions and answer them as best you can in your Science Log.

An impact site of the correct size and age of the meteorite that might have caused the extinction of the dinosaurs has been found on the Yucatán Peninsula in Mexico. The 200 to 300 km wide crater lies more than a kilometre below the surface.

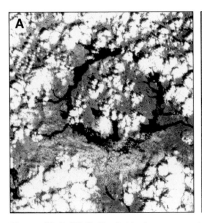

Figure 16.9 (A) Québec's Manicouagan crater, now a circular lake, is 150 km wide. (B) The Barringer crater in Arizona, only 1.5 km wide, was made by a house-sized meteorite. Debris was scattered up to 15 km away.

Check Your Understanding

1. In your own words, define the greenhouse effect.

2. Why is ozone an important part of Earth's atmosphere?

3. How does the solar wind affect Earth?

4. Describe the main way in which the Moon affects Earth.

5. Explain what is believed to have caused the extinction of the dinosaurs.

6. **Thinking Critically** Why, unlike the Sun and the Moon, do the planets of the solar system have no apparent effect on Earth?

16.2 The Use of Space

Since 1957, when the former Soviet Union sent Sputnik I into space, scientists have been using human-made **satellites** as important tools in space. Orbiting Earth, these objects are now used by many countries from all over the world for communications, observation and monitoring, navigation, and mapping. They carry instrumentation and their own power source, usually in the form of solar panels or small nuclear generators.

Communication Satellites

In 1953, a new record was set in telecommunications. Film recording the coronation of Queen Elizabeth II was rushed to a plane in London and flown across the Atlantic Ocean. The Canadian Broadcasting Corporation was the first broadcasting system in North America to show complete coverage of the coronation on television, only four hours after the ceremony ended.

Now, of course, we are able to watch the World Cup of soccer as it happens in Europe, listen to a news correspondent report live from a conference in Asia, and talk by phone with someone located just about anywhere on Earth. The world has become a "global village" of instant communications, thanks to orbiting satellites.

Satellites orbiting close to Earth take about 1.5 h to circle the planet. A moving antenna is needed to track them. **Geosynchronous satellites**, on the other hand, are in synchronized orbit with Earth's rotation. This means that they make one complete orbit for each time the Earth rotates, and so appear to be motionless over a point on Earth's surface. Stationary antennae can be used to track them. Geosynchronous satellites are placed in orbit about 42 000 km from Earth's centre, directly over the equator.

Geosynchronous satellites are far enough away that radio and television signals take a noticeable time to travel to the satellite and back. To counter this problem and provide a mobile phone network around the world, Iridium, a telecommunications company, has placed a fleet of more than 80 satellites in a low orbit (780 km high) around Earth. Thus, there are always a few above the horizon, ready to exchange long-distance communication signals with ground stations.

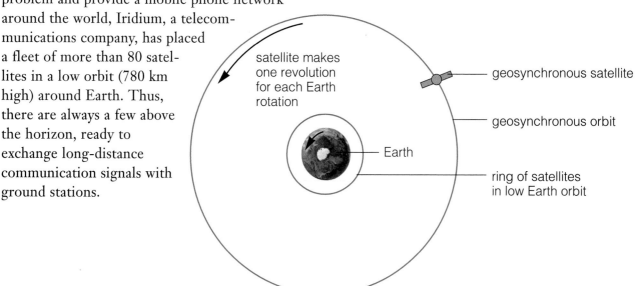

satellite makes one revolution for each Earth rotation

geosynchronous satellite

geosynchronous orbit

Earth

ring of satellites in low Earth orbit

Figure 16.10 Two orbits used for satellite communication.

For the opening of the 1996 Olympics in Nagano, Japan, choirs in five different parts of the world sang simultaneously under the direction of conductor Seiji Ozawa. Ozawa was in a television studio in Nagano and singers in Beijing, Berlin, Cape Town, New York, and Sydney watched him conduct on television screens. Their sound and images were shown on a giant television screen in the Olympic stadium. This technical achievement was made possible by satellites.

How was this done? Signals bounced back and forth between orbiting communications satellites. However, since some choirs and satellites were farther away from Nagano than others, the returning signals were out of synchronization. Technicians in Japan had to delay the picture of Ozawa until the views of all the choirs made it back to the television station. The signals were then assembled and sent to the stadium. The audience in the stadium heard the choirs' voices and watched the conductor's arm-waving about two seconds after his actual arm movements in the studio.

Word CONNECT

"Anik" means "brother" in the language of the Inuit. Research the meaning of "Sputnik" and write it in your notebook.

Canada is a world leader in the development and use of communication satellites. On November 10, 1972, Canada's domestic communication satellite, Anik 1, was launched from Cape Canaveral in Florida. On February 5, 1973, the Canadian Broadcasting Corporation started network television transmissions to the Canadian North, becoming the first in the world to use satellites to transmit television. Canada was also the first country to place a satellite in geosynchronous orbit for domestic (non-military) purposes.

More sophisticated Anik satellites have been launched since then. (See Figures 16.11A, B.)

Figure 16.11 Anik E2 makes it possible for students in Canada's North, who are often very far from a school, to participate in lessons and submit their assignments over the Internet.

Observation Satellites

Observation satellites are used for forecasting weather, carrying out research, and helping ships, aircraft, and other vehicles determine their exact location on Earth. Most people have seen the satellite photographs of weather systems displayed by television weather reports. These views of cloud patterns and areas of precipitation are useful for weather predictions and storm warnings. Ships at sea can be cautioned to avoid large cyclonic storms which show up on satellite photographs as giant pinwheels.

Satellites are also used to measure depth of snow, the extent of ice build-up in arctic waters, and the locations of forest fires. In the satellite images in Figure 16.12, you can see the smoke from fires burning in the summer of 1998 in northern Canada.

Observation satellites can do more than take photographs using the visible spectrum. Some peer at Earth's ultraviolet and infrared emissions. On infrared photographs of the ground, areas of different temperature show up as different colours. This can be used, for example, to spot where cold and warm currents meet in the ocean. Analysts of infrared satellite pictures can even tell one crop from another in farmers' fields and healthy maple forests from damaged ones.

Some satellites use spectroscopy to measure air pollution. Since hot gases emit specific colours of light, and cold gases absorb those colours, a satellite can analyze light patterns in the atmosphere to determine how abundant a particular gas is. A photograph is then produced, enhanced by false colour, to show the amounts of the target gas. Figure 16.13 shows an example of this technique.

Figure 16.12 Can you tell from this photograph in which direction the fires will probably move next?

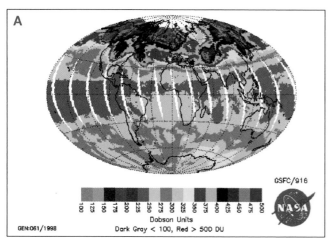

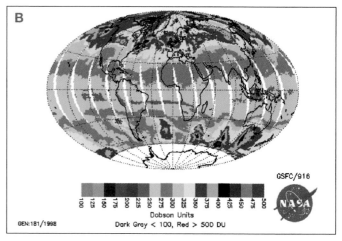

Figure 16.13 Satellite photographs showing ozone distribution in the northern hemisphere three months apart: (A) March 30 and (B) June 30. Are you better protected from ultraviolet radiation in the spring or in the summer? (A Dobson unit measures the thickness of the ozone layer)

Interpreting Satellite Photographs

Different satellites provide different information, each better suited for particular purposes. This activity lets you explore these differences for yourself.

What to Do

These two photographs were taken from two different satellites. Photo A shows a chain of three storms about to hit the U.S. east coast. Photo B, taken a week later, shows the second of the storms, Hurricane Fran, as it nears the land. Study the photographs and analyze the information each provides.

What Did You Discover?

1. Which photograph was taken by a satellite in geosynchronous orbit? Give two pieces of evidence to support your inference.

2. What are the advantages of each photograph in terms of information provided?

3. What uses can be made of the information discovered in the photographs?

Canadian observation satellites are named LANDSAT and RADARSAT. The Centre for Remote Sensing in Ottawa maintains two receiving stations for them — one in Prince Albert, Saskatchewan, and one in Gatineau, Québec. Figure 16.14 shows how LANDSAT can be used for land use interpretation and planning.

RADARSAT was launched in November 1995. It transmits and receives signals through darkness and clouds, using a powerful microwave Synthetic Aperture Radar (SAR) system. From its pole-to-pole orbit 800 km above Earth, RADARSAT produces images that are used to study ice movement, monitor pollution, and survey natural resources.

Figure 16.14 This LANDSAT image of Cape Breton Island covers a 27 km by 15 km area. The dominant coniferous forest appears in dark yellow-brown colours. The most recent forest clear-cuts show up as light blue. The purplish areas in the upper left side and lower right are treed bogs. Can you spot Margaree Harbour, the famous Cabot Trail along the ocean, and a large valley containing the Northeast Margaree River and a number of small communities?

Tools of Science

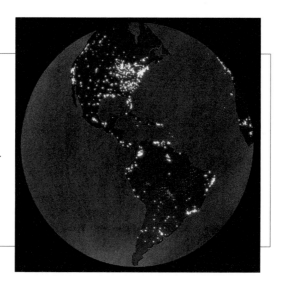

What sort of information might a satellite using infrared cameras detect? In this photograph of the Americas at night, the white patches are city lights, marking areas of urban density. The red spots in South America indicate large scale burning of vegetation as rainforests are destroyed for agriculture. The small yellow spots in Central America show burning gas flares at oil production sites.

Global Positioning System (GPS) Satellites

You need never get lost again! Using a small hand-held **Global Positioning System (GPS)** unit, you can use satellite technology to find out where you are on Earth. More than two dozen GPS satellites (called NAVSTAR, for navigation satellite tracking and ranging) are now spread out in high orbit around Earth. As a result, there are always at least three above the horizon, wherever you are in the world, whatever the time of day.

The satellites send out radio signals announcing their position and the exact time. Each hand-held GPS unit contains a receiver and a computer. It detects the radio signals and measures the distance to each satellite by comparing how long the signals take to receive. The unit then calculates your location on Earth, using the triangulation method that is programmed into the system. (Recall triangulation from Chapter 15.) Most units can pinpoint your location to within about 30 m, although more expensive units can be accurate to within 10 m.

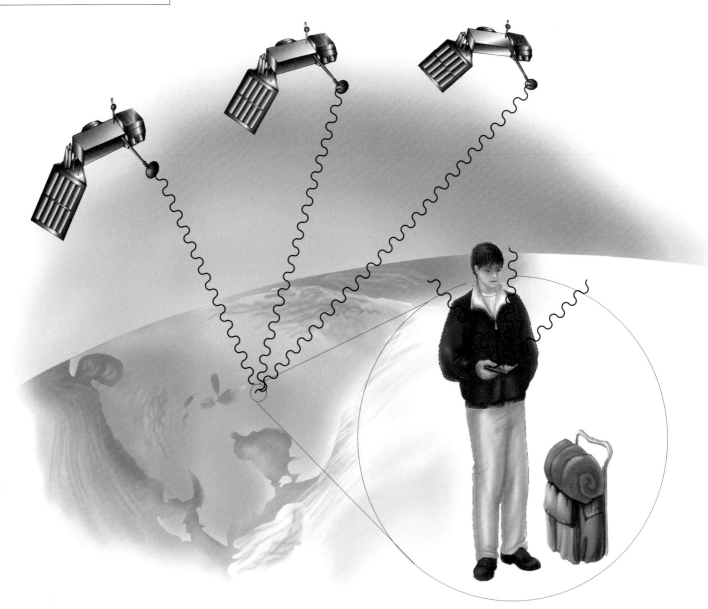

Figure 16.15 Using the GPS unit to determine your location

Photographing Space

Satellites can aim their instruments outward from Earth and take images far out into space. Orbiting above Earth's atmosphere, which distorts transmission of light waves, satellites can take much clearer pictures than telescopes on the ground. The Hubble Space Telescope, for example, has made many discoveries, from stars being born inside a nebula, to extra-solar system material orbiting around nearby stars. Other satellites photograph the Sun, and still others map the infrared, radio, and ultraviolet sources in the cosmos.

Space Travel

For generations, people have dreamed of travelling to distant parts of the universe. In 1969, when U.S. astronaut Neil Armstrong stepped onto the Moon's surface from the Apollo 11 spacecraft, the event marked a major milestone in achieving that dream. There have been five more lunar landings, the last one in 1972. Since then, no one has left Earth orbit. However, robotically-operated space probes landing on Venus and Mars have given us close-up views of the ground on these foreign worlds. In 1994, for example, the U.S. Magellan space probe used radar to make detailed maps of the surface of Venus. These showed craters, faults, and the lava flows of volcanoes.

Figure 16.16 Great strides are being made in the area of space travel. In 1969, Neil Armstrong and Edwin ("Buzz") Aldrin were the first humans to walk on the Moon. Now, with the establishment of the International Space Station, a new era of space travel and research is under way. The station might one day become a construction site for spacecraft destined for the Moon and beyond.

Space Travel of the Imagination

Space travel has fascinated people for a long time, including many writers of fiction who have used the space theme in their work. Stories about space generally fall into the category of writing known as "science fiction" or "science adventure." In many cases, the authors of these stories have a good knowledge of science and use it to develop their action. In other cases, it is clear that the authors used more imagination than science.

What to Do

1. In a small group, brainstorm a list of novels and short stories in which the setting or action involves space travel. Use the library and the Internet for assistance. Try to find at least ten titles.

2. For each story, write down the full title, the author's name, the collection in which the story appears (for short stories), and the date and place the book was published. As well, describe in one sentence what the story is about. If no member of your group has read the story, you can use the description on the book's dust jacket for guidance.

3. Bring your detailed list to class and compare your findings.

What Did You Discover?

Analyze the information you have gathered about the stories and try to determine whether there are any patterns. For example:

1. Which words, phrases, or concepts appear in the titles more often than others?

2. Are there any similarities in the plots?

3. Is there any relationship between when the stories were written and the extent of scientific knowledge about space at the time?

Extend Your Knowledge

1. Individually, select two space travel stories that interest you from your list or from the list of another group. (If these books are not available in your school or public library, your teacher might help you find a copy.) Read the stories and then write a short report, comparing how well each author has researched scientific facts about astronomy and space.

2. In a small group, brainstorm a list of songs or movies that use space travel or astronomical references. Listen to or view a selection of these and critique how accurately they portray scientific facts about astronomy and space.

For several years in the 1970s, the United States sent astronauts to Sky Lab, a small space station orbiting Earth. Space stations have living quarters, work and exercise areas, and all the equipment and support systems that humans require to live and work in space. Sky Lab eventually spiralled back to Earth, burning up over Australia and the Indian Ocean. In the 1980s and 1990s, Russian astronauts (known as "cosmonauts") lived in the Russian space station Mir for extended periods. Some stayed in space for over a year.

For the last decade, the American Space Shuttle has also been carrying astronauts and scientists into orbit. A major component of the Space Shuttle is the robotic arm outside the spacecraft that can be manipulated by remote control. The arm was developed by a Canadian company, Spar Aerospace. Shuttle crews have used the Canadarm to release and retrieve satellites from the Shuttle's cargo bay. The arm also came to the rescue when the Hubble Space Telescope was found to be defective after it was launched. Using the Canadarm, the Shuttle brought the telescope in, fixed it, and then released it back to its orbit to continue taking and relaying images to Earth.

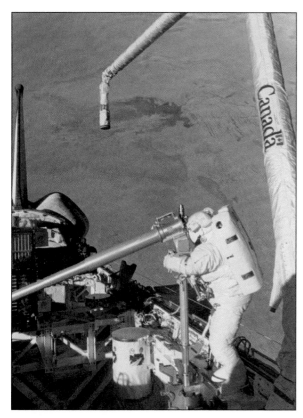

Figure 16.17 Mission specialist working in the cargo bay of the American Space Shuttle Columbia, beside the Canadarm.

Figure 16.18 Canadian astronaut Chris Hadfield "floats" through the docking mechanism, as crews from the Atlantis and Mir-20 spacecraft got together during space orbit in 1995.

The next major space project is the International Space Station, a joint project of the United States, Europe, Canada, Russia, and Japan. The Space Station will be a permanent lab where scientists can conduct long-term research experiments in space. It might also become the site of spacecraft construction and launching. The first phase of the project has involved docking missions between the Space Shuttle and Mir. In the second phase, main "Alpha" station will be constructed in orbit with modules brought from Earth. In the third phase, a crew will begin operation of the international station.

Check Your Understanding

1. There are many ways in which satellites are used. List six of these ways.

2. What are geosynchronous satellites?

3. Explain the uses of Canada's LANDSAT and RADARSAT satellites.

4. How does the Global Positioning System work?

5. What is the International Space Station and what is its purpose?

6. **Apply** A friend telephones you from the other side of the world. You notice that when you say anything, there is a slight delay before your friend answers. Your friend notices the same thing. After he or she speaks, there is brief pause before you reply. Explain why this is happening.

16.3 Issues in Space Exploration

Many scientists today expect that **extra-terrestrial life**, life other than that on Earth, exists in the universe. Certainly, one of the most exciting discoveries would be solid evidence of extra-terrestrial life. In the meantime, the possibility is just that — only a possibility.

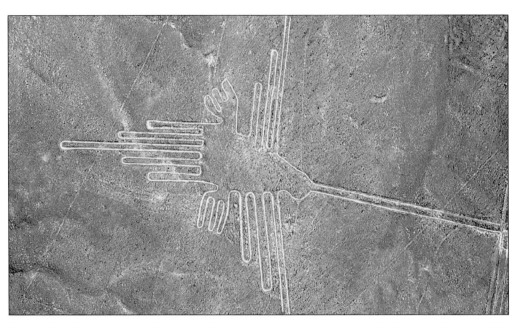

Figure 16.19 The hummingbird-like image in this aerial photograph was carved into the Peruvian plain about 2000 years ago. It is several kilometers long — so big that a ground-level observer cannot see it all. Claims have been made that it must have been created by individuals with a view from a spacecraft. How might early people have made this picture without seeing it from the air?

In the 1970s, when scientists used computer enhancement to give extra contrast to Viking photos of Mars, one photo appeared to show a human face (see figure A). This convinced many people that aliens must have visited Mars and made the markings. A later spacecraft that could have provided a better view of "the face" became lost just as it entered Mars' orbit. Believers of the "face-on-Mars" story concluded that the aliens who built the face also destroyed the spacecraft. When the Global Surveyor space probe passed Mars 25 years later, it aimed its more advanced cameras at the same spot. What appeared this time were only wind-swept hills (see figure B). Can you match the features in figure B to those in figure A?

The most intense search for extraterrestrial life was performed by the two Viking lander space probes on the surface of Mars in 1975. At each site, the little robots repeatedly performed three chemistry experiments on the planet's soil. The results indicated that Martian soil had a different composition from Earth soil. They also showed that the soil contained no metabolizing organisms and no evidence of organic material from past life.

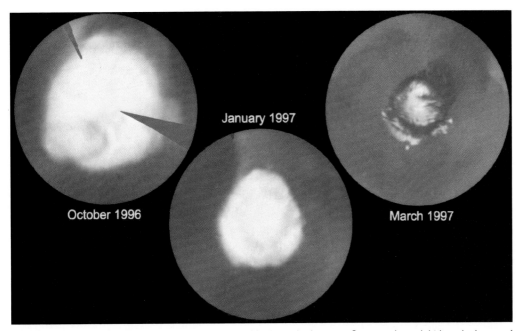

Figure 16.20 Liquid water has been detected near the Martian polar ice caps. Space probes might have had more of a chance of finding evidence of current or past life had they landed there.

Observations of Europa, a moon of Jupiter, indicate that it may have a liquid water ocean beneath an ice surface. Some scientists think this might be a place to search for life. Although another of Jupiter's moons, Callisto, appears dead, the Galileo space probe that passed it in 1996 and 1997 discovered a magnetic field. The presence of a 10 km deep salty ocean, kept warm by the decay of radioactive materials in Callisto's interior, might explain this. The existence of that ocean also had scientists wondering if Callisto, too, might have some form of life.

Off the Wall

Despite what popular television programs and movies would have you believe, expeditions in search of extra-terrestrial life are simply not possible in the foreseeable future. Even the fastest spacecraft today (the Voyagers) would take about 50 000 years to reach the nearest star. Faster spacecraft might exist in future, but the energy requirements to propel them would remain, by today's standards, completely prohibitive. For example, imagine explorers are planning a voyage to a star that is 15 light-years away. They hope to complete the one-way trip in 30 years. Some scientists have estimated that a voyage of this length would require the same amount of energy as would be consumed in more than 750 000 years in all of North America.

The Search for Extra-terrestrial Intelligence (SETI)

The existence of life elsewhere in the universe is a different matter from the existence of intelligent life. Also, intelligent life forms without a technology for space travel or telecommunication may exist. If there are intelligent forms of life, our best options for detecting them are (1) to send explorers out to find them or (2) to see if we can send messages back and forth. As you have learned earlier in this unit, the immense distances between the stars rule out space travel as a realistic option. Therefore, communication is where researchers have focussed their attention.

At several radio telescopes around the world, astronomers are listening to radio noises that come from distant stars, nebulae, pulsars, and quasars. They are attempting to detect signals in a pattern that could not be made by a naturally occurring object. This work is part of several programs under way to search the universe for radio signals from intelligent life. These programs are known collectively as the Search for Extra-terrestrial Intelligence, or **SETI.**

In 1992, the most advanced SETI project to date was begun by NASA. Although funding for the project was cut by the U.S. Congress in 1994, the SETI Institute continues the work today at a smaller scale with private funding. Two others are Project BETA, funded by the U.S. Planetary Society, and META II, an Argentinean project.

Modern searching equipment can now monitor millions of channels simultaneously. Still, the search is very ambitious and speculative. It is not just like looking for a needle in a haystack, but like looking for a needle in a million haystacks. To date, no intelligent signals have been detected. The few potential "hits" that have been recorded have all been traced to some earthly source, such as reflection of a radio wave off a large weather balloon.

Astronomers involved in the search for extra-terrestrial life are not just waiting to receive radio signals. They are also sending signals, aiming them to nearby stars where distant civilizations, if they exist, might hear them and respond.

Figure 16.21 Listening to the stars. If there are other technologically advanced civilizations on our side of the galaxy, and if they use powerful radio waves, we may some day be able to detect the presence of these neighbours.

Outside Link **ACTIVITY**

What Do We Say After "Hello"?

The radio messages that astronomers are sending into space are intended to attract the attention of potential extra-terrestrial listeners. They typically include greetings and convey information about Earth and its inhabitants. Yet, how is it possible to communicate with an extra-terrestrial intelligence that does not "speak" any of our languages?

What to Do

1. Using the resources in the library and on the Internet, research what form of communication scientists have been using to create the messages they broadcast into space. Summarize your findings in a one-page report, including illustrations as needed.

2. Create your own message using the same process. Have a classmate try to decode it.

What Did You Discover?

Outline some of the difficulties that might arise as humans attempt to establish meaningful communication with an alien civilization.

Who Might Be Picking Up Earth's Signals?

Think About It

Only since the 1930s have humans been using radio and television transmissions strong enough that they might be detectable far from Earth. If alien civilizations exist and have radio antennae pointed our way, they might be picking up our programs.

Remember that television, radio, and light waves are all forms of electromagnetic radiation. They all travel at the speed of light and cover a distance of 1 light-year in one year. A receiving dish 1 light-year away would just now be detecting the television program you were watching one year ago.

What to Do

1 Copy the diagram below into your notebook. The diagram, which is not to scale, shows Earth and a series of arcs marking the distances from Earth at intervals of 10 light-years.

2 At each distance, write down either a television program or a news broadcast that any receiving antenna at that location might be picking up now. For example, the television signal showing humanity's first step on the Moon in 1969 would have reached a distance about 30 light-years away. Any civilization farther than that would not yet know we had the capability of space travel.

Analyze

1. Suppose a civilization that picked up one of our first strong radio transmissions, emitted in 1935, immediately sent a radio message back. If that civilization were 50 light-years from Earth, in what year will we receive their reply?

2. Imagine that a radio telescope on Earth has just detected a message from a civilization which is responding to Earth's first strong radio transmission. In colour, mark on your diagram an arc that represents the farthest distance away that civilization could be.

3. Voyager, the fastest moving space probe we have created, will not reach the nearest star for about 50 000 years. To any alien civilization, Earth would be a barely visible speck near a distant star. How likely is it that an alien civilization has already detected that there is life on Earth and has actually made a visit? Explain your answer.

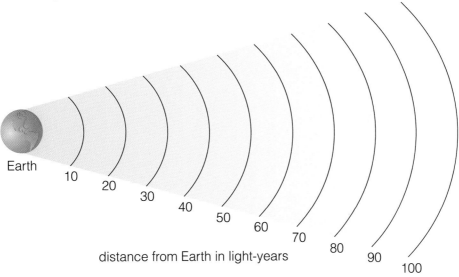

Earth

10
20
30
40
50
60
70
80
90
100

distance from Earth in light-years

Exploration by Astronauts or Robots?

Over the years, several methods of space exploration have been used. Since Galileo first pointed a telescope at the night skies 400 years ago, we have used ever larger and more sophisticated telescopes to examine the universe. Within our own solar system, we have sent space probes to visit the planets and radio back to us what they see. Our astronauts have also travelled to the Moon. Planning is now under way to send astronauts to Mars.

Should we continue using astronauts to explore the solar system? Astronomers are lined up on both sides of this question.

Some argue that the cost of these flights (like the cost of SETI work) is unjustified. Instead, they say, we could send small robots, such as Viking or Pathfinder, into space for a fraction of the cost of sending humans. Others say that humans can see and do what machines cannot. Critics of the big projects believe that they divert all the funding, expertise, and attention from many worthwhile smaller projects. Supporters believe that the public becomes more enthusiastic about big projects. Such projects, they say, result in more jobs and produce greater scientific and technological developments.

Figure 16.22 Is sending people into space worth the cost? Can robots do the job as effectively?

Check Your Understanding

1. What evidence is there of the existence of extra-terrestrial life?

2. How might radio telescopes help astronomers detect extra-terrestrial intelligence in the universe?

3. List three reasons in favour of space exploration using astronauts and three reasons against.

4. **Thinking Critically** Why might people believe that aliens regularly visit Earth, even though there is no scientific evidence?

16.4 Careers Involving Space Exploration

Space exploration is an exciting field for many reasons. For one, it requires the application of nearly all areas of science and technology to the goal of discovery and learning. For another, it involves an adventurous spirit and a great deal of resourcefulness and imagination. It is also an area of human endeavour where international cooperation and exchange is vital if advances are to be made.

Figure 16.23 A In 1962, U.S. astronaut John Glenn was the first American to orbit Earth in space. Thirty-six years later, as a member of the 1998 Discovery mission, he became the oldest person ever (at 77 years old) to go into space.

Figure 16.23 B This technologist is one of the many experts who check each piece of equipment before launching a spacecraft into space.

There are many opportunities for a career related to the space field. Depending on your own interests and aptitudes, you might find your future lies in one of the following areas.

- **Astronaut:** The ultimate space-related career for some people is being one of the individuals to travel beyond Earth's atmosphere. In addition to being scientists, astronauts must be in peak physical condition to perform the demanding tasks required in the small quarters of a spacecraft. Periodically, the Canadian Space Agency advertises for applicants to train for this job, in readiness to work on NASA missions. While very few candidates are selected from the thousands of individuals who apply, anyone with the right dedication, expertise, and education has a chance.
- **Satellite technologist:** There are many links between computer technology and satellite communication, both in the construction of the satellites and the development of software to manage the satellites and interpret the data. Engineers, physicists, mathematicians, chemists, mechanics, computer programmers, and technicians are all members of the teams that build and maintain satellites. Firms that purchase and interpret LANDSAT and RADARSAT images also employ geographers, geologists, and biologists.

What Does It Take to Become an Astronaut?

Think About It

What preparation is needed before a person would be considered to have the right qualifications to apply for the position of astronaut? Find out in this investigation.

What to Do

1 Your teacher will hand out short biographies of several Canadian astronauts.

2 Make a table with four columns. At the top of each column, write: Name, Education, Skills, and Interests/Hobbies.

3 Read each biography and summarize the information in your table. In the first column, fill in the name of the astronaut. In the next three columns, note the important qualifications of each astronaut.

4 When you have read through all the biographies and completed the table, read the information critically.

Analyze

1. What patterns do you see in the biographies of these astronauts?

2. What education, skills, and interests/hobbies would you recommend for people hoping to join the Canadian Space Agency as an astronaut?

Extend Your Knowledge

Use the library or the Internet to research the qualifications a person requires for other careers related to space exploration. If there are one or two areas of study that particularly interest you, investigate how these tie in with current needs of space research and the aerospace industry. Examples include robotics, architecture, mapping, nutrition, fitness, and sport.

Figure 16.24 Canadian astronaut Chris Hadfield in the Neutral Buoyancy lab, which simulates the experience of weightlessness. The Canadian Space Agency is the organization in Canada responsible for this country's involvement in international space exploration efforts.

- **Aerospace industry careers:** Along with constructing and launching satellites, workers in the aerospace industry design and build the spacecraft that explore the solar system and the rockets that lift them off the earth. Architects and trades people in several countries are working on the modules of the International Space Station. Everything from designing sleeping quarters to inventing recipes for the occupants must be accomplished.

- **Astronomer:** Many major universities have astronomy departments. They hire astronomers both to teach the subject and to carry out research. University science graduates working on their masters degrees or doctorates study under professors, trying to advance our knowledge of the cosmos. Many Canadian universities have excellent astronomical telescopes, and Canadian astronomers share observation time on the world's great optical and radio telescopes.

- **Careers in microgravity research:** Astronauts living and working in space must cope with the effects of **microgravity**. Microgravity refers to the condition in which objects in orbit (for example, a spacecraft and its contents) seem to be weightless. In reality, gravity is acting on them (gravity is what keeps the spacecraft in orbit), but its effect is reduced. Humans living in a microgravity environment for prolonged periods develop several health problems. For example, even after only a few days in space, astronauts' muscles and bones start to weaken. Some individuals experience back trouble. If we ever hope to launch extended space missions (think of a three-year trip to Mars), we must first learn much more about the long-term effects of microgravity on the human body.

Canadian research and development in microgravity includes investigations in fluid physics, crystal growth, glass manufacturing, ceramics, and biotechnology. The discoveries and techniques being invented by Canadian scientists have important practical potential. For example, crystals manufactured in microgravity will be used to create high precision, high power lasers, microwave broadcast devices, more sensitive heat sensors, and higher resolution video cameras. Manufacturing glass fibres in a microgravity situation will advance Canada's efficiency in fibre optics communication. Canada is already a world leader in this type of technology.

Canadian scientists have played a large role in microgravity experiments carried out in planes and drop towers and on the Space Shuttle. Canada has achieved many firsts in microgravity research and maintains a position of technical and scientific excellence.

Figure 16.25 In the seemingly weightless environment of space, astronauts have performed experiments on how microgravity affects plants, animals, people, and chemical reactions. If you have ever been in an elevator that descends rapidly, you may have felt a moment of rising off the floor of the elevator car. That sensation is similar to the feeling of microgravity.

Science Inquiry

Modelling "Artificial Gravity"

Normally, astronauts working in space must learn to adapt to microgravity conditions. What if the gravitational conditions on Earth could be recreated in space? In this activity, you have a chance to simulate "artificial gravity" and analyze what it might mean for future space travel and exploration. You will need three marbles and access to a turntable and an LP record album.

What to Do

1. Make a 4 cm high "wall" around the record by securely taping a strip of construction paper around the outside edge of the record.

2. Place the record on the turntable and put the marbles at the centre.

3. Switch the turntable on.

What Did You Discover?

1. What do you observe about the movements of the marbles?

2. Hypothesize how what you observe could be useful for simulating the effects of gravity on a space station.

Designing for the Microgravity Home

Think About It

Performing most activities in microgravity conditions is very different from performing them on Earth. Even turning a screwdriver, for example, is tricky in a microgravity environment. On Earth, you lean toward the screw and push. In space, when you do the same thing, you find yourself being pushed away. It is difficult to keep the screwdriver in contact with the screw.

Another difficulty is that, without gravity, water does not flow very well through pipes. Instead of filling the pipes, it tends to coat the inner walls, leaving "tubes" of air down the centre. You might be pumping air, unless you remove it first. And, although you might be able to lift a heavy object easily under low gravity conditions, the object's inertia (in this case, its tendency to keep going) is unchanged. Thus, an object moving toward you is just as difficult to stop in space as it would be on Earth.

The challenge in this activity is to design furniture and appliances that would enable the occupants in a "space home" to perform certain everyday activities.

What to Do

1. Organize into small groups for this brainstorming activity. Assign one person to be group recorder.

2. In a discussion with your group, analyze how gravity influences the following activities when they are performed on Earth: boiling an egg and making toast for breakfast; pouring hot tea or coffee; eating breakfast; washing and putting away the dishes.

3. Next, imagine carrying out each activity in a microgravity home. Describe what problems might occur because of the lack of gravity and how those difficulties might be overcome.

4. Brainstorm and design the furniture and appliances that would enable the occupants of a microgravity home to complete each of the above activities safely, comfortably, and efficiently. Note that you might have to change the usual procedure for an activity, or design new technology.

   Example: Must tables be horizontal? Under low gravity conditions, objects on a table tend to float off. Would the table be more effective if it were tilted toward the user?

5. Prepare a presentation for the class as though your classmates were builders looking for new products to furnish homes in a new celestial subdivision. Present sketches of the new items your group has designed and be ready to explain why you designed them as you did.

Analyze

1. Which activities are easier for humans to perform in space than on Earth. Why?

2. Which activities are more difficult to design for in a microgravity environment?

Quick! What is Canada's most important contribution to space exploration? If you are like most people around the world, you thought of the Shuttle Remote Manipulator System. SPAR Aerospace, the Canadian company that designed and built this robotic arm, is also the maker of its successor, the SSRMS (the Space Station Remote Manipulator System) and the other components that make up the station's Mobile Servicing System. This newer arm is another impressive piece of technology. It is so advanced that, once astronauts on the delivery shuttle release its travel restraints, it can get up and walk out of the cargo bay on its own.

Suppose that a similar Canadian company posted the following internship notice on the Internet. Write your application. Then exchange it with that of a friend. Discuss the possible strengths and weaknesses of your applications.

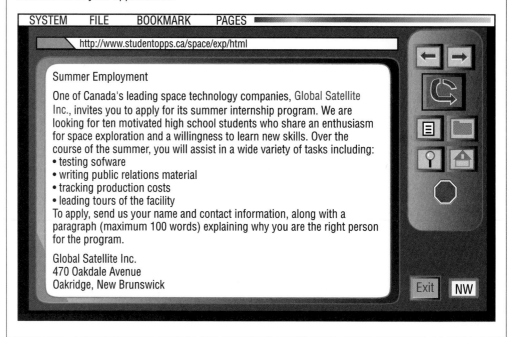

SYSTEM   FILE   BOOKMARK   PAGES

http://www.studentopps.ca/space/exp/html

Summer Employment

One of Canada's leading space technology companies, Global Satellite Inc., invites you to apply for its summer internship program. We are looking for ten motivated high school students who share an enthusiasm for space exploration and a willingness to learn new skills. Over the course of the summer, you will assist in a wide variety of tasks including:
• testing sofware
• writing public relations material
• tracking production costs
• leading tours of the facility
To apply, send us your name and contact information, along with a paragraph (maximum 100 words) explaining why you are the right person for the program.

Global Satellite Inc.
470 Oakdale Avenue
Oakridge, New Brunswick

Exit   NW

Check Your Understanding

1. Name at least five careers available in the field of satellite technology.

2. What is microgravity?

3. Explain why the effects of microgravity are a concern to the prospect of long-term space voyages.

4. Analyze How does the day-to-day work of the astronomer differ from that of the astronaut? How does the work of the astronomer and astronaut differ from that of the satellite technologist?

5. Thinking Critically Why do you think calcium loss occurs in bones when humans stay in a microgravity environment? Can you suggest how this might be prevented from happening?

Now that you have completed this chapter, try to do the following. If you cannot, go back to the sections indicated.

List the main ways in which the Sun affects Earth. (16.1)

Explain why the greenhouse effect is increasing. (16.1)

Define "magnetosphere" and make a sketch to show its appearance. (16.1)

Explain why coastal areas on Earth experience two incoming and two outgoing tides a day. (16.1)

Describe some of the purposes for which Canada's Anik satellites have been used. (16.2)

Outline how satellites can be used to determine a person's position on Earth. (16.2)

Discuss why scientists consider the existence of life elsewhere in the universe to be a likely possibility. (16.3)

Explain what SETI means and describe some of the scientific efforts it has involved. (16.3)

Compare the advantages and disadvantages of robotic and human space exploration. (16.3)

Explain the importance of microgravity research. (16.4)

Describe the types of careers that involve space exploration and research. (16.4)

Prepare Your Own Summary

Summarize this chapter by doing one of the following. Use a graphic organizer (such as a concept map), produce a poster, or write the summary to include the key chapter concepts. Here are a few ideas to use as a guide:

- What types of radiation and particles are emitted by the Sun and in what ways do they affect Earth?
- How have human activities stimulated the greenhouse effect?
- What are some of the ways that observation satellites are used?
- What is the International Space Station and how will it be used?
- Have the experiments and observations performed in the search for extra-terrestrial life produced any conclusive results? Explain.

- What are five main career areas related to space exploration and research?
- In what ways is microgravity research significant?

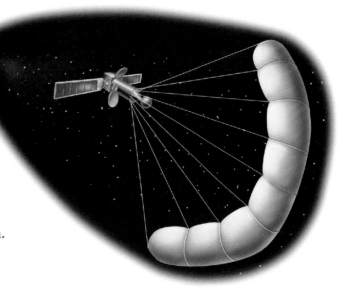

Reviewing Key Terms

If you need review, the section numbers show you where these terms were introduced.

1. In your notebook, match the phrase in column A with the correct term in column B.

A	B
• natural heating of Earth's atmosphere	• GPS (16.2)
• modified by the solar wind	• global warming (16.1)
• chemical in Earth's upper atmosphere that absorbs ultraviolet light	• ozone (16.1)
• the increase in average temperature around the world	• aurora (16.1)
• synchronized to Earth's 24 h orbit	• greenhouse effect (16.1)
• created when high-speed charged particles from Sun hit Earth's atmosphere	• magnetosphere (16.1)
	• geosynchronous (16.2)
	• microgravity (16.4)

Understanding Key Concepts

Section numbers are provided if you need to review.

2. Using a diagram, explain the cause of the tides. (16.1)

3. Which dangers to Earth do asteroids and comets pose? (16.1)

4. How might the collision of a large meteorite with Earth have caused the extinction of dinosaurs? (16.1)

5. Satellites just above Earth's atmosphere take about 1 hr to orbit. They move quickly across the sky. Where can a satellite be situated so that it does not appear to move in the sky? Of what use would such a satellite be? (16.2)

6. How might we converse with alien civilizations that are many light-years away? What type of message might they understand despite not knowing our language? (16.3)

7. What contributions have Canadians made to space exploration and research? (16.4)

Problem Solving/Applying

8. If we spotted a large rock at the distance of the Moon on a collision course with Earth, how much time would we have to prepare? Minutes? Days? Months? Follow these steps to estimate an answer:

   (a) Earth takes about 30 000 000 s to orbit the Sun. The orbit path is approximately circular, with a radius of 150 000 000 km. Estimate Earth's orbital speed.

   (b) Suppose Earth runs into an asteroid orbiting at the same speed in the opposite direction. How fast would the object appear to be approaching Earth?

   (c) How much time would the object take to cover the 400 000 km distance between the Moon and Earth?

9. What experiments could you do to test a planet's soil for living organisms? What experiments could be used to test soil for dead (but previously living) organisms?

10. Explain why, if we were to receive a radio message from a distant civilization, this would indicate that the civilization was likely more advanced than we are.

11. Make a concept map that shows the ways in which space technology and understanding contribute to making Earth a "global village."

Critical Thinking

12. Describe the effects that each of the following types of solar radiation have on the human body: infrared, ultraviolet, and visible light.

13. When we walk around, we use energy that originated in the interior of the Sun when hydrogen atoms fused to form helium. Trace the steps whereby the Sun's energy gets transformed into the energy that our bodies use.

14. There was considerable controversy about whether the International Space Station should be built. Is there any good use for a space station? What is the value of this expensive product?

15. If you were in charge of an astronaut selection process, what would you look for in applicants? Explain why.

16. Dr. Roberta Bondar was the first Canadian female astronaut in space (in January 1992). On board the space shuttle Discovery, she conducted experiments to help people suffering from inner-ear disorders, motion sickness, and some types of cancer. She also investigated the stretching of the human spine in space and, herself, became 4 cm taller while in space. Explain why you think this stretching of the human spine occurs. How do you think experimenting in space can shed light on maladies such as motion sickness?

Pause& Reflect

The space probe Galileo was the first interplanetary spacecraft to return to Earth. (A Russian spacecraft went to the Moon, scooped up samples of soil, and returned to Earth.) Galileo was on its way to Jupiter, but first it looped around Venus and then passed Earth twice. Each time it encountered a planet, its speed increased. This was a way to get the spacecraft going fast enough to reach Jupiter without burning a lot of fuel.

As Galileo neared Earth, scientists decided to see whether the craft could find any evidence of life on this planet. The probe carried optical cameras, spectroscopes, and infrared detectors. From Galileo's distance, no photograph showed any evidence of human activity. What did appear were brown, green, blue, and white markings on the surface of the planet.

(a) What tests could be done by other sensors to detect human and other life?

(b) Predict what the sensors might detect, and describe how results would be different if there were no life.

Ask an Expert

What do mapping the continent of Antarctica, fighting floods on the Red River, and searching for a downed airliner have in common? They all involved Radarsat-1, a Canadian satellite setting new standards in remote sensing. What makes this satellite so special? Ask Eric Choi, Flight Dynamics Analyst. It's Eric's job to keep Radarsat-1 up in space, and know exactly where over Earth the satellite will be at any given time.

Q Why was a Canadian satellite used to map the Antarctic?

A Radarsat-1 is the first dedicated civilian radar-imaging satellite in the world. It takes pictures of Earth's surface using radar, not light. This means we can "see" through clouds and haze, and even obtain images in the dark. Because the Antarctic is almost always covered in cloud, the first complete high resolution map of the Antarctic was made using Radarsat-1 images taken in the fall of 1997.

Q Why do we need the ability to map the South Pole, anyway?

A Radarsat's images allow us to monitor how the Antarctic ice sheet changes over time. This has huge importance to coastal areas of Canada, as well as the rest of the world. We also monitor the ice of the Arctic. In fact, Radarsat-1 helps locate and follow ice on the St. Lawrence River and Atlantic Ocean that might endanger ships.

Q What else does this satellite let us do?

A During floods, such as the Red River Flood in Manitoba, we provide engineers with images that show where they should put sandbags to protect lives and property. Radarsat-1 has also been used to help locate the wreckage of downed airliners, since the radar beam can be focused to a resolution of 8 m. Another important function is to help measure the growth of crops and forests. The numerous possibilities are amazing.

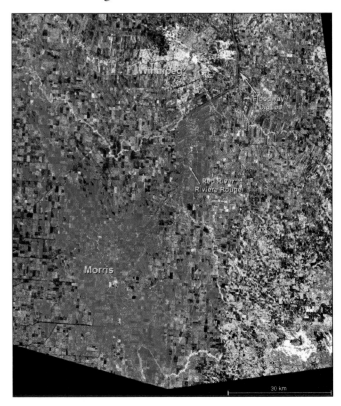

Q How do you get the satellite to where you want to take the pictures?

A Radarsat-1 orbits from pole to pole, passing over some part of Canada about 10 times a day. When we take into account how Earth is turning under the satellite, we know Radarsat-1 will pass over exactly the same spot on Earth once every 24 days. Therefore, to obtain images of a particular place, we just calculate when the satellite will next pass over that spot and order it to take its pictures then.

Q Do you control the satellite's orbit from the ground?

A Oh yes. The satellite orbits at 790 km above Earth. There is still a very thin atmosphere there, enough to slow the satellite by friction and cause it to lose height. Every once in a while, we have to order the satellite to fire its thrusters to boost it back up to its proper altitude.

Q How do you communicate with Radarsat-1?

A There are two Canadian ground stations, one in Saint-Hubert, Québec, and the other in Saskatoon, Saskatchewan. They are able to contact the satellite eight times a day for up to 15 minutes at a time. We point the dish directly at the satellite and upload instructions to it, as well as download status information. The pictures of Earth taken by Radarsat-1 are collected by another network of ground stations located around the world.

Q What's ahead for Canada's satellites?

A Thanks to Radarsat-1, Canada is a world leader in remote sensing on Earth. We are already working on Radarsat-2, a more powerful and efficient version, which is scheduled for launch in 2001. What's ahead? A new Canadian industry based in space.

EXPLORING Further

Space and Cyberspace

You can learn more about satellites for yourself. Here are two ways to start.

1. Looking up
If your night sky is clear and dark enough to allow you to see the Milky Way, you should be able to see satellites. Satellites look just like stars in size and brightness, but move steadily across the sky. The best viewing is on dry, still nights. Cold nights are even better. Although you can see satellites using only your eyes, a pair of binoculars will let you find even more. (Hint: If you have a sky chart you want to consult while you are outside viewing, tape a piece of red tissue paper over a flashlight so you can read without losing your "night vision.")

2. Into Cyberspace
You can also follow the path of satellites using maps and images from the Internet. Begin by going to **www.school.mcgrawhill.ca/resources/** Find out about projects in volcanology and ice monitoring. As well, use this site to find and follow objects in orbit, from satellites to shuttle missions. Choose a topic for a brief presentation to your class.

A DEBATE

Merits of Space Travel Using Astronauts

Think About it

In the 1960s, the United States spent billions of dollars developing the technology to send astronauts to the Moon. Five different pairs of astronauts walked on the lunar surface and returned to Earth with sample rocks. By the mid 1970s, public interest had faded, governments had changed, and the funding for big space programs had shrunk. While working on the Space Shuttle, the National Aeronautics and Space Administration Association (NASA) stopped sending people into orbit. Instead, it dispatched robots such as Voyager 1 and 2, Venus Orbiter, Viking, Galileo, and Cassini to photograph and measure the planets. These robots were much less expensive than spacecraft that could carry humans. In 1996, with an even smaller budget, a team of scientists was able to send a little vehicle to roam the surface of Mars.

Dreams of human exploration of the solar system have never died, however. By the end of the century, proposals by NASA and independent teams for a voyage to Mars had again caught people's interest. Still, the least expensive of the proposals had a price tag of over $30 billion Canadian.

Do you think we should send people to explore the Moon and planets in our solar system? What are the advantages of space travel using astronauts? What are the disadvantages? Are there better alternatives? There are no right or wrong answers to these questions. As for so many issues in society, there are several sides to the matter. In this activity, you have the opportunity to debate them.

Resolution

"Be it resolved that a modern aerospace program, to be effective, must involve sending people to explore outer space."

What to Do

1 Read the "Points For" and "Points Against" on this page and think about other points that could be made in favour of and against this resolution.

2 Two teams made up of two students each will debate the topic. One team will speak in support of the resolution and the other one will speak against it. Note: If you are on one of the teams, you must try your best to convince the jury, or the debate listeners, of the point your side is defending—no matter what side you actually believe in.

3 Two other students will be assigned to work with each team to gather background information needed to make a strong case for the point that the team is defending.

4 The rest of the class will act as the jury in hearing the debate. In preparation for the debate, they should do their own research in order to understand the science and technology behind the issues raised.

5 Your teacher will provide you with the proper *Debating Procedures* to follow.

Points For

- Space travel using astronauts puts humans "on site" to experience the mission first hand; unmanned space travel is limited by what information computers can relay to Earth.
- Space travel using astronauts is the only realistic way to study the effects of space travel on the human body and other living organisms.

Points Against

- Space travel using humans is much more costly than space travel using robots, and diverts money away from other, perhaps more beneficial, projects.
- Space travel using astronauts puts the life of humans at risk; space travel using robots does not.

Analyze

1. **(a)** Based on overall presentation, which team won the debate?

   (b) Was it the team's research or its delivery that made their case more convincing? Explain.

2. What was your position on the issue of astronaut versus robotic space travel before the debate? Did the arguments you heard from the two teams change your mind? If so, explain how. If not, did the team representing the view opposite yours still raise some good points you hadn't thought of before? What were they?

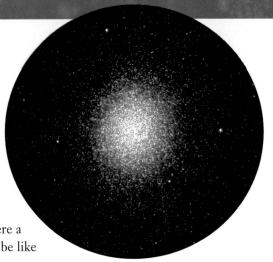

Other Worlds

In this unit you learned about moons, planets, and stars. You discovered that the universe is vast and varied. Other worlds, if they exist, are probably quite different from ours in appearance and surroundings.

Can you imagine how the night sky would appear to an inhabitant of a planet orbiting a star in the middle of the Centaurus globular cluster shown in the figure below? How would the Milky Way look if the Sun were a little above the galactic plane, out of the dust? What might the landscape be like on a planet with two suns?

Challenge

Draw or build a model of some other world, or a view of the sky as seen from that world. Use what you have learned in this unit to make your project realistic. Your project should provide a glimpse of another possible world or view in the universe.

Materials

Select a medium for your model. For a picture, you will need crayons, markers, or paint. For a model, you could use clay or papier-mâché. Tiny white decorative lights could make a star field. If you like gears and motors, you might construct a working simulation of a moon orbiting a planet orbiting a sun.

Design Criteria

A. The display: For this project, you have a wide range of choices. Be as creative as you can. Here are sample design criteria.

 Art work: Large painting or set of smaller drawings

 Model: Size up to 30 cm x 30 cm x 30 cm

 Computer presentation: Up to 10 well-designed pages

B. **Explanatory paragraph:**  Write a paragraph to accompany the display, explaining what you are depicting or demonstrating.

Plan and Construct

1. Working with a partner, define your world's location. Is it a moon orbiting a ringed planet? A planet whose sun is a red giant? A comet nearing a small, bluish-white dwarf? An asteroid rushing to collide with a planet?

2. Decide what you are going to portray. Star trails? A sunset on a distant world? Two moons circling a planet?

3. Choose your media. Paints? Clay? Wood? Computer?

4. Allocate tasks between you and your partner.

5. Create a plan for your model and write a short proposal to your teacher. Include your names and the tasks that each of you will do.

6. When your teacher approves your plan, proceed with your model.

7. Write the paragraph describing what you have depicted. Be prepared to present or demonstrate the model to the class.

Evaluate

1. List the features in your model that you incorporated based on the scientific knowledge you gained in this unit about the universe.

2. List the features in your model that are purely imaginative.

3. Consider the models your classmates have created, and evaluate the range of "other worlds" they presented. How are these imagined worlds like the one you created? How are they different?

4. How does the world you chose to create differ from our world, Earth?

Now that you have completed Chapters 13, 14, 15, and 16, you can assess how much you have learned about space by answering the following questions. Before you begin, you may find it useful to return to each Chapter at a Glance and to each Chapter Review.

True/False

In your notebook, indicate whether each statement is true or false. Correct each false statement.

1. As viewed from your location in Canada, the Sun comes directly overhead at noon.
2. All planets revolve around the Sun in the same direction.
3. Sometimes Neptune is the farthest planet from the Sun.
4. Meteors are made visible by Earth's atmosphere.

Matching

9. In your notebook, copy the the descriptions in column A. Beside each number, write the term from column B that best fits the description. A term may be used once, more than once, or not at all.

A	B
• A piece of space debris that falls to earth	• nebula
• Largest planet in our solar system	• galaxy
• Cloud of dust or gas	• asteroid
• Process of energy production in a star	• meteorite
• Last shining stage of a low mass star	• white dwarf
• Collection of billions of star	• neutron star
• Most abundant element in stars	• fusion
• Greenhouse gas	• fission
• Great Red Spot	• hydrogen
	• oxygen
	• carbon dioxide
	• Saturn
	• Jupiter

Completion

Complete the following statements with the correct term or phrase.

5. After consuming the hydrogen in its core, the Sun will begin its helium fusion stage, swelling until it becomes a ＿＿＿ ＿＿＿ star.

6. Kepler discovered that, rather than orbiting the Sun in perfect circles, planets travel in ＿＿＿ orbits.

7. The fact that the light from distant galaxies is red-shifted suggests that the galaxies are ＿＿＿.

8. Cosmic background radiation equivalent to that given off by an object at 3° above absolute zero is evidence in support of the ＿＿＿ theory.

Multiple Choice

In your notebook, write the letter of the best answer for each of the following questions.

10. Which planet has polar ice caps and old, dry river valleys?
    (a) Mars
    (b) Jupiter
    (c) Saturn
    (d) Mercury
    (e) Venus

11. The loss of ozone in Earth's upper atmosphere leads to
    (a) global warming
    (b) decreased aurora
    (c) increased ultraviolet light levels
    (d) more meteor showers
    (e) satellite failure

12. Tides are caused by
    (a) Earth's rotation
    (b) Moon's gravity
    (c) Earth's atmosphere
    (d) Moon's rotation on its axis
    (e) Earth's magnetic field

13. Which one of the following has no atmosphere?
    (a) Mercury
    (b) Venus
    (c) Mars
    (d) Jupiter
    (e) Saturn's moon, Titan

14. Large telescopes see more stars than do small telescopes because
    (a) They gather more light.
    (b) They have higher magnification.
    (c) They see a wider area of the sky.
    (d) They can see through clouds.
    (e) They have clearer eyepiece lenses.

15. What would be a good reason for building an optical observatory on the Moon?
    (a) The Moon is closer to the stars.
    (b) The Moon has a permanent dark side which could provide continuous viewing.
    (c) There would be no moon in the sky to obstruct the viewing.
    (d) The mountains of the Moon are higher than those of Earth.
    (e) There is no atmosphere

16. The astronomical unit (AU) is the
    (a) distance from Earth to the Sun
    (b) time for light to travel from the Sun to Earth
    (c) distance from Earth to the Moon
    (d) distance from the Sun to Pluto
    (e) temperature of the Sun

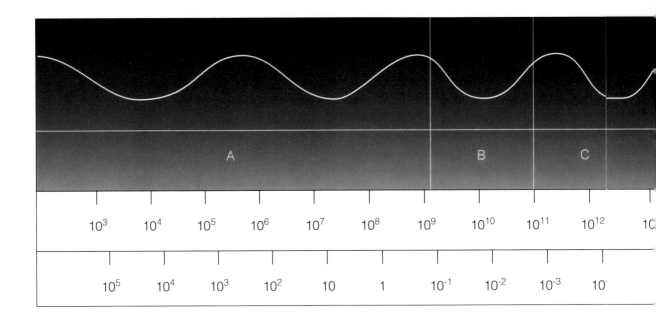

| 10^3 | 10^4 | 10^5 | 10^6 | 10^7 | 10^8 | 10^9 | 10^{10} | 10^{11} | 10^{12} | 1C |

| 10^5 | 10^4 | 10^3 | 10^2 | 10 | 1 | 10^{-1} | 10^{-2} | 10^{-3} | 10^{-} |

Short Answer

In your notebook, write a sentence or a short paragraph to answer each of the following questions.

17. Describe several factors that affect the brightness of a star as seen from Earth.

18. Why can't we see the centre of our galaxy?

19. How can we determine what chemical elements are in a star by looking at its light?

20. How can we determine the distance to nearby stars?

21. In what ways are satellites being used? What information are they providing?

22. (a) What types of radiation arrive on Earth from the Sun?

(b) What influences do they have on Earth?

23. Label the Hertzsprung-Russell diagram below with the following terms: main sequence, red giants, supergiants, and white dwarfs. Label the axes and place the Sun at the correct place on the diagram.

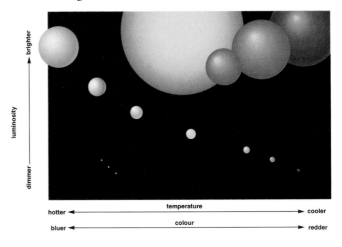

24. The figure across the top of pages 556-557 represents the electromagnetic spectrum, stretching from a low energy, low frequency, large wavelength on the left to a high energy, high frequency, small wavelength on the right. In the middle is visible light. Indicate the regions where you would find the following types of radiation on the spectrum: X-rays, infrared, ultraviolet, radio waves, microwaves, gamma rays (labelled A-F).

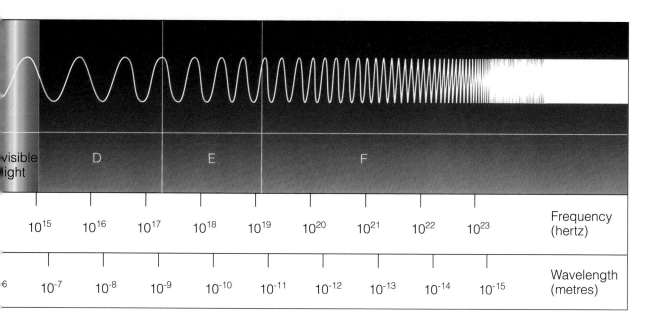

visible
light

D   E   F

| | | | | | | | | | |

10¹⁵   10¹⁶   10¹⁷   10¹⁸   10¹⁹   10²⁰   10²¹   10²²   10²³   Frequency (hertz)

⁶   10⁻⁷   10⁻⁸   10⁻⁹   10⁻¹⁰   10⁻¹¹   10⁻¹²   10⁻¹³   10⁻¹⁴   10⁻¹⁵   Wavelength (metres)

Problem Solving

Show complete solutions for all problems that involve equations and numbers. Use the GRASP problem-solving model or a model suggested by your teacher.

25. The distance from the Sun to Mars is 1.4 AU. The distance from the Sun to Jupiter is 4.48 AU. How many times farther away is Jupiter from the Sun than Mars?

26. The distance of Earth from the Sun is 1.49×10^8 km.

   (a) What is the distance from the Sun to Mars in kilometres?

   (b) What is the closest distance that Mars comes to Earth in kilometres?

Critical Thinking

27. The time for the Moon to rotate once is about 271/2 days, but the time between one full Moon and the next is about 29 full days. Explain why the time between full moons is greater than the time it takes the Moon to rotate once. Hint: Use the Sun-centred model.

28. What is the significance of the following observations.

   (a) Most stars we see are in a band that runs north-south across the sky.

   (b) Globular clusters are all located in one direction in the sky and not all around Earth.

Applications

29. A refracting telescope is made with a large lens that focuses the light that passes through it. A reflecting telescope is made with a large mirror that focuses the light that bounces off it. Why are the largest optical telescopes reflectors, rather than refractors?

30. New developments and discoveries are constantly occurring in the area of space exploration. To keep up to date, make a chart in your notebook and record the names, destinations, launch dates, arrival dates, and discoveries made by the latest space probes. Detailed information can be found on the Internet.

Classifying Living Things

Over 2000 years ago, the Greek philosopher Aristotle developed a system of classification that grouped organisms according to whether they were plant or animal. Scientists used Aristotle's system for hundreds of years, but as they discovered more and more living things, the system did not work well because it did not show probable relationships between similar organisms.

In 1735, Carolus Linnaeus produced a new system that also classified all organisms as plant or animal, but this new system was very different in other ways from Aristotle's system.

Linnaeus' system gives a two-word name to each type of organism. This system of naming organisms is still in use today. The two-word name is called the organism's scientific name, and it is given in Latin, a language that is no longer spoken. The first word of the organism's name is its genus, and the second word is its specific name. A **genus** is a group of organisms that are very similar. A **species** is the smaller, more limiting classification grouping. The Canada lynx, shown on the right, and the bobcat, shown on the left, are members of the same genus, *Lynx*, but they are considered different species. The lynx is the species *Lynx canadensis* and the bobcat is *Lynx rufus*.

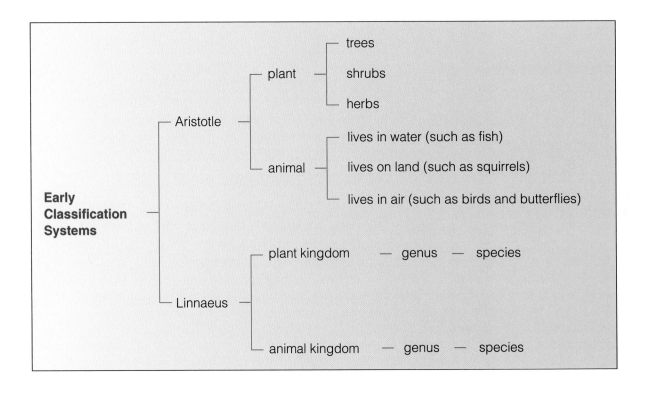

Early Classification Systems

- Aristotle
  - plant
    - trees
    - shrubs
    - herbs
  - animal
    - lives in water (such as fish)
    - lives on land (such as squirrels)
    - lives in air (such as birds and butterflies)
- Linnaeus
  - plant kingdom — genus — species
  - animal kingdom — genus — species

In the 1900s, as knowledge about the great diversity of organisms on Earth exploded, it became clear that separating organisms into only two kingdoms, plant and animal, was inadequate. For example, bacteria are just too different from either plants or animals to be grouped with either. Likewise, fungi such as bread mould, yeast, and the many kinds of mushrooms are very different from plants and animals. Influential scientists like Robert Whittaker and Lynn Margulis supported the idea that new criteria for classifying organisms were needed. Thus, since the 1960s, a system that classifies organisms into five different kingdoms, still using Linnaeus' basic system at its roots, is largely accepted and used. The organisms and their kingdoms are shown in the table below.

Life's Five Kingdoms

	Monera	Protista	Fungi	Plant	Animal
Type of cells	Prokaryotic	Eukaryotic	Eukaryotic	Eukaryotic	Eukaryotic
Number of cells	One-celled	One- and many-celled	One- and many-celled	Many-celled	Many-celled
Movement	Some move	Some move	Don't move	Don't move	Move
Nutrition	Some members make their own food; others obtain it from other organisms.	Some members make their own food; others obtain it from other organisms.	All members obtain food from other organisms.	Members make their own food.	Members eat plants or other organisms.

Using Resources and the Internet Effectively

Using Resources Effectively

You probably have some books and periodicals in your classroom that you can use to find out more about certain topics, but for much of the information you need, you will want to use the library in your school or a branch of your local library.

A library can be overwhelming, but if you approach it in an organized way, you can quickly and efficiently find what you need.

First, be aware of the huge amount of material you can access through the library: general and specialized encyclopedias, directories (telephone, city, postal code), almanacs, atlases, handbooks, periodicals, newspapers, government publications, pamphlets, tapes, videos, CD-ROMs, databases, and the ever-changing store of information on the Internet.

To make the best use of your time and the resources available to you, ask yourself these questions before you start your research:

- *What* information do I need? In how much detail?

- *When* is the assignment due? (That might help you decide how much detail you need.)

- *Why* do I need the information? Am I preparing something for an audience (my teacher, another group, or another class)?

- *How* will I be presenting the information (as a written report, a poster, an oral presentation, a multimedia presentation)?

Next, identify which kinds of resources will give you what you need. Librarians are extremely knowledgeable and helpful, so consider them an initiating resource by asking them questions about library use when you cannot find out what you need.

What Is the Internet?

The Internet is an extensive network of interlinked yet independent computer networks. In less than two decades, the Internet went from being a highly specialized communications network used mostly for military and academic applications to a massive electronic bazaar. Today, the network includes

- educational and government computers
- computers from research institutions
- computerized library catalogues
- businesses
- homes
- community-based computers (called *freenets*)
- a diverse range of local computer bulletin boards.

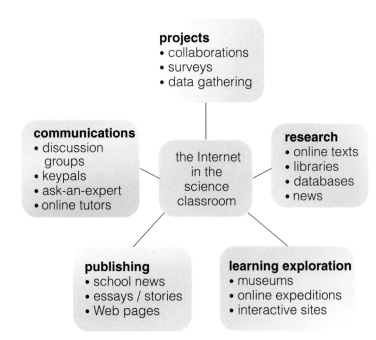

projects
- collaborations
- surveys
- data gathering

communications
- discussion groups
- keypals
- ask-an-expert
- online tutors

the Internet in the science classroom

research
- online texts
- libraries
- databases
- news

publishing
- school news
- essays / stories
- Web pages

learning exploration
- museums
- online expeditions
- interactive sites

Anyone who has an account on one of these computers can send electronic mail throughout the network and access resources from hundreds of other computers on the network. Here are some of the ways you will find the Internet most useful as a learning tool.

Using the Internet Effectively

The web site address for the publisher of this textbook is: http://www.mcgrawhill.ca This URL (Universal Resource Locator, or web site address) will take you to the headquarters of McGraw-Hill Ryerson Limited in Whitby, Ontario. You can use the site to obtain information about specific topics in the textbook. When "surfing" the Internet yourself, remember that anyone, anywhere can develop a web site or post information on the Internet. They can use it to "publish" their own opinions. Sometimes, it is difficult to distinguish accurate scientific information from these opinions. Always check the source of the information. Be wary of an individual publishing alone. Government sites and educational association sites tend to contain much more reliable information. Follow your own school's guidelines for "surfing" the Internet to do your research, and make good use of McGraw-Hill Ryerson's School Division web site of www.school.mcgrawhill.ca/resources/ to streamline your search.

INTERNET ⋅ CONNECT

www.school.mcgrawhill.ca/resources/

To see the latest Hubble Space Telescope photographs, go to Science Resources, then to **SCIENCEPOWER 9** to know where to go next. An excellent link is the Astronomy Picture of the Day. At this site, you can search through all previous Astronomy Pictures of the Day photographs. Each is accompanied by an informative description. What are the latest findings about quasars and gamma ray bursts? Write a short update on both topics, based on your research.

Answers to Quiz, page 434

1. (b) June 22
2. (c) south
3. (b) six months
4. (c) 10:00 pm
5. (c) 12 to 16
6. (e) all year
7. (b) a month
8. (c) 24 h

Periodic Table of the Elements

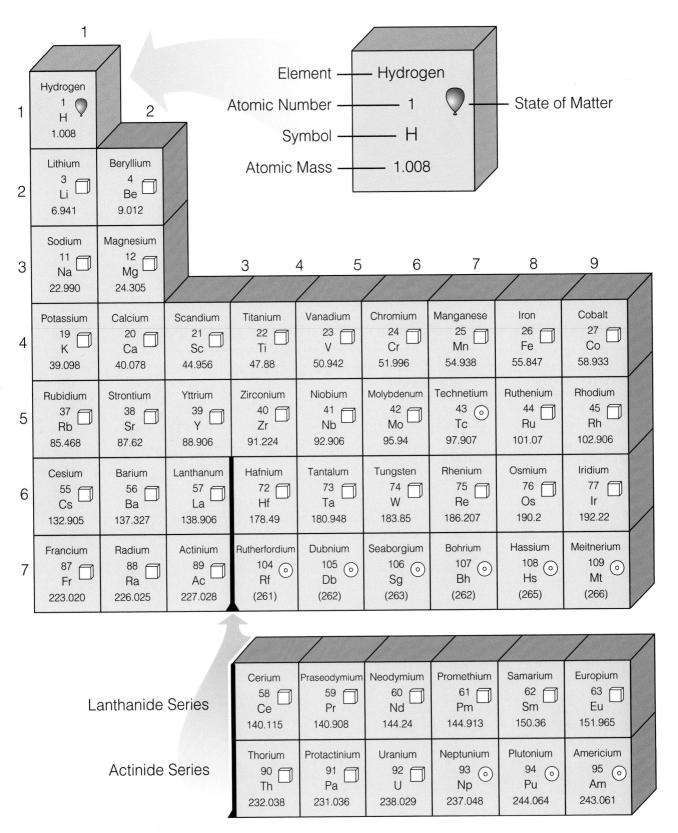

	1	2		3	4	5	6	7	8	9
1	Hydrogen 1 H 1.008									
2	Lithium 3 Li 6.941	Beryllium 4 Be 9.012								
3	Sodium 11 Na 22.990	Magnesium 12 Mg 24.305								
4	Potassium 19 K 39.098	Calcium 20 Ca 40.078		Scandium 21 Sc 44.956	Titanium 22 Ti 47.88	Vanadium 23 V 50.942	Chromium 24 Cr 51.996	Manganese 25 Mn 54.938	Iron 26 Fe 55.847	Cobalt 27 Co 58.933
5	Rubidium 37 Rb 85.468	Strontium 38 Sr 87.62		Yttrium 39 Y 88.906	Zirconium 40 Zr 91.224	Niobium 41 Nb 92.906	Molybdenum 42 Mo 95.94	Technetium 43 Tc 97.907	Ruthenium 44 Ru 101.07	Rhodium 45 Rh 102.906
6	Cesium 55 Cs 132.905	Barium 56 Ba 137.327		Lanthanum 57 La 138.906	Hafnium 72 Hf 178.49	Tantalum 73 Ta 180.948	Tungsten 74 W 183.85	Rhenium 75 Re 186.207	Osmium 76 Os 190.2	Iridium 77 Ir 192.22
7	Francium 87 Fr 223.020	Radium 88 Ra 226.025		Actinium 89 Ac 227.028	Rutherfordium 104 Rf (261)	Dubnium 105 Db (262)	Seaborgium 106 Sg (263)	Bohrium 107 Bh (262)	Hassium 108 Hs (265)	Meitnerium 109 Mt (266)

Element — Hydrogen
Atomic Number — 1
Symbol — H
Atomic Mass — 1.008
State of Matter

Lanthanide Series

Cerium 58 Ce 140.115	Praseodymium 59 Pr 140.908	Neodymium 60 Nd 144.24	Promethium 61 Pm 144.913	Samarium 62 Sm 150.36	Europium 63 Eu 151.965

Actinide Series

Thorium 90 Th 232.038	Protactinium 91 Pa 231.036	Uranium 92 U 238.029	Neptunium 93 Np 237.048	Plutonium 94 Pu 244.064	Americium 95 Am 243.061

Metal
Metalloid
Nonmetal

Gas
Liquid } (At room temperature and pressure)
Solid

Synthetic Elements

18
Helium
2
He
4.003

13	14	15	16	17
Boron	Carbon	Nitrogen	Oxygen	Fluorine	Neon
5	6	7	8	9	10
B	C	N	O	F	Ne
10.811	12.011	14.007	15.999	18.998	20.180
Aluminum	Silicon	Phosphorus	Sulfur	Chlorine	Argon
13	14	15	16	17	18
Al	Si	P	S	Cl	Ar
26.982	28.086	30.974	32.066	35.453	39.948

10	11	12	13	14	15	16	17	18
Nickel	Copper	Zinc	Gallium	Germanium	Arsenic	Selenium	Bromine	Krypton
28	29	30	31	32	33	34	35	36
Ni	Cu	Zn	Ga	Ge	As	Se	Br	Kr
58.693	63.546	65.39	69.723	72.61	74.922	78.96	79.904	83.80
Palladium	Silver	Cadmium	Indium	Tin	Antimony	Tellurium	Iodine	Xenon
46	47	48	49	50	51	52	53	54
Pd	Ag	Cd	In	Sn	Sb	Te	I	Xe
106.42	107.868	112.411	114.82	118.710	121.757	127.60	126.904	131.290
Platinum	Gold	Mercury	Thallium	Lead	Bismuth	Polonium	Astatine	Radon
78	79	80	81	82	83	84	85	86
Pt	Au	Hg	Tl	Pb	Bi	Po	At	Rn
195.08	196.967	200.59	204.383	207.2	208.980	208.982	209.987	222.018
(unnamed)	(unnamed)	(unnamed)		(unnamed)				
110	111	112		114				
Uun	Uuu	Uub		Uuq				

Gadolinium	Terbium	Dysprosium	Holmium	Erbium	Thulium	Ytterbium	Lutetium
64	65	66	67	68	69	70	71
Gd	Tb	Dy	Ho	Er	Tm	Yb	Lu
157.25	158.925	162.50	164.930	167.26	168.934	173.04	174.967
Curium	Berkelium	Californium	Einsteinium	Fermium	Mendelevium	Nobelium	Lawrencium
96	97	98	99	100	101	102	103
Cm	Bk	Cf	Es	Fm	Md	No	Lr
247.070	247.070	251.080	252.083	257.095	258.099	259.101	260.105

Properties of Common Substances

KEY TO SYMBOLS:
Common names of substances are enclosed in parentheses.

(*) Water solution of a pure substance   (e) Element   (c) Compound   (n) Not a pure substance

Name	Formula	Melting point (°C)	Boiling point (°C)	Density (g/cm³ or g/mL)
acetic acid (vinegar) (c)	CH_3COOH	16.6	118.1	—
alcohol (see ethanol) (c)				
aluminum (e)	Al	659.7	2519	2.7
aluminum oxide (alumina) (c)	Al_2O_3	2015	—	—
ammonia (c)	NH_3	−77.8	−33.4	less dense than air
ammonium nitrate (c)	NH_4NO_3	169.6	210	
antimony (e)	Sb	631	1587	6.70
argon (e)	Ar	−189	−185	denser than air
arsenic (e)	As	—	—	5.727 (grey) 4.25 (black) 2.0 (yellow)
barium (e)	Ba	727	1897	3.62
berkelium (e)	Bk	1050	—	14.78
beryllium (e)	Be	1280	2471	1.85
bismuth (e)	Bi	271	1560	9.7
boron (e)	B	2075	4000	2.37 (brown) 2.34 (yellow)
bromine (e)	Br	−7.2	58.8	3.12
calcium (e)	Ca	845	1484	1.55
calcium carbonate (limestone) (c)	$CaCO_3$	decomposes at 900°C	—	2.93
calcium hydroxide (slaked lime) (c)	$Ca(OH)_2$	decomposes at 522°C	—	2.24
calcium oxide (lime) (c)	CaO	2580	2850	3.3
carbon (diamond) (e)	C	3500	3930	3.51
carbon (graphite) (e)	C	4492	4492	2.25
carbon dioxide (c)	CO_2	—	—	—
chlorine (e)	Cl_2	−101.6	−34.6	denser than air
chromium (e)	Cr	1907	2671	7.2
cobalt (e)	Co	1480	2927	8.9
copper (e)	Cu	1084	2562	8.95
copper (II) nitrate (c)	$Cu(NO_3)_2$	—	—	—
copper (II) sulfate (bluestone) (c)	$CuSO_4.5H_2O$	decomposes at 150°C	—	2.28
diamond (see carbon) (e)				
ethanol (ethyl alcohol) (c)	C_2H_5OH	−114.5	78.4	0.789
ethylene (ethene) (c)	C_2H_4	−169	−103.9	—
fluorine (e)	F_2	−270	−188	—
gold (e)	Au	1063	2856	19.3
glucose (c)	$C_6H_{12}O_6$	146	decomposes before it boils	1.54
graphite (see carbon) (e)				
helium (e)	He	−272.2	−268.93	—
hematite (c)	Fe_2O_3	1565	—	5.24

Appearance (at room temperature: 20°C)	Comments
colourless liquid with pungent smell	used in the manufacture of cellulose ethanoate; vinegar is a 5–7 percent solution in water
silver-white metal	used in aircraft, cooking utensils, and electrical apparatus
white, crystalline substance	used in refining of aluminum and in cement
very soluble gas with pungent smell	used as refrigerant and in manufacture of resins, explosives, and fertilizers
white, soluble, crystalline salt	used in explosives and as a fertilizer
silver-grey solid	used in infra-red detectors
inert gas	used in electric lights
grey, black, or yellow solid	used in semiconductors and alloys; compounds are very poisonous and are used in medicine and as pesticides
silver-white solid	used in X-ray diagnosis
—	—
hard, white metal	used for corrosion-resistant alloys
brittle, white, crystalline metal with reddish tinge	used in alloys, catalysts, nuclear reactors; compounds used in medicine
brown amphorous powder or yellow crystals	used for hardening steel and for producing enamels and glasses
red-brown liquid	liquid causes severe chemical burns; vapour is harmful to lungs; used to make certain pain-relieving drugs
soft, white metal that tarnishes easily	very abundant; essential to life
white solid	main ingredient in chalk, marble
white solid	aqueous solution used to test for CO_2
white solid	used in cement and to mark lines on playing fields
colourless, solid crystals	very hard; used for drilling through rock
grey-black solid	very soft; used in lubricants, pencil leads, electrical apparatus
colourless gas with a faint tingling smell and taste	does not support combustion and is denser than air; used in fire extinguishers and as a refrigerant at −78.5°C
green gas	poisonous; used to kill harmful organisms in water
shiny, silvery solid	very hard metal; used to make stainless steel
hard, silver-white, magnetic metal	used in alloys; compounds used to produce the colour blue in glass and ceramics
shiny, reddish solid	soft metal; good conductor of heat
blue, solid crystals	used in pesticides
colourless liquid	derived from fermentation of sugar; used as solvent or fuel; found in wine
colourless, flammable gas with a sweetish smell	made from petroleum; used in manufacture of ethanol and other organic chemicals
greenish yellow gas	similar to chlorine
shiny, yellow solid	very soft metal; highly resistant to tarnishing
white solid	simple sugar; human body converts most sugars and starches to glucose
nonflammable inert gas	used as refrigerant; provides inert atmosphere for welding; used to fill air ships and balloons
rusty red colour	found in iron ore; rusty iron

Name	Formula	Melting point (°C)	Boiling point (°C)	Density (g/cm³ or g/mL)
hydrochloric acid (*)	HCl	varies	varies	varies
hydrogen (e)	H_2	−259	−253	much less dense than air
hydrogen peroxide (c)	H_2O_2	−0.4	150.2	1.45
iodine (e)	I	114	184	4.95
iron (e)	Fe	1535	2861	7.86
lead (e)	Pb	327.4	1750	11.34
lead (II) nitrate (c)	$Pb(NO_3)_2$	—	—	—
limestone (see calcium carbonate)				
lithium (e)	Li	179	1340	0.534
magnesium (e)	Mg	651	1107	1.74
magnesium chloride (c)	$MgCl_2$	708	1412	2.3
magnetite (c)	Fe_3O_4	—	—	5.18
manganese (e)	Mn	1246	2061	7.43
mercury (e)	Hg	−38.9	356.6	13.6
methane (c)	CH_4	−182.5	−161.5	—
molybdenum (e)	Mo	2623	4679	10.28
neon (e)	Ne	−248	−246	—
nickel (e)	Ni	1455	2913	8.90
nitrogen (e)	N_2	−209.9	−195.8	slightly less dense than air
nitrogen dioxide (c)	NO_2	—	—	—
oxygen (e)	O_2	−218	−183	slightly denser than air
ozone (e)	O_3	−192.5	−112	denser than air
phosphorus (e)	P	44	280	1.82 (white) 2.20 (red)
platinum (e)	Pt	1769	3824	21.41
polyethylene (polythene) (c)	$(C_2H_4)_n$	—	—	—
potassium (e)	K	63.5	759	0.86
propane (c)	C_3H_8	—	−42.17	—
selenium (e)	Se	217	684.9	4.81
silicon (e)	Si	1410	3265	2.33
silicon dioxide (silica) (c)	SiO_2	1600	—	—
silver (e)	Ag	961	2162	10.5
sodium (e)	Na	97.5	892	0.971
sodium chloride (table salt) (c)	NaCl	801	1465	2.16
sodium fluoride (c)	NaF	988	1695	2.56
steel (n)	varies	varies	varies	varies
strontium (e)	Sr	777	1412	2.6
sucrose (sugar) (c)	$C_{12}H_{22}O_{11}$	170	decomposes at 186°C	1.59
sulfur (brimstone) (e)	S	112.8	444.6	2.07
technetium (e)	Tc	2157	4265	11.5
tellurium (e)	Te	450	990	6.25
tin (e)	Sn	231.9	2602	7.31
titanium (e)	Ti	1666	3287	4.5
tungsten (e)	W	3422	5555	19.25
uranium (e)	U	1130	4131	19.05
water (c)	H_2O	0	100	1.00
xenon (e)	Xe	−111.9	−107.1	—
zinc (e)	Zn	419	907	7.14
zirconium (e)	Zr	1852	4400	6.51

Appearance (at room temperature: 20°C)	Comments
colourless liquid	corrosive acid; properties vary according to concentration
colourless gas	highly flammable; liquid form is used as rocket fuel
colourless liquid	thick and syrupy when pure; an antiseptic
violet-black, solid crystals	crystals sublime readily to form poisonous violet vapour
shiny, silver solid	rusts readily; soft when pure
shiny, blue-white solid	soft metal; forms poisonous compounds
white or colourless crystals	easily decomposed by heat; soluble in water
silver-white metal (least dense solid known)	used in alloys; its salts have various medical uses
light, silvery white metal that tarnishes easily in air	used in alloys, photography; compounds used in medicine; essential to life
white, deliquescent substance	
shiny, black crystalline solid	strongly magnetic
grey-white solid	used in alloys with special magnetic properties
shiny, silvery liquid	only liquid metal; forms poisonous compounds
odourless, flammable gas formed from decaying organic matter	main constituent in natural gas
silver-white solid	used in high-strength steel alloys
colourless, odourless gas	discharge of electricity at low pressures through neon produces an intense orange-red glow
silvery white, magnetic metal that resists corrosion	used for nickel plating, coinage, in alloys, and as a catalyst
colourless gas	will not burn or support burning; makes up 80 percent of air
brown gas	causes reddish brown colour in smog
colourless gas	must be present for burning to take place; makes up 20 percent of air
bluish gas	used for purifying air and water and in bleaching; atmospheric layer blocks most of Sun's ultraviolet light
dark red powder	highly poisonous, flammable
white, waxy, luminous in the dark	nonpoisonous, less flammable; compounds used in fertilizers and detergents; occurs only in combined state, mainly calcium phosphate $Ca_3(PO_4)_2$; essential to life
silver-white solid	used in jewellery; alloyed with cobalt, used in pacemakers
tough, waxy, thermoplastic material	polymer of ethylene; used as insulating material; flexible and chemically resistant
silvery white, soft, highly reactive, alkali metal	essential to all life; found in all living matter; salts used in fertilizers
colourless gas	flammable; used as fuel
non-metal resembling sulfur; silvery grey, crystalline solid	used in manufacture of rubber and ruby glass; used in photoelectric cells and semiconductors
steel-grey metalloid similar to carbon in its chemical properties	used in pure form in semiconductors and alloys and in the form of silicates in glass
hard, granular powder; insoluble in water	main constituent of sand; used in clocks and watches as quartz
shiny, white solid	soft metal; best known conductor of electricity
soft, silvery-white metal; very reactive	used in preparation of organic compounds, as coolant, and in some types of nuclear reactors
white, crystalline solid	used to season or preserve foods
colorless, crystalline substance	used in water fluoridation and as an insecticide
metallic grey solid	alloys of iron with carbon and other elements; widely used as structural materials
silver-white solid	used in the manufacture of colour television tubes
white solid	made from sugar cane or sugar beets
yellow solid	used to make dyes, pesticides, and other chemicals
silver-grey solid	used in gamma ray diagnosis of bone abnormalities
silver-white solid	used in semiconductors
shiny, slightly yellow solid	soft metal; rust resistant
lustrous white solid	alloys are widely used in the aerospace industry
grey-white solid	used in light bulb filaments
metallic grey solid	used as a nuclear fuel (usually converted into plutonium)
colourless liquid	good solvent for non-greasy matter
inert gas	used in fluorescent tubes and light bulbs
hard, bluish-white metal	used in alloys such as brass and galvanized iron
silver-white solid	used in the chemical industry as anti-corrosive material

SCIENCE SKILLS GUIDE

USING GRAPHIC ORGANIZERS TO IMPROVE YOUR LEARNING

A good way to organize information you are learning is to represent it using a **graphic organizer**. One kind of graphic organizer you will find useful is a **concept map**. A concept map is a diagram that visually represents how science concepts are related. Because the concept map shows the relationships among science ideas, it can clarify the meaning of the ideas and terms and help you to understand what you are studying.

Look at the construction of a concept map below, called a **network tree**. Notice how some words are circled while others are written on connecting lines. The circled words are ideas or terms called concepts. The lines in the map show related concepts, and the words written on them describe relationships between the concepts. The following network tree shows how simple machines can be categorized.

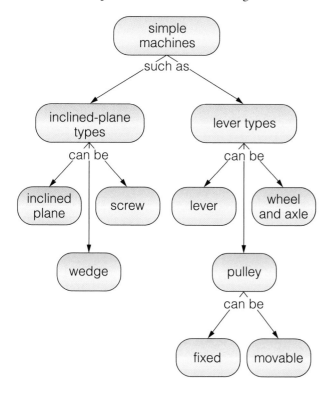

As you learn more about the topic, your concept map will grow and change. Concept maps are just another tool for you to use. There is no one "correct" concept map; it just represents the connections that make sense to you. Make your map as neat and clear as possible and make sure you have good reasons for suggesting the connections between its parts.

When you have completed the concept map, you may have dozens of interesting ideas. Your map is a record of your thinking. Although it may contain many of the same concepts as other students' maps, your ideas may be recorded and linked differently. You can use your map for study and review. You can refer to it to help you recall concepts and relationships. At a later date, you can use your map to see what you have learned and how your ideas have changed.

Here are other types of concept maps that you will find useful.

An **events chain** is used to describe ideas in order. In science, an events chain can be used to describe a sequence of events, the steps in a procedure, or the stages of a process. When making an events chain, you first must find out the one event that starts the chain. This event is called the initiating event. You then find the next event in the chain and continue until you reach an outcome. Here is a chain-of-events concept map showing what happens when popcorn is popped in a microwave oven.

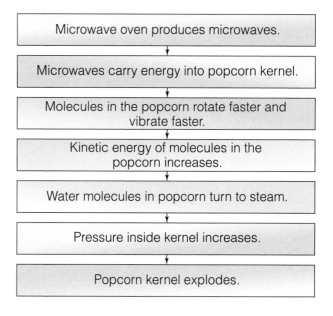

A **cycle concept map** is a special type of events chain map. In a cycle concept map, the series of events do not produce a final outcome. There is no beginning and no end to a cycle concept map.

To construct a cycle map, you first decide on a starting point and then list each important event in order. Since there is no outcome and the last event relates back to the first event, the cycle repeats itself. Look at the cycle map below of the processes involved in photosynthesis.

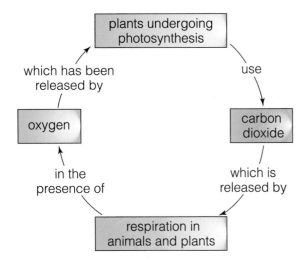

A **spider map** is a concept map that you may find useful for brainstorming. You may, for example, have a central idea and a jumble of related concepts, but they may not necessarily be related to each other. By placing these related ideas outside the main concept, you may begin to group these ideas so that their relationships become easier to understand. Examine the following spider map of the circulatory system to see how various concepts related to this organ system may be grouped to provide clearer understanding.

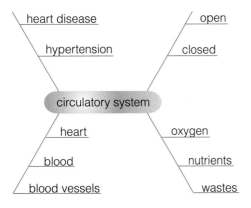

Another method to help you solidify your learning is comparing and contrasting. When you compare, you look for similarities between two things. When you contrast, you look for differences. This method can involve listing the ways in which two things are similar or ways in which they are different. You can also use a graphic organizer called a **Venn diagram** to do this, using two circles. The following Venn diagram can help you distinguish the similarities and differences between cows and cats.

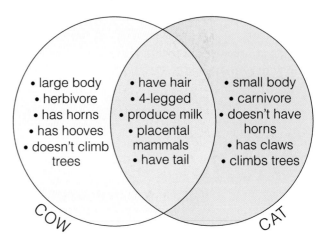

Instant Practice

1. Use the following terms to produce a network tree concept map: transportation vehicles, has, airplane, internal combustion engine, bicycle, car, steering wheel, jet engine, tires, rudder, pedals and gears.

2. Produce an events chain concept map that starts with the end of the school day and ends with you going to bed.

3. Make a Venn diagram to compare and contrast soccer and basketball.

HOW TO USE A SCIENCE LOG

Scientists keep logs, or detailed records, of their observations, new data, and new ideas. This helps them organize their thinking and keep track of the progress of their research. You can also keep a *Science Log* (or *Science Journal*) to help you organize your thinking.

Your *Science Log* should be a place where you can record what you already know about a topic, and add to that information as you continue through this course. Your *Science Log* can be a special booklet or a marked-off section of your science notebook. Your teacher can advise you on which approach to take.

You will find that recording something that you have learned will help you solidify it in your own mind and will often help to clarify ideas and concepts. It is also very useful to indicate what you already know about a topic. You may discover that you know more than you realized. On the other hand, you might discover that a particular topic needs close attention because you do not know very much about it. The value of a *Science Log* is that you find out for yourself how clear your understanding is, and, like scientists, keep track of the progress of your learning. You do not have to wait until your teacher assesses your knowledge through a formal test or examination.

Here are some ways in which **SCIENCEPOWER**™ **9** makes sure you can add to your *Science Log* effectively. Each chapter begins with a set of questions called "Opening Ideas...".

Are you able to answer any of these questions from your previous studies? You can write, draw a sketch, or use whatever means suits you best to explain what you know. This is *your* log, so you can feel free to record that you know very little about a particular topic at this point. This is an important study tool because learning and understanding become easier when you have an idea of what you do and do not know.

Pause& Reflect

Bacteria, such as *Clostridium botulinum,* can cause a serious form of food poisoning. Other bacteria, such as *Lactobacillus acidophilus,* help digest food and destroy other harmful bacteria in your intestinal tract. In your Science Log, write a one-page essay explaining why bacteria can be both harmful and beneficial to humans. Search the Internet for information about "useful" bacteria, such as those that are used to break down toxins in the environment.

Opening Ideas...

- How do organisms grow?
- How do broken bones mend?
- How do people age?
- What is cancer?
- How do organisms make more of themselves?

Throughout each chapter, *Pause & Reflect* features help you keep thinking about what you now know. They are designed to help you make connections and organize your thoughts. Your teacher will guide you on your use of *Pause & Reflect* questions.

As the final question in each Chapter Review, a *Pause & Reflect* item asks you to look back over the new concepts you have learned. A question may ask you to review your original answers to the *Opening Ideas* questions. Some questions may direct your thinking to *Key Concepts* in the chapter. You may be amazed at how much your original ideas have changed based on the new knowledge you have gained by studying the chapter.

Here are some other things you might want to include in your *Science Log:*

- Questions that occur to you that you would like to be able to answer.

- Sketches and notes about models and processes in science.

- Graphic organizers (see ***SkillPower 1***, for a few examples).

- Thoughts on what you find difficult and ideas on how you might overcome the barriers to learning a new topic.

- Notes about interesting items in the news that involve a chapter topic and that spark more questions or answers to some existing questions.

- Profiles of leading Canadian scientists or technologists that you learn about in the media, plus profiles of careers related to science and technology that you find interesting.

- Connections between science and other subject areas that occur to you in the course of your learning.

Your *Science Log* will help you become a better learner, so take the time to make entries on a regular basis.

Instant Practice

1. How would you define science? How would you define technology? How can both science and technology help answer questions about societal issues? Why is it useful to have scientific input on societal issues? Formulate your own questions about science, technology, and societal issues to produce a set of *Opening Ideas* questions. Then exchange your questions with a classmate so each of you can start your own *Science Log* using these questions.

2. Think of something that you consider to be an example of a simple technology. It can be any tool or device that you may have used. Do you necessarily have to be a scientist to produce such technological devices? How about an example of sophisticated technology? How do you think scientific knowledge might be of benefit to produce such technology? Write responses to these questions in your *Science Log.*

3. After you have finished reading pages xxii–IS-14, produce a set of *Pause & Reflect* questions comparing and contrasting science and technology. (How are they similar and how are they different?) Again, exchange your set of questions with a classmate to continue the development of your *Science Log.*

WORKING IN GROUPS

In this program, you are often asked to work in a group to complete a task. Studies have found that students improve in problem solving and critical thinking when co-operative groups are used. As well, students retain learned material for a longer period of time than when working individually or competitively. However, students must follow some important rules for effective learning in groups.

In a co-operative group, each of you will have one or more assigned tasks for which you are responsible. This means that a group can make the best use of each member's special skills, and help develop new skills. Teams often develop a special ability to work together, so that each presentation or project completed together is an improvement over the last.

Working well in a group is not always easy. The best way to develop your skills is to consider carefully what makes a group succeed at a task.

Assessing Group Performance

These are some behaviours you should aim toward when doing group work in this course and others:

- Share your ideas with others in the group.
- Show others respect, even if you disagree with them.
- Listen to another group member when that person is speaking.
- Encourage others to speak.
- Stay on the group's task.
- Help the group to stay on task.
- Do not allow yourself to be distracted.
- Keep your voice low enough that it will not distract other groups.
- Allow others to present their ideas, even when you think you know the answers.

Instant Practice

1. The first time you are asked to work in a group in this course, assess yourself on how well you did. Your teacher will provide a *Performance Task Self-Assessment* form for you to use. Before you begin your assessment, read over the form to note how you will be assessed.

2. Use the *Performance Task Group Assessment* form provided by your teacher to assess your whole group.

UNITS OF MEASUREMENT AND SCIENTIFIC NOTATION

Sometimes when you're working with numbers, you just need an approximate idea about a quantity. At other times, you need to be very precise. For example, what size shoes do you wear? Your answer is probably very precise. Imagine how uncomfortable you would be if you wore shoes only generally approximated to your size. Obviously you need shoes that are carefully measured to fit your foot.

The Metric System

When you take measurements in science, you use the **metric system**, which is a decimal system of measurement.

In the metric system, all units are multiples of 10. Therefore, if you need to express a quantity using a larger unit, you multiply by a multiple of 10. To express a quantity using a smaller unit, you divide by a multiple of ten. For example, the prefix *kilo-* means multiplied by 1000; thus, one kilogram equals one thousand grams.

$$1 \text{ kg} = 1000 \text{ g}$$

The prefix *milli-* means divided by 1000; thus, one milligram equals one one thousandth of a gram.

$$1 \text{ mg} = \frac{1}{1000} \text{ g}$$

The table on the right lists some frequently used units of measurement in the metric system.

Frequently Used Metric Quantities, Units, and Symbols

Quantity	Unit	Symbol
length	nanometre	nm
	micrometre	μm
	millimetre	mm
	centimetre	cm
	metre	m
	kilometre	km
mass	gram	g
	kilogram	kg
	tonne	t
area	square metre	m^2
	square centimetre	cm^2
	hectare	ha (10 000 m^2)
volume	cubic centimetre	cm^3
	cubic metre	m^3
	millilitre	mL
	litre	L
time	second	s
temperature	degree Celsius	°C
force	newton	N
energy	joule	J
	kilojoule	kJ
pressure	pascal	Pa
	kilopascal	kPa
electric current	ampere	A
quantity of electric charge	coulomb	C
frequency	hertz	Hz
power	watt	W

The following table shows the most commonly used metric prefixes. (Adding metric prefixes to a base unit is a way of expressing powers of ten.)

Metric Prefixes

Prefix	Symbol	Relationship to the base unit
giga-	G	10^9 = 1 000 000 000
mega-	M	10^6 = 1 000 000
kilo-	k	10^3 = 1 000
hecto-	h	10^2 = 100
deca-	da	10^1 = 10
–	–	10^0 1
deci-	d	10^{-1} = 0.1
centi-	c	10^{-2} = 0.01
milli-	m	10^{-3} = 0.001
micro-	μ	10^{-6} = 0.000 001
nano-	n	10^{-9} = 0.000 000 001

Example 1

The distance across Canada is 5514 km. How would you express this distance in metres?

Solution

5514 km = ? m

$$5514 \text{ km} \times \frac{1000 \text{ m}}{1 \text{ km}} = 5\ 514\ 000 \text{ m}$$

Example 2

You have 10.5 g of salt. To express this mass in kilograms, remember that 1000 g = 1 kg.

Solution

10.5 g = ? kg

$$10.5 \text{ g} \times \frac{1 \text{ kg}}{1000 \text{ g}} = 0.0105 \text{ kg}$$

Instant Practice

1. 35 cm = ? m
2. 20 m = ? mm
3. 55 g = ? mg
4. 0.5 kg = ? g
5. 6.5 L = ? mL
6. 1750 cm³ = ? m³
7. 750 mL = ? L
8. 1250 kg = ? t

SI Units

In science classes, you will often be instructed to report your measurements and answers in **SI** units. The term, SI, is taken from the French name *Systéme international d' unités*. SI uses the metre as the basic unit of length, the kilogram as the basic unit of mass, and the second as the basic unit of time. Most other units are related to the basic units.

Example

Convert $42.5 \frac{\text{cm}}{5}$ to SI Units.

Solution

$$42.5 \frac{\text{cm}}{5} \times \frac{\text{m}}{100 \text{ cm}} = 0.425 \frac{\text{m}}{5}$$

Instant Practice

Convert the following to SI Units

1. 275 cm
2. 22 min
3. $21 \frac{\text{km}}{\text{h}}$
4. 6937 g

Exponents of Scientific Notation

An **exponent** is the symbol or number denoting the power to which another number or symbol is to be raised. The exponent shows the number of repeated multiplications of the base. In 10^2, the exponent is 2 and the base is 10. The place table below shows the powers of 10 as numbers in standard form and in exponential form.

	Standard Form	Exponential Form
ten thousands	10 000	10^4
thousands	1000	10^3
hundreds	100	10^2
tens	10	10^1
ones	1	10^0
tenths	0.1	$\frac{1}{10^1}$
hundredths	0.01	$\frac{1}{10^2}$
thousandths	0.001	$\frac{1}{10^3}$
ten thousandths	0.0001	$\frac{1}{10^4}$

Why use exponents? Consider this. Mercury is about 58 000 000 km from the Sun. If a zero were accidentally added to this number, the distance would appear to be ten times larger than it actually is. To avoid mistakes when writing many zeros, scientists express large numbers in scientific notation.

Example 1

Mercury is about 58 000 000 km from the Sun. Write 58 000 000 in scientific notation.

Solution

In scientific notation, a number has the form $x \times 10^n$, where x is greater than or equal to 1 but less than 10, and 10^n is a power of 10.

58 000 000. ⟵ The decimal point starts here. Move the decimal point 7 places to the left.

$= 5.8 \times 10\ 000\ 000$

$= 5.8 \times 10^7$

Example 2

The electron in a hydrogen atom is, on the average, 0.000000000053 m from the nucleus. Write 0.000000000053 in scientific notation.

Solution

To write the number in the form $x \times 10^n$, move the decimal point to the right until there is one, non-zero number to the left of the decimal point.

The decimal point starts here. 0.000000000053
Move the decimal point 11 places to the right.

$= 5.3 \times 0.00000000001$

$= 5.3 \times 10^{-11}$

Notice that, when you move the decimal point to the left, the exponent of ten is positive. When you move the decimal point to the right, the exponent of ten is negative. The number of places you move the decimal point is the number in the exponent.

Instant Practice

1. Express each of the following in scientific notation.
   (a) Our galaxy, the Milky Way, contains more than 400 000 000 000 stars.
   (b) The distance of the Andromeda Galaxy from Earth is about:
   23 000 000 000 000 000 000 km
   (c) The distance across the universe has been estimated at:
   800 000 000 000 000 000 000 000 km
   (d) The mass of a proton is about:
   0.000 000 000 000 000 000 000 0017 g

2. Change the following to standard notation.
   (a) 9.8×10^5 m
   (b) 2.3×10^9 kg
   (c) 5.5×10^{-5} L
   (d) 6.5×10^{-10} s

USING A MICROSCOPE

Part 1 Parts of a Microscope

The **light microscop**e is an optical instrument that greatly increases our powers of observation by magnifying objects that are usually too small to be seen with the unaided eye. The microscope you will use is called a compound light microscope because it uses a series of lenses (rather than only one as in a magnifying glass) and it uses light to view the object. A microscope is a delicate instrument, so proper procedure and care must be practised. This *SkillPower* reviews the skills that you will need to use a microscope effectively. Before you use your microscope,

you need to know the parts of a microscope and their functions. Do the *Instant Practice* below to familiarize yourself with your microscope.

Instant Practice

1. Study the photograph of the compound light microscope. Learn the names and functions of the parts of the microscope.

2. Before you go any further, close your book and draw and label as many parts of a microscope as you can.

3. Explain to a classmate the function of each part.

A. Eyepiece (or ocular lens)
You look through this part. It has a lens that magnifies the object, usually by 10 times (10×). The magnifying power is engraved on the side of the eyepiece.

B. Tube
Holds the eyepiece and the objective lenses at the proper working distance from each other.

C. Revolving nosepiece
Rotating disk holds two or more objective lenses. Turn it to change lenses. Each lens clicks into place.

D. Objective lenses
Magnify the object. Each lens has a different power of magnification, such as 4×, 10×, 40×. (Your microscope may instead have 10×, 40×, and 100× objective lenses). For convenience, the objective lenses are referred to as low, medium, and high power. The magnifying power is engraved on the side of each objective lens. Be sure you can identify each lens.

E. Arm
Connects the base and the tube. Use the arm for carrying the microscope.

F. Coarse-adjustment knob
Moves the tube up and down to bring the object into focus. Use it only with the low-power objective lens.

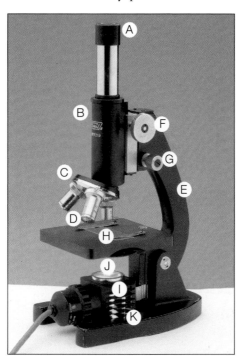

G. Fine-adjustment knob
Use with medium- and high-power magnification to bring the object into sharper focus.

H. Stage
Supports the microscope slide. Stage clips hold the slide in position. An opening in the centre of the stage allows light from the light source to pass through the slide.

I. Condenser lens
Directs light to the object being viewed.

J. Diaphragm
Controls the amount of light reaching the object being viewed.

K. Light source
Shining a light through the object being viewed makes it easier to see the details. Your microscope might have a mirror instead of a light. If it does, it must be adjusted to direct the light source through the lenses. **CAUTION:** Use an electric light, not sunlight, as the light source for focussing your mirror.

Part 2 Now, practise!

You are now ready to practise proper use of your microscope to view an object. In this activity, you will also practise calculating magnification and the **field of view** — the size of the area that can be seen using your microscope. By doing these calculations, you will be able to estimate the actual size of the objects you have magnified using the microscope.

What You Need

microscope, lens paper, prepared microscope slide, plastic ruler

Safety Precautions

- Be sure your hands are dry when you plug in or disconnect the cord of the microscope.
- Handle microscope slides carefully so that they do not break or cause cuts or scratches.

What to Do

1. Obtain a microscope and carry it to your work area. Use both hands to carry the microscope upright and support it properly. One hand should hold the arm of the microscope firmly and the other should support the base.

   (a) Do not turn any knobs until you have read through the rest of this procedure.

   (b) If the microscope has an electric cord for the light source, make sure the cord is properly connected and plugged in.

   (c) Use lens paper to clean the lenses and the light source (or mirror). Do not touch the lenses with your fingers.

2. The microscope should always be left with the low-power objective lens in position. If it is not, rotate the revolving nosepiece until the low-power objective lens clicks into place, as shown in the photograph.

   (a) Use the coarse-adjustment knob to lower the objective lens until the lens is about 1 cm above the stage.

   (b) Look through the eyepiece (ocular lens) and adjust the diaphragm until the view is as bright as you can get it.

When you rotate the nosepiece on a microscope, watch from the side to make sure the objective lenses do not hit the slide. The medium- and high-power objective lenses are long enough to touch the slide if they are lowered too much. Therefore, *only* the fine-adjustment knob is used when observing specimens under these lenses.

3. Place a prepared slide on the stage. Make sure the object to be viewed is centred over the opening.

   (a) Look through the eyepiece and slowly turn the coarse-adjustment knob until the object is in focus.

   (b) Use the fine-adjustment knob to sharpen the focus.

4. View the object under higher magnification. **CAUTION:** Do not use the coarse-adjustment knob with the medium- or high-power objective lens.

   (a) Watch from the side and rotate the revolving nosepiece to the medium-power objective lens. Do not change the focus first.

   (b) After the medium-power objective lens has clicked into place, adjust the focus using only the fine-adjustment knob.

   (c) Next, the object may be viewed under the high-power objective lens. Rotate the nose-piece (while watching from the side) until it clicks into place. Focus only with the fine-adjustment knob.

(d) When you have finished viewing the object, remove the slide and return it to the proper container before proceeding to step 5.

(e) If you do not continue to step 5, carefully unplug the microscope, click the low-power objective lens in place, and return the microscope to its storage area.

5. To calculate the total magnification of the object on your slide, multiply the number on the eyepiece by the number on the objective lens. For example, a 10× eyepiece and a 4× objective lens give a total magnification of 40×.

6. You are now ready to calculate the size of the field of view. Set your microscope to the low-power objective and place a clear plastic ruler on the stage.

7. Focus on the ruler and position it so that one of the centimetre markings is at the left edge of the field of view.

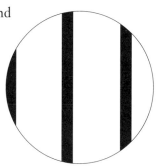

The diameter of the field of view under low power illustrated here is 2.5 mm.

8. Measure and record the diameter of the field of view in millimetres (mm). If the field of view is 2.5 mm in diameter, then an object that occupies about half the field of view would be about 1.25 mm in diameter.

9. Millimetre markings are too far apart to permit direct measurement of the field of view for lenses with magnifications higher than 10×. However, if you know the diameter of the field of view for the low-power lens, you can calculate the field of view for the other lenses. Before doing so, unplug the microscope by pulling out the plug. **CAUTION:** Never tug on the electrical cord to unplug it. Use the following formula to calculate the field of view for the medium-power objective lens:

Troubleshooting

You may encounter difficulties when using your microscope. The following list details the more common problems and how you can deal with them.

- *You cannot see anything.* Make sure the microscope is plugged in and the light is on. If the microscope has no light, adjust your mirror.

- *Are you having trouble finding anything on the slide?* Be patient. Follow all of the steps outlined in this procedure from the beginning and make sure the object being viewed is in the middle of the stage opening. While watching from the side, lower the low-power objective as far as it will go. Then look through the ocular lens and slowly raise the objective lens using the coarse-adjustment knob.

- *Are you having trouble focussing, or is the image very faint?* Try closing the diaphragm slightly. Some objects that you will examine are almost transparent. If there is too much light, a specimen may be difficult to see or will appear "washed out."

- *Do you see lines and specks floating across the slide?* These are probably structures in the fluid of your eyeball that you see when you move your eyes. Do not worry; this is normal.

- *Do you see a double image?* Check that the objective lens is properly clicked into place.

- *Do you close one eye while you look through the microscope with the other eye?* You might try keeping both eyes open. This will help prevent eye fatigue. It also lets you sketch an object while you are looking at it.

- Always place the part of the slide you are interested in at the centre of the field of view before changing to a higher-power objective lens. When you turn to medium and high power, you otherwise may not see the object you were viewing under low power. Why not?

Medium-power field of view = Low-power field of view × $\dfrac{\text{Magnification of low-power objective lens}}{\text{Magnification of medium-power objective lens}}$

CONTINUED

If, for example, your low-power objective lens is a 4×
lens with a field of view of 4 mm, and your medium-
power objective lens is a 10× lens, then the field of
view for the medium-power lens would be:

Medium-power field of view = 4 mm × $\frac{4}{10}$

$$= 4 \text{ mm} \times 0.4$$

$$= 1.6 \text{ mm}$$

Do a similar calculation to determine your high-power
field of view. Record the value.

Instant Practice

A **scale drawing** is a drawing in which you keep constant the proportions of what you see through the
microscope. This is important because it allows you to
compare the sizes of different objects and helps you
form an idea of the actual size of an object. Also, a
scale drawing makes it easier to explain what you see
to someone else. Do the following to make a scale
drawing.

1. Draw a circle (the size does not matter) in your
   notebook. The circle represents the microscope's
   field of view.

2. Imagine that the circle is divided into four equal
   sections (see the diagram below). Use a pencil and
   a ruler to draw these sections in your circle, as
   shown below.

3. Using low or medium power, locate a sample
   from the prepared slide that interests you.
   Imagine that the field of view is also divided into
   four equal sections.

4. Note in what part of the field of view the object
   lies and how much of the field of view the object
   occupies.

5. Draw the object in the circle. Position it so that it
   is in the same part of the circle as it appears in the
   field of view. Draw the object to scale. This means
   that it should take up the same proportion of space
   on the circle as it does in the field of view.

6. Label your drawing.

7. Estimate the size of the object in your drawing.

drawing made to scale

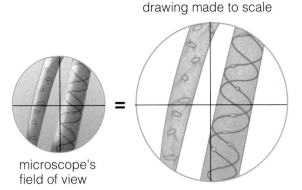

microscope's
field of view

Part 3 Preparing A Wet Mount

Now that you have learned how to use a microscope properly, you are ready to prepare and view slides of your own, using a variety of materials.

What You Need

microscope, microscope slides, cover slips, medicine dropper, tweezers

small piece of newspaper, tap water, other samples, lens paper

Safety Precautions

- Be careful when using sharp objects such as tweezers.
- Handle microscope slides and cover slips carefully so that they do not break and cause cuts or scratches.

What to Do

1. To prepare a wet mount, begin with a clean slide and cover slip. Wash the slide and cover slip with water and dry them carefully with lens paper. **CAUTION:** The cover slip is very thin. It is safest to dry both of its surfaces at the same time by holding the lens paper between your thumb and forefinger. Once cleaned, hold the slide and cover slip by their edges to avoid getting fingerprints on their surfaces.

2. Tear out a small piece of newspaper containing a single letter. Use an *e*, *f*, *g*, *s*, or *h*. Pick up the letter with the tweezers and place it in the centre of the slide.

3. Use the medicine dropper to place a very small drop of tap water on the newspaper sample. Then, hold a cover slip gently by its edges and place it at an angle of 45° on the surface of the slide near the edge of the newspaper sample.

4. Slowly and carefully lower the cover slip over the sample. Make sure there are no air bubbles trapped underneath the cover slip. This type of sample preparation is called a **wet mount**.

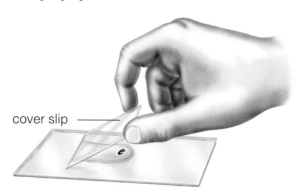

cover slip

5. Set your microscope on the low-power objective lens. Place the slide on the microscope stage and centre the sample over the opening in the stage.

   (a) Look through the eyepiece and move the slide until you can see the letter. Adjust the coarse-adjustment knob until the letter is in focus.

   (b) Move the slide until you can see the torn edge of the newspaper. Slowly turn the fine-adjustment knob about one-eighth turn either way. Do you see the whole view in sharp focus at one time?

6. View the letter under the medium-power objective lens. Remember to observe from the side while you rotate the nosepiece into position. Use only the fine-adjustment knob to focus.

7. Examine the letter and note that it is made up of many small dots. To reveal the structure of small objects, the microscope must do more than magnify. It must also reveal detail. The capacity to distinguish detail is called **resolution**, and the measure of resolution is known as **resolving power**. The resolving power of a microscope is defined as the minimum distance two objects can be apart and still be seen as separate objects.

Troubleshooting

- *Do you see round or oval shapes on the slide?* These are likely to be air bubbles. Move the cover slip gently with your finger to get rid of them, or study another area of the slide.

- *Do you see a straight line?* This could be the edge of your cover slip.

Instant Practice

1. Before rotating the nosepiece to a higher magnification, it is best to have the object you are examining at the centre of the field of view. Why?

2. To view a letter torn out of a newspaper (such as *e*) through the microscope the right way up, how would you position the slide on the stage?

3. The letters in a newspaper are composed of numerous small dots. How do you think newspapers produce colour photographs? Prepare a wet mount using a piece of a colour print from a newspaper and find out how the colour print is composed.

4. Prepare and examine microscope slides of different samples of materials, such as strands of hair, cotton, Velcro™, and grains of salt or sand. Obtain your teacher's approval of the material you select.

ESTIMATING AND MEASURING

The gathering of scientific data often involves the measurement of different quantities. Special tools and techniques have been developed to take accurate measurements. **Accuracy** refers to how close a measurement is to the true value of a particular quantity, such as the length or volume of an object. Some of the measurements scientists need to make are more complex than others. Whether complex or simple, measurements must be taken properly. In this *SkillPower*, you will learn and practise some of these techniques so that you may gather your own data.

Estimating

In some cases, it may not be essential or possible to take exact measurements. In such cases, scientists make estimates. For example, suppose you were an ecologist and needed to know the number of individuals of a tree species in a large provincial park. It would not be practical to count every single tree of that species. It would take too much time and money, and you probably would not need to know the *exact* number. If you define a study area, say 100 m^2 and if you know the total area of the park, then you could obtain a good estimate by multiplying the number of trees in your study area by the number of 100 m^2 blocks in the total area of the park.

Instant Practice

1. You need to estimate the number of micro-organisms on a petri dish. It is impractical to examine the whole dish with a microscope, but you can easily count the micro-organisms in a 1 mm × 1 mm square. Suppose you count 15 micro-organisms in this area, and you know that the area of the dish is 20 cm^2. Estimate the number on the whole dish. Remember that you must use the same units in your estimate.

2. Suppose you are an ornithologist studying parental behaviour in American robins. You observe that in an 8 h period, a robin visits its nest 29 times. Estimate how many times per hour the robin visits the nest.

3. A 1 L (1000 mL) jar is filled with dried kidney beans. How can you make a good estimate of the number of beans in the jar using a 10 mL container?

Measuring Area

As you know, length is the distance between two points. **Area** is the number of square units required to cover a surface. Area can be calculated easily for a square or rectangular shape: measure the lengths of two neighbouring sides (in other words, the length and width) and multiply them together. For example, the area of a rectangle with a length of 5 cm and a width of 4 cm is

$$5 \text{ cm} \times 4 \text{ cm} = 20 \text{ cm}^2$$

Notice that the values for area are expressed in square units.

The area of a right-angled triangle is obtained by multiplying the base and height (which are the neighbouring sides joined at the right angle) and dividing by 2. In other words:

$$\text{Area of triangle} = \tfrac{1}{2} \times \text{height} \times \text{base}$$

A special formula is required to calculate the area of a circle. Measure the radius — the distance between the centre of the circle and its circumference — (or halve the diameter instead), square this value, and multiply by the special number pi (3.14), which is symbolized by π.

$$\text{Area of a circle} = \pi r^2$$

Instant Practice

1. What is the area of a rectangle with a width of 2 cm and a length of 3.5 cm?

2. What is the area of a square with sides of 1 cm?

3. The area of a square or a rectangle is calculated by multiplying length by width. Why is a triangle's area half the area of a rectangle? To find out, draw a rectangle and create two triangles from it by drawing a line between two opposite corners.

4. You are responsible for supervising the renovation of your classroom into a laboratory. An end wall will serve as the sink area, and it needs to be tiled to a height of 1.5 m. Standard laboratory

tiles, 10 cm in height and 20 cm in width, will be used. How many tiles will you need?

(a) First, decide what kind of measurement would be most practical for the area — mm^2, cm^2, or m^2.

(b) Measure the length of the wall.

(c) Calculate the area of the wall to be tiled.

(d) How many tiles would you need to cover 1 m^2?

(e) Multiply that number by the number of square metres of wall area.

(f) Remember to use the same units. Using centimetres and metres in the same calculation will lead to incorrect calculations.

Measuring Volume

The **volume** of an object is the amount of space that the object occupies. Volume involves three dimensions: height, length, and width. The units for measuring the volume of a solid are called **cubic units** (for example, cm^3). The units used to measure the volume of liquids are called **capacity units**. The basic unit for liquids is the litre (L), but in this course, you will probably be working in millilitres (mL). Cubic units and capacity units are interchangeable, as indicated below:

$$1 \text{ cm}^3 = 1 \text{ mL}$$
$$1 \text{ dm}^3 = 1 \text{ L}$$
$$1 \text{ m}^3 = 1 \text{ kL}$$

To measure the volume of a liquid, you need a graduated cylinder. Once you have poured in the liquid sample, place the cylinder on a flat surface. Read the level at the top of the column of the liquid, but make sure that your eye is level with the top — do not measure from above or below. Finally, you need to consider the **meniscus**, the slight curve at the top of a liquid where the liquid meets the sides of the cylinder. For most liquids, such as water, the sides curve slightly upward, so measure at the lowest level of the meniscus, as shown in the diagram above.

In a mercury thermometer, the edges of the mercury curve slightly downward. In this case, read from the top of the meniscus.

The volume of solids can be measured in several ways, depending on shape and form. A solid that pours, such as sugar, can be measured like a liquid, but the surface of the substance being measured must be as flat as possible.

For a rectangular solid, measure the length, width,

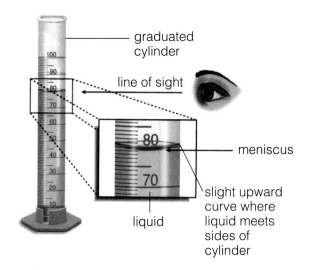

line of sight

graduated cylinder

meniscus

liquid

slight upward curve where liquid meets sides of cylinder

Take a reading from the bottom of the meniscus with your line of sight at the level of the meniscus.

and height, then multiply the values together. You may also calculate the volume of a cylinder. Calculate the area of its circular base (see the formula on page 583) and multiply it by the height of the cylinder.

The volume of irregularly shaped objects may be determined by the amount of liquid they displace. The displacement for a small object, such as a coin or a pebble, may be determined with a graduated cylinder. The water displaced equals the volume of the object, as shown in the diagram below.

Instant Practice

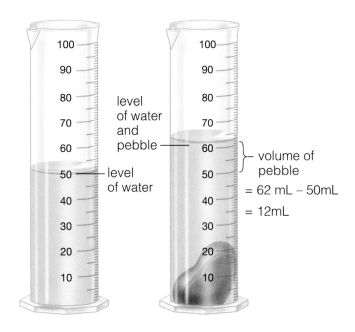

level of water and pebble

level of water

volume of pebble
= 62 mL – 50mL
= 12mL

The volume of larger objects can be determined by displacement as well, by using an overflow can. The spout allows water displaced by an object to be caught and measured in a graduated cylinder, as shown in the two diagrams directly below.

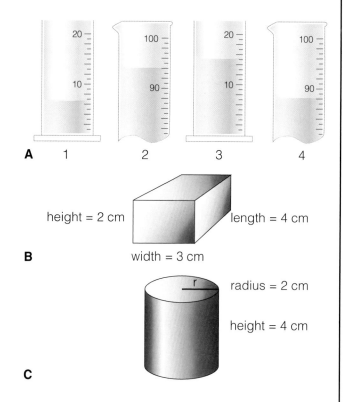

A   1   2   3   4

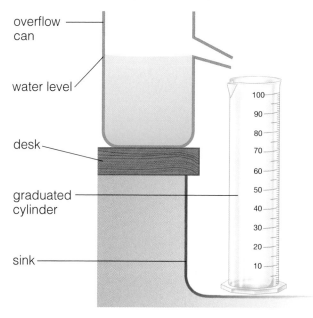

height = 2 cm   length = 4 cm

B   width = 3 cm

radius = 2 cm

height = 4 cm

C

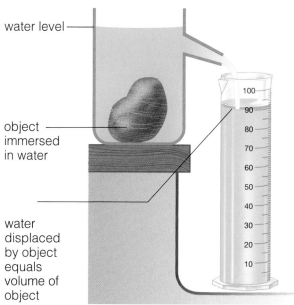

For questions 1 to 3, refer to the diagrams on the top right.

1. What is the volume indicated by each of the graduated cylinders in diagram A?

2. Calculate the volume of the object in diagram B.

3. Calculate the volume of the cylinder in diagram C.

4. To measure the volume of an object, follow these steps:

(a) Place a carefully measured amount of water, say 50 mL, into a 100 mL graduated cylinder. To do this, fill the cylinder to just under 50 mL and use a medicine dropper to bring the level to 50 mL.

(b) Tilting the cylinder slightly, gently immerse an object. The object will displace the water by an amount equal to its volume, and the level of the water (50 mL) in the cylinder will rise by this amount.

(c) Read the new volume level and subtract the original amount of water from this new value. This will give you the volume of the object.

5. You can use an overflow can and a graduated cylinder to measure the volume of an object.

(a) Place your finger over the spout and fill the can above the level of the spout. Position the can on a level surface and remove your finger to allow the excess water to drain into a sink.

(b) Place a graduated cylinder beneath the spout and carefully immerse the object in the water. Be careful that you do not immerse your fingers. The volume of the water displaced into the cylinder equals the volume of the object.

Measuring Mass

The **mass** of an object is the measure of the amount of material that makes up the object, but not the space occupied by the objects. For example, which has more mass: a cube of wood or a cube of lead of the same size? In this case, you know that the cube of lead has more mass because lead is much more dense than wood. What about a marble and a quarter? This comparison is not as easy to make. To measure the mass of each object accurately, you need to use a balance or a scale. You will probably use a triple beam balance similar to the one shown below.

The balance has a pan on one side and a set of three beams on the other. Each of the beams has a scale marked off and a rider or weight that can be moved along the beam. You can find the mass of an object by placing it directly on the pan. What if you needed to determine the mass of one cup of sugar? There is an easier way than dumping the sugar on the pan! Learn how to find mass by doing the following.

Instant Practice

1. Before you begin, set the balance to zero by sliding all three riders back to their zero points, at the left side of the beams. The pointer at the right side of the beams should swing slowly an equal amount above and below the zero. If it does not, turn the adjusting screw until it does so.
    (a) Place your object on the pan. The pointer will rise above the zero mark.
    (b) Slide the largest rider along until the pointer falls below zero. Then move it back one notch.
    (c) Repeat with the next heaviest rider, and then with the lightest rider. Adjust the last rider until the pointer swings equally above and below zero.
    (d) Add the readings of the three beams to find the mass.

2. What is the mass of half a cup of sugar?
    (a) Place an empty beaker (or cup) on the pan of the balance. Determine the mass of the beaker and record it.
    (b) Remove the beaker and half-fill it with sugar. Place the beaker on the pan of the balance and determine the mass of the sugar and the beaker together.
    (c) Determine the mass of the sugar only.

3. You may use the balance "in reverse" to measure out a known quantity. Suppose you needed to measure out 100 g of sugar (see the diagrams below).
    (a) Place an empty beaker on the pan and determine its mass.
    (b) Now move the appropriate slider along and add 100 g to the right side of the scale. The pointer will fall below zero.
    (c) Carefully pour sugar into the beaker until the pointer begins to move. You need to add exactly 100 g to balance the scales again.

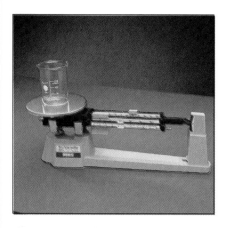

A Determine the mass of the empty beaker.

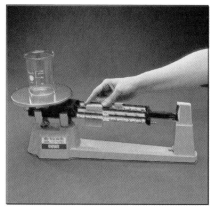

B Add 100 g to the mass measurement by moving the appropriate rider along the beam.

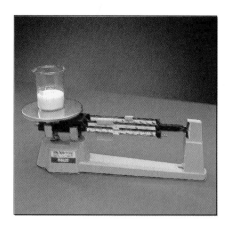

C Carefully add the solid to the beaker on the pan of the balance. The scales will be balanced again when 100 g of solid have been added to the beaker.

ORGANIZING AND COMMUNICATING SCIENTIFIC RESULTS

Scientific data have little value unless they are reported clearly and concisely. While learning about science, you will also learn to communicate scientific information in a manner that is easy to follow. To communicate results successfully, you must first organize them in an appropriate way. When the information contains numerical values, you may report it in the form of a table, bar graph, circle graph, or line graph.

Tables

Regardless of the final form in which the data are presented, they are often arranged in a table first. Tables also provide a convenient way to organize data for use in further calculations.

Example

Table 1 contains data necessary to determine the number of people per square kilometre of land area in each province and territory in Canada. To find out how to construct such a table, read the following steps and compare the instructions to the completed table.

1. Decide on the number of columns and rows for your table. Remember to leave one row for column headings.

2. Gather data on population and land area for all provinces and territories. Place the data in your table.

3. Calculate the value for the last column by dividing the population by the land area. For example, for Alberta, the number of people per land area is 2 696 826 people ÷ 644 390 km^2 = 4.19 people/km^2. Repeat the procedure for every province and territory.

4. Which province or territory has the largest number of people per square kilometre? Which province or territory has the smallest number of people per square kilometre?

Instant Practice

1. Organize the following data into a table. In the table, include a column that gives the greatest temperature range in each province and territory.

The following temperatures are the warmest ever recorded in Canada to date: Newfoundland, 41.7°C; Prince Edward Island, 36.7°C; New Brunswick, 39.4°C; Nova Scotia, 38.3°C; Québec, 40.0°C; Ontario, 42.2°C; Manitoba, 44.4°C;

Table 1 People per Square Kilometre of Land in Provinces and Territories in Canada (prior to April 1, 1999)

Name	Population	Land area (km^2)	People per km^2
Alberta	2 696 826	644 390	4.19
British Columbia	3 724 500	929 730	4.00
Manitoba	1 113 898	548 360	2.03
New Brunswick	738 133	72 090	10.2
Newfoundland	551 792	371 690	1.48
Northwest Territories	64 402	3 293 020	0.020
Nova Scotia	909 282	52 840	17.2
Ontario	10 753 573	891 190	12.1
Prince Edward Island	134 557	5 660	23.8
Québec	7 138 795	1 356 790	5.26
Saskatchewan	990 237	570 700	1.74
Yukon Territory	30 766	478 970	0.060

Saskatchewan, 45.0°C; Alberta, 43.3°C; British Columbia, 44.4°C; Yukon Territory, 36.1°C; Northwest Territories, 39.4°C.

The following temperatures are the coldest ever recorded in Canada: Newfoundland, –51.1°C; Prince Edward Island, –37.2°C; New Brunswick, –47.2°C; Nova Scotia, –41.1°C; Québec, –54.4°C; Ontario, –58.3°C; Manitoba, –52.8°C; Saskatchewan, –56.7°C; Alberta, –61.1°C; British Columbia, –58.9°C; Yukon Territory, –63.0°C; Northwest Territories, –57.2°C.

2. Why would some of the data in this table be different after April 1, 1999?

Graphing

Graphs communicate data in a visual way. In designing a graph, your goal is to communicate a large amount of information in a simple, clear manner.

Constructing a Bar Graph

Bar graphs are most useful when you have numerical values associated with categories of places or things. In the following example, the categories are the world's continents.

Example

Table 2 provides the data for the bar graph shown on the right, showing the land areas of the world's continents. To learn how the bar graph was prepared, read the following steps and compare them to the graph.

Table 2 Land Area of Continents

Continent	Land area (millions of square kilometres)
Africa	30.3
Antarctica	13.2
Asia	44.5
Europe	10.5
Oceania	7.8
North and Central America	24.2
South America	17.8

1. Draw your x-axis and y-axis on a sheet of graph paper. Label the x-axis "Continents" and the y-axis "Land area." Remember to include units.

2. Select an appropriate scale. Write the numerical values to show the scale on your y-axis. For example, the number 10 represents: 10 000 000 km².

3. Decide on a width for the bars that will make the graph easy to read. Leave the same amount of space between each bar.

4. To draw the bar representing Africa, move along the x-axis the width of your first bar, then go up the y-axis just above 30 to represent 30.3. Use a pencil and a ruler to draw in the first bar lightly. Repeat the procedure for the other continents.

5. When you have drawn all the bars, you might wish to colour them so that each one stands out. If you do decide to use different colours, you may need to make a legend or a key to explain the meaning of the colours. Give your graph a title.

Instant Practice

Make a bar graph showing the greatest temperature range recorded for each province and territory. Use the data table that you prepared in the *Instant Practice* for making data tables (page 587).

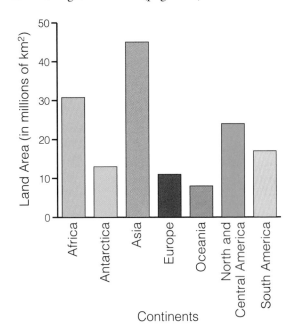

Constructing a Histogram

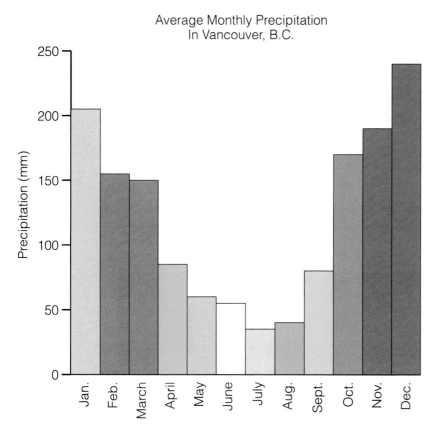

Average Monthly Precipitation
In Vancouver, B.C.

The *x*-axis in this histogram represents time, which is a continuous variable. The precipitation data have been grouped by the month.

How does a histogram, such as the one shown above, differ from a bar graph? You probably noticed that there is no space between the bars. The reason for placing the bars in contact with each other is that the *x*-axis represents a continuous quantity. In this histogram, the continuous quantity is time and each group is one month. The total of the data is represented by the height of a bar. In this case, the heights of the bars represent the total precipitation during each month. The procedure for constructing a histogram is the same as the procedure for making a bar graph.

Instant Practice

The following data represent the masses, in grams, of 30 mature laboratory rats that have been fed a special test diet. Make a histogram to display the masses of the rats. Use mass groupings of 100 g for the bars along the *x*-axis. Choose an appropriate scale on the *y*-axis for the number of rats in each mass group.

756, 677, 811, 472, 591, 744, 714, 891, 903, 623, 767, 819, 922, 717, 858, 727, 512, 907, 537, 735, 681, 913, 836, 654, 789, 827, 638, 701, 873

Constructing a Circle Graph

Circle graphs are an excellent way to communicate categories in terms of percentages of a whole.

Example

To learn how to construct a circle graph, follow the steps below while examining the circle graph showing the percentage of each blood type in the North American population.

Table 3 Blood Types in North America

Blood type	Percentage of total	Degrees (°) in "piece of pie"
A	38	137
B	14	51
AB	4	14
O	44	158

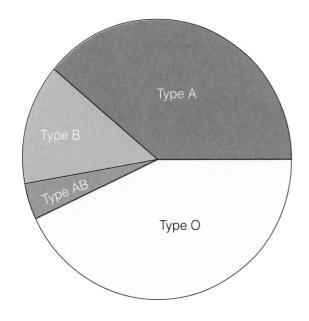

1. Make a large circle on a piece of paper and put a dot in the centre.

2. To determine the number of degrees in each "piece of the pie" that represents each section, use the following formula:

$$\text{Degrees for "piece of pie"} = \frac{\text{Percentage of total}}{100\%} \times 360°$$

Round your answer to the nearest whole number. For example, the degrees in the section representing blood type A are:

$$\text{Degrees for type A} = \frac{38\%}{100\%} \times 360° = 137°$$

3. Draw a straight line from the centre to the edge of the circle. Place a protractor on this line and use it to mark a point on the edge of the circle at 137°. Connect the point to the centre of the circle. This is the "piece" that represents the portion of the population having type A blood.

4. Repeat steps 2 and 3 for the remaining blood types.

Instant Practice

Make a circle graph using the following data on the elements in the human body: hydrogen (H), 63%; oxygen (O), 25.4%; carbon (C), 9.4%; nitrogen (N), 1.4%; calcium (Ca), 0.31%; phosphorus (P), 0.22%; other, 0.23%.

Drawing a Line Graph

Line graphs, or co-ordinate graphs, show relationships between two variables, such as time and distance. You can use a line graph to predict the value of one variable at any desired value of the other variable. The following examples will show you how to create line graphs from data tables, as well as how to use the graphs.

Example 1

Suppose that park wardens in a provincial park counted the number of hikers that passed certain points along a popular trail in one day. Their data are shown in Table 4, along with a graph of the data shown on the right below. Examine the table and the graph while you read the following steps describing how the graph was made.

Table 4 Number of Hikers on a Trail in One Day

Distance from trail head (km)	Number of hikers
0 (at the trail head)	38
1	36
2	36
3	25
5	22
8	19
10	3
12	2

1. With a ruler, draw an x-axis and a y-axis on a piece of graph paper.

2. Label the x-axis "Distance" and the y-axis "Number of hikers."

3. Decide on a scale to use. You are working with two numbers, distance on the x-axis and number of people on the y-axis. The scale on the x-axis will go from zero to 12, and the scale on the y-axis will go from zero to at least 38. It is usually convenient to use a round number, such as 40, to end the graph. Choose the scale so that the height and the width of the graph are similar.

4. To plot your graph, carefully move a pencil up the y-axis until you reach 38. Since this is the number of hikers at the trail head, you can say that they went zero kilometres. Make a mark on the y-axis, which represents zero kilometres. Notice that the co-ordinates of this point are (0, 38). Repeat the procedure for each pair of values in the table.

5. Since there is no way of knowing where individual hikers turned back in between observation points, we do not know where the line should go between data points. Therefore, simply draw straight lines directly from one data point to the next.

6. Give your graph a title.

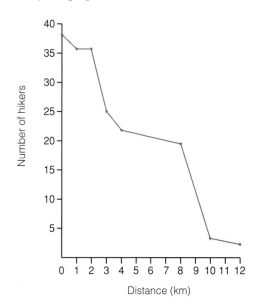

Example 2

Suppose that, while hiking, you dropped a rock from a cliff above a river after making sure that it was safe to do so. Another hiker said she could calculate exactly how far a rock would fall after any number of seconds. The results of her calculations are shown in Table 5. The points on the line graph below were taken from the table and plotted according to the procedure described in Example 1. However, the line on this graph is not drawn straight from point to point. The difference between these two examples is the fact that we know that a rock falls with a smooth, continuous motion. Therefore, the lines between the data pointsshould be drawn as a smooth curve connecting the points.

Table 5 Distance that a Rock Falls in Certain Amounts of Time

Time (s)	Distance (m)
0	0.00
2	19.6
4	78.4
6	176
8	314
10	490

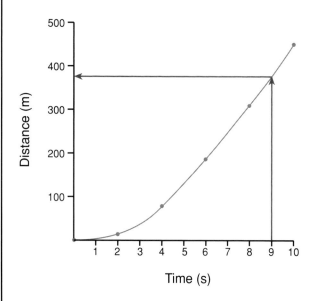

This graph is useful for making accurate predictions. For example, imagine that another hiker used the second hand on his watch to measure the time between the release of the rock and the time when he heard a splash. He said that it took 9 s for the rock to hit the water. You can use this information and the graph to determine the height of the cliff. Find 9 s on the x-axis and draw a line straight up to the curve. Then draw another straight line from that point to the y-axis. The line reaches the y-axis just below 400 m. Therefore, the height of the cliff is about 395 m.

Instant Practice

The data in Table 6 give the speed of a ball every second after it was thrown straight upward with an initial speed of 49 m/s. Make a graph of the speed of the ball with time. Use your graph to estimate the speed of the ball after 3.5 s.

Table 6 Speed of Ball Thrown Upward

Time (s)	Speed (m/s)
0.0	49.0
1.0	39.2
2.0	29.4
3.0	19.6
4.0	9.80
5.0	0.00

Straight Line Graphs

When a graph makes a straight line, you can obtain important information by determining the slope of the line.

Example

A group of students used an instrument called a spark timer to make measurements of the position of a cart on an air track at 0.1 s intervals. The points on the graph below were plotted from their data. Draw a line of best fit and determine the speed of the cart from the slope of the line. Examine the graph while you read the steps in the procedure below.

1. Since the data points do not lie on a straight line, you must estimate the best place for the line. Place a ruler on the graph and move it around until there are about as many data points above the ruler as below the edge of the ruler. Draw the line. This is the line of best fit. Do NOT simply connect the first and last points and do NOT assume that the line must go through the origin.

2. The slope of a straight line is defined as the "rise" over the "run." To find this ratio, pick any two points on the line. Do NOT use two data points. None of them really lie on the line. Your calculations will be more accurate if you pick points relatively far apart. Write the co-ordinates of these points. The selected points on this graph are circled. Their co-ordinates are (0.3, 0.4) and (1.3, 1.6).

3. The rise is the vertical distance between the points. You can calculate the rise by subtracting the y co-ordinate of the first point from that of the second point. The value is 1.6 - 0.4 = 1.2. Since the units on the y-axis are metres, the rise is 1.2 m.

4. The run is the horizontal distance between the points. You can calculate the run by subtracting the x co-ordinate of the first point from that of the second. The value is 1.3 – 0.1 = 1.0. Since the units on the x-axis are seconds, the run is 1.0 s.

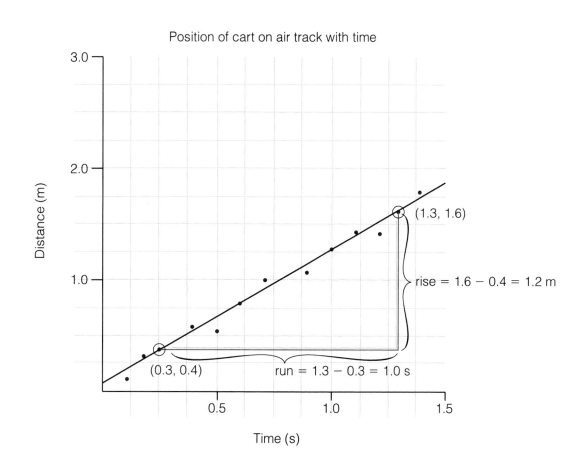

Position of cart on air track with time

5. Calculate the slope of the line by using the following equation.

$$\text{slope} = \frac{\text{rise}}{\text{run}}$$

$$\text{slope} = \frac{1.2 \text{ m}}{1.0 \text{ s}}$$

$$\text{slope} = 1.2 \text{ m/s}$$

6. The units of the slope are metres per second. These are the units of speed. The slope of any straight line graph of time against distance is the speed. If the line is not straight, you cannot determine a slope. A curved line would mean that the speed of the object is changing.

Instant Practice

To help time pass while on a long trip by car, you watch road signs and keep track of the time. Imagine that you collected the data in Table 7. Plot your data on a graph and draw a line of best fit. Use the graph to estimate the speed of the car.

Table 7 Distance Travelled and Time Passed

Distance travelled (km)	Time passed (h)
50	0.5
75	1.0
125	1.25
175	2.0
200	2.25
250	2.5
300	3.25
325	3.75
375	4.0

USING MODELS IN SCIENCE

In science, a model is anything that helps you to better understand a scientific concept. A model can be a picture, a mental image, a structure, or even a mathematical expression. Sometimes you need a model because the objects you are studying are too small to see or too large to envision. Sometimes they are hidden from view, like the interior of Earth or the inside of a living organism.

Scientists use models to help them communicate their ideas to other scientists and/or to students. They also use models to test an idea and to find out if it can work. Models help scientists plan new experiments in order to learn more about the subject they are studying. Sometimes, when scientists learn more, they have to modify their models.

$$E = mc^2$$

This equation is probably one of the most famous mathematical models in all of science. It is part of Einstein's theory of relativity. The theory proposes that matter can be converted into energy. The equation allows you to calculate the amount of energy, E, that is produced when an amount of matter, m, is annihilated (made to disappear) and converted into energy. The c in the equation is the speed of light. Einstein's equation has been tested extensively and has never been shown to be incorrect.

Examples

An atom is too small to see, even with the most powerful microscope. Scientists have used a variety of techniques to learn about the atom. This is a model in development that helped scientists describe what they had learned about the atom.

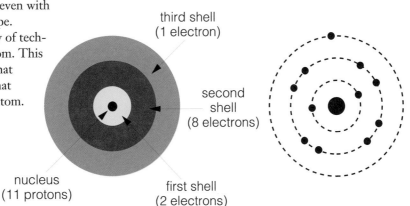

third shell
(1 electron)

second
shell
(8 electrons)

nucleus
(11 protons)

first shell
(2 electrons)

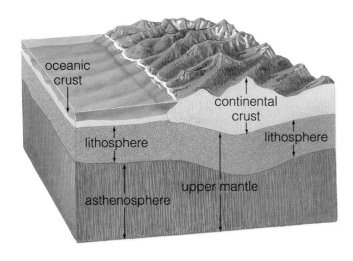

oceanic
crust

continental
crust

lithosphere

lithosphere

asthenosphere

upper mantle

Scientists have used many techniques to probe Earth's internal structure. They have been able to create this model by combining results from many experiments and observations.

Instant Practice

Early astronomers believed that the paths, or orbits, travelled by planets were circles. However, many astronomical observations could not be explained by supposing that orbits were circular. In order to explain these observations, the famous astronomer Johannes Kepler reasoned that the orbits were ellipses. With this knowledge, you can construct a model that simulates the planetary orbits. Start by constructing a circle and then use a similar method to construct ellipses.

You will need two thumbtacks, a 25 cm length of string, pencil, paper, ruler, and cardboard. If possible, use a cork board under your cardboard. Carry out the following steps.

1. Tie the ends of the string together to form a loop.

2. Place a blank sheet of paper on the cardboard. Insert a thumbtack near the centre of the paper.

3. Loop the string around the thumbtack. If you have a cork board, push the thumbtack into the cork. If you do not have a cork board, have a partner hold the thumbtacks steady.

4. Put the tip of the pencil in the loop and pull it taut. Move the pencil around the thumbtack, keeping the string taut, until you have drawn a perfect circle.

5. Place a second thumbtack about 5 cm from the first one.

6. Loop the string around both thumbtacks.

7. Put the tip of the pencil in the loop and pull the string taut, as shown in the diagram.

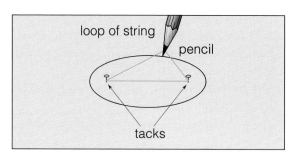

8. Move the pencil all the way around the thumbtacks, keeping the string taut.

   You have just drawn an ellipse. Any closed, smooth curve drawn in this manner is an ellipse. To accurately model Earth's orbit, the two thumbtacks would have to be very close together. To model the orbit of a comet, the thumbtacks would have to be very far apart.

9. Use what you have just learned to construct a model of Earth's orbit.

10. Use the information above to construct a model of a comet's orbit.

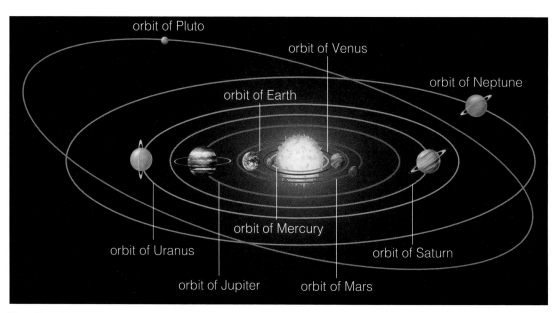

The orbits of the planets around the Sun are elliptical.

SAFETY SYMBOLS

The following safety symbols are used in the *SCIENCEPOWER*™ *9* program to alert you to possible dangers. Be sure you understand each symbol used in an activity or investigation before you begin.

	Disposal Alert This symbol appears when care must be taken to dispose of materials properly.
	Biological Hazard This symbol appears when there is danger involving bacteria, fungi, or protists.
	Thermal Safety This symbol appears as a reminder to use caution when handling hot objects.
	Sharp Object Safety This symbol appears when a danger of cuts or punctures caused by the use of sharp objects exists.
	Fume Safety This symbol appears when chemicals or chemical reactions could cause dangerous fumes.
	Electrical Safety This symbol appears when care should be taken when using electrical equipment.
	Skin Protection Safety This symbol appears when use of caustic chemicals might irritate the skin or when contact with micro-organisms might transmit infection.
	Clothing Protection Safety A lab apron should be worn when this symbol appears.
	Fire Safety This symbol appears when care should be taken around open flames.
	Eye Safety This symbol appears when a danger to the eyes exists. Safety goggles should be worn when this symbol appears.
	Poison Safety This symbol appears when poisonous substances are used.
	Chemical Safety This symbol appears when chemicals used can cause burns or are poisonous if absorbed through the skin.

WHMIS Symbols

Look carefully at the WHMIS (Workplace Hazardous Materials Information System) safety symbols shown here. The WHMIS symbols are used throughout Canada to identify dangerous materials used in all workplaces, including schools. Make certain you understand what these symbols mean. When you see these symbols on containers in your classroom, at home, or in a workplace, use safety precautions.

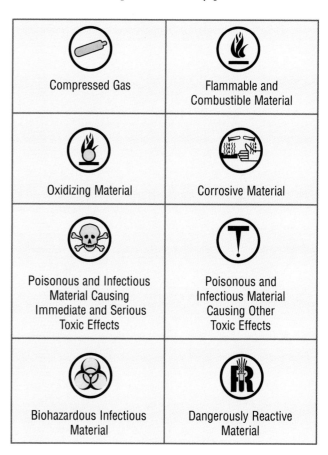

Compressed Gas	Flammable and Combustible Material
Oxidizing Material	Corrosive Material
Poisonous and Infectious Material Causing Immediate and Serious Toxic Effects	Poisonous and Infectious Material Causing Other Toxic Effects
Biohazardous Infectious Material	Dangerously Reactive Material

Instant Practice

1. Find four of the *SCIENCEPOWER*™ *9* safety symbols in activities or investigations in this textbook. What are the possible dangers in the activity or investigation that relate to each symbol?

2. Find any two WHMIS symbols on containers in your school, or ask a parent or guardian to look for WHMIS symbols in a workplace. Record the name of the substance on which the symbols are used. What dangers are associated with the substance in each container?

SCIENTIFIC DRAWING

A clear, concise drawing can often illustrate or replace words in a scientific explanation. In science, drawings are especially important when you are trying to explain difficult concepts or describe something that contains a lot of detail. It is important to make scientific drawings clear, neat, and accurate.

Making a Scientific Drawing

Follow these steps to make a good scientific drawing.

1. Use unlined paper and a sharp pencil with an eraser.

2. Give yourself plenty of space on the paper. You need to make sure that your drawing will be large enough to show all necessary details. You also need to allow space for labels. Labels identify parts of the object you are drawing. Place all of your labels to the right of your drawing, unless there are so many labels that your drawing looks cluttered.

3. Carefully study the objects that you will be drawing. Make sure you know what you need to include.

4. Draw only what you see, and keep your drawing simple. Do not try to indicate parts of the object that are not visible from the angle you observed. If you think it is important to show another part of the object, do a second drawing, and indicate the angle from which each drawing is viewed.

5. Shading or colouring is not usually used in scientific drawings. If you want to indicate a darker area, you can use stippling (a series of dots). You can use double lines to indicate thick parts of the object.

6. If you do use colour, try to be as accurate as you can and choose colours that are as close as possible to the colours in the object you are observing.

7. Label your drawing carefully and completely, using lower-case (small) letters. Pretend you know nothing about the object you have just observed, and think about what you would need to know if you were looking at it for the first time. Remember to place your labels to the right of the drawing, if possible. Use a ruler to draw a

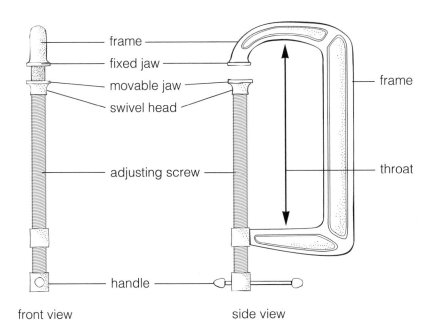

front view   side view

horizontal line from the label to the part you are identifying. Make sure that none of your label lines cross.

8. Give your drawing a title. **Note:** The drawing of an amoeba shown here is from a Grade 9 student's notebook. The student used stippling to show darker areas, horizontal labels for the cell parts viewed, and a title — all elements of an excellent final drawing.

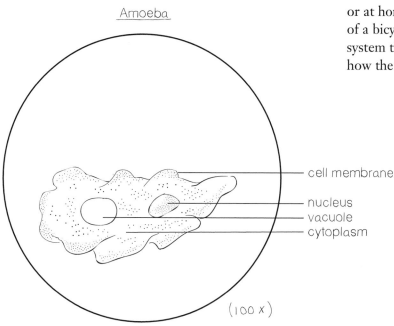

Amoeba

cell membrane
nucleus
vacuole
cytoplasm

(100 X)

The stippling on this drawing of an amoeba as observed under a microscope shows that some areas are darker than others.

Instant Practice

1. Make a drawing of an object in your classroom and use stippling as a way of indicating that it has three dimensions.

2. Draw a spoon in front view and back view. Show how you can use stippling to give the impression of the concave and convex surfaces of the bowl of the spoon.

3. Select any mechanical system in your classroom or at home; for example, the brakes or the gears of a bicycle. Show two different views of the system that would help someone else understand how the system works.

CONNECTING AND READING AMMETERS AND VOLTMETERS

Meters in a Circuit

An **ammeter** is an instrument used to measure the electric current flowing through a component (for example, a light bulb) in a circuit. A **voltmeter** is an instrument used to measure the electric potential difference between two points in a circuit (for example, across a light bulb or across a battery). Figure 1 shows a simple circuit containing a battery, a switch, a light bulb, an ammeter to measure the current flowing through the light bulb, and a voltmeter to measure the potential difference across it.

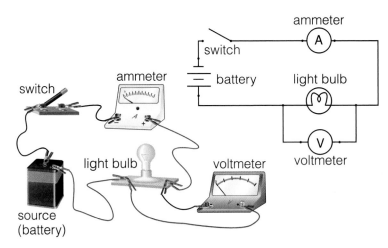

Figure 1 To measure the current flowing through the light bulb, the ammeter must be connected in series with the light bulb. To measure the potential difference across the light bulb, the voltmeter must be connected in parallel with the light bulb.

Polarity of the Meters

Both ammeters and voltmeters have two terminals that must be connected to the circuit. The negative terminal (–) is black and the positive terminal (+) is red. The electrons must enter any meter at the negative terminal and exit from the positive terminal to prevent damage to the meter. Since electrons leave the negative terminal of the source, the negative terminal of a meter must be connected to the negative terminal of the source. As well, the positive terminal of a meter must be connected to the positive terminal of the source. However, there may be other circuit elements between the source and the meter. If you trace the connecting wires in Figure 1 you will see that they are connected correctly.

Connecting an Ammeter

Because electric current is measured at a point, all of the current must pass through the ammeter at that point. When connecting an ammeter to a circuit, open the circuit by disconnecting a wire at the point at which you wish to measure the current. Then connect the ammeter so that the electrons will enter at the negative terminal and leave at the positive terminal. You will usually need one additional connecting wire to connect an ammeter to a circuit. Figure 2 shows a circuit that has been disconnected and an ammeter that is about to be added to the circuit in series with the light bulb.

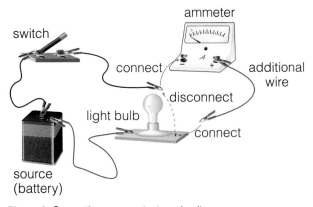

Figure 2 Connecting an ammeter to a circuit.

Connecting a Voltmeter

Because potential difference is measured between two points in a circuit, the terminals of the voltmeter must be connected at these two points. You do not need to open a circuit to connect a voltmeter. Using two additional wires, connect the terminals of the voltmeter on opposite sides of the component across which you want to measure the potential difference. Be sure that the negative terminal of the voltmeter is connected to the negative terminal of the source, and that the positive terminal of the voltmeter is connected to the positive terminal of the source. Figure 3 shows a circuit with an open switch and a voltmeter about to be connected in parallel with the light bulb.

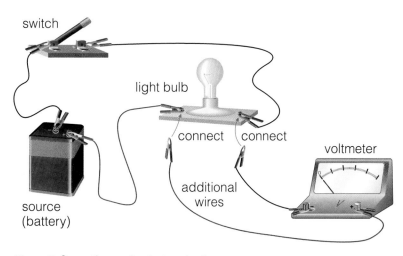

Figure 3 Connecting a voltmeter to a circuit

Reading Meters

Voltmeters and ammeters come in a wide variety of sizes and shapes. Some meters display values directly as numbers, as shown in Figure 4A. Other meters display results with a needle pointing to numbers on a dial, as shown in Figure 4B.

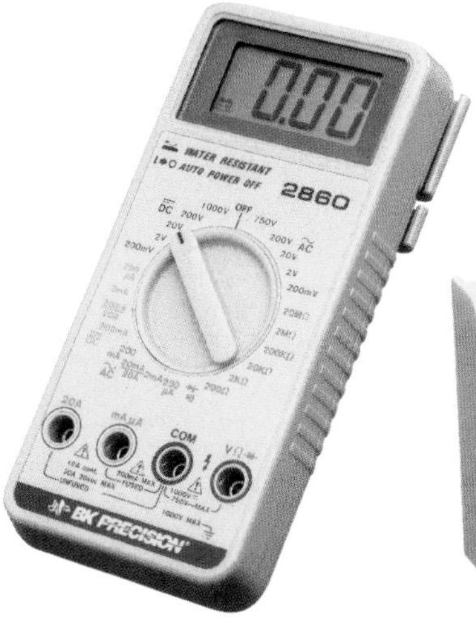

Figure 4A Meters that display numerical values directly are called digital meters.

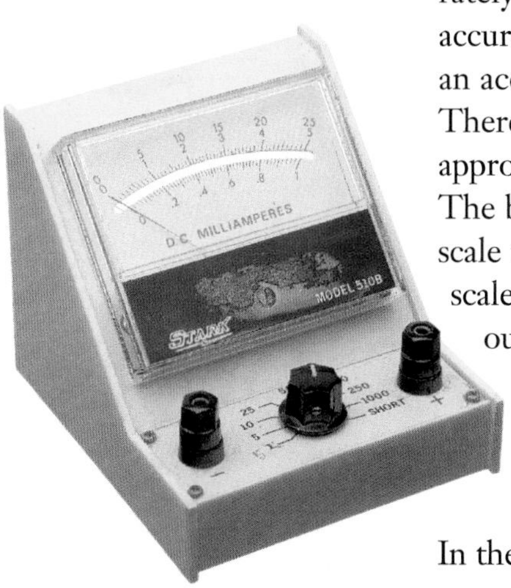

Figure 4B Meters that have needles pointing to a dial are called analog meters.

When looking at the digitial meter in Figure 4A, you might wonder why there are three sets of numbers on the dial. The numbers represent different scales of measurement. For example, one scale might report values of potential difference between zero and 2.5 V, while another scale will report values between zero and 10 V. Several different scales are needed because meters have electric circuits inside that allow them to measure different levels of current or voltage accurately. For example, a circuit that provides an accurate measurement of a large current cannot give an accurate measurement of a very small current. Therefore, when using meters, you must select the appropriate circuit by setting the scale on the meter. The best approach is to set the meter at the largest scale to get an approximate value. Then lower the scale until you have the highest possible reading without going off the scale.

Figure 5, on the next page, illustrates meters that have two different ways to change the scale. The meter in Figure 5A is a voltmeter with a dial that you can set at a particular value. In the figure, the dial is set at 10.

Therefore, the maximum potential difference for that scale is 10 V. To determine the potential difference, look for a number at the top of the scale with the same first digit as 10. The top scale has a maximum value of 1, so now "1" represents 10 V. To read the scale, multiply the number the needle is pointing to by 10. This dial is reporting 7.2 V.

Figure 5B shows an ammeter with six different ranges of current. To change the scale on this meter, you choose among six positive terminals. In the example, the circuit wire is connected to the 500 mA terminal. Remember that mA represents milliamperes or thousandths of an ampere. So 500 mA is the same as 0.500 A. The "5" on the bottom scale is the first digit in 500 mA, so the 5 now represents 500 mA. The needle is pointing to 4.7, so the meter is reporting 470 mA of current.

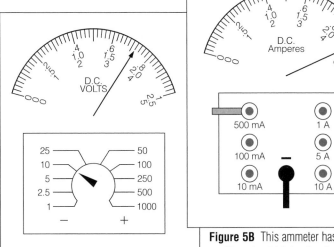

Figure 5A This voltmeter has a dial that changes the scale.

Figure 5B This ammeter has different positions in which to plug the positive lead.

Instant Practice

Determine the values of current or potential difference indicated by the meters in Figures 6A, B, C, and D.

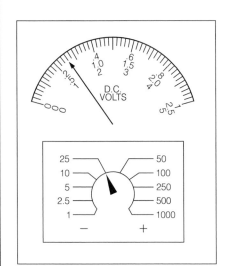

Figure 6A

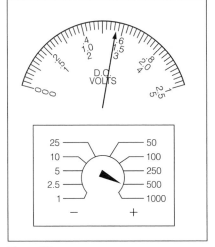

Figure 6B

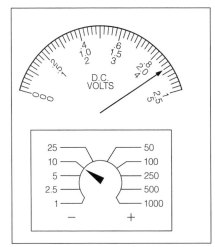

Figure 6C

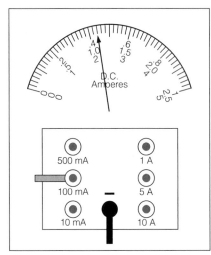

Figure 6D

SOLVING NUMERICAL PROBLEMS (GRASP)

Problem-solving skills are important in everyday life, in the workplace, and in school. Whether you realize it or not, you solve many problems every day. For example, one of the first problems you solve each day is deciding what to wear. The "given" information that you use to make your decision is a knowledge of what items of clothing you own and which ones are clean. Then you have to think about what is required of you on that day. If you are going to a job interview, you dress differently than you would if you were going to play soccer or softball. After you have analyzed all of the information, you make a decision, get dressed, and go out to start your the day.

Although solving numerical problems seems more difficult than deciding what to wear, you can use the same methods to solve both types of problems. Solving any problem is easier when you establish a logical, step-by-step procedure. One excellent method for solving numerical problems includes five basic steps called: Given, Required, Analysis, Solution, and Paraphrase. You can easily remember these steps because the first letter of each word spells the word **GRASP**. The following steps will help you get a "grasp" on quantitative or numerical problem solving.

The GRASP method

Given

The first step in solving a numerical problem is to organize the given data. Read the problem carefully and make a list of all of the numerical quantities given in the problem statement, as well as any other important, qualitative information. Include the symbols, numerical values, and units for each numerical quantity. For example, if you are told that the mass of a rock is 3.5 kg, you would list: Mass of rock, m = 3.5 kg.

Required

The second step in the GRASP method is to identify exactly what information the problem requires you to find. Write the name of the quantity, the symbol, and the units. For example, if you are asked to find the velocity of an object, write: Velocity, v (m/s).

Analysis

To carry out the third step, analyze the problem statement by breaking it down into individual phrases. A single phrase may contain important information. You can use the following strategies to help you analyze the problem:

- Look at the given data and the required value. Write down any relationships between these quantities. For example, if you are given values for area and pressure and you need to determine the force, write down: $P = F/A$.

- If possible, make a sketch or a diagram. A good diagram can often provide the key to solving a problem.

- Ensure that the units in the given data are consistent with each other and with the units you will use in your final answer. If the units are not consistent, make the necessary conversions.

- Analyze the problem statement to determine if you need any information that can be found in a table, appendix, or other reference. For example, the densities of many substances are listed in tables in science textbooks. The masses of many objects, from an electron to the Sun can be found in reference materials, both print, and electronic. Look up and record any numerical values that you will need.

- Write down any assumptions you will have to make in order to solve the problem.

Solution

In the fourth step, use all of the data and information you have accumulated to find the solution. Convert all units to the units required in your final answer. Then substitute the given values into the relationships you have written down and carry out the mathematical operations. Include units in every step.

Paraphrase

The purpose of the fifth and final step is to clarify the meaning of the calculations you have done. The word "paraphrase" means to restate in a different way. Paraphrase your solution, including the quantity, value, and units, in the form of a sentence.

Example of the GRASP Problem-Solving Method

A small, shiny, gold-coloured, metallic crown was uncovered at an excavation site. To determine whether the crown was made of either pure gold or copper, the excavators decided to calculate its density and compare it to the published densities of the two metals. They measured the mass of the crown and found it to be 2.00 kg. The measured volume was 225 cm^3. Was the crown made of copper or gold?

Given

Mass of crown, m = 2.00 kg

Volume of crown, V = 225 cm^3

Required

Density, D (g/cm^3)

Analysis

Units are not consistent.

Convert mass in kilograms to grams.

Use the conversion factor 1 kg = 1000 g.

Write it in the form $\dfrac{1000 \text{ g}}{1 \text{ kg}}$ = 1

$D = m/V$

Densities of copper and gold are needed for comparison. Published values are:

Density of copper, D$_{Cu}$ = 8.90 g/cm^3

Density of gold, D$_{Au}$ = 19.30 g/cm^3

Assume that any dirt was removed from the crown before its mass and volume were determined.

Solution

1. Convert units.

$$m = 2.00 \; \cancel{\text{kg}} \times \frac{1000 \text{ g}}{1 \; \cancel{\text{kg}}}$$

$$= 2000 \text{ g}$$

2. $D = \dfrac{m}{V}$

$$= \frac{2000 \text{ g}}{225 \text{ cm}^3}$$

$$= 8.90 \text{ g/cm}^3$$

The density of the crown is the same as the published density of copper.

Paraphrase

The density of the gold-coloured crown is 8.90 gm/cm^3, the same as the published density of copper. Since the published density of gold, 19.30 g/cm^3, is much larger than the calculated density of the crown, the crown could not be made of gold. The colour and the density of the crown are consistent with the colour and density of copper. However, more tests should be done to confirm this conclusion.

Instant Practice

Use the GRASP method to solve the following problems.

1. A cube of aluminum has a mass of 2.0 kg and a volume of 741 cm^3. What is the density of the aluminum in g/cm^3?

2. An armoured vehicle can carry a maximum mass of 10 000 kg. The security safe in the vehicle has an inside volume of 0.600 m^3. Can this safe hold 10 000 kg of gold?

3. A statue weighing 10 000 N stands on a platform. The statue has a circular base with a radius of 30 cm. How much pressure, in Pa, does the statue exert on the platform? (Hint: 1 Pa = $\frac{1 \text{ N}}{\text{m}^2}$)

Photo Credits

Bank of Canada, photography by James Zagon, Ottawa, **centre right** Coin design courtesy of the Royal Canadian Mint, photography by Don Ford; **217** CORBIS-BETTMANN; **226** VALAN/Phillip Norton, **inset** Michael Busselle/Tony Stone Images; **228** Alfred Pasienka/Science Photo Library/Photo Researchers; **229** Richard Megna/Fundamental Photographs; **231** CORBIS-BETTMANN; **234** Courtesy of IBM Corporation, Almaden Research Center; **237** Paul Silverman/Fundamental Photographs; **238 left** CORBIS-BETTMANN, **right** AIP Emilio Segrè Visual Archives; **240** COMSTOCK/Russ Kinne; **241** Photo used with the permission of Ontario Power Generation; **246** Oxford Museum of Science/CORBIS-BETTMANN; **249** VALAN/Richard Nowitz; **252** Sylvia Fedoruk; **253** Alfred Pasienka/Science Photo Library/Photo Researchers; **256** Christopher Bissell/Tony Stone Images; **261 left** Jim Krantz/Tony Stone Images, **right** Stephen Johnson/Tony Stone Images; **262 left** Charles D. Winters/Science Source/Photo Researchers, **right** VALAN/Joyce Photographics; **263 left** Lawrence Migdale/Science Source/Photo Researchers, **right** Charles D. Winters/Science Source/Photo Researchers; **266** Claudia Kunin/Tony Stone Images; **267** Dr. Jeremy Burgess/Science Photo Library/Photo Researchers; **272** Rosemary Weller/Tony Stone Images; **273** Paul Silverman/Fundamental Photographs; **277 top** VALAN/Phillip Norton; **278** VALAN/Anthony Scullion; **279 top** Scott Winter/*Great Careers for People Interested in the Human Body* by Lois Edwards, published by Trifolium Books Inc./Weigl Educational Publishers Limited; **284, 285** Reprinted by permission of Canadian Conservation Institute, Department of Canadian Heritage, and André Lepine, Marine Archaeologist, Committee of Underwater Archaeology of Québec Inc.; **286** Canapress Photo Service; **292** Christopher Morris; **293** Martin Paquette; **294 left** Courtesy CN Tower, **right** Ontario Science Centre; **296 top** Dick Hemingway, **bottom** Metro Toronto Library Board; **297 top right** Hartmann Sachs/Phototake/First Light; **306** John Cunningham/Visuals Unlimited; **309** Paul Silverman/Fundamental Photographs; **312** Courtesy Petro Canada; **313** Charles O'Rear/First Light; **316 left** Dick Hemingway, **right** Ontario Hydro; **317** Tony Stone Images; **322 centre** Bill Ross First Light, **inset** Bill Ivy/Ivy Images; **325** Bill Ivy/Ivy Images; **336** Monique Frize; **338** Bill Ivy/Ivy Images; **339** Ken Cole/VALAN; **343** Canadian Sport Images; **352** Greg Ranieri/Picture It Photography Inc.; **364 bottom left and bottom centre** Bill Ivy/Ivy Images; **368** Dick Hemingway; **380 centre** Kristen Brochmann/Fundamental Photographs, **inset** Darwin Wigget/First Light; **382 bottom** CORBIS-BETTMANN; **386** Public Archives of Canada PA 93160; **387 both** Jet Propulsion Laboratory/Caltech; **393 bottom** Courtesy Mercedes Benz Canada Inc.; **394 top** NASA **396 top** Ward's Natural Science Establishment; **399** Bill Ivy/Ivy Images; **401** Brian Simmons/Manitoba Hydro; **402** British Columbia Ministry of Energy, Mines and Petroleum Resources; **403 top and bottom left** Ontario Hydro, **bottom right** Arthus Bertrand/Explorer/Photo Researchers Inc.; **404 top** Ken Cole/VALAN, **bottom** Ontario Ministry of Energy, Science and Technology; **406** Ontario Hydro; **407 bottom** John McDermott/Tony Stone Images; **410 top left** Hank Morgan/Science Source/Photo Researchers; **411 centre left** Ontario Ministry of Energy, **centre right** John Fowler/Valan, **bottom right** James R. Page/Valan; **412 top** Nova Scotia Tourism/Canapress; **413 bottom** CORBIS/Roger Ressmeyer; **420** Gerry Kitchen/Trans Alta Utilities Corp.; **426-427** NASA; **430 top** V. Wilkinson/Valan, **bottom** Joseph Needham, *Science and Civilization of China*; **428** Wendy Roberts/Cerro Tololo Inter-American Observatory, Chile; **432 top** James R. Page/Valan, **bottom** NASA; **433 top** NASA; **437 bottom** Yerkes Observatory; **438 top** Rob Smythe, **bottom** Andreas Celarius/Mary Evans Picture Library; **443-444 both** NASA; **448-457 all** NASA; **459** Rob Smythe; **460** NASA; **462 top** University of Toronto, Department of Public Affairs; **463 top** NASA; **466 bottom** Rob Smythe/TERSCH; **468 top** NASA; **470 top left** NASA, **bottom left** Bill Iberg/Science Photo Library/Photo Researchers, **right** Space Telescope Science Institute/NASA/Science Photo Library/Photo Researchers; **471** Celestial Image Co/Science Photo Library/Photo Researchers; **472** Jerry Lodriguss/Photo Researchers; **473** Photo by Barry Shell from *Great Canadian Scientists*, Polestar, 1997; **474-475 all** NASA; **478** Pam E. Hickman/Valan; **479 top** NASA, **bottom** Mark McCaughrean (Max Planck Institute for Astronomy), C. Robert O'Dell (Rice University), and NASA; **485** Rob Smythe/TERSCH; **486** Vincent van Gogh, *The Starry Night* (1889). Oil on canvas, 29 X 36¼". The Museum of Modern Art, New York. Acquired through the Lillie P. Bliss Bequest. Photograph ©1999 the Museum of Modern Art, New York;

488 National Optical Astronomy Observatories; **489 top** American Institute of Physics; **496 top** Celestial Image Co/Science Photo Library/Photo Researchers, **bottom** NASA; **497 bottom** CP Picture Archive; **498 top** NASA, **bottom** TV Ontario; **499 top left** Fred Espenar/Science Photo Library/Photo Researchers, **right** Dennis Di Ciccio/First Light **bottom left** Chris Butler/Science Photo Library/Photo Researchers; **500** NASA; **503 top** Cal Millar/Canapress; **506** UPI/CORBIS-BETTMANN; **507** Dick Hemingway; **511 top** Painting © 1999 by Don Dixon, **bottom left** John Bova/Photo Researchers, satellite NASA, professional astronomer Dennis Milon/Visuals Unlimited; **512** Sudbury Neutrino Observatory; **513** TV Ontario; **516 centre** NASA/Tony Stone Images, **inset** Chuck O'Rear/First Light; **521 left** Canadian Tourism Commission, **right** Dick Hemingway; **522 top centre** Jack Finch/Science Photo Library/Photo Researchers, **bottom** NASA; **523 bottom** Bill Ivy/Ivy Images; **526 left** NASA/Photo Researchers, **right** Photo Researchers; **528 top** Jan Bauer/Associated Press/Canapress/Photo Service, **bottom** Photo courtesy of Telesat Canada; **529** CORBIS; **530 top and bottom right** NASA, **bottom left** National Oceanographic and Atmospheric Administration; **531 top** Radarsat International/Canadian Centre for Remote Sensing, **bottom** NASA/Mark Marten/Photo Researchers; **533 centre** CORBIS, **inset** NASA; **535 left** NASA, **right** Associated Press AP/Canapress/Photo Service; **536 top** Georg Gerster/Photo Researchers, **bottom left** NASA, **bottom right** Malin Space Science Systems/Jet Propulsion Laboratory; **537** NASA; **538** Chuck O'Rear/First Light; **540 both** NASA; **541 left** NASA, **right** JPL/First Light; **542-543** Canadian Space Agency; **544** NASA/Science Photo Library/Photo Researchers; **550 top** Eric Choi, **bottom left and right** Radarsat International; **553** galaxy Science Photo Library/Photo Researchers, star trails Frank Zullo/Photo Researchers; **558** Daniel J. Cox/Tony Stone Images.

Text Credits

IS-2, IS-15 Galbraith et al, *Analyzing Issues: Science, Technology, & Society*, Trifolium Books Inc., 1997, portions adapted with permission; **IS-2, IS-9** Williams, Peter and Jacobson, Saryl, *Take a Technowalk to Learn About Material and Structures*, Trifolium Books Inc., 1997, portions adapted with permission; **99** From *Life Science*, Laboratory Manual, © 1997 Glencoe/McGraw-Hill; **115** Adapted from Alberta Agriculture in the Classroom Program; **139** Data provided by Dr. Karen Goodrowe; **214** Excerpted from "Truffles Without Tears" by Russ Parsons. Copyright © 1999, Los Angeles Times. Reprinted by permission.

Illustration Credits

12 From *Life Science* by Lucy Daniel, © 1997 Glencoe/McGraw-Hill; **17** From Mader, *Human Biology*, Fourth Edition, © The McGraw-Hill Companies Inc.; **18-19, 23, 30, 33** From *Life Science* by Lucy Daniel, © 1997 Glencoe/McGraw-Hill **48-49, 50** From Mader, *Human Biology*, Fourth Edition, © The McGraw-Hill Companies Inc.; **50** From Mader, *Inquiry Into Life*, © The McGraw-Hill Companies Inc.; **56, 57, 58, 63, 66, 82, 83, 84 top** From *Life Science* by Lucy Daniel, © 1997 Glencoe/McGraw-Hill; **88** From Mader, *Human Biology*, Fourth Edition, © The McGraw-Hill Companies Inc.; **89, 91** From *Life Science* by Lucy Daniel, © 1997 Glencoe/McGraw-Hill; **93 bottom** From Mader, *Inquiry Into Life*, © The McGraw-Hill Companies Inc.; **100** From Starr, *Biology: The Unity and Diversity of Life*, Sixth Edition, © Wadsworth Publishing; **109** From *Science Interactions* 3 by Bill Aldridge, © 1998 Glencoe/McGraw-Hill; **112-113** From *Life Science* by Lucy Daniel, © 1997 Glencoe/McGraw-Hill; **172 top** From *Physical Science* by Charles W. McLaughlin, © 1997 Glencoe/McGraw-Hill; **229 bottom, 231 top** From *Science Interactions* 3 by Bill Aldridge, © 1998 Glencoe/McGraw-Hill; **342, 394, 445** From *Science Interactions* 3 by Bill Aldridge, © 1998 Glencoe/McGraw-Hill; **501, 509, 519** From *Earth Science* by Ralph Feather, Jr., © 1997 Glencoe/McGraw-Hill; **504** From *Earth Science* by Ralph Feather, Jr., © 1997 Glencoe/McGraw-Hill; **522 top** from *Earth Science* by Ralph Feather, Jr., © 1997 Glencoe/McGraw-Hill; **559** From *Life Science* by Lucy Daniel, © 1997 Glencoe/McGraw-Hill; **595, 596** From *Earth Science* by Ralph Feather, Jr., © 1997 Glencoe/McGraw-Hill.

Glossary

This Glossary defines each key term found in **bold face** type in the units of this text book. It also includes additional helpful terms.

A

acid rain rain that contains higher than normal levels of acid; caused by waste gases released into the atmosphere

afterbirth the placenta, so called because it is usually expelled from the uterus after the birth of a baby

alchemist in the past, a researcher who tried to discover ways of changing some elements into others (e.g., base metals into gold)

alkali metal any of the Group 1 metallic elements: lithium, sodium, potassium, rubidium, cesium, and francium; all are strongly reactive, soft, low-density metals

alkaline earth metal any of the Group 2 elements beryllium, magnesium, calcium, strontium, barium, and radium; all are reactive soft, low-density metals

allantois a membrane rich in blood vessels which helps remove wastes from the developing embryo

alloy a homogeneous mixture of a metal with one or more metals or non-metals

alloying the process of producing an alloy by mixing a metal with one or more metals or non-metals (e.g., brass is produced by alloying copper and zinc)

alpha particle a positively charged particle emitted by the nucleus of some radioactive atoms

alternating current electrical current in which electrons rapidly change direction back and forth

amino acids complex compounds that combine in many ways to make different proteins

ammeter an instrument for measuring electric current

amniocentesis examination of a sample of fluid surrounding a fetus, for genetic testing

amnion the membrane that forms a protective fluid-filled sac surrounding the developing embryo

ampere (A) the basic unit for measuring the strength of an electric current; short form is amp

anaphase the stage in mitosis when the duplicated chromosomes move apart to opposite ends of the cell

angiosperm a flowering plant that produces seeds inside an ovary, which ripens into a fruit

anode in most power supplies, the positively charged electrode

anther the part of a flower stamen that bears the pollen

antibiotic chemical that can inhibit the growth of certain bacteria

aquaculture growing and harvesting of fish and shellfish for use by humans, fish farming

aqueous term applied to solutions in which water is the solvent

area the number of squared units (e.g., m^2) required to cover a surface

asexual reproduction the formation of a new individual from a single organism

asterism a distinctive star pattern

asteroid any of the millions of small planets between the orbits of Mars and Jupiter

astronomical unit (AU) one astronomical unit is equal to the distance from the centre of Earth to the centre of the Sun (149 599 000 km)

atmosphere a gaseous envelope surrounding a planet

atom the smallest unit of matter that can take part in a chemical change

atomic mass the mass of an average atom of an element, in atomic mass units

atomic mass unit (u) the unit used to measure the mass of atoms relative to $\frac{1}{12}$ the mass of an atom of carbon-12

atomic number the number of protons in the nucleus of an atom

atomic structure the arrangement of subatomic particles within an atom (e.g., an atom of hydrogen has one proton in its nucleus and one electron in its shell).

aurora borealis shifting patterns of coloured light that appear in the night sky in northern latitudes; caused by collisions between charged particles and molecules in the upper atmosphere

aurora australanis the same as aurora borealis but in southern latitudes

B

bar graph diagram consisting of horizontal or vertical bars representing data

battery a combination of electric cells that produce a potential difference

beta particle an electron ejected by the nucleus of some radioactive atoms

Big Bang theory scientific explanation for the origin of the universe; according to this theory, the universe and everything in it began in an instantaneous event that occurred between 15 and 20 billion years ago

binary fission the splitting of an organism into two new organisms approximately equal in size; bacteria reproduce asexually through this process

binary stars two single stars orbiting one another

bioremediation the process of using micro-organisms to break down the complex compounds in toxic waste

biosphere the portion of the planet Earth that supports life

biotechnology using or modifying living organisms to produce marketable goods

black dwarf the final phase of a white dwarf (star)

black hole in space, an object having such strong gravity that nothing, not even light, can escape it

blastocyst during embryonic development, the arrangement of cells into an inner and outer layer

bonding pattern the particular way in which atoms combine to form a molecule

bovine growth hormone (BGH) a hormone used to promote growth and milk production in cattle

budding asexual reproduction process in which a bud forms on an organism, grows, and eventually breaks away

C

CANDU reactor Canadian Deuterium Uranium reactor, in which the nuclear fission of uranium is used to produce electrical energy

capacity units the units that are used to report the volume of a liquid (e.g., cm^3)

carbon dating a method of determining the age of organic objects that relies on the radioactive decay of carbon-14; the half-life of carbon-14 is about 5600 years

cathode in most power supplies, the negatively charged electrode

cathode ray in a gas discharge tube, a beam of electrons emitted from the cathode when an electric field is applied

celestial bodies the collective term for the Sun, Moon, stars, planets, natural satellites, and comets

celestial object a naturally occurring body in the skies, such as a star, planet, or asteroid

celestial sphere an imaginary sphere once thought to enclose the universe and in which the planets and stars seem to be fastened

cell cycle in a cell, the continuous process of mitosis, cell division, growth and interphase

cell plate in plant cell division, develops to form a cell wall between the two new cells

cell wall rigid structure surrounding the cell membrane of plants, fungi, and some unicellular organisms; protects and supports the cell

cell membrane the selectively permeable structure enclosing the cell contents

cell theory a major theory of living things, formulated in the 1800s; all living things are composed of one or more cells; the cell is the basic unit of life; all cells come from other cells

centrioles in animal cells, organelles that organize spindle fibres during mitosis

centromere in a chromosome, the point at which spindle fibres attach

Cepheid variable a star that pulses, changing its brightness in a regular cycle

cervix the muscular neck at the base of the uterus

Caesarean section an operation involving an incision through the abdomen and uterus to deliver a baby when normal birth cannot take place

charged term referring to matter having an excess of electrons (a negative charge) or a deficiency of electrons (a positive charge)

chemical change a change in matter in which at least one new substance, with new properties, is formed

chemical family a term referring to a group of related elements; for example, the coinage metals

chemical formula a formula that uses symbols and numerals to represent the elements in a pure substance (e.g., H$_2$0 is the chemical formula for water)

chemical property a characteristic of a substance that describes its ability to react chemically with other substances (e.g., whether the substance will burn in air)

chemical reaction a process in which new substances with new properties are formed (e.g., the burning of wood to form smoke and ash)

chloroplast in plant cells, an organelle that contains chlorophyll and enables plants to make carbohydrates through the process of photosynthesis

chorion the outermost of three layers of protective tissues around an embryo during early development

chromatin long strands of DNA scattered throughout a cell's nucleus

chromosome in a cell nucleus, a double-stranded, threadlike structure that carries genetic material (instructions for producing new cells with the same characteristics as the parent cell)

circuit a path over which an electric current flows

circuit breaker a switch that automatically breaks an electric circuit when a dangerous amount of current flows through; used as a safety device

circuit diagram a diagram showing a path over which an electric current flows

classify to group ideas, information, or objects based on their similarities

cleavage the process of rapid cell division that occurs soon after an egg is fertilized

clone identical copy of a molecule, gene, cell, or entire organism

cloning the process of producing a clone

codon in a molecule of DNA or RNA, a triplet of bases controlling the placement of a specific amino acid during the making of a protein

colloid a type of mechanical mixture in which extremely small particles of one or more substances are evenly and stably distributed in one or more others (e.g., whipped cream is a colloid of cream particles in air)

combustibility the ability of a substance to burn in air

comet a small celestial body that orbits the Sun and has a bright nucleus and a fainter tail, which always points away from the Sun

complete metamorphosis process by which an organism develops into an adult by changing from one form to another (e.g., from tadpole to frog)

compound a pure substance made up of two or more elements that are chemically combined (e.g., water is a compound consisting of two elements, hydrogen and oxygen)

computer spreadsheet software that helps to organize information, using rows and columns

concept map a diagram that shows relationships among concepts

conductor a material that allows electric charges or heat to move freely on and through it

congenital defects abnormalities present at birth

conjugation method of reproduction in single-celled organisms; involves transfer of DNA from one individual to another

consortium in bioremediation a group of organisms such as fungi and bacteria that work together to break down toxic wastes

constellation a group of stars that form a pattern (e.g., Ursa Major)

coordinate graph a grid that has data points named as ordered pairs of numbers, for example, (4,3)

corona an irregularly shaped halo around the Sun

corpus luteum a yellowish body formed from the follicle after ovulation

cotyledon in the embryo of a seed plant, a structure that may develop into the plant's first leaf

coulomb (C) the unit of electric charge; one coulomb is the amount of charge passing a point in one second when one ampere of current is flowing

covalent bond attraction between atoms caused by the sharing of electrons

crossing over the exchange of DNA between paired homologous chromosomes during meiosis

crystal lattice the regular, repeating pattern in which ions in ionic compounds fit together

cubic units the units used to report the volume of a solid (e.g., cm^3)

current a flow of electric charge

cytoplasm the gel-like substance within the cell membrane that supports the structures of the cell

D

Dalton's atomic theory the proposal advanced by John Dalton (1766-1844) to explain matter; it states that all matter is made up of small particles called atoms

density the amount of mass in a certain unit volume of a substance (density equals mass divided by volume)

dependent (or **responding**) **variable** the factor in an experiment or study that changes in response to a change in the independent variable

diamond a precious stone consisting of a crystalline form of carbon

differentiation the process by which generalized cells become specialized to form structures such as tissues and organ systems

diploid having two sets of chromosomes; the diploid number for a human cell is 46 (2 x 23)

direct current electrical current in which electrons travel continuously in one direction

DNA (deoxyribonucleic acid) a molecule that determines the inherited characteristics of an organism

Doppler effect the apparent change in frequency of sound, light, and other waves due to relative motion between, the observer and the wave source

ductility the capacity of a metal to be shaped or stretched into a wire without breaking or fracturing

dry cell device in which chemical reactions create a potential difference; chemical agent is in the form of a paste to prevent spills (e.g., flashlight battery)

E

ectoderm the outermost layer of a gastrula

ectopic pregnancy refers to an embryo that has implanted in the wall of the oviduct

eggs the gametes in female animals

electric charge a property of matter having an excess of electrons (a negative charge) or a deficiency of electrons (a positive charge)

electric potential energy the electric energy stored in a battery

electrode either of the two (metal) terminals in a battery or other electricity source; in a battery, they are called the anode and the cathode

electrolysis the process of decomposing a chemical compound by passing an electric current through it

electrolyte a solution that can conduct an electric current

electromagnetic spectrum the arrangement by wavelength of the different forms of electromagnetic radiation

electron cloud in Rutherford's nuclear model of an atom, a negatively charged "envelope" that is relatively large in volume, light compared to the nucleus, and negatively charged

electron rearrangement the process by which the outer shells of atoms lose, gain, or share electrons

electron shell in Bohr's model of an atom, a fixed, three-dimensional, sphere-like region around an atom's nucleus; electrons move rapidly within the electron shell

electron a negatively charged particle found orbiting the nucleus of an atom

electroscope a device for detecting the presence of electric charge

electrostatic precipitator a device to control air pollution using stationary electric charges (not currents)

electrostatics the study of electrical charges that move very little

element a type of pure substance that can not be broken down into simpler parts by ordinary chemical means (e.g., oxygen, gold)

element symbol a symbol used to stand for an element (e.g., H for hydrogen, Na for sodium)

embryo a fertilized egg during early development

endoderm the innermost layer of a gastrula

endometrium the lining of the uterus

endoplasmic reticulum within a cell's cytoplasm, a folded membrane that forms a system of canals which transport materials to different parts of the cell

enzyme protein that increases the rate of chemical reactions in cells

epicycle a smaller circle whose centre rolls around the circumference of a larger circle

epididymis a structure next to the testis in which sperm are collected and stored before moving to the vas deferens

equivalent resistance in a series or parallel electric circuit, the resistance of one resistor that would yield exactly the same current and potential difference readings as the readings that the circuit produces

Escherichia coli species of bacteria found in the human large intestine; used in genetic research

estrogen a hormone that directs the development and function of the female sex organs and secondary sex characteristics

external fertilization a form of fertilization in which sperm and egg cells meet outside the bodies of both parents

extra-solar planet a planet that orbits a star other than the Sun

extra-terrestrial life life other than that on Earth

F

fact a verifiable statement, or event known to have really happened

fair test investigation carried out under strictly controlled conditions to ensure accuracy

feedback the return of information from the output of a system to the input

fertilization the process by which gametes from two parents combine to form one new cell

filament the part of a flower stamen that supports the anther

fission products the atoms left after nuclear fission takes place; fission products are highly radioactive and can damage living tissues

follicle a structure in the ovary where an egg cell develops

follicle stimulating hormone (FHS) a hormone produced by the pituitary to stimulate the development of egg cells in females and sperm cells in males

fossil fuel a fuel made of the partly decomposed remains of organisms buried hundreds of millions of years ago (e.g., coal, crude oil)

fragmentation an asexual reproduction process in which a small piece, or fragment, breaks away and grows into a new individual; fungi can reproduce this way

fruit in a flowering plant, the ripened ovary, which contains one or more seeds

fuel cell an electric cell that is continually fed with fuel, usually hydrogen and oxygen, from tanks outside it

fuel rod in a nuclear reactor, a device which contains pellets of uranium fuel

fuse in an electric circuit, a device containing a wire or strip of metal that melts in order to break the connection when a dangerous amount of current flows through; used as a safety device

G

galaxy a huge accumulation of stars, gas, and dust held together by gravity

gamete a specialized cell for reproduction (e.g., egg cell, sperm cell)

gametophyte the haploid stage of a plant's life cycle during which gametes are produced

gamma ray burst a powerful pulse of gamma rays that can come from anywhere in the sky

gamma ray camera a device that detects gamma rays; in medicine, used to diagnose bone abnormalities

gamma rays the rays having the shortest frequency and highest energy of all waves in the electromagnetic spectrum; gamma rays come from nuclear reactions

gas discharge tube a sealed tube containing a gas at low pressure, through which an electric current is passed

gastrula the structure of the developing embryo, consisting of the ectoderm, mesoderm, and endoderm

gene a segment of DNA on a chromosome that encodes a particular protein

gene splicing the cutting of a segment of DNA from one organism and inserting it into the DNA of another organism

gene therapy a technique allowing scientists to block defective genes or add healthy ones

genetic defects disorders caused by abnormalities in the DNA

genetic engineering the process of artificially combining genes in a cell

genetic screening identifying human genetic conditions by examining the genes in an individual's cells

genome all of the genes found in a complete set of chromosomes

genus a biological group of similar, related species (e.g., the genus *Canis* includes species such as the wolf and the domestic dog)

geocentric model Earth-centred model of the solar system

geomagnetic storm a cascade of particles sent into space during solar flares and drawn towards Earth by its magnetic field

geosynchronous satellite a satellite orbiting in synchrony with Earth's rotation so it remains above the same spot on Earth's equator

germ layers the three layers of a developing embryo in the early stages; ectoderm, mesoderm, endoderm

germination the process in which a seed begins to grow

gestation the period during which the embryo develops in the uterus

Global Positioning System (GPS) a network of artificial satellites revolving around Earth, sending out continuous location and time signals; used as a navigation system

global warming an increase in worldwide temperatures attributed to the trapping of heat in the atmosphere by greenhouse gases

globular cluster a collection of 100 000 to a million stars arranged in a distinctive spherical shape and not appearing along the band of the Milky Way

Golgi body in a cell, an organelle that packages up and moves (secretes) materials out of the cell

gonad a reproductive organ; in humans, male gonads are called testes and female gonads are called ovaries

grafting the transplantation of living tissue from one individual to another or to a different location on the same individual

graphic organizer a visual learning tool that helps clarify the relationship between a central concept and related ideas or terms

graphite soft, blackish-grey form of carbon; used for pencil lead and as a lubricant

greenhouse effect a natural process in the atmosphere that traps some of the Sun's heat near the Earth's surface

greenhouse gas a gas that traps heat in the atmosphere and prevents it from escaping into outer space (e.g., carbon dioxide)

ground to connect a conductor through some conducting material directly to the ground, or Earth

group a vertical column of elements in the periodic table

gymnosperm a plant that produces exposed seeds, rather than seeds inside an ovary; (e.g., conifers)

H

halogen any of the Group 17 non-metallic elements: fluorine, chlorine, bromine, iodine, and astatine

haploid having a single set of chromosomes; the haploid number for a human cell is 23

heliocentric model Sun-centred model of the solar system

hermaphrodite an organism having the reproductive organs of both sexes

herbicide chemical that can kill a plant or inhibit its growth

heterogeneous term applied to mixtures that are not of a uniform composition throughout (e.g., metal ores)

histogram a type of bar graph in which each bar represents a range of values and in which the data are continuous

homogeneous term applied to pure substances and to mixtures that are of a uniform composition throughout (e.g., solutions and alloys)

homologous pairs matching pairs of chromosomes

hormone substance released from specific glands to control particular body activities

Hubble constant the ratio of the speed at which galaxies are receding to the distance away of those galaxies

Hubble's law a law stating that galaxies are moving apart at rates that increase in direct proportion to the distance between them

Human Genome Project a project with the aim of locating the approximately 100 000 genes found on one set of human chromosomes

hybrid an organism resulting from crossing individuals of two different but closely related species (e.g., crossing a horse with a donkey produces a mule)

hydro-electric term applied to the use of water power to generate electricity

hydrosphere all the water that occurs at Earth's surface

hypothesis a testable proposal used to explain an observation or to predict the outcome of an experiment

I

implantation the process by which a developing embryo becomes anchored to the lining of the uterus

inbreeding breeding among closely related individuals

incomplete metamorphosis organism develops into an adult through a series of stages having slightly different forms (e.g. from nymph to grasshopper)

independent (or manipulated) variable a factor in an experiment or study that can be changed or selected

induction the process by which an object having an electric charge produces the same charge in a neighbouring object without actually touching it

inner planets Mercury, Venus, Earth, Mars

insecticide chemical used to kill insects

insulator a material that does not allow electric charges or heat to move freely on or through it

inter-stellar medium the space between the stars and the material it contains

internal fertilization a form of fertilization in which the sperm travels into the female's body to meet the egg

insulin hormone that regulates the level of glucose in the blood

interphase in a cell, the period of time during which it is not actively dividing by mitosis

in vitro refers to a biological process that occurs outside the living organism or cell, such as in a test tube

in vivo refers to a biological process that occurs inside the living organism or cell

ion an atom with a positive or negative charge due to loss or gain of electrons

ionic bond the attraction between positive and negative ions

ionic compound a compound made up of oppositely charged ions (e.g., table salt)

isotope any of two or more forms of an element that have the same number of protons but a different number of neutrons (e.g., deuterium is an isotope of hydrogen)

IUPAC International Union of Pure and Applied Chemistry; a body that specifies rules for chemical names and symbols

K

karyotype a photograph of a cell's chromosomes showing their arrangement from largest to smallest

kilowatt hour the unit of energy for electric meters; the amount of energy transmitted by one thousand watts of power over a period of one hour

kingdom one of the five major subdivisions (plants, animals, protists, fungi, monerans) that include all living organisms

L

labour a sequence of muscle contractions that open the cervix in preparation for childbirth

law an action or condition that has been observed so consistently that scientists are convinced it will always happen

law of attraction and repulsion a law stating that like electric charges repel and unlike electric charges attract

law of conservation of mass a law stating that, in a chemical change, the total mass of the new substances is always the same as the total mass of the original substances

law of definite proportions a law stating that compounds are pure substances that contain two or more elements combined in fixed (or definite) proportions

layering a method of growing roots from the branches or shoots of a parent plant by covering those parts with soil

light-year the distance that a beam of light travels in a vacuum in one year; about 63 240 AUs, or 9.46 trillion km

lightning in the sky, a flash of bright light caused by the discharge of electricity between clouds, or between clouds and the ground

lightning rod a metal rod or wire attached to a building to prevent lightning damage by conducting the electrons to the ground

load in an electric circuit, a device that resists the flow of current and converts electrical energy to another form of energy (e.g., a light bulb)

luminosity a measure of the total amount of energy a star radiates per second

luteinizing hormone (LH) a pituitary hormone that promotes production of egg cells by the ovaries and development of the corpus luteum

lysosome in a cell, an organelle that breaks down food and digests wastes and worn-out cell parts

M

magnetosphere the space surrounding a celestial body, such as the Earth, in which that body's magnetic field exists

main sequence on the Hertsprung-Russell diagram, a narrow band of stars into which fall most stars including our Sun

malleability how easily a metal can be hammered, pressed, or rolled into thin plates

mass the amount of matter in a substance; often measured with a balance

mass number the number of protons and neutrons in the nucleus of an a atom

mating the process by which organisms combine their gametes to each other for fertilization

mechanical mixture a substance made of more than one kind of particle in which the particles are not uniformly scattered

meiosis in cell division, the process that ensures each gamete is haploid

meniscus the slight curve at the top of a liquid where the liquid meets the sides of a container

menstrual cycle the cycle in which a female mammal's body is prepared for the possible fertilization of an egg and resulting pregnancy

menstruation the monthly shedding of the uterine lining that occurs if fertilization has not occurred

meristem unspecialized cells found in the tips of roots and shoots that produce new growth in plants

mesoderm the middle layer of cells in a gastrula

metal a chemical element such as aluminum, gold, or iron; metals share certain properties including a metallic lustre, malleability, ductility, and a good ability to conduct heat and electricity

metalloid a chemical element such as silicon or antimony; metalloids can have properties of both metals and non-metals

metallurgy the science and technology of obtaining metals and making them useful; includes the processes of extraction, modification, and alloying

metaphase the stage in mitosis when the duplicated chromosomes are in line across the middle of the cell

meteor a solid body that enters Earth's atmosphere from outer space, becoming hot and bright because of friction with the atmosphere

meteorite the remnant of a meteor that does not burn up completely in Earth's atmosphere; it falls to Earth as a solid body made up mainly of stone or iron

meteorology the study of the atmosphere and weather systems

microgravity the condition in which objects in orbit (e.g., a spacecraft) seem to be weightless; in fact, gravity is acting on them, but its effects are greatly reduced

Milky Way the galaxy that includes our Sun and Earth; appears as a hazy white band in the night sky

mineral a natural, pure inorganic substance with a particular chemical composition (e.g., silicon, quartz, hematite)

mitochondrion an oval-shaped organelle that transforms energy for a cell (plural: mitochondria)

mitosis the process by which genetic material duplicated divides into two identical sets of chromosomes

model a verbal, mathematical, or visual representation of a scientific structure or process, which allows scientists to construct and test inferences and theories

modification in metallurgy, the process of altering the properties of a pure metal without using a chemical change (e.g., by heating and sudden cooling)

molecular compound a compound that is not ionic

molecule the smallest independent unit of a pure substance; generally a cluster of atoms bonded together

monoculture the use of land for growing only a single variety of a crop

moulting the periodic shedding of a body covering, such as an exoskeleton or skin

mutagenic agent a cause of mutations (e.g., radiation temperature extremes, or exposure to chemicals such as pesticides)

mutation a change in genes, produced by an error occuring during the process of copying DNA

N

nebula a vast cloud of gas and dust, which may be the birth place of a star (plural: nebulae)

negative charge charge carried by electrons

negative feedback a system in which the products of a reaction cause the rate of that reaction to decrease

negative terminal in a battery or other source of electricity, the plate having an excess of electrons

neutral term referring to matter having neither a negative nor a positive electric charge

neutrino an elementary particle that carries no electric charge

neutron a particle carrying no electric charge and forming part of the nucleus of an atom

neutron star a small super-dense star thought to be the crushed remnant of a large star that has exploded as a supernova

nitrogen base the part of the DNA molecule that joins the two strands

noble gases the elements helium, neon, argon, krypton, xenon, and radon

non-metal a chemical element such as oxygen or sulfur; non-metals do not possess the properties of metals

non-renewable a term applied to resources that cannot be replaced or that are being used much faster than they are forming (e.g., coal, oil)

nuclear energy the release of large amounts of energy from splitting or colliding atomic nuclei

nuclear fusion a reaction in which two small atomic nuclei combine; it is accompanied by the release of enormous amounts of energy and may be an important energy source in the future

nuclear fission the process in which a large atomic nucleus such as uranium splits into two or more parts; accompanied by the release of two or three neutrons and a tremendous amount of energy

nuclear medicine the controlled application of certain radioactive isotopes for the diagnosis or treatment of cancer and other serious medical conditions, such as osteoporosis

nuclear membrane the thin, double membrane that separates the nuclear contents from the cytoplasm

nucleolus a darker, condensed area within the nucleus of a cell; it manufactures ribosomes

nucleotide a segment of DNA composed of a sugar molecule, a phosphate group, and one of four nitrogen bases

nucleus (1) the central part of an atom (2) in a cell, an organelle with a double-layered porous membrane surrounding the cell's DNA

O

ohm (Ω) a unit of electrical resistance; one ohm is the resistance of a conductor through which a current of one ampere flows when a potential difference of one volt is applied

ohmic resistor a term applied to any electric device that has a constant resistance regardless of potential difference

Ohm's law a law stating that the ratio of the potential difference between the ends of a conductor and the current flowing in the conductor is constant

open cluster a collection of 50 to 1000 stars that appear dispersed along the main band of the Milky Way

open pit mining mining done at or just beneath the surface

operational definition a way of defining physical quantities which shows how they are observed and measured

ordinary mechanical mixture a mixture in which the different parts are big enough to see and stay mixed rather than separating out

ore a body or deposit of rock, gravel, sand, or earth worth mining for the mineral or minerals it contains

organelle a structure within a cell that has a specific function

outer planets Jupiter, Saturn, Uranus, Neptune

ovary in a female animal, the organ in which eggs are produced; in a plant, the part that holds the young seeds

oviducts (Fallopian tubes) the tubes that carry eggs from the ovaries to the uterus

ovulation the process of releasing a mature egg from an ovary

ovule the plant part that develops into a seed

ovum a female gamete, produced in the ovaries (plural: ova)

oxytocin a hormone that stimulates the uterus to contract and open the birth canal in preparation for giving birth

ozone (O_3) a form of oxygen that absorbs much of the Sun's ultraviolet light

P

parallax the apparent shift in position of a nearby object against a distant background when it is viewed from two different points

parallel circuit an electric circuit in which current branches to two or more paths

particle theory of matter a scientific model of the structure of matter; one part of this theory states that all matter is made up of extremely small particles

period a horizontal row of elements in the periodic table

periodic table a table in which the elements are organized into rows and columns according to their atomic numbers and their patterns of similar properties

pesticide chemical used to kill pests

philosopher a person who studies the nature and meaning of existence, or the principles of the universe

photosphere around the Sun, the region from which the Sun's light originates

physical change a change in matter in which no new substance is formed

physical property a characteristic of a substance, that can change without forming a new substance (e.g., the density of water changes when water turns from a liquid to a gas)

pistil the seed-producing part of a flower

pituitary gland in the brain, a pea-sized gland that secretes hormones controlling several body functions including the production of sex hormones

placenta in mammals, the organ developed by a growing embryo; it attaches to the uterus, absorbing food and oxygen from the mother's blood, as well as removing wastes

planet a celestial body that orbits a star and does not produce its own light (e.g., Mercury, Venus)

planetary nebula a fuzzy object that is not a planet but that, through a telescope, resembles a planet such as Neptune

plasmid an independent loop of DNA in an organism such as a bacterium

pollen tube in a plant, a tube that grows from a pollen grain toward the ovule

pollen grain a structure formed on flower anthers that contains the sperm

pollination in a flower, the process by which pollen grains from the anther reach the stigma of the pistil

polymer a giant molecule created by the union of many similar or identical molecules (e.g., proteins, plastics, nylon)

population all the individuals of one species that occupy a certain geographic area during a certain time

positive charge charge carried by protons

positive feedback a system in which the products of a reaction cause the rate of that reaction to increase

positive terminal in a battery or other source of electricity, the plate having a deficiency of electrons

potential difference the difference in electric potential energy per coulomb of charge at one point in a circuit compared to the potential energy per coulomb of charge at another point in the circuit

power the rate of doing work or using energy (power equals energy divided by time)

precipitate an insoluble substance formed as a result of a chemical change when two soluble substances react

primary cell a non-rechargeable electric cell that can be used only once

progesterone a hormone produced by the corpus luteum to prepare the uterus for pregnancy and help maintain the uterine lining during pregnancy

prophase the first stage in mitosis, during which the chromosomes contract and the nucleolus and nuclear membrane disappear

prostate a gland near the upper end of the male urethra; it produces fluids found in semen

protein long chain of amino acids; necessary in the diet; protein is an essential part of animal and plant cells

proton a positively charged particle forming part of the nucleus of an atom

puberty the period when an individual becomes capable of sexual reproduction and develops secondary sex characteristics

purebred a variety of an animal or plant species that produces offspring with the same characteristics as the parents

Q

qualitative data information gathered in observations in which no measurement takes place

qualitative physical property a characteristic of a substance that can be described but not measured

quantitative data data that consist of numbers and/or units of measurements; obtained through measurement and mathematical calculations

quantitative physical property a characteristic of a substance that can be measured (e.g., density)

quasar a celestial object that looks like a star but emits much more energy; quasars are thought to be the explosively erupting cores of colliding galaxies

R

radioactive emitting highly energetic charged particles or rays from the nucleus; can be dangerous to living tissues (e.g., uranium and radium are radioactive elements)

radioactivity the property of spontaneous emission of radiation; this property is possessed by certain elements and isotopes including uranium and radium

reactivity the tendency of an element to enter into chemical reactions

recombinant DNA DNA having genes from different sources put together by genetic engineering

red dwarf a small, cool star that is not very bright

red giant a large, bright star that is not very hot

red-shifted a shifting of light from an object toward the red (longer-wavelength) end of the spectrum as the object moves away from Earth

regeneration the process of repairing injured cells or growing lost body parts

renewable a term applied to resources that can be replaced as fast or faster than they are being used (e.g., energy from the Sun and wind)

replication the process by which a cell nucleus makes copies of its genetic material so that there are two complete sets of DNA

reproductive technology techniques to increase the probability of reproduction

resistance (R) potential difference across the load, V, to the current through the load, I ($R=V/I$)

resistor a component that resists the passage of a current, converting electric energy into other energy forms (e.g., a lamp converts electric energy into light energy)

resolution the power of an optical device, such as a microscope, to produce separate images of objects that are very close to each other

retrograde motion in a celestial body's orbit, an actual or apparent movement opposite to that of the usual east-to-west direction

ribosomes small, granular cell structures involved in the manufacture of proteins

S

satellite a small body that orbits a larger one; it may be a natural satellite such as the Earth's Moon, or an artificial satellite sent into orbit for communications or research

scale drawing a drawing in which the objects appear in the same proportions as they are in reality

scientific investigation an investigation that involves the systematic application of concepts and procedures (e.g., experimentation and research, observation and measurement, analysis and dissemination of data)

scrotum a sac of skin on the outside of the male's body which contains the testes

scrubber an anti-pollution system that can remove sulfur dioxide from industrial smoke stack emissions

secondary cell a rechargeable electric cell

seed in plants, a complete reproductive package containing an embryo, food supply, and seed coat

self-pollination transfer of pollen from the stamen to the pistil of the same flower, or another flower of the same plant

semen a mixture composed of sperm and nourishing glandular secretions which help them move

seminal vesicle a gland that produces fluids that enter the vas deferens and mix with the sperm

seminiferous tubules in the testes, a mass of coiled tubes in which sperm cells are formed

series circuit an electric circuit with only one path for the flow of current

SETI (Search for Extra-terrestrial Intelligence) collective term for a group of programs under way to search the universe for radio signals from intelligent life

sexual reproduction reproductive process involving two sexes (in most organisms) and resulting in offspring genetically different from both parents

short circuit in an electric circuit, the bypassing of a load, often caused by the touching of two connecting wires

SI the international system of measurement units, including such terms as kilogram, metre and second (from the French *Le Système International d'Unités*)

smelting the process of melting ore to obtain the metal from it

solar cell an electric cell that runs on solar, or light, energy

solar flare near sun spots, a high-temperature eruption of gases on the Sun; solar flares usually cause radio and magnetic disturbances on Earth

solar mass the basis of comparison for measuring star mass; the Sun has a solar mass of one

solar nebula theory the hypothesis that many astronomers currently hold about how our solar system developed

solar plane an imaginary, flat disk extending out from the Sun's equator on all sides, along which our solar system's planets (except Pluto) orbit the Sun

solar prominence a large eruption of glowing gas that starts on the Sun and rises high above it

solar system the family of the Sun and all the planets and other celestial bodies that revolve around it

solar wind streams of electrically charged protons and electrons discharged by the Sun, often associated with sun spots and solar flares

solute a substance that dissolves in a solvent (e.g., salt is a solute that dissolves in water)

solution a homogeneous mixture of two or more pure substances

solvent a substance that dissolves a solute to form a solution (e.g., water is a solvent that dissolves salt)

somatic cell body cell and not a reproductive cell, such as egg or sperm

spark an electric discharge; caused by electrons jumping from one conductor to another through the air

species a group of organisms that can interbreed and produce fertile offspring

spectroscope a device for producing and observing the spectrum of radiation from any source

spectrum the series of coloured bands produced when white light is separated into its component wavelengths

sperm the gametes in male animals

spindle fibres tiny tubules that attach themselves to the chromosomes during mitosis

sporangium a structure where spores are stored and produced

spore a haploid cell that can develop into a new organism without fertilization

sporophyte the diploid stage of a plant's life cycle during which spores are formed

stable octet the stable arrangement of eight electrons in the outer shell of an atom or ion

stamen the part of a flower that contains the pollen

static electricity term referring to electric charges that are stationary, or at rest

stigma the part of a plant pistil that receives pollen

style the stemlike part of a plant pistil

subatomic particles particles such as protons, neutrons, and electrons, called subatomic because they are smaller than atoms

sun spot a region on the Sun that is cooler and therefore looks darker than its surroundings

supergiant an extremely large red giant (star)

supernova a huge explosion constituting the death of a star

suspension a mechanical mixture consisting of a liquid or gas with small particles that are distributed through it, but that separate out if the suspension is left undisturbed

switch a device for turning electric current on and off; in effect, for closing and opening a circuit

synthesis the combining of parts to make a unified new product

T

table an orderly arrangement of facts set out for easy reference

technology the application of knowledge toward the solution of practical problems

telophase the final stage of mitosis, during which new nuclei are formed

tempering a process that increases the hardness and toughness of a metal

testes the male gonads

testosterone a hormone that directs the development of male secondary sex characteristics

theory an explanation of an event that has been supported by consistent, repeated experimental results and has therefore been accepted by a majority of scientists

thermal pollution an unwanted increase in the temperature of a lake, river, or other body of water; may result from a thermonuclear or thermo-electric generating plant discharging warm water into it

thermo-electric term applied to the use of heat to generate electricity

thermonuclear term applied to the use of nuclear reactions to generate electricity

tidal range the difference in the water level between high tide and low tide

toxic a chemical that is harmful to organisms

trait a distinct type of a characteristic, such as eye colour

transformer a device that increases or decreases the potential difference across the conducting wires of power transmission lines

transgenic an organism produced by moving DNA from one organism to another in order to create a new combination

triangulation a method of indirectly measuring distance by creating an imaginary triangle between an observer and an object whose distance is to be estimated

trimester any one of the three-month segments of pregnancy

Tyndall effect the scattering of light by colloid particles

U

ultrasound a diagnostic technique in which sound waves are reflected off tissues and organs, and a computer image is generated

umbilical cord a structure containing blood vessels and associated tissues that connect a placenta to an embryo

urethra a tube leading from the bladder to the outside of the body

uterus the thick-walled, muscular organ of female mammals in which a fetus develops before birth

V

vacuole in a cell, a fluid-filled organelle that stores water, food, wastes, and other materials

vagina the muscular passageway leading from the uterus to the outside of a female's body

valence electrons the electrons in the outer shell of an atom, which determine its power to combine with other elements

variable a factor that can influence the ourcome of an experiment

variation differences in characteristics caused by genetic and environmental factors

vas deferens either of two tubes that transport sperm from the epididymis to the urethra

volt (V) the unit of potential difference; one volt causes a current of one ampere to flow through a conductor with a resistance of one ohm

voltaic cell a cell containing two electrodes in a liquid electrolyte; uses chemical action to produce electric energy

voltmeter an instrument for measuring the potential difference between two points in an electric circuit

volume the measurement of the amount of space occupied by a substance

W

watt (W) a unit of electric power equivalent to one joule per second; one watt equals the power in a circuit in which one ampere of current flows across a potential difference of one volt

wet cell an electric cell with a liquid electrolyte (e.g., automobile battery)

wet mount a type of sample preparation using a microscope slide, a cover slip, and water

white dwarf a small, hot star that is not very bright

WHMIS an acronym that stands for Workplace Hazardous Materials Information System.

X

X-ray an electromagnetic ray having a very short wavelength; can penetrate substances such as skin and muscle

Y

yolk sac a structure that contains nutrients for the developing embryo

Z

zygote the new cell formed by the process of fertilization

Index

The page numbers in **boldface** type indicate the pages where the terms are defined.
Terms that occur in investigations (*inv.*) and activities (*act.*) are also indicated.